Organic Reactions

Organic Reactions

VOLUME II

KRIEGER PUBLISHING COMPANY
MALABAR, FLORIDA

Original Edition 1944
Reprint Edition 1981

Printed and Published by
KRIEGER PUBLISHING COMPANY
KRIEGER DRIVE
MALABAR, FLORIDA 32950

Library of Congress Cataloging-In-Publication Data

LCN 42-20265
ISSN 0073-8077
ISBN 0-89874-375-3

10   9   8   7   6   5   4   3

PREFACE TO THE SERIES

In the course of nearly every program of research in organic chemistry the investigator finds it necessary to use several of the better-known synthetic reactions. To discover the optimum conditions for the application of even the most familiar one to a compound not previously subjected to the reaction often requires an extensive search of the literature; even then a series of experiments may be necessary. When the results of the investigation are published, the synthesis, which may have required months of work, is usually described without comment. The background of knowledge and experience gained in the literature search and experimentation is thus lost to those who subsequently have occasion to apply the general method. The student of preparative organic chemistry faces similar difficulties. The textbooks and laboratory manuals furnish numerous examples of the application of various syntheses, but only rarely do they convey an accurate conception of the scope and usefulness of the processes.

For many years American organic chemists have discussed these problems. The plan of compiling critical discussions of the more important reactions thus was evolved. The volumes of *Organic Reactions* are collections of about twelve chapters, each devoted to a single reaction, or a definite phase of a reaction, of wide applicability. The authors have had experience with the processes surveyed. The subjects are presented from the preparative viewpoint, and particular attention is given to limitations, interfering influences, effects of structure, and the selection of experimental techniques. Each chapter includes several detailed procedures illustrating the significant modifications of the method. Most of these procedures have been found satisfactory by the author or one of the editors, but unlike those in *Organic Syntheses* they have not been subjected to careful testing in two or more laboratories. When all known examples of the reaction are not mentioned in the text, tables are given to list compounds which have been prepared by or subjected to the reaction. Every effort has been made to include in the tables all such compounds and references; however, because of the very nature of the reactions discussed and their frequent use as one of the several steps of syntheses in which not all of the intermediates have been isolated, some instances may well have been missed. Nevertheless, the investigator will be able to use the tables and their accompanying bibliographies in place of most or all of the literature search so often required.

Because of the systematic arrangement of the material in the chapters and the entries in the tables, users of the books will be able to find information desired by reference to the table of contents of the appropriate chapter. In the interest of economy the entries in the indices have been kept to a minimum, and, in particular, the compounds listed in the tables are not repeated in the indices.

The success of this publication, which will appear periodically in volumes of about twelve chapters, depends upon the cooperation of organic chemists and their willingness to devote time and effort to the preparation of the chapters. They have manifested their interest already by the almost unanimous acceptance of invitations to contribute to the work. The editors will welcome their continued interest and their suggestions for improvements in *Organic Reactions*.

CONTENTS

CHAPTER 1

THE CLAISEN REARRANGEMENT

D. Stanley Tarbell

The University of Rochester

CONTENTS

INTRODUCTION

Allyl ethers of enols and phenols undergo rearrangement to C-allyl derivatives when heated to sufficiently high temperatures. The reaction, named after its discoverer (Claisen, 1912), was first observed when ethyl O-allylacetoacetate was subjected to distillation at atmospheric pressure in the presence of ammonium chloride.[1, 2]

$$\underset{CH_3C=CHCO_2C_2H_5}{\overset{OCH_2CH=CH_2}{|}} \rightarrow \underset{CH_3C-CHCO_2C_2H_5}{\overset{O \quad CH_2CH=CH_2}{\| \quad |}}$$

The allyl ethers of phenols rearrange smoothly at temperatures of about 200°, in the absence of catalysts. If the ether has an unsubstituted *ortho* position, the product is the *o*-allylphenol. One of the most interesting features of the rearrangement of allyl phenyl ethers to *o*-allylphenols

(*ortho* rearrangement) is the fact that the carbon atom which becomes attached to the aromatic nucleus is not the one attached to the oxygen atom of the ether, but rather the one in the γ-position with respect to the oxygen atom (p. 9). During the rearrangement the double bond of the allyl group shifts from the β,γ-position to the α,β-position. The *inversion* of the allyl group is apparent, of course, only when substituents are present on either the α- or γ-carbon atom. Crotyl phenyl ether (I), for example, rearranges to the branched-chain *o*-methylallylphenol (II).

[1] Claisen, *Ber.*, **45**, 3157 (1912).
[2] Claisen, *Beilstein*, Supplementary Volume III–IV, p. 256.

$$\overset{\alpha}{OCH_2}\overset{\beta}{CH}{=}\overset{\gamma}{CHCH_3}$$

(benzene ring structure)

I

$\rightarrow$

OH

(benzene ring) $-\overset{\gamma}{C}H\overset{\beta}{C}H{=}\overset{\alpha}{C}H_2$
                     |
                     CH_3

II

Allyl ethers of *ortho*-disubstituted phenols rearrange to the corresponding *p*-allylphenols. It is noteworthy that the *para* rearrangement is not usually accompanied by inversion of the allyl group.[3, 4, 5, 6, 7] For example, cinnamyl 2-carbomethoxy-6-methylphenyl ether (III) rearranges without inversion [3] to yield the *p*-cinnamyl derivative (IV).

$OCH_2CH{=}CHC_6H_5$

CH_3 (benzene ring) CO_2CH_3

$\rightarrow$

OH

CH_3 (benzene ring) CO_2CH_3

$CH_2CH{=}CHC_6H_5$

III   IV

The crotyl ether of the same phenol also rearranges without inversion.[3] The only known example of *para* rearrangement accompanied by inversion is the reaction of α-ethylallyl 2-carbomethoxy-6-methylphenyl ether (V), which yields the *p*-(γ-ethylallyl) derivative (VI).[6]

$OCH(C_2H_5)CH{=}CH_2$

CH_3 (benzene ring) CO_2CH_3

$\rightarrow$

OH

CH_3 (benzene ring) CO_2CH_3

$CH_2CH{=}CHC_2H_5$

V   VI

This is also the only known example of *para* rearrangement in which a substituent is present on the α-carbon atom of the allyl group in the ether. Although the number of known *para* rearrangements in which inversion or non-inversion can be detected hardly justifies a generalization, it does appear that a substituent on the γ-carbon atom of the allyl group prevents inversion, whereas a substituent on the α-carbon atom favors inversion. In other words, the *para* rearrangement appears to operate in such a way that either an α- or γ-substituted allyl group leads to a straight-chain substituent in the product.

The occurrence of inversion in the rearrangement of enol ethers appears to be dependent upon the experimental conditions, at least in some instances. This question is discussed on p. 7.

[3] Mumm and Möller, *Ber.*, **70**, 2214 (1937).
[4] Späth and Holzer, *Ber.*, **66**, 1137 (1933).
[5] Späth and Kuffner, *Ber.*, **72**, 1580 (1939).
[6] Mumm, Hornhardt, and Diederichsen, *Ber.*, **72**, 100 (1939).
[7] Mumm and Diederichsen, *Ber.*, **72**, 1523 (1939).

STRUCTURAL REQUIREMENTS FOR REARRANGEMENT;
RELATED REARRANGEMENTS

The group of atoms which allows rearrangement is

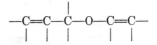

In this group the double bond on the right may be an aliphatic double bond, as in the enol ethers [1, 8, 9] and the allyl vinyl ethers,[10] or part of an aromatic ring, as in the phenol ethers. The double bond on the left must be aliphatic, i.e., must be part of an allyl or substituted allyl group. The position or character of the double bonds in the reactive group cannot be changed without destroying the ability of the compound to rearrange. These generalizations are based (in part) on the following observations. Allyl cyclohexyl ether,[11] methyl O-propylacetoacetate,[1, 12] and n-propyl phenyl ether are stable to heat. Butenyl phenyl ethers of the type $C_6H_5OCH_2CH_2CH=CH_2$ and vinyl phenyl ether, $C_6H_5OCH=CH_2$, do not rearrange.[13] The double bond in the allyl group cannot be replaced by a triple bond without destroying the ability to rearrange;[13, 14] the phenyl propargyl ethers $C_6H_5OCH_2C\equiv CH$ do not rearrange on refluxing, although they do give some phenol and other decomposition products. The benzyl phenyl ethers, $C_6H_5CH_2OC_6H_5$, contain the requisite group of atoms for rearrangement but do not rearrange under conditions effective for the allyl ethers;[13, 15] under more drastic conditions rearrangement does take place [16] but a mixture of *ortho*- and *para*-substituted phenols is formed, while the allyl ethers rearrange almost exclusively to the *ortho* position, if one is free.

The double bond of the vinyl (or aryl) portion of the reactive system may be replaced by a carbon-nitrogen double bond, forming the system

$$-\overset{|}{C}=\overset{|}{C}-\overset{|}{C}-O-\overset{|}{C}=N-,$$ without destroying the tendency toward

rearrangement. For example, allyl N-phenylbenzimino ether (VII) rearranges to an amide (VIII) when heated to 210–215° for three hours.[3]

[8] Lauer and Kilburn, *J. Am. Chem. Soc.*, **59**, 2586 (1937).

[9] Bergmann and Corte, *J. Chem. Soc.*, **1935**, 1363.

[10] Hurd and Pollack, *J. Am. Chem. Soc.*, **60**, 1905 (1938).

[11] Claisen, *Ann.*, **418**, 97 (1919).

[12] Enke, *Ann.*, **256**, 208 (1889).

[13] Powell and Adams, *J. Am. Chem. Soc.*, **42**, 646 (1920).

[14] Hurd and Cohen, *J. Am. Chem. Soc.*, **53**, 1068 (1931).

[15] Claisen, Kremers, Roth, and Tietze, *Ann.*, **442**, 210 (1925).

[16] Behagel and Freiensehner, *Ber.*, **67**, 1368 (1934).

$$\underset{\text{VII}}{\overset{\displaystyle OCH_2CH=CH_2}{\underset{|}{C_6H_5C=NC_6H_5}}} \quad \rightarrow \quad \underset{\text{VIII}}{\overset{\displaystyle O \quad CH_2CH=CH_2}{\underset{|}{C_6H_5C—NC_6H_5}}}$$

A further resemblance of this rearrangement to the Claisen type is to be observed in the occurrence of inversion when the crotyl ether rearranges (IX → X).

$$\underset{\text{IX}}{\overset{\displaystyle OCH_2CH=CHCH_3}{\underset{|}{C_6H_5C=NC_6H_5}}} \quad \rightarrow \quad \underset{\text{X}}{\overset{\displaystyle O \quad CH(CH_3)CH=CH_2}{\underset{|}{C_6H_5C—NC_6H_5}}}$$

Similar reactions are known of compounds in which the carbon-nitrogen bond is part of a heterocyclic nucleus.[17, 18]

The oxygen atom of the reactive system may be replaced by a sulfur atom, with, however, some reduction in the tendency toward rearrangement. Allyl p-tolyl sulfide rearranges (XI → XII) to the extent of 27% (50% based on sulfide not recovered) when subjected to refluxing at 228–264° for four hours.[19]

$$\underset{\text{XI}}{\overset{SCH_2CH=CH_2}{\underset{CH_3}{\bigcirc}}} \quad \rightarrow \quad \underset{\text{XII}}{\overset{SH}{\underset{CH_3}{\bigcirc}CH_2CH=CH_2}}$$

Allyl thiocyanate, $CH_2=CHCH_2SC\equiv N$, on distillation rearranges to allyl isothiocyanate, $CH_2=CHCH_2N=C=S$.[20] Cinnamyl[21] and crotyl[22] thiocyanates also rearrange: the rearrangement of the former occurs without inversion, yielding cinnamyl isothiocyanate; that of the latter is accompanied by inversion, yielding α-methylallyl isothiocyanate.

A reaction similar to the Claisen rearrangement but involving the migration of an allyl group from one carbon atom to another has been discovered recently;[23] for example, ethyl 1-cyclohexenylallylcyanoacetate (XIII) rearranges quantitatively in ten hours at 170° to ethyl (2-allyl-cyclohexylidene)-cyanoacetate (XIV).

[17] Tschitschibabin and Jeletzsky, Ber., **57**, 1158 (1924).

[18] Bergmann and Heimhold, J. Chem. Soc., **1935**, 1365.

[19] Hurd and Greengard, J. Am. Chem. Soc., **52**, 3356 (1930).

[20] Billeter, Ber., **8**, 462 (1875).

[21] Bergmann, J. Chem. Soc., **1935**, 1361.

[22] Mumm and Richter, Ber., **73**, 843 (1940).

[23] Cope and Hardy, J. Am. Chem. Soc., **62**, 441 (1940); Cope, Hoyle, and Heyl, ibid., **63**, 1843 (1941); Cope, Hofmann, and Hardy, ibid., **63**, 1852 (1941).

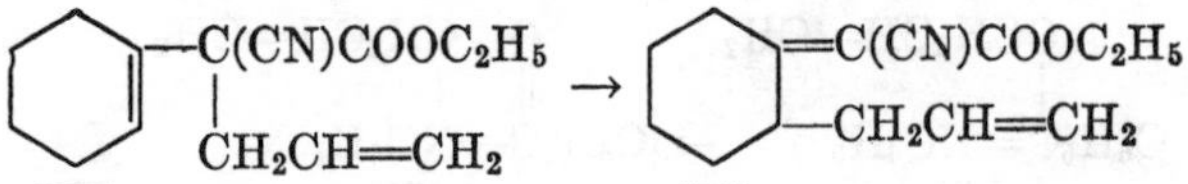

$$\text{XIII} \qquad\qquad \rightarrow \qquad\qquad \text{XIV}$$

XIII structure: cyclohexene ring with $-C(CN)COOC_2H_5$ and $CH_2CH=CH_2$
XIV structure: cyclohexane ring with $=C(CN)COOC_2H_5$ and $-CH_2CH=CH_2$

This type of rearrangement has been shown to take place with inversion; it is a first-order reaction and is believed to be intramolecular because the rearrangement of mixtures yields no mixed products.[23]   In all these respects it resembles the Claisen rearrangement (see p. 16).

The following compounds have systems formally similar to that present in the allyl aryl ethers, but they do not undergo rearrangement on pyrolysis.   N-Allylaniline has the group $-C=C-C-N-C=C-$ but evolves propylene, at temperatures above 275°, instead of rearranging.[24]   Phenoxyacetonitrile contains the group $N\equiv C-C-O-C=C-$ but is unchanged by long refluxing.[13]   p-Tolyloxyacetone [25] does not rearrange, although it does form a little p-cresol; it has the group $O=C-C-O-C=C-$.

SCOPE AND LIMITATIONS

Rearrangement in Open-Chain Compounds (Table I)

Although the Claisen rearrangement was first observed in the enol allyl ethers,[1, 2] the reaction is much more useful and important in the aromatic series.   Some interesting observations have been made, however, with the open-chain systems.   The original reports concerned the rearrangement of ethyl O-allylacetoacetate, O-allylacetylacetone (XIVa), and O-allyloxymethylenecamphor (XV).

$$\begin{array}{cc} CH_3C=CHCOCH_3 & \\ \quad| & \\ \quad OC_3H_5 & \\ \text{XIVa} & \text{XV} \end{array}$$

XIVa structure: $CH_3C=CHCOCH_3$ with OC_3H_5
XV structure: camphor ring with CH_3, $=O$, and $=CHOC_3H_5$

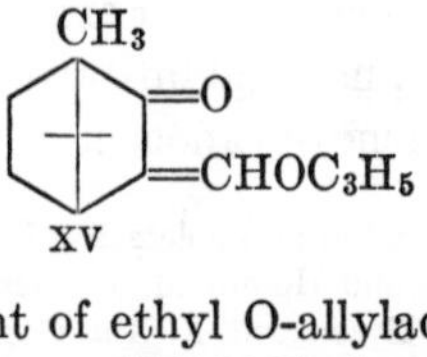

Experimental details of the rearrangement of ethyl O-allylacetoacetate were worked out later; it was found that at 150–200° there is a slow reaction which is more rapid in the presence of ammonium chloride.[8]

[24] Carnahan and Hurd, *J. Am. Chem. Soc.*, **52**, 4586 (1930).
[25] Tarbell, *J. Org. Chem.*, **7**, 251 (1942).

In the rearrangement of ethyl O-cinnamylacetoacetate (XVI), carried out at 110° in the presence of ammonium chloride, the substituted allyl group migrates with inversion to give XVII.

$$CH_3C{=}CHCO_2C_2H_5$$
$$|$$
$$OCH_2CH{=}CHC_6H_5$$
XVI

$$CH_3C{-}CHCO_2C_2H_5$$
$$\parallel \quad |$$
$$O \quad CH(C_6H_5)CH{=}CH_2$$
XVII

$$CH_3C{-}CHCO_2C_2H_5$$
$$\parallel \quad |$$
$$O \quad CH_2CH{=}CHC_6H_5$$
XVIII

However, when the rearrangement is effected by heating at 260° for four hours the product (XVIII) is formed by migration without inversion.[9] There is evidence that, when XVI is hydrolyzed with alcoholic alkali, rearrangement takes place with inversion.[9] Apparently the occurrence of inversion here depends on the experimental conditions.

The simplest compounds to undergo the Claisen rearrangement are the vinyl allyl ethers.[10] Vinyl allyl ether itself rearranges cleanly at 255° in the gas phase (XIX → XX).

$$CH_2{=}CHOCH_2CH{=}CH_2 \rightarrow CH_2{=}CHCH_2CH_2CHO$$
$$\text{XIX} \qquad\qquad\qquad \text{XX}$$

α-Methylvinyl allyl ether and α-phenylvinyl allyl ether behave similarly. Inversion has been found to accompany the rearrangement of vinyl γ-ethylallyl ether (XXI → XXII).

$$CH_2{=}CHOCH_2CH{=}CHC_2H_5 \rightarrow CH_2{=}CHCHCH_2CHO$$
$$|$$
$$C_2H_5$$
$$\text{XXI} \qquad\qquad\qquad\qquad \text{XXII}$$

The rearrangement of ketene diallylacetal is of the Claisen type; it occurs so readily that the ketene acetal cannot be isolated from the products of reaction of diallylbromoacetal with potassium t-butoxide in t-butyl alcohol.[25a]

$$BrCH_2CH(OCH_2CH{=}CH_2)_2 + KOC_4H_9(t)$$
$$\rightarrow KBr + t\text{-}C_4H_9OH + [CH_2{=}C(OCH_2CH{=}CH_2)_2]$$
$$\rightarrow CH_2{=}CHCH_2CH_2CO_2CH_2CH{=}CH_2$$

Allyl allylacetate is obtained in 43% yield. The dibenzylacetal also rearranges, but the migrating benzyl group appears as an o-tolyl group, the product being benzyl o-tolylacetate.

[25a] McElvain, Anthes, and Shapiro, *J. Am. Chem. Soc.*, **64**, 2525 (1942).

A different type of rearrangement in which the allyl group migrates to an open-chain carbon atom has been reported.[26] Allyl ethers of the type XXIII with a propenyl group in the *ortho* position can be rearranged to phenols with the allyl group attached to the side chain; XXIII yields XXIV in 37% yield when refluxed under diminished pressure at 177° for one hour.

Two other examples of this type of rearrangement have been reported.[26] The reaction is interesting because it is analogous to the rearrangement of allyl phenyl ethers to the *para* position of the benzene ring.

Rearrangement of Allyl Aryl Ethers

The *ortho* Rearrangement (Table II).   In the rearrangement of allyl (or substituted allyl) ethers of phenolic compounds, the allyl group usually migrates exclusively to the *ortho* position if one is free, and the product is obtained generally in good yield.   Thus, the simplest aromatic allyl ether, allyl phenyl ether, rearranges almost quantitatively at 200° in an inert atmosphere *, [27, 28, 29] to give *o*-allylphenol; no detectable amount of the *para* isomer is formed.   A few compounds are known which rearrange with some migration of the allyl group to the *para* position although a free *ortho* group is available.   It may be significant that all such compounds, γ,γ-dimethylallyl 2-methoxyphenyl ether,[30] allyl 2-hydroxyphenyl ether,[31, 32] and allyl 2,3-methylenedioxyphenyl ether,[33] are derivatives of polyhydroxybenzenes.

The *para* Rearrangement (Table III).   If both *ortho* positions of an allyl aromatic ether are blocked, the allyl group migrates to the *para* position.   If both *ortho* positions and the *para* position are occupied, complex decomposition ensues, but the allyl group never goes to the

---

* See p. 79 of the article cited in reference 11.

[26] Claisen and Tietze, *Ann.*, **449**, 81 (1926).

[27] Lauer and Leekley, *J. Am. Chem. Soc.*, **61**, 3042 (1939).

[28] Adams and Rindfusz, *J. Am. Chem. Soc.*, **41**, 648 (1919).

[29] Hurd and Hoffman, *J. Org. Chem.*, **5**, 212 (1940).

[30] Staudinger, Kreis, and Schilt, *Helv. Chim. Acta*, **5**, 743 (1922).

[31] Kawai, *Sci. Papers Inst. Phys. Chem. Research Tokyo*, **3**, 263 (1926) [*Chem. Zentr.*, I, 3144 (1926)].

[32] Perkin and Trikojus, *J. Chem. Soc.*, **1927**, 1663.

[33] Baker, Penfold, and Simonsen, *J. Chem. Soc.*, **1939**, 439.

meta position.[26, 34]   The *para* rearrangement usually is as satisfactory as the *ortho* rearrangement, with yields sometimes in excess of 85%.

Effect of Substituents in the Allyl Group.   Ethers with the allyl group substituted by alkyl groups in the α- or γ-position, $ArOCH(R)CH=CH_2$ or $ArOCH_2CH=CHR$, rearrange to give products in which the γ-carbon atom of the allyl group is attached at the *ortho* position of the ring.   This phenomenon of inversion (see p. 2) was first noted [35] in the rearrangement of cinnamyl phenyl ether (XXV) to 2-(α-phenylallyl)-phenol (XXVI).

The structure of XXVI was deduced from the fact that it was different from the 2-cinnamylphenol obtained by direct C-cinnamylation of phenol.[15]   Later investigators showed that XXVI is the sole product; ozonization yielded formaldehyde but not benzaldehyde.   γ-Methyl-allyl phenyl ether also rearranges with inversion, yielding 2-(α-methyl-allyl)-phenol;[36] the structure of the rearrangement product has been definitely established [37, 38] by a combination of degradative and synthetic procedures.

Study of many substituted allyl ethers has shown that in no case in rearrangement to the *ortho* position is the substituted allyl group attached to the nucleus after rearrangement by the same carbon which was attached to the oxygen; usually the attachment is by the γ-carbon (inversion).   The first example of the abnormal rearrangement (attachment by other than the γ-carbon atom) was found in the rearrangement of γ-ethylallyl phenyl ether (XXVII).[39, 40]   The product is 2-(α,γ-dimethylallyl)-phenol (XXVIII), which must be formed as a result of attachment of the δ- (or β-) carbon to the nucleus.

[34] Hurd and Yarnall, *J. Am. Chem. Soc.*, **59**, 1686 (1937).
[35] Claisen and Tietze, *Ber.*, **58**, 275 (1925).
[36] Claisen and Tietze, *Ber.*, **59**, 2344 (1926).
[37] Lauer and Ungnade, *J. Am. Chem. Soc.*, **58**, 1392 (1936).
[38] Lauer and Hansen, *J. Am. Chem. Soc.*, **61**, 3039 (1939).
[39] Hurd and Pollack, *J. Org. Chem.*, **3**, 550 (1939).
[40] Lauer and Filbert, *J. Am. Chem. Soc.*, **58**, 1388 (1936).

OH

$\text{CH}(C_2H_5)\text{CH}=\text{CH}_2$

XXIX

The presence of the normal product, 2-(α-ethylallyl)-phenol (XXIX), in the rearrangement mixture from XXVII has been demonstrated.[39] The allylic isomer of (XXVII), α-ethylallyl phenyl ether (XXX), rearranges normally [40] to give only the expected product (XXXI).

$\text{OCH}(C_2H_5)\text{CH}=\text{CH}_2$ OH

                                              $\text{CH}_2\text{CH}=\text{CHC}_2H_5$

XXX   XXXI

In the rearrangement of the γ-propylallyl ether derived from ethyl 4-hydroxybenzoate, the abnormal product with the side chain —$\text{CH}(\text{CH}_3)\text{CH}=\text{CHCH}_2\text{CH}_3$ predominates over the normal product [side chain, —$\text{CH}(\text{CH}_2\text{CH}_2\text{CH}_3)\text{CH}=\text{CH}_2$] by a ratio of two to one.[41] The corresponding γ-ethylallyl ethers behave similarly. The α-substituted allyl ethers, however, such as $\text{ArOCH}(\text{CH}_2\text{CH}_3)\text{CH}=\text{CH}_2$, yield only the normal product with γ-attachment.

The structures of the rearrangement products in studies on inversion and the abnormal rearrangement are assigned by identification of the aldehyde formed by ozonization. Sometimes the substituted arylacetic acid obtained by oxidation of the rearrangement product (after methylation) has been characterized and/or synthesized. Another method of proving structures consists in ozonization, followed by oxidation of the aldehydes with silver oxide; the mixture of acids [39] (formic, acetic, and propionic) is analyzed by selective oxidation.

The generalizations above apply only to the migration to the *ortho* position. When a substituted allyl ether of the type $\text{ArOCH}_2\text{CH}=\text{CHR}$ rearranges to the *para* position, inversion does *not* occur. As mentioned earlier (p. 3), the only known *para* rearrangement of an ether of the type $\text{ArOCH}(R)\text{CH}=\text{CH}_2$ proceeds *with* inversion. No evidence for the formation of abnormal products in the *para* rearrangement has been reported.

The presence of an alkyl group on the β-carbon of the allyl group, as in the β-methylallyl ethers, $\text{ArOCH}_2\text{C}(\text{CH}_3)=\text{CH}_2$, introduces no complications due to inversion, because the β-substituted allyl group is symmetrical. A number of β-methylallyl ethers have been made, and they rearrange in good yield.

[41] Lauer and Leekley, *J. Am. Chem. Soc.*, **61**, 3043 (1939).

Allyl aryl ethers with halogen atoms in the allyl group rearrange very poorly; β-bromoallyl phenyl ether is reported to give 30% rearrangement after ninety minutes at 215°, 50% being recovered unchanged.[42] Later experiments have not confirmed this, phenolic resins being the only product observed; however, by rearrangement of the corresponding chloro compound, a 24% yield was obtained.[43] The γ-halogen ethers, such as $C_6H_5OCH_2CH=CHCl$, do not rearrange, although they do decompose and yield some phenol.[43]

Effect of Substituents in the Aromatic Nucleus. Substituents in the aromatic nucleus do not affect the ease of rearrangement greatly, and it is noteworthy that *meta* directing groups in the nucleus do not hinder the reaction, nor do the strongly *ortho-para* directing groups seem to favor it greatly. Rearrangements have been reported for allyl aryl ethers with the following substituents in the aromatic nucleus (Table II): hydroxyl, methoxyl, methylenedioxy, allyloxy (rearrangement involving migration of two allyl groups), formyl, carboxyl, acetyl, propionyl, γ-hydroxypropyl, carbethoxyl, β-carbomethoxyvinyl, halo, nitro, amino, acetamino, and azo. Allyl ethers derived from the following aromatic and heterocyclic nuclei have been rearranged: benzene, toluene, xylene, allylbenzene, naphthalene, anthracene, phenanthrene, fluorene, biphenyl, hydrindene, fluorescein, quinaldine, flavone, chromone, dibenzofuran, coumarin, and benzothiazole.

Displacement of Substituents. No complications are caused by the presence of ester groups in the aromatic nucleus, but, if a free carboxyl or aldehyde group is present in the position *ortho* or *para* to the ether linkage, it may be displaced by the allyl group (Table II, Section C). O-Allyl-3,5,-diallylsalicylic acid (XXXII) gives a quantitative yield of 2,4,6-triallylphenol (XXXIII), the evolution of carbon dioxide starting at 100°.[44] O-Allylsalicylic acid (XXXIV) when heated at 175–180° gives 23% of 2-allylphenol, with loss of carbon dioxide, and 64% of 3-allylsalicylic acid (XXXV).[45] A carboxyl group in the *para* position also is eliminated easily; thus 3,5-diallyl-4-allyloxybenzoic acid (XXXVI)

XXXII

XXXIII

XXXIV

XXXV

[42] v. Braun, Kuhn, and Weismantel, *Ann.*, **449**, 264 (1926).
[43] Hurd and Webb, *J. Am. Chem. Soc.*, **58**, 2190 (1936).
[44] Claisen and Eisleb, *Ann.*, **401**, 79 (1913).
[45] Tarbell and Wilson, *J. Am. Chem. Soc.*, **64**, 607 (1942).

rearranges and evolves 99% of the theoretical amount of carbon dioxide.[*]

The displacement reaction is accompanied by inversion when migration is to the *ortho* position; thus the crotyl ether of 3,5-dichlorosalicylic acid (XXXVII) gives XXXVIII.[45] In the rearrangement of the isomer of XXXVII, in which carbon dioxide is evolved from the *para* position, inversion does not occur.[46] These results parallel those in the ordinary rearrangement. It is interesting to note that the benzyl *ether* corresponding to XXXVII rearranges on heating to give the benzyl *ester* of 3,5-dichlorosalicylic acid, and carbon dioxide is not evolved in appreciable amounts.[46a]

The displacement reactions with the ethers having aldehyde groups in the positions *ortho* or *para* to the ether linkage are similar, although they do not go as smoothly and the temperatures required seem to be higher. Thus allyl 2-formyl-4-allyl-6-methoxyphenyl ether (XXXIX) gives XL in 60% yield when heated at 170–285°.[†]

A displacement of the chlorine atom has been observed in the rearrangement of allyl 2,6-dichlorophenyl ether (XLI), which is converted to the normal product (XLII, 60% yield) along with a little (10% yield) of 2-allyl-6-chlorophenol (XLIII).[46] Some hydrogen chloride is evolved, also.

Allyl 2,6-dibromophenyl ether behaves similarly.[43, 47]

[*] See p. 91 of the article cited in reference 44.
[†] See p. 115 of the article cited in reference 44.
[46] Tarbell and Wilson, *J. Am. Chem. Soc.*, **64**, 1066 (1942).
[46a] Tarbell and Wystrach, *J. Am. Chem. Soc.*, **65**, 2146 (1943).
[47] Hurd and Webb, *J. Am. Chem. Soc.*, **58**, 941 (1936).

Although the effect of ring substituents, other than carboxyl and aldehyde groups, upon the rearrangement is usually small, provided that one or more unsubstituted *ortho* or *para* positions are available, poor results have been reported with the following ethers of substituted phenols; it is probable that further study will disclose satisfactory reaction conditions for at least some of these rearrangements. Allyl 2-allyl-4-methylphenyl ether and the allyl ether of allyl-*m*-cresol give poor reactions, probably because of polymerization.* Allyl 4-nitro-phenyl ether rearranges in 30 to 40% yield on refluxing in paraffin oil at 230°; the 2-nitro compound gives a 73% yield at 180°.† Allyl 2-(hydroxymethyl)-phenyl ether yields formaldehyde and decomposition products when heated,‡ but it is reported [48] that allyl 2-methoxy-4-(γ-hydroxypropyl)-phenyl ether rearranges (in unspecified yield), so that a hydroxyl group in a side chain does not necessarily preclude rearrangement.

Relation of Bond Structure to Rearrangement. Numerous examples have been found, in the allyloxy derivatives of polycyclic aromatic compounds in particular, where rearrangement does not take place although it would be expected if the aromatic nucleus could react in all of the possible Kekulé bond structures. From the introductory discussion, it is clear that the reaction requires the ether oxygen to be attached to a double bond and that after rearrangement the allyl group is attached to the same double bond. The failure of 1-allyl-2-allyloxynaphthalene (XLIV) to rearrange even after long heating [1] is explained by assuming

XLIV   XLV   XLVI

that the naphthalene nucleus cannot react in the unsymmetrical form (XLV) with a double bond in the 2,3-position. While 2,6-diallyloxy-naphthalene [49] rearranges smoothly in 85% yield, 1,5-diallyl-2,6-diallyl-oxynaphthalene (XLVI) does not rearrange in five minutes at 200° and, on longer heating, decomposes without forming any alkali-soluble material. This supports the conclusion that naphthalene does not undergo reactions which would require double bonds in the 2,3- and 6,7-positions.

---

* See pp. 45 and 58 of the article cited in reference 44.

† See pp. 40 and 59 of the article cited in reference 44.

‡ See p. 106 of the article cited in reference 44.

[48] Kawai, Nakamura, and Sugiyama, *Proc. Imp. Acad. Tokyo*, **15**, 45 (1939) [*C. A.*, **33**, 5394 (1939)].

[49] Fieser and Lothrop, *J. Am. Chem. Soc.*, **57**, 1459 (1935).

Similar studies of the relationship between bond structures and the Claisen rearrangement have been made with allyloxy derivatives of other aromatic compounds, among them anthracene,[50] phenanthrene,[51] hydrindene,[52] fluorene,[53] chromone,[54] flavone,[54] fluorenone,[55] and 2-methylbenzothiazole.[55a]

The monoallyl ether of resacetophenone [56, 57] rearranges with migration of the allyl group to the 3-position instead of to the 5-position which is usually favored in reactions of substitution. This is attributed to formation of a chelate ring containing a double bond, which stabilizes one Kekulé structure and directs the allyl group to the 3-position (XLVII → XLVIII). With the methyl ether (XLIX) of XLVII, chelation being impossible, there is no stabilization of the bond structure; the allyl group migrates to the 5-position and L is formed.

XLVII   XLVIII   XLIX   L

Side Reactions. A side reaction that often accompanies the rearrangement of substituted allyl ethers is the cleavage of the allyl group from the oxygen with the formation of a phenol and a diene; the cleavage reaction is favored by increased substitution in the allyl group.[58, 59, 60, 61] Thus, α,γ-dimethylallyl 4-carbethoxyphenyl ether (LI) gives a 59% yield of

LI   LII   LIII

[50] Fieser and Lothrop, *J. Am. Chem. Soc.*, **58,** 749 (1936).
[51] Fieser and Young, *J. Am. Chem. Soc.*, **53,** 4120 (1931).
[52] Lothrop, *J. Am. Chem. Soc.*, **62,** 132 (1940).
[53] Lothrop, *J. Am. Chem. Soc.*, **61,** 2115 (1939).
[54] Rangaswami and Seshadri, *Proc. Indian Acad. Sci.*, **9A,** 1 (1939) [*C. A.*, **33,** 4244 (1939)].
[55] Bergmann and Berlin, *J. Am. Chem. Soc.*, **62,** 316 (1940).
[55a] Ochiai and Nisizawa, *Ber.*, **74,** 1407 (1941) [*C. A.*, **36,** 5475 (1942)].
[56] Baker and Lothian, *J. Chem. Soc.*, **1935,** 628.
[57] Baker and Lothian, *J. Chem. Soc.*, **1936,** 274.
[58] Hurd and Puterbaugh, *J. Org. Chem.*, **2,** 381 (1937).
[59] Hurd and McNamee, *J. Am. Chem, Soc.*, **54,** 1648 (1932).
[60] Hurd and Schmerling, *J. Am. Chem. Soc.*, **59,** 107 (1937).
[61] Hurd and Cohen, *J. Am. Chem. Soc.*, **53,** 1917 (1931).

1,3-pentadiene and ethyl 4-hydroxybenzoate.[62] 2-Cyclohexenyl phenyl ether (LII) gives a 50–60% yield of phenol and cyclohexadiene, with 5% of the expected rearrangement product (LIII) and 15% of hexahydrodibenzofuran (LIV).[63] The very highly substituted ether, $\alpha,\alpha,\gamma,\gamma$-tetra-

LIV   LV

methylallyl phenyl ether (LV) undergoes only the cleavage reaction without any rearrangement, 33% of the diene being obtained after one hour at 160–170°.[61] It has been reported,[36, 64] but without experimental details, that γ,γ-dimethylallyl phenyl ether yields phenol and isoprene on heating, but that when heated with sodium carbonate it undergoes rearrangement. Recently it has been shown[64a] that pyrolysis of γ,γ-dimethylallyl 4-carbethoxyphenyl ether (LVa) gives

LVa   LVb

mainly the cleavage products, isoprene and ethyl 4-hydroxybenzoate; the dihydrobenzofuran derivative (LVb) is produced in small yield, apparently as the result of an abnormal rearrangement with attachment by the β-carbon, followed by ring closure. The cleavage of a substituted allyl ether and formation of the phenol have been observed also in an attempted catalytic reduction at low temperature and pressure with a palladium[6] or a platinum catalyst.[65, 18]

The other side reaction which is sometimes troublesome is illustrated by the formation of LIV (see p. 18). The rearrangement of allyl phenyl ether itself yields, in addition to 2-allylphenol,* a small amount (4–6%) of the methyldihydrobenzofuran (LVI), which is probably produced

LVI

* See p. 79 of the article cited in reference 11.

[62] Lauer and Ungnade, *J. Am. Chem. Soc.*, **61**, 3047 (1939).

[63] Cornforth, Hughes, and Lions, *J. Proc. Royal Soc. N. S. Wales*, **71**, 323 (1938) [*C. A.* **33**, 148 (1939)].

[64] Claisen, *J. prakt. Chem.*, [2] **105**, 65 (1922).

[64a] Lauer and Moe, *J. Am. Chem. Soc.*, **65**, 289 (1943).

[65] Tarbell and Wilson, unpublished observation.

by ring closure of the initial product. Compounds with substituted allyl groups seem to form the dihydrobenzofurans more readily than the unsubstituted allyl compounds; [43, 63, 66] thus 2-(β-methylallyl)-phenol [66] forms the corresponding dihydrobenzofuran on heating or even on standing in petroleum ether solution over anhydrous magnesium sulfate.

Mechanism of the Rearrangement *

The Claisen rearrangement to the *ortho* position is a first-order reaction,[67, 68] and the process does not require catalysis by acids and bases. The rearrangement is intramolecular, since rearrangement of mixtures of ethers such as allyl β-naphthyl ether and cinnamyl phenyl ether,[60] or cinnamyl 4-methylphenyl ether and allyl 4-aminophenyl ether,[68] yields none of the cross products which would result from an intermolecular reaction. The process is best represented by the cyclic mechanism, in which the following processes take place, with the electronic shifts during reaction indicated by the arrows.[23, 39, 69]

LVII   LVIII   LIX

The breaking of the carbon-oxygen bond and the attachment of the γ-carbon atom to the *ortho* position must be simultaneous, and this step, rather than the enolization of the hydrogen, must be the rate-determining step. If the latter were the slow step, the reaction would be speeded up by dimethylaniline, and this is not observed. The cyclic mechanism accounts for the occurrence of inversion.

The mechanism is in agreement with the observation [45] that crotyl ethers rearrange more rapidly than allyl ethers, because the γ-methyl group would promote the electronic shifts indicated. The cyclic mechanism as written does not explain the abnormal rearrangement, which involves the shift of two hydrogens, but this may involve a cyclic intermediate in which the β-carbon becomes attached to the *ortho* carbon atom.

* Cf. Tarbell, *Chem. Revs.*, **27**, 495 (1940), for a more detailed discussion.

[66] Bartz, Miller, and Adams, *J. Am. Chem. Soc.*, **57**, 371 (1935).

[67] Kincaid and Tarbell, *J. Am. Chem. Soc.*, **61**, 3085 (1939).

[68] Kincaid and Morse, Abstracts of the Atlantic City meeting, September, 1941.

[69] Watson, *Ann. Repts. Chem. Soc.*, **1939**, 206.

The *para* rearrangement is also a first-order reaction, and the rate is not greatly affected by acetic acid or dimethylaniline.[70] The non-occurrence of inversion, and the atomic distances involved, make a cyclic mechanism improbable. The rearrangement may go through a first-order dissociation of the allyl ether into either radicals or ions, which must then be assumed to recombine, with the allyl group entering the *para* position, before any secondary reactions can take place. If allyl radicals (or ions) actually were free during the reaction, they should combine with a reactive solvent such as dimethylaniline, and the yield of rearrangement product would be low, which is contrary to the observed facts. A study[70a] of the decomposition of quaternary ammonium compounds of the type $[Me_2\overset{+}{N}(C_6H_5)C_3H_5]$ $[OAr]^-$ indicates that ions are not intermediates in the Claisen rearrangement. From the rearrangement of benzyl phenyl ether in quinoline at 250°, Hickinbottom[71] isolated benzylquinolines, hydroxyphenylquinolines, and toluene, indicating the intermediate formation of benzyl radicals. There is no evidence for the formation of similar products in the Claisen rearrangement.

Synthetic Application

The usefulness of the Claisen rearrangement in synthetic work depends on the following facts. The allyl aryl ethers, such as phenyl allyl ether (LX), can be prepared easily in high yields and can be transformed readily in good yields to the 2-allylphenols (LXI). The reaction thus

furnishes a convenient method of introducing allyl groups into a wide variety of phenolic compounds. Among the naturally occurring allylphenols which have been synthesized by this method are elemicin,[72, 73] eugenol,* croweacin,[33] and dill apiole.[74] The allylphenols serve as easily accessible starting materials for other synthetic operations. Reduction converts them to propyl (or substituted propyl) phenols (LXII), and this

* See p. 118 of the article cited in reference 11.
[70] Tarbell and Kincaid, *J. Am. Chem. Soc.*, **62**, 728 (1940).
[70a] Tarbell and Vaughan, *J. Am. Chem. Soc.*, **65**, 231 (1943).
[71] Hickinbottom, *Nature*, **143**, 520 (1939).
[72] Mauthner, *Ann.*, **414**, 250 (1917).
[73] Hahn and Wassmuth, *Ber.*, **67**, 696 (1934).
[74] Baker, Jukes, and Subrahmanyam, *J. Chem. Soc.*, **1934**, 1681.

provides a convenient method of introducing a propyl group into a phenol.

Because of the occurrence of inversion, compounds of the structure $HOArCH_2CH{=}CHR$ cannot be prepared by rearrangement of ethers containing substituted allyl radicals such as farnesyl and phytyl groups. β-Methylallyl ethers are not subject to this disadvantage, because inversion does not change the structure of the group, and rearrangement of the ethers followed by reduction has been employed as a convenient method of introducing the isobutyl group into phenols.[66]

The allyl group in the allylphenols can be oxidized, after protecting the hydroxyl group, to yield substituted phenylacetaldehydes [73, 75, 76] and phenylacetic acids. Thus, homogentisic acid LXIII is prepared readily by ozonizing the dibenzoate of allylhydroquinone LXIV, which is obtained by rearrangement of the allyl ether of hydroquinone mono-

LXIII   LXIV   LXV

benzoate followed by benzoylation.[77] The ozonization procedure has been developed to give a good yield of 3,4,5-trimethoxyphenylacetalde-hyde (LXV) from the corresponding allyl compound.[73]

The 2-allylphenols in the presence of acid catalysts such as pyridine hydrochloride,[*, 66] hydrobromic acid-acetic acid, or formic acid [36] form 2-methyldihydrobenzofurans (coumarans) such as LXVI. In the pres-

LXVI   LXVII   LXVIII

ence of hydrogen bromide and a peroxide, 2-allylphenyl acetate gives the isomeric dihydrobenzopyran or chroman (LXVII).[29, 78, †] Ring

---

* See p. 26 of the article cited in reference 44.

† This problem of ring closure of allylphenols is of importance in the chemistry of vitamin E and has been discussed in detail by Smith (reference 78).

[75] Schöpf and co-workers, *Ann.*, **544**, 30 (1940).

[76] Mauthner, *J. prakt. Chem.*, [2] **148**, 95 (1937).

[77] Hahn and Stenner, *Z. physiol. Chem.*, **181**, 88 (1929).

[78] Smith, *Chem. Revs.*, **27**, 287 (1940).

closure of 2-(γ,γ-dimethylallyl)-phenol gives only the chroman LXVIII, irrespective of the presence or absence of peroxides.[29]

Treatment of 2-allylphenols with mercuric salts gives mercurimethyl-

LXIX   LXX

dihydrobenzofurans such as LXIX.[79, 80, 81] The halomercuri group can be replaced by iodine by treatment with potassium iodide, and this is a method of preparing iodo compounds like LXX.

Another occasionally useful transformation of allylphenols is the isomerization to propenylphenols by strong alkali, as in the well-known isomerization of eugenol to isoeugenol. For example, 2-methoxy-6-allylphenol (LXXI) is changed to the propenyl compound LXXII by

LXXI   LXXII

heating 1 part of the phenol with 2 parts of powdered potassium hydroxide and 1 of water for one hour at 170°.* This isomerization also can be brought about by heating with soda lime without solvent, but the phenolic hydroxyl must be etherified.[64] A solution of sodium or potassium hydroxide in diethylene glycol may be used for the isomerization.[81a] The propenylphenols can be distinguished from the allylphenols by their different behavior toward mercuric acetate.[82] The propenyl compounds are oxidized to glycols, and mercurous acetate is precipitated; the allyl compounds can add the elements of basic mercuric acetate, giving a solid addition product from which the allyl compound can be recovered by reduction with zinc and alkali. If a mixture of propenyl and allyl compounds is present, and less than the necessary amount of mercuric acetate is used, the allyl compound reacts preferentially and the unchanged propenyl compound can be separated by extraction or steam distillation. This makes possible a separation of the two isomers. However, the γ,γ-dimethylallyl aromatic derivatives are oxidized by mer-

* See p. 52 of the article cited in reference 44.
[79] Adams, Roman, and Sperry, J. Am. Chem. Soc., 44, 1781 (1922).
[80] Mills and Adams, J. Am. Chem. Soc., 45, 1842 (1923).
[81] Nesmejanow and Sarewitsch, Ber., 68, 1476 (1935).
[81a] Fletcher and Tarbell, J. Am. Chem. Soc., 65, 1431 (1943).
[82] Balbiano, Ber., 48, 394 (1915), and previous papers.

curic acetate, with formation of mercurous acetate, so that the test must be used with caution.[64]   The propenylphenols can be ozonized to the hydroxyaldehydes,[48, 76] but these usually can be prepared more easily by standard methods.

OTHER METHODS OF SYNTHESIS OF ALLYLPHENOLS

Allylphenols and derivatives with substituents in the allyl group can be prepared by direct C-alkylation of the sodium salt of the phenol in benzene solution.[15]   This method is not as good for the preparation of allylphenols themselves as the one involving preparation of the allyl ether followed by rearrangement, because a mixture of several products is obtained in C-alkylation.   Thus the alkylation of p-cresol in benzene with sodium and allyl bromide yields 20% of allyl 4-methylphenyl ether, 8% of allyl 2-allyl-4-methylphenyl ether, 40% of 2-allyl-4-methyl-phenol, and 15% of 2,6-diallyl-4-methylphenol.[15]   The rearrangement of allyl 4-methylphenyl ether, however, yields 2-allyl-4-methylphenol in practically quantitative yield, and the ether is easily obtained.

The substituted allylphenols such as cinnamyl (LXXIII, R = C_6H_5) and crotyl (LXXIII, R = CH_3) can be prepared by C-alkylation more

LXXIII   LXXIV

easily than the allyl compounds, because the more reactive substituted allyl halides give rise to more C-alkylation and less O-alkylation. Thus 2-cinnamylphenol (LXXIII, R = C_6H_5) can be made in 60% yield from sodium phenoxide and cinnamyl bromide in benzene.[15]   It is interesting to note that chloro- and bromo-acetones do not yield C-alkyl derivatives when treated with the sodium salt of a phenol in benzene.[25]

Compounds of type LXXIII cannot be made by the rearrangement of the γ-substituted allyl ethers, because these compounds yield LXXIV by inversion.[83]   α,γ-Dimethylallyl bromide,[15] γ,γ-dimethylallyl bromide,[29] cinnamyl chloride,[84] and phytyl bromide [85] (a vitamin K synthesis) have been used in C-alkylation procedures.   The silver salt of 2-hydroxy-1,4-naphthoquinone is converted to a mixture of C-alkylation product and two isomeric ethers by treatment with allylic halides and benzyl halides.[84]

[83] Makino and Morii, Z. physiol. Chem., 263, 80 (1940), disregarded this fact.
[84] Fieser, J. Am. Chem. Soc., 48, 3201 (1926).
[85] MacCorquodale et al., J. Biol. Chem., 131, 357 (1939).

The condensation of allylic alcohols with phenolic compounds in the presence of an acid catalyst yields allylphenols.   This reaction was used [86] in a synthesis of vitamin K (LXXVa) by condensing phytol with 2-methyl-1,4-naphthohydroquinone in dioxane with oxalic or trichloroacetic acid as catalyst; the hydroquinone first formed was oxidized to

$CH_2CH=C(CH_3)CH_2C_{15}H_{31}$
CH_3

LXXVa

CH_3
$CH_2CH=C(CH_3)CH_2C_{15}H_{31}$

LXXVb

the quinone LXXVa.   An interesting side reaction here was the formation of the isomeric diketone LXXVb.[87]   This method of synthesis seems to be superior to the C-alkylation by the use of phytyl bromide and the sodium salt of the hydroquinone,[85] and to the condensation of phytyl bromide with the hydroquinone with zinc as a catalyst.[88]   Frequently, however, condensation of an allylic alcohol with a phenol leads to a chroman derivative, as in the synthesis of vitamin E (LXXVII) from phytol and trimethylhydroquinone.[89, 90]   The reaction of an allylic halide with a free phenol in the presence or absence of an acid catalyst (in contrast to the C-alkylation of the sodium salt of the phenol) frequently gives the chroman instead of the allylphenol.

Dienes also condense with phenolic compounds, but the product is usually a chroman.   Isoprene[91] condenses with phenol to yield 2,2-dimethylchroman LXXVI, and phytadiene[92] condenses with trimethyl-

CH_3
CH_3

LXXVI

CH_3
HO
CH_3
$C_{16}H_{33}$
CH_3
CH_3 O

LXXVII

hydroquinone under acid conditions to give the chroman LXXVII (vitamin E).   In some instances, however, allylphenols can be obtained by the condensation of a phenol and a diene;[92a, 93] butadiene and tri-

[86] Fieser, J. Am. Chem. Soc., 61, 3467 (1939).
[87] Tishler, Fieser, and Wendler, J. Am. Chem. Soc., 62, 1982 (1940).
[88] Almquist and Klose, J. Biol. Chem., 132, 469 (1940).
[89] Bergel, Jacob, Todd, and Work, J. Chem. Soc., 1938, 1382.
[90] Smith and Ungnade, J. Org. Chem., 4, 298 (1939).
[91] Claisen, Ber., 54, 200 (1921).
[92] Smith, Ungnade, Hoehn, and Wawzonek, J. Org. Chem., 4, 311 (1939).
[92a] Fieser, Campbell, Fry, and Gates, J. Am. Chem. Soc., 61, 2559, 3216 (1939).
[93] Smith and King, J. Am. Chem. Soc., 63, 1887 (1941).

methylhydroquinone yield LXXVIII, and the same product is obtained from the hydroquinone and crotyl alcohol.[93]

$$
\begin{array}{c}
\text{CH}_3 \\
\text{H}_3\text{C} \overset{}{\diagdown}\!\!\!\overset{}{\diagup} \text{OH} \\
\text{HO} \overset{}{\diagup}\!\!\!\overset{}{\diagdown} \text{CH}_2\text{CH}{=}\text{CHCH}_3 \\
\text{CH}_3
\end{array}
$$

LXXVIII

In summary, it can be said that the γ-substituted allylphenols can be prepared by C-alkylation of the sodium salt of the phenol in benzene, and they usually cannot be prepared by the Claisen rearrangement. The condensation of free phenols with allylic halides, allylic alcohols, and dienes may give allylphenols, but frequently yields other products.[*, 94]

EXPERIMENTAL CONDITIONS AND PROCEDURES

Preparation of Allyl Ethers

The most widely used method † of preparing allyl aryl ethers consists in refluxing the phenol with allyl bromide and anhydrous potassium carbonate in acetone for several hours; allyl bromide may be replaced advantageously by allyl chloride and sodium iodide,[76, 95] and acetone may be replaced by the higher-boiling methyl ethyl ketone. The method usually gives very good yields but is unsatisfactory for weakly acidic phenols; these can be treated with sodium ethoxide in ethanol solution, then with the allyl halide. The procedure is also unsatisfactory for phenolic aldehydes, which condense with acetone in the presence of potassium carbonate. Substituted allyl chlorides and bromides usually can be employed successfully,[36, 40, 58, 66] although the yields are poorer, probably owing to C-alkylation.

Secondary ethers of the type $ArOCH(R)CH{=}CH_2$, where R is ethyl or n-propyl, are prepared from the chlorides instead of the bromides [6, 40, 41, 62] because the isomeric chlorides $ClCH(R)CH{=}CH_2$ and $RCH{=}CHCH_2Cl$ can be separated by distillation.[96] The corresponding primary and secondary bromides are in very mobile equilibrium,[97, 98] and, although

* The topic discussed in this section is of great importance in the chemistry of vitamin E and vitamin K, and more detailed information is available in the reviews of vitamin E by Smith (reference 78) and of vitamin K by Doisy, Binkley, and Thayer (reference 94).

† See p. 29 of the article cited in reference 44.

[94] Doisy, Binkley, and Thayer, *Chem. Revs.*, **28**, 477 (1941).

[95] Smith, Hoehn, and Whitney, *J. Am. Chem. Soc.*, **62**, 1863 (1940).

[96] Meisenheimer and Link, *Ann.*, **479**, 254 (1930).

[97] Winstein and Young, *J. Am. Chem. Soc.*, **58**, 104 (1936).

[98] Young, Richards, and Azorlosa, *J. Am. Chem. Soc.*, **61**, 3070 (1939).

the allylic isomers can be separated by careful distillation, the chlorides are much more useful for synthetic work.

The Williamson synthesis, using a sodium phenoxide and allyl bromide in methanol solution, is more rapid than the procedure using acetone and potassium carbonate and gives good results.[15, 35, 44, 66] Aqueous acetone also has been used as the reaction medium with allyl bromide and sodium hydroxide; this method likewise is rapid and sometimes leads to better yields than the procedure using potassium carbonate and acetone.[34] Allylation of 2-hydroxy-1,4-naphthoquinone has been carried out by treating the silver salt, in benzene, with allyl bromide;[84] some C-alkylation as well as O-alkylation was observed.

The extent of C-alkylation as a side reaction in etherification varies; about 1% of allyl 2-allylphenyl ether is formed when phenol is used in the acetone and potassium carbonate method with allyl bromide; * with cinnamyl bromide or γ,γ-dimethylallyl bromide the extent of C-alkylation is greater.[15] A complicated mixture of C- and O-alkylation products results from the treatment of phenol with 4-bromo-2-hexene and 4-chloro-2-hexene.[99] 4-Hexenylresorcinol has been obtained in about 40% yield from the reaction of 1-bromo-2-hexene, resorcinol, and potassium carbonate in boiling acetone.[99a] An appreciable amount of C-alkylation occurs when 2,6-dimethylphenol is treated with allyl bromide and sodium ethoxide in ethanol.[70] Since, in general, the amount of C-alkylation is greatly increased by carrying out the alkylation on the sodium salt of the phenol in benzene,[15] this method is unsuitable for the preparation of allyl aryl ethers.

In preparing ethers of o-carbomethoxyphenols it has been found that the slow dropwise addition of aqueous sodium hydroxide or potassium carbonate to a refluxing mixture of the proper phenol and halide in methyl ethyl ketone gives a smoother reaction with yields much better than those obtained when all the alkali is added before refluxing is begun.[46a]

Conditions of Rearrangement

The simpler allyl aryl ethers can be rearranged by refluxing at atmospheric pressure until the boiling point becomes constant; since the boiling point of the product is higher than that of the ether, the boiling point rises until the reaction is complete. The rearrangement is nearly always exothermic—so much so that it may become troublesome when large batches are run without solvent.

* See p. 78 of the article cited in reference 11.
[99] Smith, Ungnade, Lauer, and Leekley, J. Am. Chem. Soc., **61**, 3079 (1939).
[99a] Hurd and McNamee, J. Am. Chem. Soc., **59**, 104 (1937).

Ethers of higher boiling point frequently undergo undesirable side reactions when refluxed at atmospheric pressure, and often better yields are obtained by refluxing under diminished pressure.* The same result can be obtained more conveniently by mixing the ether with a solvent to act as diluent, the solvents most frequently employed being dimethylaniline (b.p. 193°) and diethylaniline (b.p. 215°). Better yields have been reported * with these basic solvents as compared to hydrocarbon solvents.[36] Kinetic studies of the rearrangement [67, 68, 70] have shown that dimethylaniline has only a negligible effect on the rate, but it has been found [100] that dimethylaniline reduces polymerization during the rearrangement of cinnamyl phenyl ether and greatly improves the yield. Paraffin oil,† tetralin,[47] and kerosene [101] have been employed as solvents with satisfactory results.

The reaction mixture is usually worked up by removing the basic solvent, if present, by extraction with dilute mineral acid, solution of the residue in petroleum ether, and extraction with aqueous alkali to separate the phenolic product from any neutral by-products and unchanged ether. When the phenols are highly substituted, especially the 2,6-disubstituted ones, their acidity may be so greatly diminished that they are practically insoluble in aqueous alkali; "Claisen's alkali" ‡ (p. 28) has proved of great service in isolating weakly acidic phenols.[11, 29, 99, 101] Petroleum ether or benzene should be the solvent for the organic material when Claisen's alkali is used for an extraction.

A non-oxidizing atmosphere, such as hydrogen, carbon dioxide, or nitrogen, usually results in a better product.[29] In the rearrangement of 1,5-diallyloxyanthracene,[50] no pure product was obtained when the ether was heated in diethylaniline, but, when the reaction was carried out in the presence of acetic anhydride and diethylaniline, the rearrangement product was readily isolated in the form of its diacetate. The very sensitive dihydroxy compound formed was protected from decomposition by acetylation. This device has been employed in work on naphthohydroquinone [101] and hydroquinone derivatives.[102]

The thermal rearrangement of allyl ethers is a process entirely different from the rearrangement of saturated alkyl phenyl ethers by acidic catalysts.[103] The latter process seems to be intermolecular, gives consider-

---

* See p. 72 of the article cited in reference 11.
† See p. 111 of the article cited in reference 11.
‡ See p. 96 of the article cited in reference 11.
[100] Kincaid and Morse, private communication.
[101] Fieser, Campbell, and Fry, J. Am. Chem. Soc., **61**, 2206 (1939).
[102] Sealock and Livermore, private communication.
[103] Wallis, in Gilman's " Organic Chemistry," p. 997 ff., John Wiley & Sons, New York, 1943.

able *para* substitution and disubstitution, and does not give a high yield of a pure product.   In the only instance [103a] noted in the literature in which an acid catalyst was used to rearrange an allyl phenyl ether, allyl 2-methoxyphenyl ether (LXXIX) rearranged at 78° in the presence of boron fluoride and acetic acid to give 38% of eugenol (LXXX), with guaiacol, 6-allyleugenol, and the allyl ether of allylguaiacol as by-products.   When the rearrangement of LXXIX is carried out thermally,

LXXIX   LXXX   LXXXI

an excellent yield of LXXXI is obtained (Table I). The presence of acids in the Claisen rearrangement might be disadvantageous because the 2-allylphenols might be isomerized to the heterocyclic compounds (see p. 18).

Experience with a variety of allyl ethers has indicated that in general it is not necessary to heat ethers above 200° to effect rearrangement, and that many preparations in the literature probably would give better yields if they were run at lower temperatures.   Allyl 4-methylphenyl ether rearranges completely in thirteen hours at 200° without solvent,[67] and the corresponding 2,4- and 2,6-dimethyl compounds react more rapidly.   The allyl ethers of 2-phenanthrol and 3-phenanthrol rearrange at 100°.[51] Allyl 2-nitrophenyl ether gives a 73% yield after heating five hours at 180°, but the 4-nitro compound rearranges much more slowly. The allyl ethers of the isomeric hydroxynaphthoquinones (LXXXII and LXXXIII) rearrange in a few minutes at 135–145° to give the same compound (LXXXIV).[84]

LXXXII   LXXXIII   LXXXIV

Substitution in the α- or γ-position of the allyl group increases the rate of rearrangement; the crotyl ether of 2,4-dichlorophenol rearranges more rapidly than the allyl ether.[45]   α-Ethylcrotyl phenyl ether rearranges to the extent of 10% in twenty-four hours at 120°.[99] α-Ethyl-

[103a] Bryusova and Joffe, *J. Gen. Chem. U.S.S.R.*, **11**, 722 (1941) [*C.A.*, **36**, 430 (1942)].

allyl 2-carbomethoxy-6-methylphenyl ether (LXXXV) undergoes the *para* rearrangement when the ester group is saponified with alcoholic alkali.[6] A similar rearrangement accompanied by loss of carbon dioxide is observed during hydrolysis of LXXXVI.[73]

LXXXV   LXXXVI

These variations in reactivity are usually not large enough to be of practical importance. The behavior of ethers of hydroxy acids, some of which rearrange at temperatures not far above 100°, has been discussed (p. 11).

Experimental Procedures *

Preparation of Allyl Phenyl Ether.† A mixture of 188 g. of phenol, 242 g. of allyl bromide, 280 g. of finely ground calcined potassium carbonate, and 300 g. of acetone is refluxed on the steam bath for eight hours. A heavy precipitate of potassium bromide begins to form soon after the refluxing is started. After cooling, water is added; the product is taken up in ether and washed twice with 10% aqueous sodium hydroxide solution. The ether solution is dried over potassium carbonate, and, after removal of the ether, the residue is distilled under diminished pressure. The yield is 230 g. (86%), b.p. 85°/19 mm., d_{15}^{15} 0.9845. The residue is so small (6 g.) that the distillation might be omitted unless a very pure product is desired. About 1% of allyl 2-allylphenyl ether (a product of C-alkylation) is formed by this procedure.

Preparation of Allyl 2,4-Dichlorophenyl Ether.[45] A mixture of 10.8 g. (0.066 mole) of 2,4-dichlorophenol, 9.7 g. (0.080 mole; 21.5% excess) of allyl bromide, 9.4 g. of powdered anhydrous potassium carbonate, and 50 cc. of methyl ethyl ketone is refluxed for four and one-half hours. After cooling, 100 cc. of water is added and the organic layer is separated. The aqueous layer is extracted twice with 50-cc. portions of petroleum ether (b.p. 90–100°) and the extracts are combined with the organic layer, which is then extracted twice with 50-cc. portions of 10% sodium hydroxide to remove any unreacted phenol and washed twice with water. After drying over calcium chloride, the solvent is evaporated and the residual oil is distilled under diminished pressure, giving 11.4 g. (85%) of colorless liquid, b.p. 98–99°/2 mm.; d_{25}^{25} 1.258; n_D^{25} 1.5522.

* Procedures checked, in part, by Ann T. Tarbell.
† See p. 78 of the article cited in reference 11.

Preparation of 2-Allylphenol. The allyl ether is boiled in a flask under a reflux tube, the course of the rearrangement being conveniently followed by noting the refractive index at frequent intervals. When n_D has risen to 1.55 (five to six hours) the rearrangement is substantially complete with the minimum formation of undesirable by-products. To separate a small amount of 2-methyldihydrobenzofuran, the product is dissolved in twice its volume of 20% sodium hydroxide solution and extracted twice with petroleum ether (30–60°), from which the dihydrobenzofuran residue may be obtained by distillation. Ether should not be used for this extraction as it removes some of the phenol from the alkaline solution. The alkaline solution is acidified and the phenol extracted with ether; the extract is dried over calcium chloride and distilled under diminished pressure. A 73% yield of material boiling at 103–105.5°/19 mm., n_D^{24} 1.5445, is obtained. 2-Allylphenol is a colorless liquid, of guaiacol-like odor, with the following properties: b.p. 220°/760 mm., 99°/12 mm., n_D^{20} 1.5453.[27, *]

Contrary to the usual situation, this procedure was found more satisfactory than the rearrangement of allyl phenyl ether by refluxing in diethylaniline. When the ether was refluxed for six hours in three times its volume of diethylaniline, a 61% yield of 2-allylphenol was obtained.

2-Methyldihydrobenzofuran. 2-Allylphenol is dissolved in four times its volume of acetic acid and treated with twice its volume of 45% aqueous hydrobromic acid. The mixture is refluxed 20 minutes, during which an oily layer separates on top; then an excess of water is added, and the mixture is extracted with ether. The ether solution is washed with sodium hydroxide solution, dried, and distilled under reduced pressure. A 51% yield of material boiling at 86.5–87.5°/19 mm., 198–199°/740 mm.[28] is obtained; n_D^{22} 1.5307. A considerable amount of tarry residue remains after distillation.

The same procedure, with a refluxing time of one hour, gives a 73% yield of 2,3-dimethyldihydrobenzofuran when applied to 2-(α-methylallyl)-phenol.[36]

Isomerization of 2-Allylphenol to 2-Propenylphenol. 2-Allylphenol is dissolved in three times its volume of a saturated solution of potassium hydroxide in methanol; part of the solvent is distilled off until the temperature of the liquid rises to 110°, and the residue is refluxed six hours at this temperature. The reaction product is washed free of the base, dried, and distilled, giving a 75% yield of 2-propenylphenol boiling over a range 110–115°/15–16 mm. The compound solidifies in the receiver, and on recrystallization from ligroin forms shining needles melting at 36.5–37° (corr.); in fused state n_D^{21} 1.5823, b.p. 230–231° at atmospheric

* See p. 80 of the article cited in reference 11.

pressure. v. Auwers [103b] reports b.p. 119.4–119.8°/18 mm., m.p. 37–38°, n_D^{20} 1.5811.

C-Alkylation. Preparation of 2-Cinnamylphenol.[15] The sodium salt from 18.8 g. of phenol in 100 cc. of benzene is treated with 39.4 g. of cinnamyl bromide dissolved in a small amount of benzene. After refluxing for five hours, water is added and the layers are separated. The benzene is distilled *completely* (by operating at reduced pressure near the end of the distillation), and the residue is treated with four times its volume of Claisen's alkali.* The resulting solution is extracted twice with petroleum ether to remove the small amount of neutral material (2–3 g.). This procedure requires fewer extractions than the alternative method of dissolving the reaction product in petroleum ether and extracting the solution with Claisen's alkali to remove the phenolic material. The phenol is recovered from the alkaline solution by acidification and ether extraction; the ether solution is dried, the solvent is removed, and the residue is distilled. Twenty-five grams (60%), b.p. 207–212°/12 mm., of 2-cinnamylphenol is obtained, with a small residue probably consisting of dicinnamylphenol. On redistillation the product has a constant b.p. of 208–209°/11 mm. and crystallizes to a solid, which, when recrystallized from hot petroleum ether or hot absolute formic acid, melts at 55.5–56.5°. The phenylurethan melts at 131.5–132°.

---

* Claisen's alkali is prepared by dissolving 350 g. of potassium hydroxide in 250 cc. of water and diluting to 1000 cc. with methanol.

[103b] v. Auwers, *Ann.*, **413**, 298 (1917).

TABLE I. REARRANGEMENT OF OPEN-CHAIN COMPOUNDS

A. Ethers of Enols

Compound	Conditions			Product	Yield	Reference *
	Time, hours	Temperature, °C.	Solvent (or Catalyst)			
Ethyl O-allylacetoacetate	—	150–200	(NH₄Cl)	Ethyl allylacetoacetate	>85%	1, 2, 8
Ethyl O-cinnamylacetoacetate	4	110	(NH₄Cl)	Ethyl α-phenylallylacetoacetate	—	8
	6	260	—	Ethyl cinnamylacetoacetate	20%	9
O-Allylacetylacetone	—	At b.p.	—	Allylacetylacetone	>85%	1
O-Allyloxymethylenecamphor	—	255	—	C-Allyloxymethylenecamphor	—	1
Allyl vinyl ether	—	255	—	Allylacetaldehyde	—	10
Allyl α-methylvinyl ether	1	255	—	Allylacetone	>85%	10
Allyl α-phenylvinyl ether	¼	<175	—	γ-Butenyl phenyl ketone	71%	10
γ-Ethylallyl vinyl ether containing 23% of α-isomer	—	220	—	3-Ethyl-4-pentenal	76%	39
				3-Methyl-4-hexenal	4%	39
				4-Heptenal	18%	39

B. Rearrangements Involving Migration to an Unsaturated Side Chain

Aryl Group in ArOCH₂CH=CH₂	Conditions		Product	Yield	Reference *
	Time, hours	Temperature, °C.			
2-Propenyl-4-propyl-6-methoxy-phenyl	—	168–178	See p. 8	28%	26
2-Propenyl-4,6-dichlorophenyl	5	160–173	See p. 8	28%	26
2-Propenyl-4,6-dimethylphenyl	7	177	See p. 8	37%	26

* References 104–129 appear on p. 48.

TABLE II

ortho REARRANGEMENTS OF ALLYL ARYL ETHERS

A. Benzene Derivatives

Ring Substituents in CH_2=$CHCH_2OC_6H_5$	Conditions			Product Substituents in Phenolic Ring	Yield	Reference *
	Time, hours	Temperature, ° C.	Solvent (or Other Special Condition)			
None	Several	190–220	(Inert atmosphere)	2-Allyl (dimer)	>85%	11 (p. 79), 27, 28, 29, 60
2-Methyl	1.3	207–231	—	6-Allyl-2-methyl	78%	44 (p. 56)
3-Methyl	1	210–240	—	2-Allyl-3-methyl, 6-Allyl-3-methyl	70%	44 (p. 58)
4-Methyl	13	200	(Inert atmosphere)	2-Allyl-4-methyl	>85%	44 (p. 43), 34, 67
2-Hydroxymethyl	—	—	—	(CH_2O, decomposition products)	—	44 (p. 106)
2-Allyl	0.5	237	Diethylaniline	2,6-Diallyl	80%	11 (p. 91)
2,4-Dimethyl	3	200–210	(Inert atmosphere)	6-Allyl-2,4-dimethyl	>85%	26, 104
3,5-Dimethyl	—	—	—	2-Allyl-3,5-dimethyl	—	105
2-Allyl-3- (and -5-) methyl †	—	230–270	—	2,6-Diallyl-3-methyl	30%	44 (p. 58)
2-Allyl-4-methyl	"Long refluxing"	—	—	2,6-Diallyl-4-methyl	10%	44 (p. 45)
2-Propyl-4-methyl	1¼	230–252	(Inert atmosphere)	6-Allyl-2-propyl-4-methyl (2-Propyl-4-methyl-phenol)	67% 10%	34

Substituent	Time (hr.)	Temp. (°C)	Conditions	Product	Yield	References
2,3,5-Trimethyl	¼	270	—	6-Allyl-2,3,5-trimethyl	55%	95, 106
4-(β-Carbomethoxyvinyl)	2	230–245	—	2-Allyl-4-(β-carbomethoxyvinyl)	82%	80
2-Chloro	0.15	220–224	—	6-Allyl-2-chloro	>85%	46
4-Chloro	0.4	Reflux (to 256°)	—	2-Allyl-4-chloro	>85%	44 (p. 37)
2,4-Dichloro	"Long"	200–210	(Inert atmosphere)	6-Allyl-2,4-dichloro	—	26, 45, 107
2-Bromo	1.8	210–220	—	6-Allyl-2-bromo	82%	47
4-Bromo	Few minutes at reflux	—	—	2-Allyl-4-bromo	>85%	44 (p. 38)
2,4-Dibromo	2	213–220	Tetralin	6-Allyl-2,4-dibromo (phenolic by-product)	69% 11%	47
3,5-Dibromo	1.6	210–220	—	2-Allyl-3,5-dibromo	72%	47
2-Nitro	5	180	—	6-Allyl-2-nitro	72%	44 (p. 59)
4-Nitro	1.5	230	Paraffin oil	2-Allyl-4-nitro	30–40%	44 (p. 40)
3-Acetamino	—	—	Refluxed in dimethylaniline (inert atmosphere)	6-Allyl-3-acetamino	>85%	107a
4-Amino	6	185	Paraffin oil (inert atmosphere)	2-Allyl-4-amino	70%	11 (p. 111)
4-Acetamino	6	180	Dimethylaniline (inert atmosphere)	2-Allyl-4-acetamino	>85%	11 (p. 107); 100
2,3,5-Trimethyl-4-formamino	2	225	Kerosene	6-Allyl-2,3,5-trimethyl-4-formamino	>85%	95
2,3,5-Trimethyl-4-acetamino	7	225	Kerosene	6-Allyl-2,3,5-trimethyl-4-acetamino	>85%	95
2-Allyl-4-acetamino	5	—	Dimethylaniline (inert atmosphere)	2,6-Diallyl-4-acetamino	—	11 (p. 112)
4-Phenylazo	0.5–1	230	Paraffin oil	2-Allyl-4-phenylazo	70%	44 (p. 42)

* References 104–129 appear on p. 48.
† A mixture of the two isomers was used.

TABLE II—*Continued*

ortho REARRANGEMENTS OF ALLYL ARYL ETHERS

Ring Substituents in $CH_2=CHCH_2OC_6H_5$	Conditions			Product	Yield	Reference *
	Time, hours	Temperature, ° C.	Solvent (or Other Special Condition)	Substituents in Phenolic Ring		
2-Hydroxy	—	170–265	—	6-Allyl-2-hydroxy	>85% †	31, 32, 108
				4-Allyl-2-hydroxy	>85% †	108
3-Hydroxy	0.1	200–280	—	6-Allyl-3-hydroxy	45%	81, 108
4-Hydroxy-2,3,5-trimethyl	1.5	230	—	6-Allyl-4-hydroxy-2,3,5-trimethyl		109
2-Methoxy	1	230	—	6-Allyl-2-methoxy ‡	>85%	1
2-Methoxy-4-methyl	—	220–230	—	6-Allyl-2-methoxy-4-methyl	>85%	109a
3-Methoxy	0.75	—	Refluxing dimethylaniline	6-Allyl-3-methoxy	"Good"	110
3-Methoxy-6-carbomethoxy	6	—	Refluxing dimethylaniline (inert atmosphere)	2-Allyl-3-methoxy-6-carbomethoxy	68%	110a
4-Methoxy	0.75	—	Refluxing dimethylaniline	2-Allyl-4-methoxy	"Good"	110
2-Allyloxy	—	180	—	3,6-Diallyl-2-hydroxy §	—	31, 108
3-Allyloxy	—	210	—	4,6-Diallyl-3-hydroxy	—	108
4-Allyloxy	2.25	210–215	Kerosene	2,3-Diallyl-4-hydroxy and 2,5-diallyl-4-hydroxy (in equal amounts)	>85%	101
4-Acetoxy	—	—	—	2-Allyl-4-acetoxy	80%	102
4-Benzoyloxy	2	130–280	—	Mixture of benzoyl derivatives of 2-allyl-4-hydroxy	>85%	77

Ether		Temperature / Method	Product	Yield	Reference
3-Hydroxy-4-nitro	0.8	185	6-Allyl-3-hydroxy-4-nitro	26%‖	57
2-Hydroxy-3-allyl	—	Distillation in vacuum	3,6-Diallyl-2-hydroxy	—	108
2-Methoxy-4-allyl	1 ¼	200	4,6-Diallyl-2-methoxy	70%	44 (p. 47)
2-Methoxy-4-propyl	4	190–200 (Inert atmosphere)	6-Allyl-2-methoxy-4-propyl	>85%	26
2-Methoxy-4-(γ-hydroxypropyl)	—	—	6-Allyl-2-methoxy-4-(γ-hydroxypropyl)	—	48
2-Allyloxy-3-allyl	—	Distillation in vacuum	3,5,6-Triallyl-2-hydroxy	—	108
3-Allyloxy-4,6-diallyl	—	Distillation in vacuum	2,4,6-Triallyl-3-allyloxy	—	108
2,3-Methylenedioxy	—	220–240	Mixture of 6-allyl-2,3-methylenedioxy (80%) and 4-allyl-2,3-methylenedioxy (20%)	79%	33, 111
2-Allyloxy-3-methoxy (?)	—	200		—	112
2-Allyloxy-3-hydroxy (?)	—	200		—	112
2-Formyl	—	220–230	6-Allyl-2-formyl	>85%	44 (p. 96)
4-Formyl	—	250–270	2-Allyl-4-formyl	66%	44 (p. 107)
4-Acetyl	5	200–210 (Inert atmosphere)	2-Allyl-4-acetyl	78%	112a
2-Allyl-4-formyl	1	250–310	2,6-Diallyl-4-formyl	<60%	44 (p. 108)
2-Carbethoxy		230	6-Allyl-2-carbethoxy	—	1
2-Carbomethoxy	—	—	6-Allyl-2-carbomethoxy	—	44 (p. 70)

* References 104–129 appear on p. 48.
† The mixture contained the 6-allyl and 4-allyl derivatives in the ratio 5 : 4.
‡ For products with boron fluoride-acetic acid (103a), see p. 25.
§ The product was not isolated from the reaction mixture, which contained other substances also.
‖ The yield based on ether not recovered was 52%.

TABLE II—*Continued*

ortho REARRANGEMENTS OF ALLYL ARYL ETHERS

Ring Substituents in $CH_2=CHCH_2OC_6H_5$	Conditions			Product	Yield	Reference*
	Time, hours	Tempera-ture, °C	Solvent (or Other Special Condition)	Substituents in Phenolic Ring		
4-Carbethoxy	0.5	220–250	—	2-Allyl-4-carbethoxy	>85%	44 (p. 87) ; 27
2-Allyl-4-carbethoxy	0.5	220–230	—	2,6-Diallyl-4-carbethoxy	>85%	44 (p. 89)
2-Methoxy-4-formyl	—	210–300	—	6-Allyl-2-methoxy-4-formyl	80%	44 (p. 116)
2-Methoxy-4-formyl-5-bromo	0.5	230–250	—	6-Allyl-2-methoxy-4-formyl-5-bromo	54%	113
2-Methoxy-4-acetyl	—	230	—	6-Allyl-2-methoxy-4-acetyl	85%	113a
3-Hydroxy-4-formyl	1	190–200	—	2-Allyl-3-hydroxy-4-formyl	50%	57
3-Methoxy-4-formyl	1	200	—	6-Allyl-3-methoxy-4-formyl	59%	57
3-Hydroxy-4-acetyl	1.5	210–215	—	2-Allyl-3-hydroxy-4-acetyl	>85%	56
3-Methoxy-4-acetyl	0.75	215	—	6-Allyl-3-methoxy-4-acetyl	60%	56
2-Allyl-3-hydroxy-4-acetyl	6	210	—	2,6-Diallyl-3-hydroxy-4-acetyl	20%	56
3-Methoxy-4-acetyl-6-allyl	0.75	210	—	2,6-Diallyl-3-methoxy-4-acetyl	30%	56
3-Hydroxy-4-propionyl	2	205	—	2-Allyl-3-hydroxy-4-propionyl	>85%	57
3-Methoxy-4-propionyl	2	200	—	6-Allyl-3-methoxy-4-propionyl	80%	57
3-Acetyl-4-hydroxy	0.75	180–230	—	2-Allyl-3-acetyl-4-hydroxy	74%	57
3-Acetyl-4-methoxy	0.33	220–230	—	2-Allyl-3-acetyl-4-methoxy	75%	57

B. Polycyclic and Heterocyclic Derivatives

Compound	Conditions			Product	Yield	Reference *
	Time, hours	Temperature, °C	Solvent (or Other Special Condition)			
5-Allyloxy-6-methylindan	1	245	Dimethylaniline	4-Allyl-5-hydroxy-6-methylindan	>85%	52
4,7-Dimethyl-5-allyloxyindan	—	280	Dimethylaniline	4,7-Dimethyl-5-hydroxy-6-methylindan	75%	52
1-Allyloxynaphthalene	1	230	—	2-Allyl-1-naphthol	50–60%	44 (p. 61)
2-Allyloxynaphthalene	—	—	—	1-Allyl-2-naphthol	>85%	1
1-Allyl-2-allyloxynaphthalene	—	"Long heating"	—	No reaction	0	1
2-Allyloxy-1,4-naphthoquinone	0.15	135	—	2-Hydroxy-3-allyl-1,4-naphthoquinone	—	84
4-Allyloxy-1,2-naphthoquinone	0.5	135–145	(Inert atmosphere)	2-Hydroxy-3-allyl-1,4-naphthoquinone	70%	84
1-Allyloxy-3,7-dimethylnaphthalene	2.75	240	Dimethylaniline	2-Allyl-3,7-dimethyl-1-naphthol	49%	101
1-Allyloxy-5-methoxynaphthalene	1.5	240	—	2-Allyl-5-methoxy-1-naphthol	73%	114
1,4-Diallyloxynaphthalene	5	200	Diethylaniline (acetic anhydride, inert atmosphere)	2,3-Diallyl-1,4-diacetoxynaphthalene	>85%	101
1,4-Diallyloxy-5,8-dihydronaphthalene	2	240–250	Kerosene (inert atmosphere)	2,3-Diallyl-1,4-dihydroxy-5,8-dihydronaphthalene	>85%	101
2,6-Diallyloxynaphthalene	Few minutes	190	(Inert atmosphere)	1,5-Diallylnaphthalene-2,6-diol	85%	49
1,5-Diallyloxy-2,6-diallyloxynaphthalene	—	—	—	Decomposition products	0	49
2-Allyloxy-3-carbomethoxynaphthalene	—	Distillation at 162	—	1-Allyl-3-carbomethoxy-2-naphthol	—	115
4-Allyloxybiphenyl	—	—	—	3-Allyl-4-hydroxybiphenyl (mainly)	—	116

* References 104–129 appear on p. 48.

TABLE II—*Continued*

ortho REARRANGEMENTS OF ALLYL ARYL ETHERS

Compound	Conditions			Product	Yield	Reference *
	Time, hours	Tempera-ture, °C.	Solvent (or Other Special Condition)			
2-Allyloxybiphenyl	0.15	250–300	—	3-Allyl-2-hydroxybiphenyl	—	117
2-Allyloxyphenanthrene	—	100	—	1-Allyl-2-phenanthrol	—	51
3-Allyloxyphenanthrene	—	100	—	4-Allyl-3-phenanthrol	—	51
1-Methyl-7-isopropyl-9-allyloxy-phenanthrene	1.5	150	(Inert atmosphere)	10-Allyl-1-methyl-7-isopropyl-9-phenanthrol	—	51
1-Allyl-2-allyloxyphenanthrene	—	—	—	Decomposition products	0	51
2,6-Diallyloxyanthracene	2.5	160–180	Diethylaniline (acetic anhydride)	1,5-Diallyl-2,6-diacetoxyanthracene	55%	50
1,5-Dimethyl-2,6-diallyloxyanthra-cene	—	—	—	Decomposition products	0	50
2-Allyloxyfluorene	0.1	235–238	—	1-Allyl-2-hydroxyfluorene	60%	53
				3-Allyl-2-hydroxyfluorene	25%	53
1-Allyl-2-allyloxyfluorene and 3-allyl-2-allyloxyfluorene	—	—	—	1,3-Diallyl-2-hydroxyfluorene	—	53
1,2-Dimethyl-3-allyloxyfluorene	—	230	—	4-Allyl-1,2-dimethyl-3-hydroxyfluo-rene	78%	53
1,4-Dimethyl-3-allyloxyfluorene	—	215	(Inert atmosphere)	2-Allyl-1,4-dimethyl-3-hydroxyfluo-rene	62%	53
2-Allyloxyfluorenone	3	200	—	Mixture of 1- and 3-allyl-2-hydroxyfluorenone	60%	55
1,6-Diallyloxydihydropleiadene	—	—	—	Decomposition products	0	49
7-Allyloxyquinoline	—	230	—	8-Allyl-7-hydroxyquinoline	64%	118
7-Allyloxy-8-allylquinoline	0.1	250	—	No reaction	0	118

	Time	Temp.	Conditions	Product	Yield	Ref.
2-Methyl-4-allyloxyquinoline	"Short time"	200	—	3-Allyl-2-methyl-4-hydroxyquino-line	>85%	119
8-Allyloxyquinoline	—	190–290	—	7-Allyl-8-hydroxyquinoline	>85%	119a
4-Allyloxy-2,3-dimethylquinoline	—	180	—	5-Allyl-4-hydroxy-2,3-dimethyl-quinoline (?)	—	119a
4-Allyloxy-2-methylquinoline methiodide	0.3	175	—	Allyl iodide and 1,2-dimethyl-4-quinolone	—	119a
6-Allyloxy-2-methylbenzothiazole	0.1	240–245	Sealed tube	7-Allyl- and 5-allyl-6-hydroxy-2-methylbenzothiazole †	—	55a
6-Allyloxy-5-allyl-2-methylbenzo-thiazole	—	235–250	—	5,7-Diallyl-6-hydroxy-2-methyl-benzothiazole	—	55a
6-Allyloxy-7-allyl-2-methylbenzo-thiazole	—	235–250	—	Same compound as above	—	55a
2-Allyloxydibenzofuran	0.25	220–230	—	1-Allyl-2-hydroxydibenzofuran	34%	120
7-Allyloxycoumarin	1.5	195–200	—	8-Allyl-7-hydroxycoumarin	20%	121
4-Methyl-7-allyloxycoumarin	1.5	210–240	—	8-Allyl-4-methyl-7-hydroxycou-marin	—	56
2-Methyl-3-methoxy-7-allyloxy-chromone	2.5	200	—	8-Allyl-2-methyl-3-methoxy-7-hydroxychromone	—	54
2-Methyl-3-methoxy-7-allyloxy-8-allylchromone	—	200–205	—	6,8-Diallyl-2-methyl-3-methoxy-7-hydroxychromone	—	54
7-Allyloxyflavone	2.5	210–215	—	8-Allyl-7-hydroxyflavone	—	54
7-Allyloxy-8-allylflavone	2.5	210–215	—	6,8-Diallyl-7-hydroxyflavone	75%	54
3-Methoxy-7-allyloxyflavone	—	—	—	8-Allyl-7-hydroxy-3-methoxy-flavone	80%	121
3-Allyloxy-6-hydroxyfluoran	1	210–220	—	2-Allylfluorescein	—	122
3,6-Diallyloxyfluoran	1	210–220	—	2,7-Diallylfluorescein	—	122
Allyl 6-allyloxy-9-phenylfluorone-11-carboxylate	1	210–220	—	Allyl ester of 2-allylfluorescein	—	122

* References 104–129 appear on p. 48.

† Formed in ratio of 20 : 1; structures were assigned to the isomers from relative melting points.

TABLE II—*Continued*

ortho REARRANGEMENTS OF ALLYL ARYL ETHERS

C. *ortho Rearrangements with Displacement of Carbon Monoxide or Carbon Dioxide*

Ring Substituents in $CH_2=CHCH_2OC_6H_5$	Conditions		Product Substituents in Phenolic Ring	Yield	Reference *
	Time, hours	Temperature, °C			
2-Formyl-6-allyl	—	>180	2,6-Diallyl	60%	44 (p. 102)
			4,6-Diallyl-2-formyl	20%	44 (p. 102)
2-Formyl-4-allyl-6-methoxy	—	180–295	2,4-Diallyl-6-methoxy	60%	44 (p. 118)
2-Formyl-6-methoxy	—	170–240	2-Allyl-6-methoxy	35%	44 (p. 112)
			2-Allyl-4-formyl-6-methoxy	20%	44 (p. 112)
			4-Allyl-2-formyl-6-methoxy	27%	44 (p. 112)
2-Carboxy	0.5	175–180	6-Allyl-2-carboxy	64%	45
			2-Allyl	23%	45
2-Carboxy-4,6-dichloro	—	118	2-Allyl-4,6-dichloro	>85%	11 (p. 85); 45
2-Carboxy-6-methyl	—	>100	2-Allyl-6-methyl	80%	44 (p. 83)
			4-Allyl-2-carboxy-6-methyl	20%	44 (p. 83)
2-Carboxy-6-allyl	—	100–180	2,6-Diallyl	53%	44 (p. 75)
			4,6-Diallyl-2-carboxy	30%	44 (p. 75)
2-Carboxy-4,6-diallyl	—	>100	2,4,6-Triallyl	>85%	44 (p. 79)
2-Carboxy-4-methoxy	6	Refluxing in dimethylaniline	2-Allyl-4-methoxy	—	110a
2-Carboxy-6-methoxy	—	110–250	2-Allyl-6-methoxy	76%	11 (p. 117)
			4-Allyl-2-carboxy-6-methoxy	2%	11 (p. 117)

D. Rearrangements of Ethers Containing Monosubstituted Allyl Groups

1. β-METHYLALLYL ETHERS

| Ring Substituents in CH₂=C—CH₂OC₆H₅ with CH₃ | Conditions | | | Product Substituents in (OH, CH₂C=CH₂ / CH₃) | Yield | Reference* |
	Time, hours	Temperature, °C	Solvent (or Other Special Condition)			
None	2.5	200–215	Diethylaniline (inert atmosphere)	None	82%	66, 123
4-Chloro	0.5	200–240	—	4-Chloro	60–70%	66
2-Methyl	0.5	200–240	—	2-Methyl	60–70%	66
3-Methyl	0.5	200–240	—	3-Methyl	60–70%	66
4-Methyl	0.5	200–240	—	4-Methyl	60–70%	66
2-(β-Methylallyl)	0.15	210–235	Diethylaniline	2-(β-Methylallyl)	50–60%	66
2,4-Dimethyl	0.15	210–235	Diethylaniline	2,4-Dimethyl	50–60%	66
2,5-Dimethyl	0.15	210–235	Diethylaniline	2,5-Dimethyl	50–60%	66
3,4-Dimethyl	0.15	210–235	Diethylaniline	3,4-Dimethyl	50–60%	66
2-Isopropyl-5-methyl	0.15	210–235	Diethylaniline	2-Isopropyl-5-methyl	50–60%	66
2-(β-Methylallyl)-4-methyl	0.15	210–235	Diethylaniline	2-(β-Methylallyl)-4-methyl	50–60%	66
2-(β-Methylallyl)-5-methyl	0.15	210–235	Diethylaniline	2-(β-Methylallyl)-5-methyl	50–60%	66
2-Methoxy	0.5	205	—	2-Methoxy	60–70%	66
3-(β-Methylallyloxy)	0.5	205	—	4-(β-Methylallyl)-3-hydroxy	60–70%	66

* References 104–129 appear on p. 48.

TABLE II—_Continued_

ortho REARRANGEMENTS OF ALLYL ARYL ETHERS

2. MISCELLANEOUS ETHERS, BENZENE DERIVATIVES

Reactant: $CH_2=CHCH_2O$—benzene ring
Product: HO—benzene—$CH_2=CHCH_2$

Substituents in (reactant)		Conditions			Substituents in (product)		Yield	Reference [*]
Allyl Group	Ring	Time, hours	Temperature, °C	Solvent (or Other Special Condition)	Allyl Group	Ring		
β-Chloro	None	2	216–223	—	β-Chloro	None	24%	43
β-Bromo	None	—	—	Tetralin	(2-Methylbenzofuran)		20%	43
γ-Chloro	None	—	—	—	(Phenolic products)		18–29%	42, 43
γ-Chloro	4-Methyl	—	—	—	(Phenolic products)		—	43
γ-Bromo	None	—	—	—	(Polymeric products)		8%	43
					(1,3-Dibromopropene)		9–18%	43
					(Phenol)			
α-Methyl	4-Carbethoxy	1.5	222–240	Refluxed at 50 mm.	γ-Methyl	4-Carbethoxy	>85%	123a
					(Butadiene)		Trace	40
α-Ethyl	None	3.5	201–225	Diethylaniline	γ-Ethyl	None	84%	62
α-Ethyl	4-Carbethoxy	1	200–236	—	γ-Ethyl	4-Carbethoxy	70%	62
					(1,3-Pentadiene)		9%	41
α-n-Propyl	4-Carbethoxy	—	220–246	—	γ-n-Propyl	4-Carbethoxy	—	
γ-Phenyl	None	4	—	Refluxing diethylaniline	α-Phenyl	None	58%	35, 60, 68

γ-Phenyl	4-Methyl	0.33	200	Dimethylaniline (inert atmosphere)	α-Phenyl	4-Methyl	85%	35, 68
γ-Methyl	None	3	200–210	Diethylaniline	α-Methyl	None	85%	36, 37, 124
γ-Methyl	2,4-Dichloro	2	Refluxing	Diethylaniline	α-Methyl	2,4-Dichloro	83%	45
γ-Methyl	4-Carbethoxy	1.2	210–227	Refluxed at 50 mm.	α-Methyl	4-Carbethoxy	>85%	123a
γ-Ethyl	None	1.75	220–235	Dimethylaniline	α-γ-Dimethyl	None	>85%	39, 40, 58
γ-Ethyl	2-Methyl	—	—	—	α-Ethyl	2-Methyl	44%	58
					α-Ethyl (o-Cresol)		12%	58
γ-Ethyl	4-Carbethoxy	—	195–233	—	α-Ethyl	4-Carbethoxy	>85%	62
					α,γ-Dimethyl (1,3-Pentadiene)	4-Carbethoxy	13%	
γ-n-Propyl	None	0.5–0.8	—	—	α-n-Propyl	None	40%	58, 59
					α-n-Propyl (Phenol)		19%	58, 59
γ-n-Propyl	2-Methyl	—	—	—	α-n-Propyl	2-Methyl	27%	58
					α-n-Propyl (o-Cresol)		Trace	58
γ-n-Propyl	4-Carbethoxy	1.5	213–241	—	α-n-Propyl	4-Carbethoxy	—†	41
					α-Methyl-γ-ethyl	4-Carbethoxy	—†	41
γ-n-Butyl	None	0.5–0.8	230–260	—	α-n-Butyl	None	28	58
					α-n-Butyl (Phenol)		Trace	58
γ-n-Butyl	2-Methyl	0.5–0.8	230–260	—	α-n-Butyl	2-Methyl	15	58
					α-n-Butyl (o-Cresol)		Trace	58
γ-n-Propyl	2-(γ-n-Propylallyloxy)-3-hydroxy (?)	Distillation in vacuum			x,x-Dihexenyl-2,3-dihydroxy		—	112
γ-n-Butyl	2-(γ-n-Butylallyloxy)-3-hydroxy (?)	Distillation in vacuum			x,x-Diheptenyl-2,3-dihydroxy		—	112
Geranyl	2-Hydroxy	Distillation in vacuum			6-Geranyl-2-hydroxy (?)		—	125

* References 104–129 appear on p. 48.

† The mixture contained the normal (inverted) and abnormal products in the ratio 1 : 2.

TABLE II—*Continued*

ortho REARRANGEMENTS OF ALLYL ARYL ETHERS

3. MISCELLANEOUS ETHERS, DERIVATIVES OF POLYCYCLIC HYDROCARBONS

Compound	Conditions			Product	Yield	Reference *
	Time, hours	Tempera-ture, °C	Solvent			
2-Cinnamyloxy-3-carbomethoxy-naphthalene	Distillation in vacuum		—	1-(α-Phenylallyl)-2-hydroxy-3-carbomethoxynaphthalene	—	115
1-(γ-Methylallyloxy)-naphthalene	Distillation in vacuum		—	2-(α-Methylallyl)-1-naphthol	—	36, 124
2-(γ-Methylallyloxy)-1,4-naphthoquinone	0.5	140	—	3-(α-Methylallyl)-2-hydroxy-1,4-naphthoquinone	>85%	126
4-(γ-Methylallyloxy)-1,2-naphthoquinone	0.5	125	—	Same compound as above	>85%	126
3-(γ-Ethylallyloxy)-6-hydroxy-fluoran	—	—	—	2-Pentenylfluorescein	—	122
3,6-Di-(γ-n-propylallyloxy)-fluoran	1	210–220	—	2,7-Dihexenylfluorescein	—	122
1,4-Difarnesyloxynaphthalene	3	190–200	Diethylaniline, acetic anhydride	2,3-Difarnesyl-1,4-diacetoxynaphthalene (?)	—	83

E. Rearrangements of Ethers Containing Disubstituted Allyl Groups, Benzene Derivatives

Allyl Group	Ring	Time, hours	Temperature, °C	Solvent	Product	Yield	Reference*
α,γ-Dimethyl	None	1	200	—	2-(α,γ-Dimethylallyl)-phenol	70–80%	15
		—	Refluxing	Diethylaniline (inert atmosphere)	Same product as above	28%	40, 61
α,γ-Dimethyl	4-Carbethoxy	1	208–213	—	1,3-Pentadiene	59%	62
					Ethyl p-hydroxybenzoate	38%	62
					$1,2,4\text{-}C_6H_3(OH)\text{-}[CH(CH_3)CH{=}CHCH_3](CO_2C_2H_5)$	"Much"	62
					$1,2,4\text{-}C_6H_3(OH)\text{-}[CH(C_2H_5)CH{=}CH_2](CO_2C_2H_5)$	"Little"	62
α-Ethyl-γ-methyl	None	0.5	200–205	—	2-(α-Methyl-γ-ethylallyl)-phenol	75%	61, 99
					(Phenol)		58
α-Ethyl-γ-methyl	2-Methyl	0.5	200–230	—	(o-Cresol)	10–20%	58
α-n-Propyl-γ-methyl	None	0.5	228–230	—	2-(α-Methyl-γ-propylallyl)-phenol	54%	58, 61
					(Phenol)		127
α-n-Propyl-γ-methyl	2-Methyl	0.5	200–230	—	(o-Cresol)	10–20%	58
α-n-Butyl-γ-methyl	None	0.5	200–230	—	(Phenol)	—	58
α-n-Butyl-γ-methyl	2-Methyl	0.5	200–230	—	(o-Cresol)	—	58
α,γ-Trimethylene (2-Cyclohexenyloxybenzene)	None	—	—	—	(Cyclohexadiene, Phenol)	50–60%	63
					(Hexahydrobenzofuran)	15%	63
					o-(2-Cyclohexenyl)-phenol	5%	63
γ,γ-Dimethyl	None	—	—	—	(Phenol and isoprene)	—	35, 36
			(With calcined soda)		o-(α,α-Dimethylallyl)-phenol	70%	64
γ,γ-Dimethyl	4-Carbethoxy	3.5	197–224	—	(Isoprene, Ethyl 4-hydroxybenzoate, 2,2,3-Trimethyl-5-carbethoxydihydrobenzofuran)	65%	64a
						23%	64a
							64a
α,α,γ,γ-Tetramethyl	—	1	160–170	—	(2,4-Dimethylpentadiene)	33%	61
					(Phenol)	20%	61

* References 104–129 appear on p. 48.

TABLE III

para REARRANGEMENTS OF ALLYL ARYL ETHERS

A. Allyl Ethers of Phenols and Substituted Phenols

Compound Ring Substituents in $CH_2=CHCH_2OC_6H_5$	Conditions			Product	Yield	Reference [*]
	Time, hours	Temperature, °C	Solvent (or Other Special Condition)			
2,6-Dichloro	1	195–200	(Inert atmosphere)	4-Allyl-2,6-dichlorophenol	57%	46
				2-Allyl-6-chlorophenol	10%	46
2,6-Dibromo	—		(Refluxing tetralin)	4-Allyl-2,6-dibromophenol } 2-Allyl-6-bromophenol	37%	53, 107
2-Bromo-6-methyl	—		(Refluxing tetralin)	4-Allyl-2-bromo-6-methylphenol	23%	43
				2-Bromo-6-methylphenol	Trace	43
2,6-Dimethyl	7	172	(Inert atmosphere)	4-Allyl-2,6-dimethylphenol	>85%	70
2,6-Diallyl	0.5	225–248		2,4,6-Triallylphenol	50%	11 (p. 96)
2-Methyl-6-methoxy	2.5	230–250	Diethylaniline	4-Allyl-2-methyl-6-methoxyphenol	56%	109a
2-Allyl-6-methoxy	2	200	—	2,4-Diallyl-6-methoxyphenol	83%	44 (p. 55)
2-Allyloxy-3,6-diallyl	—	180–200	—	3,4,5,6-Tetraallyl-2-hydroxyphenol	—	108
2-Hydroxy-6-methoxy (?)	—	—	—	4-Allyl-2-hydroxy-6-methoxyphenol	—	128
2,6-Dimethoxy	1	(Refluxed at 75 mm.)		4-Allyl-2,6-dimethoxyphenol	>85%	72, 73
2,3-Dimethoxy-6-hydroxy	"Few minutes"	165–200	—	4-Allyl-2,3-dimethoxy-6-hydroxyphenol	30%	74
2-Carbomethoxy-6-methyl	(Distillation at 275–290)			4-Allyl-2-carbomethoxy-6-methylphenol	76%	44 (p. 83)
2-Carbomethoxy-6-allyl	—	250	—	4,6-Diallyl-2-carbomethoxyphenol	69%	44 (p. 77)
2-Carbomethoxy-6-methoxy	0.75	201–212	—	4-Allyl-2-carbomethoxy-6-methoxyphenol	>85%	129, 11 (p. 118)

B. Ethers Containing Substituted Allyl Groups

1. BENZENE DERIVATIVES

Substituents in $CH_2=CHCH_2O$ (γ β α) ring		Conditions			Product HO— ring, $CH_2CH=CH_2$ (α β γ) Substituents in		Yield	Reference [*]
Allyl Group	Ring	Time, hours	Temperature, °C	Solvent (or Other Special Condition)	Allyl Group	Ring		
α-Ethyl	2-Carbomethoxy-6-methyl			(Alkaline hydrolysis)	γ-Ethyl	2-Carbomethoxy-6-methyl	—	6, 7
β-Methyl	2-(β-Methylallyl)-6-methyl	0.5	210–235	Diethylaniline	β-Methyl	2-(β-Methylallyl)-6-methyl	70–80%	66
γ-Phenyl	2-Carbomethoxy-6-methyl	4	—	Diethylaniline	γ-Phenyl	2-Carbomethoxy-6-methyl	—	3
γ-Methyl	2-Carbomethoxy-6-methyl	3		(Refluxing diethylaniline)	γ-Methyl	2-Carbomethoxy-6-methyl	85%	3
γ-Ethyl	2-Carbomethoxy-6-methyl	3		(Refluxing diethylaniline)	γ-Ethyl	6-Carbomethoxy-2-methoxy	59%	6, 7
γ,γ-Dimethyl	2-Methoxy	2.5	220	—	γ,γ-Dimethyl	2-Methoxy	—†	30

* References 104–129 appear on p. 48.
† The pure product was not isolated.

TABLE III—*Continued*

para REARRANGEMENTS OF ALLYL ARYL ETHERS

2. HETEROCYCLIC DERIVATIVES

Compound	Conditions		Product	Yield	Reference *
	Time, hours	Temperature, °C.			
γ,γ-Dimethylallyloxyfuranocoumarin (Imperatorin)	0.1	200–205	Alloimperatorin	>85%	4, 5
8-Allyloxy-7-allylquinoline	0.1	190–240	4,7-Diallyl-8-hydroxyquinoline	—	119a

C. *Rearrangements Involving Displacement*

$$\underset{\gamma}{CH_2}=\underset{\beta}{CH}\underset{\alpha}{CH_2}O$$

Substituents in ring (positions 1–6)

Allyl Group	Substituents in Ring	Conditions Time, hours	Conditions Temperature, °C.	Product	Yield	Reference*
None	2,6-Diallyl-4-formyl	—	>170	2,4,6-Triallylphenol	50%	44 (p. 108)
None	2-Methoxy-4-formyl-6-allyl	—	>180	4,6-Diallyl-2-methoxyphenol	58%	44 (p. 118)
None	2,6-Diallyl-4-carboxy	—	150–300	2,4,6-Triallylphenol	>85%	44 (p. 91)
None	2,6-Dimethoxy-4-carbomethoxy	(Heating 10 hr. with 2 N NaOH)		4-Allyl-2,6-dimethoxyphenol	>85%	73
γ-Methyl	2,6-Dichloro-4-carboxy	1.5	165–175	4-Crotyl-2,6-dichlorophenol (2,6-Dichloro-4-carboxyphenol)	75% 10%	46 46

* References 104–129 appear on p. 48.

[104] Kincaid and Oberseider, private communication.
[105] v. Auwers and Borsche, *Ber.*, **48**, 1716 (1915).
[106] Smith, Ungnade, Hoehn, and Wawzonek, *J. Org. Chem.*, **4**, 305 (1939).
[107] Raiford and Howland, *J. Am. Chem. Soc.*, **53**, 1051 (1931).
[107a] Arnold, McCool, and Schultz, *J. Am. Chem. Soc.*, **64**, 1023 (1942).
[108] Hurd, Greengard, and Pilgrim, *J. Am. Chem. Soc.*, **52**, 1700 (1930).
[109] Bergel, Jacob, Todd, and Work, *J. Chem. Soc.*, **1938**, 1375.
[109a] Kawai and Sugiyama, *Ber.*, **72**, 367 (1939).
[110] Mauthner, *J. prakt. Chem.*, [2] **102**, 41 (1921).
[110a] Arnold and Moran, *J. Am. Chem. Soc.*, **64**, 2986 (1942).
[111] Baker and Savage, *J. Chem. Soc.*, **1938**, 1602.
[112] Hurd and Parrish, *J. Am. Chem. Soc.*, **57**, 1731 (1935).
[112a] Arnold and McCool, *J. Am. Chem. Soc.*, **64**, 1315 (1942).
[113] Kawai, Nakamura, Kitazawa, and Nomatsu, *Ber.*, **73**, 1328 (1940).
[113a] Kawai, Yoshimura, and Ashino, *Ber.*, **71**, 324 (1938).
[114] Hill, Short, and Stromberg, *J. Chem. Soc.*, **1937**, 937.
[115] Bergmann and Berlin, *J. Org. Chem.*, **3**, 246 (1938).
[116] Gilman and Kirby, *J. Am. Chem. Soc.*, **48**, 2190 (1926).
[117] v. Auwers and Wittig, *J. prakt. Chem.*, [2] **108**, 99 (1924).
[118] Ochiai and Kokeguti, *J. Pharm. Soc. Japan*, **60**, 271 (1940) [*C.A.*, **35**, 458 (1941)].
[119] Mander-Jones and Trikojus, *J. Am. Chem. Soc.*, **54**, 2570 (1932).
[119a] Mander-Jones and Trikojus, *J. Proc. Roy. Soc. N.S. Wales*, **66**, 300 (1932) [*C.A.*, **27**, 1350 (1933)].
[120] Gilman and Van Ess, *J. Am. Chem. Soc.*, **61**, 1365 (1939).
[121] Krishnaswamy and Seshadri, *Proc. Indian Acad. Sci.*, **13A**, 43 (1941) [*C.A.*, **35**, 5499 (1941)].
[122] Hurd and Schmerling, *J. Am. Chem. Soc.*, **59**, 112 (1937).
[123] Schales, *Ber.*, **70**, 116 (1937).
[123a] Lauer and Sanders, *J. Am. Chem. Soc.*, **65**, 198 (1943).
[124] v. Braun and Schirmacher, *Ber.*, **56**, 538 (1923).
[125] Kawai, *Sci. Papers Inst. Phys. Chem. Research Tokyo*, **6**, 53 (1927) [*Chem. Zentr.*, **II**, 2188 (1927)].
[126] Fieser, *J. Am. Chem. Soc.*, **49**, 857 (1927).
[127] Hurd and Williams, *J. Am. Chem. Soc.*, **58**, 2636 (1936).
[128] Trikojus and White, *Nature*, **144**, 1016 (1939).
[129] Freudenberg and Klink, *Ber.*, **73**, 1369 (1940).

CHAPTER 2

THE PREPARATION OF ALIPHATIC FLUORINE COMPOUNDS

Albert L. Henne

Ohio State University

CONTENTS

INTRODUCTION

Reactions of four types have been used for introducing fluorine atoms into aliphatic molecules. These are listed below in the order of their practical importance at the present time.

1. Interaction of organic halides or polyhalides with inorganic fluorides.

$$RX + MF \rightarrow RF + MX$$

2. Addition of hydrogen fluoride to olefins and acetylenes.

$$RCH{=}CHR' + HF \longrightarrow RCH_2{-}CHFR'$$

$$RC{\equiv}CR' \xrightarrow{HF} RCF{=}CHR' \xrightarrow{HF} RCF_2{-}CH_2R'$$

3. Direct fluorination of saturated compounds or addition of fluorine to unsaturated compounds.

$$RH + F_2 \rightarrow RF + HF$$

$$RCH{=}CHR' + F_2 \rightarrow RCHF{-}CHFR'$$

4. Replacement of the hydroxyl group of alcohols.

$$ROH + HF \leftrightarrows RF + H_2O$$

METHODS OF PREPARATION

Interaction of Organic Halides or Polyhalides with Inorganic Fluorides

The replacement of a halogen atom in an organic compound by fluorine may be effected by treatment with any of several inorganic fluorides. The most important are mercury, silver, antimony, and hydrogen fluoride. The last is used whenever possible because of its low cost, ease of handling, and high fluorine content. The fluorides of thallium,[1] zinc,[2] and potassium[3, 4, 5] have been used in isolated instances. The choice of the reagent is based on the reactivity of the halogen to be replaced. Iodine is most easily and chlorine least easily replaced; however, side reactions are most prevalent with iodides, which in consequence have not been used extensively. Bromides occupy an intermediate place both with respect to ease of replacement and extent of side reactions; they have been used most often in replacement reactions carried out in open equipment. With the increased availability of pressure equipment, particularly in commercial practice, the use of chlorides has now become general.

All replacement reactions of this type must be carried out under completely anhydrous conditions. The difficulty of removing the last traces of water from oxygen compounds, and the possibility of producing water by decomposition, account for the fact that it is often difficult to utilize halogen compounds which contain oxygen in the molecule.

THE USE OF POTASSIUM FLUORIDE, ZINC FLUORIDE, ANTIMONY FLUO-RIDES, AND HYDROGEN FLUORIDE

A very reactive halogen atom, such as that of an acyl or sulfonyl halide, is replaced by fluorine by the action of almost any inorganic fluoride. The most convenient method consists in heating gently a mixture of an acyl or sulfonyl chloride with zinc or antimony fluoride in an apparatus which permits the acyl fluoride to distil as it is formed. The acyl fluoride usually boils about 40° lower than the chloride, and its removal from the reaction mixture results in quantitative yields. Complete interchange also can be effected with hydrogen fluoride, but more elaborate equipment is required. Good results have been reported for the synthesis of formyl and acetyl fluorides from mixtures of formic or

[1] Ray, *Nature*, **132**, 173 (1933).
[2] Meslans, *Ann. chim.*, [7] **1**, 411 (1894).
[3] Dumas and Peligot, *Ann. chim.*, [2] **61**, 193 (1836).
[4] Fremy, *Ann. chim.*, [3] **47**, 13 (1856).
[5] Nesmejanov and Kahn, *Ber.*, **67**, 370 (1934).

acetic acid and benzoyl chloride, treated with potassium fluoride in boiling acetic anhydride,[5] but an extension of this work to higher homologs disclosed that the reaction is first retarded and then stopped by the formation of a coating of potassium chloride on the reagent.[5a]

Allyl fluoride has been obtained by gentle heating of a mixture of allyl chloride and silver fluoride.[6] Hydrogen fluoride cannot be used with allyl halides because the first reaction is addition to the double bond; thus, methallyl chloride and hydrogen fluoride react to form the chlorofluoride, $(CH_3)_2CHFCH_2Cl$.[5a] An equimolecular mixture of hexachloropropene and antimony trifluoride, heated under reflux, generates the trifluoride, $CCl_2{=}CClCF_3$, quantitatively;[7] by allowing the intermediate mono- or di-fluoride to distil as formed, either of them can be produced quantitatively.[7] Since the replacement of each chlorine atom by fluorine lowers the boiling point by about 40°, the reaction is easily directed. Similarly, the substituted allyl chloride, $CF_2{=}CClCF_2Cl$, when heated overnight in a closed steel container at 180–200° with an excess of antimony trifluoride, is transformed quantitatively to the fluoride, $CF_2{=}CClCF_3$.[7]

Benzotrichloride resembles the allyl chlorides just described. It reacts with antimony trifluoride so rapidly that control of the reaction is difficult.[8] Benzotrifluoride is obtained in yields of about 60%, the remainder being lost through decomposition. The intermediate chlorofluorides, $C_6H_5CCl_2F$ and $C_6H_5CClF_2$, are seldom found and then only in small amounts. Benzotrifluoride is obtained also from the chloride and hydrogen fluoride.[9] The reaction of benzal chloride with antimony fluoride is even more difficult to control, but benzal fluoride can be obtained in 40% yield by skillful manipulation.[10] Diphenyldichloromethane is transformed to diphenyldifluoromethane in 60% yield when it is rapidly heated with antimony trifluoride to 140° and held at this temperature only until the mixture is completely liquefied.[11] In all the above preparations antimony trifluoride may be replaced by hydrogen fluoride, since hydrogen fluoride does not add to the double bonds of the benzene ring. The operation consists in mixing the chloride with a large excess (300%) of hydrogen fluoride in a copper vessel equipped with a fractionating device which permits the escape of hydrogen chloride but returns hydrogen fluoride to the reaction mixture.[5a, 9]

[5a] Unpublished observations of the author.

[6] Meslans, *Compt. rend.*, **111**, 882 (1890); *Ann. chim.*, [7] **1**, 374 (1894).

[7] Henne, Whaley, and Stevenson, *J. Am. Chem. Soc.*, **63**, 3478 (1941).

[8] Swarts, *Bull. acad. roy. Belg.*, **35**, 375 (1898); **1920**, 389.

[9] Simons and Lewis, *J. Am. Chem. Soc.*, **60**, 492 (1938).

[10] Van Hove, *Bull. acad. roy. Belg.*, **1913**, 1074.

[11] Henne and Leicester, *J. Am. Chem. Soc.*, **60**, 864 (1938).

Vinyl halides are so inert that none has been converted to a fluoride by halogen exchange. Vinyl fluorides have been synthesized from saturated polyhalides by dehalogenation with zinc and by dehydrohalogenation with alcoholic alkali, and from acetylene by addition of one molecule of hydrogen fluoride.[12-18]

Next to allyl halides in ease of replacement are saturated polyhalides of the types RCX_2R' and RCX_3. They are transformed to the corresponding polyfluorides RCF_2R' [19, 20] and RCF_3 [5a, 21] by long refluxing with antimony trifluoride or hydrogen fluoride. The reaction is so slow, however, that it would be of little practical importance if it could not be accelerated by the addition of small amounts (2 to 5%) of a pentavalent antimony salt; this procedure, discovered by Swarts about 1890,[22] has proved the most important means of synthesizing organic fluorides. The pentavalent antimony salt is usually produced by adding free halogen to the antimony trifluoride. Swarts recommended the addition of about 5% of bromine or antimony pentachloride. The current practice involves the addition of chlorine in amounts commensurate with the difficulty encountered in the halogen exchange. With the types just mentioned, in which all the halogen atoms are attached to one carbon atom, not more than 1% of chlorine should be added to the antimony trifluoride. The interchange then gives nearly quantitative yields, and little or no chlorination occurs as a side reaction. In more difficult preparations enough chlorine is added to transform the trifluoride to antimony trifluorodichloride, SbF_3Cl_2. When more halogen atoms are present in the molecule, or when halogen and hydrogen are present on the same carbon atom, the exchange becomes more difficult and side reactions (chlorination and loss of hydrogen halide) increase in significance. The reagent frequently must contain a high percentage of pentavalent antimony salt.

The behavior of a number of chlorine derivatives of methane, ethane, and propane toward antimony trifluoride activated by the trifluorodichloride is shown in Table I. The yield given for each product is the maximum obtained when the reaction was adjusted for the preparation

[12] Swarts, *Mém. couronnés acad. roy. Belg.*, **61** (1901).
[13] Ger. pat., 641,878 (1937) [*C. A.*, **31**, 5809 (1937)].
[14] Fr. pat., 805,563 (1936) [*Chem. Zentr.*, I, 2258 (1937)].
[15] Brit. pat., 469,421 (1937) [*C. A.*, **32**, 587 (1938)].
[16] U. S. pat., 2,118,901 (1937) [*C. A.*, **32**, 5409 (1938)].
[17] U. S. pat., 2,005,710 (1935) [*C. A.*, **29**, 5123 (1935)].
[18] Grosse and Lind, Baltimore meeting of American Chemical Society, 1939.
[19] Henne and Renoll, *J. Am. Chem. Soc.*, **59**, 2434 (1937).
[20] Henne, Renoll, and Leicester, *J. Am. Chem. Soc.*, **61**, 938 (1939).
[21] Henne and Renoll, *J. Am. Chem. Soc.*, **58**, 889 (1936).
[22] Swarts, *Bull. acad. roy. Belg.*, [3] **24**, 474 (1892).

of the particular product. The yields from bromides, and particularly from iodides, were much lower, owing to concurrent decomposition reactions.

TABLE I

PREPARATION OF ALIPHATIC FLUORIDES BY THE USE OF ANTIMONY FLUORIDES

Starting Material	Products	Note	Reference
CCl_4	CCl_3F (quant.)	2	23, 24
	CCl_2F_2 (quant.)	2	23, 24
$CHCl_3$	$CHCl_2F$ (quant.)	2	25, 26
	$CHClF_2$ (quant.)	2	25, 26
CH_2Cl_2	CH_2ClF (80%)	1, 2	26
	CH_2F_2 (80%)	1, 2	26
CH_3Cl	No reaction		
CCl_3CCl_3	CCl_3CCl_2F (quant.)	2	27
	CCl_2FCCl_2F (quant.)	2	27
	$CClF_2CCl_2F$ (quant.)	3	27
	$CClF_2CClF_2$ (quant.)	3	27
$CHCl_2CCl_3$	$CHCl_2CCl_2F$ (85%)	1, 2	28
	$CHCl_2CClF_2$ (70%)	1, 2	28
$CHCl_2CHCl_2$	$CHCl_2CHClF$ (60%)	1, 2	12
	$CHCl_2CHF_2$ (60%)	1, 2	12
CH_2ClCCl_3	CH_2ClCCl_2F (80%)	1, 2	29
	$CH_2ClCClF_2$ (80%)	1, 2	29
$CH_2ClCHCl_2$	$CH_2ClCHClF$ (60%)	1, 2	21
	CH_2ClCHF_2 (30%)	1, 2	21
CH_3CCl_3	CH_3CCl_2F (90%)	2	21
	CH_3CClF_2 (90%)	2	21
	CH_3CF_3 (90%)	2	21
CH_2ClCH_2Cl	No reaction		5a
CH_3CH_2Cl	No reaction		5a
$CCl_3CCl_2CCl_3$	$CCl_2FCCl_2CCl_3$ (quant.)	2	30
	$CCl_2FCCl_2CCl_2F$ (quant.)	2	30
	$CCl_2FCCl_2CClF_2$ (quant.)	2	30

TABLE I—*Continued*

PREPARATION OF ALIPHATIC FLUORIDES BY THE USE OF ANTIMONY FLUORIDES

Starting Material	Products	Note	Reference
$CHCl_2CCl_2CCl_3$	$CHCl_2CCl_2CCl_2F$ (quant.)	2	30
	$CHCl_2CCl_2CClF_2$ (quant.)	2	30
	$CHCl_2CClFCClF_2$ (75%)	1, 2	31
	$CHClFCClFCClF_2$ (20%)	1, 2	32
$CCl_3CHClCCl_3$	$CCl_3CHClCCl_2F$ (75%)	1, 2	30
	$CCl_2FCHClCCl_2F$ (75%)	1, 2	30
	$CClF_2CHClCCl_2F$ (30%)	1, 2	31
	$CClF_2CHClCClF_2$ (30%)	1, 2	31
$CH_3CH_2CCl_3$	$CH_3CH_2CCl_2F$ (40%)	2, 4	5a
	$CH_3CH_2CClF_2$ (40%)	2, 4	5a
	$CH_3CH_2CF_3$ (40%)	2, 4	5a
$CH_3CCl_2CH_3$	$CH_3CClFCH_3$ (quant.)	2	19
	$CH_3CF_2CH_3$ (quant.)	2	19
$CH_3CF_2CCl_3$	$CH_3CF_2CCl_2F$ (60%)	1, 2	19, 33
	$CH_3CF_2CClF_2$ (10%)	1, 2	5a, 33
$CCl_3CH_2CF_3$	$CCl_2FCH_2CF_3$ (quant.)	2	5a
	$CClF_2CH_2CF_3$ (quant.)	2	5a
$CCl_3CCl_2CF_3$	$CCl_2FCCl_2CF_3$ (quant.)	2	5a
	$CClF_2CCl_2CF_3$ (quant.)	2, 3	5a

1. The remainder of the material underwent chlorination.

2. For the preparation of this product, antimony trifluoride containing 10% of SbF_3Cl_2 was used.

3. For the preparation of this product, the antimony trifluoride must be converted completely to SbF_3Cl_2.

4. The remainder of the material underwent loss of hydrogen chloride.

[23] Swarts, *Mém. couronnés acad. roy. Belg.*, **51** (1895).

[24] Midgley and Henne, *Ind. Eng. Chem.*, **22**, 542 (1930).

[25] Swarts, *Bull. acad. roy. Belg.*, [3] **24**, 474 (1892).

[26] Henne, *J. Am. Chem. Soc.*, **59**, 1400 (1937).

[27] Locke, Brode, and Henne, *J. Am. Chem. Soc.*, **56**, 1726 (1934).

[28] Henne and Ladd, *J. Am. Chem. Soc.*, **58**, 402 (1936).

[29] Henne and Hubbard, *J. Am. Chem. Soc.*, **58**, 404 (1936).

[30] Henne and Ladd, *J. Am. Chem. Soc.*, **60**, 2491 (1938).

[31] Henne and Renoll, *J. Am. Chem. Soc.*, **61**, 2489 (1939).

[32] Henne and Haeckl, *J. Am. Chem. Soc.*, **63**, 3476 (1941).

[33] McBee, Henne, Hass, and Elmore, *J. Am. Chem. Soc.*, **62**, 3340 (1940)

From these experiments it is clear that, in the reaction of a poly-chloroparaffin with antimony trifluoride activated by a pentavalent antimony salt:

1. —CCl_3 groups are most reactive; they are converted to —CCl_2F and —$CClF_2$ groups, but rarely to —CF_3 groups.

2. —$CHCl_2$ groups are changed slowly to —$CHClF$ groups and with greater difficulty to —CHF_2 groups.

3. —CH_2Cl and —$CHCl$— groups are not affected.

4. The presence of fluorine decreases the ease of replacement of halogen attached to an adjacent carbon atom, or prevents such replacement.

5. Side reactions and decompositions increase as the hydrogen content of the molecule increases.

Hydrogen fluoride alone undergoes exchange reactions only with very reactive organic halides. However, because it reacts with antimony chloride to form antimony fluoride and hydrogen chloride,[34] it can be used to transform a large amount of organic halide to the fluoride with the aid of only small amounts of antimony salts. This is the method used in industry for the preparation of dichlorodifluoromethane.[34, 35]

$$3CCl_4 + 2SbF_3 \rightarrow 2SbCl_3 + 3CCl_2F_2$$

$$6HF + 2SbCl_3 \rightarrow 2SbF_3 + 6HCl$$

The process is carried out continuously by supplying carbon tetrachloride and hydrogen fluoride to a vessel originally charged with a quantity of antimony trifluoride containing a little pentavalent salt. The product (CCl_2F_2, b.p. $-30°$) and hydrogen chloride (b.p. $-85°$) are removed continuously by means of a fractionating column which returns hydrogen fluoride (b.p. $20°$), trichlorofluoromethane (b.p. $25°$), and carbon tetrachloride (b.p. $76°$). The distillate is washed with water to remove hydrogen chloride, and the dichlorodifluoromethane is finally purified by distillation.

The Use of the Fluorides of Silver and Mercury

Silver and mercury fluorides are capable of effecting all the replacements which can be accomplished by the other inorganic fluorides and in addition some replacements which are not effected by the others. Thus, alkyl halides are transformed by silver fluoride into alkyl fluorides, and difluoromethyl bromide is transformed to fluoroform by mercuric

[34] Daudt and Youker, U. S. pat., 2,005,705 (1935) [C. A., 29, 5123 (1935)].
[35] Midgley, Henne, and McNary, U. S. pats., 2,007,208 (1935), 1,930,129 (1933), 1,833,847 (1931) [C. A., 29, 5459 (1935); 28, 179 (1934); 26, 1047 (1932)].

fluoride; the last reagent converts difluoroethyl iodide, CHF_2CH_2I, and difluoroethylidene bromide, CHF_2CHBr_2, to trifluoro- and tetrafluoro-ethane, respectively. Vinyl halides are not affected. With respect to the relative ease of replacement, the various halogen-containing groups fall into the order discussed in connection with antimony trifluoride.

Silver fluoride is difficult to prepare in anhydrous form, and it has the further disadvantage that only half of its fluorine is available because the exchange reaction stops with the formation of the compound AgF· AgCl. Mercuric fluoride and mercurous fluoride are, therefore, more convenient reagents despite the lower fluorine content of mercurous fluoride.

Mercurous fluoride [36, 37, 38] converts alkyl iodides readily to alkyl fluorides; with alkyl bromides the yields range from 60 to 90%; alkyl chlorides have not been extensively studied. Mercurous fluoride is not a satisfactory reagent for polyhalides because it tends to remove halogens from adjacent carbon atoms, forming mercuric salts and olefins. Thus, acetylene tetrabromide is converted to a mixture of dibromethylene, $CHBr{=}CHBr$, and dibromoethylidene fluoride, $CHBr_2CHF_2$.[38] All the above reactions are carried out by refluxing the halogen compound with mercurous fluoride, usually at temperatures below 130°.

Mercuric fluoride is by far the most effective reagent.[39] It reacts rapidly, often violently, but its action is easily controlled. It reacts readily with alkyl chlorides and with polyhalides; it does not produce olefins, and all its fluorine is available for interchange. The reagent can be used in the presence of such solvents as hydrocarbons or their fluorine derivatives, but its action is impeded by ethers and stopped completely by ketones. Substances capable of generating water decompose it rapidly. Mercuric fluoride is an expensive reagent, because the only good method of preparation known consists in the treatment of mercuric chloride with fluorine. Consequently, it is used only after the cheaper fluorides have proved ineffective, or to complete a reaction which can be brought to an intermediate stage with the cheaper reagents. For example, a good method of preparing fluoroform consists in converting bromoform to difluorobromomethane by treatment with antimony trifluoride and transforming this intermediate to fluoroform by reaction with mercuric fluoride.[40] Similarly, 1,1,2-trifluoroethane is best synthe-sized by treatment of 1,1,2-tribromoethane with antimony trifluoride to give 1,1-difluoro-2-bromoethane, which is converted to the desired

[36] Henne and Renoll, J. Am. Chem. Soc., 58, 887 (1936).
[37] Swarts, Bull. acad. roy. Belg., [3] 31, 675 (1896).
[38] Henne and Renoll, J. Am. Chem. Soc., 60, 1060 (1938).
[39] Henne and Midgley, J. Am. Chem. Soc., 58, 884 (1936).
[40] Henne, J. Am. Chem. Soc., 59, 1200 (1937).

product by reaction with mercuric fluoride,[21] and 1,1,2,2-tetrafluoro-ethane is prepared from acetylene tetrabromide by way of the difluoro-dibromide, $CHBr_2CHF_2$, through the same sequence of treatments.[34]

Several procedures have been devised to circumvent the necessity of synthesizing mercuric fluoride. The nascent salt, prepared by passing hydrogen fluoride into a mixture of mercuric oxide and the organic reagent, may be employed.[41] The oxide is instantly converted to the fluoride, which reacts at once with the organic halide. The reaction is strongly exothermic, and adequate mechanical means of dissipating the heat must be provided in order to keep the reaction under control. The mercury halide produced can be recovered and used for the preparation of mercuric oxide for another run. Examples of preparations effected by this method are given in Table II.

TABLE II

PREPARATION OF ALIPHATIC FLUORIDES BY THE USE OF MERCURIC OXIDE
AND HYDROGEN FLUORIDE [41]

Starting Material	Products	Yield
$CHBr_2CHBr_2$	$CHBr_2CHBrF$	80%
	$CHBr_2CHF_2$	80%
$CH_2BrCHBr_2$	$CH_2BrCHBrF$	80%
	CH_2BrCHF_2	80%
$CH_3COCH_2CH_2Br$	$CH_3COCH_2CH_2F$	60–70%
CH_2Cl_2	CH_2F_2	70–80%
$CHCl_3$	$CHClF_2$	70–80%
CH_3CHCl_2	CH_3CHF_2	70%
$CH_3(CH_2)_5CHCl_2$	$CH_3(CH_2)_5CHF_2$	80%
$(C_6H_5)_2CCl_2$	$(C_6H_5)_2CF_2$	75%
$(C_6H_5)_3CCl$	$(C_6H_5)_3CF$	40–50%
$CHCl_2CClF_2$	CHF_2CClF_2	
CHF_2CCl_3	CHF_2CClF_2	

Another procedure consists in adding a halogen to mercurous fluoride in order to generate a mercuric fluorohalide; such a salt acts substantially as a mixture of mercuric fluoride and mercuric halide.[38] Methyl fluoride was prepared in yields of better than 80% by dissolving one equivalent of iodine in a large quantity of methyl iodide and progressively feeding one equivalent of mercurous fluoride into the solu-

[41] Henne, J. Am. Chem. Soc., 60, 1569 (1938).

tion.[42] Mercuric fluorochloride, prepared from mercurous fluoride and chlorine,[38] proved capable of converting methylene chloride and methylene bromide quantitatively to CH_2F_2, tribromoethane to CHF_2CH_2Br, and acetylene tetrabromide to CHF_2CHBr_2. A side reaction appeared, especially in the case of ethylene bromide which was transformed to a mixture of ethylene fluoride and ethylene chlorobromide.

It has not yet been possible to employ hydrogen fluoride in conjunction with mercuric fluoride in a process comparable to that with hydrogen fluoride and antimony fluorides (p. 56). At room temperature there is practically no reaction between hydrogen fluoride and mercuric chloride, and at temperatures high enough to permit the reaction the practical difficulties of operation are such that the process is without value.[5a]

Construction of Apparatus and Preparation of Reagents

Equipment. All interchange reactions must be carried out under rigorously dry conditions. The very easy interchanges can be done in glass, but this is not recommended. The great majority of reactions reported in the literature were performed in platinum equipment, and some of the results which were difficult to duplicate in other equipment were due to the very beneficial effect of platinum itself. Clean steel equipment is most convenient in the laboratory and can be built inexpensively from standard pipe fittings. Copper has been used successfully, as have also magnesium, nickel, stainless steel, and Monel metal. Steel equipment with silver lining is convenient when mercury salts are handled.

When an organic bromide is transformed into a fluoride, the boiling point usually is lowered by about 70° for each halogen replacement. The boiling points of chlorides are lowered by about 40° for each replacement by fluorine. It is, therefore, advantageous to run the interchange in a reaction chamber surmounted by a column and to allow the desired fluorides to distil as formed. This mode of operation often permits a quantitative conversion. When very low-boiling compounds are involved, the dephlegmator is equipped with a pressure gauge, a thermometer well, and a releasing needle valve. The combined readings of the thermometer and the gauge indicate the progress of the reaction when referred to a pressure-temperature chart such as that illustrated (Fig. 1). Since the lines are practically straight, it is possible to draw the vapor curve of any fluoride whose boiling point at one pressure can be estimated with a degree of accuracy sufficient to be of great help in the synthesis.

[42] Swarts, *Bull. soc. chim. Belg.*, **46**, 10 (1937).

Reagents. Hydrogen fluoride can be obtained in convenient steel containers equipped with dependable needle valves. Excellent grades of the crystalline anhydrous fluorides of zinc and antimony are available commercially.

Preparation of Mercurous Fluoride.[38] A solution of 40 g. of red mercuric oxide in a mixture of 28 cc. of concentrated nitric acid and 60 cc. of

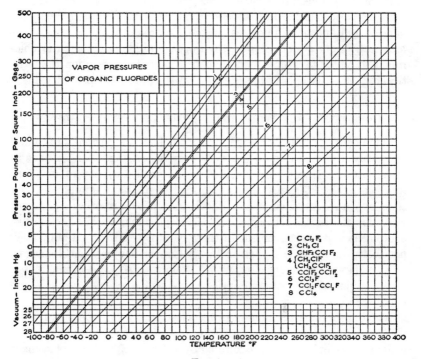

Fig. 1.

water is shaken vigorously in a bottle with 40 g. of mercury until the mercury ceases to dissolve readily, at which point mercurous nitrate starts to crystallize. A solution of 4 cc. of concentrated nitric acid in 45 cc. of water is then added to redissolve the crystals, and the excess mercury is decanted. The reaction mixture is next poured into a freshly prepared solution of 48 g. of potassium bicarbonate in 200 cc. of water; the resulting mercurous carbonate is filtered by suction in the presence of a few pieces of solid carbon dioxide and finally washed thoroughly with 1400 cc. of water saturated with carbon dioxide. All operations should be carried out in diffused light. The moist mercurous carbonate is added immediately in small portions and with constant stirring to a mixture of

100 cc. of 48% hydrofluoric acid and 260 cc. of water in a platinum dish, which is then heated on the water bath. The mixture is stirred and heated until a dry, sandy powder is obtained. This powder is immediately scraped off the walls, crushed in the bottom of a platinum crucible, and then heated for an hour on the water bath. The salt must be removed from the dish and stored immediately in tightly stoppered copper or resin containers. The yield is about 80 g. Analysis indicates the product to be essentially pure mercurous fluoride. The use of organic solvents for washing and drying does not simplify the process, and the use of chemical reagents inferior to the chemically pure grade causes complications.

Preparation of Antimony Trifluorodichloride (SbF_3Cl_2). This is made in the steel reaction vessel described on p. 59. A known quantity of antimony fluoride is placed in the vessel; the vessel is evacuated, the needle valve is closed, and the whole is weighed. Connection is established to a chlorine cylinder, and the needle valve is opened to permit chlorine to fill the vessel. Part of it is absorbed rapidly by the salt, with evolution of heat. Soon the reaction slows down as indicated by the rate of pressure fall when the needle valve is closed. Weighing indicates the amount of chlorine present in the vessel. When the absorption practically ceases, the valve is closed, and the connection with the chlorine tank is removed. The reaction vessel is alternately heated gently, then allowed to cool in order to permit SbF_3Cl_2, which is a viscous liquid, to flow and expose fresh surfaces of crystalline antimony trifluoride. The operation is ended after the absorption of the desired quantity of chlorine.

Experimental Procedures

Acetyl Fluoride. (a) [2] In a pressure bottle stoppered with rubber is placed 150 g. of acetyl chloride. It is cooled to $-15°$, and 10 g. of anhydrous zinc fluoride is introduced; the bottle is stoppered and allowed to warm to room temperature with shaking. It is then cooled, a second 10-g. portion of the salt is added, and the bottle is stoppered and shaken as before. When 100 g. of zinc fluoride has been added in this way the temperature is allowed to rise gradually to 50°. The reaction mixture is cooled, and the product is distilled. Acetyl fluoride boils at 20°; the yield is quantitative.

(b) [43] One mole of hydrogen fluoride is condensed into 10 moles of acetic anhydride cooled to 0°. The container is closed and allowed to stand overnight at room temperature. The mixture is cooled to 0°, and a few grams of sodium fluoride is added. After vigorous shaking to

[43] Colson, *Ann. chim.* [7] 255 (1897).

remove any residual trace of hydrogen fluoride, the mixture is subjected to distillation. The yield of acetyl fluoride, b.p. 20°, is quantitative.

1,1,2-Trichloro-3,3,3-trifluoro-1-propene $(CCl_2=CClCF_3)$.[7] In a dry flask equipped with an efficient dephlegmator an equimolecular mixture of hexachloropropene and antimony trifluoride is heated in an oil bath. The temperature of the bath is adjusted to maintain a steady distillation at about 90° at the top of the dephlegmator. The crude distillate is mostly the desired product, distilling at 87.9°, together with a small amount of $CCl_2=CClCClF_2$. If the difluoride is wanted instead of the trifluoride the distillation is adjusted at 130°. If the monofluoride is desired, the distillation is made as rapid as possible. The fluorine utilization is complete, and there are no side reactions.

Benzotrifluoride $(C_6H_5CF_3)$. *Laboratory Procedure.*[5a, 8] Benzotrichloride and antimony trifluoride, in the molecular proportion of 1.5 to 1, are placed in a metal container fitted with a 30-cm. vertical pipe to act as a mild dephlegmator. The pipe is connected to a downward metal condenser whose flared end comes in contact with the surface of a large quantity of water in a wide-mouthed bottle. The reaction mixture is brought rapidly to 130–140°, at which temperature the reaction starts in a lively fashion. Benzotrifluoride distils at 103° and collects in the bottom of the water bottle. Heating is regulated in such a fashion that distillation proceeds rapidly; prolonged heating is distinctly detrimental. At the end of the operation, the water is drained from the condenser, so that some unchanged antimony trichloride will distil over. Otherwise an appreciable amount of organic material remains and is difficult to remove from the antimony trichloride. For purification, benzotrifluoride is subjected to steam distillation, washed with dilute carbonate, dried, and distilled (b.p. 103°). The yields computed on the basis of the benzotrichloride are from 60 to 65%. The fluorine utilization is about 90%. Considerable decomposition of the benzotrichloride occurs, but this is compensated by its low cost, the speed of the reaction, and the purity of the product.

Industrial Procedure.[44] Into 500 parts of benzotrichloride cooled to 0° in a copper flask equipped with a stirrer, an outlet tube, and an inlet tube reaching to the bottom, is introduced 200 parts of hydrogen fluoride over a period of seventy-two hours. At first, only hydrogen chloride escapes; later, a mixture of hydrogen fluoride and benzotrifluoride distils and is condensed in a metal receiver cooled with ice and salt. After completion of the reaction, the contents of the receiver and the reaction flask are united and gently warmed to drive off most of the hydrogen fluoride. The remainder is eliminated by agitation with powdered

[44] Ger. pat., 575,593 [*Chem. Zentr.*, II, 609 (1933)].

sodium fluoride. After filtration, the product is distilled; yield, 300 parts of benzotrifluoride, b.p. 103°. The distillation tailings contain chlorofluorides which can be reworked in a subsequent operation.

2,2-Difluoropropane ($CH_3CF_2CH_3$).[19] In a reaction vessel equipped with an ice-cooled reflux condenser is placed 1.25 moles of antimony trifluoride containing 5% of bromine by weight. The vessel is cooled in ice, and 1.5 moles of 2,2-dichloropropane, cooled to 0°, is added. The reaction starts promptly and is regulated by means of an ice bath intermittently applied. At the end of the operation the vessel is heated to about 70°. The vapors passing through the condenser are caught in a water gasometer or in a receiver cooled with solid carbon dioxide. This operation, quickly performed, yields about 85% of 2,2-difluoropropane (b.p. $-0.5°$) and 10 to 15% of 2-fluoro-2-chloropropane (b.p. 35.2°).

1,1,2,2,3,3-Hexachloro-3-fluoropropane ($CHCl_2CCl_2CCl_2F$).[30] In a 1-l. flask, a mixture of 1160 g. of 1,1,2,2,3,3,3-heptachloropropane and 740 g. of antimony trifluorodichloride is vigorously stirred so that the temperature does not exceed 50°. After the mixture has cooled to 30°, it is slowly heated to 130–140° and maintained at this temperature for five hours. It is then cooled, poured into water, washed with hydrochloric acid—to remove antimony salts—then with water, and dried. The yield is 907 g. of reaction product containing approximately 60 g. of 1,1,2,2-tetrachloro-3,3,3-trifluoropropane (b.p. 130°), 315 g. of 1,1,2,2,3-pentachloro-3,3-difluoropropane (b.p. 168°), and 435 g. of 1,1,2,2,3,3-hexachloro-3-fluoropropane (b.p. 210°).

1,1,2,2,3-Pentachloro-3,3-difluoropropane ($CHCl_2CCl_2CClF_2$).[30] In a 3-l. flask a mixture of 1970 g. of 1,1,2,2,3,3,3-heptachloropropane and 1245 g. of SBF_3Cl_2 is heated to 140–150° and held at this temperature for eight hours. The subsequent operations are identical with those of the preceding procedure. The crude product (weight 1740 g.) contains approximately 400 g. of trifluoride and 1000 g. of difluoride; the remainder of the material consists of ethylenic derivatives and of fluorine derivatives of ethane, resulting from the cleavage of the propane molecule. The more abundant by-products are $CCl_2{=}CCl_2$, CCl_3CCl_2F, CCl_2FCCl_2F, and C_2Cl_6.

1,1,1,2,2,3,3-Heptachloro-3-fluoropropane ($CCl_3CCl_2CCl_2F$).[30] In a round-bottomed flask equipped with an air-cooled reflux condenser a mixture of 960 g. of octachloropropane, 180 g. of antimony trifluoride, and 40 g. of antimony pentachloride is heated for eight hours at 140°. The following day, 30 g. of SbF_3Cl_2 is added, and the heating is continued at 140° for another six hours. During this treatment, the lower layer containing most of the antimony trifluoride gradually liquefies and dissolves in the upper layer of organic material. The liquid reaction mixture is poured into commercial hydrochloric acid while still hot and is washed free of antimony salt. The crude product, amounting to 910 g., solidifies at room temperature. By fractional distillation at 90 mm., it is separated into about equal parts of the monofluoride (b.p. 237°, m.p. 97°) and unchanged octachloropropane.

1,1,2,2,3,3-Hexachloro-1,3-difluoropropane ($CCl_2FCCl_2CCl_2F$).[30] In a round-bottomed flask equipped with an air-cooled reflux condenser a mixture of 1500 g. of octachloropropane, 560 g. of antimony trifluoride, and 75 g. of antimony pentachloride is heated for five hours on a steam bath. A further quantity of 100 g. of antimony pentachloride is then added in small portions, and the heating is continued for twenty hours. The reaction mixture, which gradually becomes homogeneous, is allowed to cool before it is poured into aqueous acid, then is washed and dried. The crude product amounts to 1092 g., from which about 750 g. of difluoride is obtained by fractional distillation at 90 mm. The boiling point at 760 mm. is 194°, and the freezing point is 29.8°.

1,1,2,2,3-Pentachloro-2,3,3-trifluoropropane ($CCl_2FCCl_2CClF_2$).[30] In a round-bottomed flask equipped with an air-cooled reflux condenser a mixture of 1220 g. of octachloropropane, 500 g. of antimony trifluoride, and 75 g. of antimony pentachloride is heated on a steam bath for twelve hours. A further portion of 80 g. of antimony pentachloride is added, and heating on the steam bath is continued for two hours. The mixture is then cooled, and to the liquid layer, decanted from the crystalline antimony salts into a flask equipped with a water-cooled reflux condenser, is added 400 g. of SbF_3Cl_2. The reaction mixture is then heated slowly to 140°, because the reaction is quite active at the start. It is advisable to have ice water ready to chill the mixture if it threatens to escape control. After the temperature of 140° is reached, the heating is continued for two hours. Then, after cooling, the washing, drying, and distillation are performed as in the preceding cases. The crude product amounts to 700 g. and contains about 300 g. of the trifluoride (b.p. 152.3°, f.p. −5°).

Dichlorodifluoromethane and Trichlorofluoromethane.[5a] In a flask connected to an ice-cooled reflux condenser, a mixture of 2 moles of carbon tetrachloride and 1 mole of antimony trifluoride is cooled to 0°. After addition of 0.1 mole of antimony pentachloride, the mixture is allowed to warm until the reaction starts. The reaction is regulated by intermittent cooling and heating in order not to overtax the reflux condenser. The uncondensed vapors are led to a receiver cooled with solid carbon dioxide. The distillate is a mixture of CCl_3F(b.p. 25°) and CCl_2F_2(b.p. −30°) whose composition depends on the efficiency of the dephlegmation but is usually 50–50 in a laboratory operation. At the end of the operation, a small amount of trichlorofluoromethane can be distilled from the excess carbon tetrachloride. The utilization of the antimony fluoride is complete.

1,2-Dichloro-1,1,2,2-tetrafluoroethane ($CClF_2CClF_2$).[5a] A known quantity of SbF_3Cl_2 is prepared as described on p. 61. When this is complete the reaction vessel is evacuated, and an equimolecular quantity of $CClF_2CCl_2F$ is drawn in. The needle valve is closed, and the mixture is heated gradually to 140°, then to 160°. The pressure rises. The temperature and pressure readings at the top of the equipment are referred to the vapor-tension diagram, Fig. 1. The needle valve is opened in such way as to permit the passage of $CClF_2CClF_2$ vapors. These vapors (b.p. 3.6°) are condensed in Dry Ice. When the tetrafluoride vapors are withdrawn, the trifluoride (b.p. 47°) starts to distil, the temperature rises, and the pressure falls. The valve is closed until more tetrafluoride is formed. The transformation of the trifluoride into the tetrafluoride is quantitative. The residual SbF_2Cl_3 is utilized to convert hexachloroethane to trichlorotrifluoroethane which is then available for the next operation.

1,1-Difluoro-2,2-dibromoethane and 1-Fluoro-1,2,2-tribromoethane.[5a, 41] To 3 gram molecules of acetylene tetrabromide in a tall metal container (preferably nickel) cooled externally with water, 1 gram molecule of red mercuric oxide is added and the mixture immediately stirred to prevent the formation of a heavy paste or cake. Dry hydrogen fluoride from a commercial cylinder is led into the liquid through a metal tube (flexible copper tubing is convenient). The flow of gas is regulated so that the temperature of the reaction mixture does not exceed 40° to 50°. The red color of the mercuric oxide fades progressively to pink, yellow, grayish white, and finally gleaming white at the end of the reaction. At this point it is found that about 2.3 gram molecules of hydrogen fluoride has been used, which is an excess of 15% over the theoretical quantity required. The white salt is pure mercuric bromide. An aqueous layer of concentrated hydrofluoric acid floats on the surface. At the end of the reaction, the mixture is poured onto cracked ice and washed roughly by decantation to remove the excess acid. It is then placed in a distilling flask with twice its volume of water and heated with a free flame kept in constant motion to prevent foaming. Steam distillation of the product takes place promptly and carries along some acetylene tetrabromide. The distillate is decanted from the water, dried, and rectified; it yields 0.6 gram molecule of CHF_2CHBr_2 (b.p. 107°) and 0.4 gram molecule of $CHFBrCHBr_2$ (b.p. 174°), which is an 80% yield, based on the mercuric oxide. The material left in the distilling flask is cooled overnight, preferably in ice; this causes the mercuric bromide to crystallize out completely and facilitates filtration. The aqueous layer is separated as completely as practicable, and the remainder is filtered with suction and air-dried on the filter. The filtrate separates into a layer of acetylene tetrabromide and a layer of water. The solid material is removed from the filter, placed in a bottle, covered with chloroform, vigorously shaken for twenty minutes, and then filtered by suction. Pure mercuric bromide is left on the filter. The filtrate is a chloroform solution containing from 75 to 100 cc. of acetylene tetrabromide. By distillation of the chloroform it is possible to recover the acetylene tetrabromide.

1,2-Dibromofluoroethane and 1-Bromo-2,2-difluoroethane. By a procedure analogous to that just described, 1,2,2-tribromoethane was converted to the mono- and di-fluoro derivatives. The reaction temperature had to be lower for good results. At 0°, the yield of mixed products was 50%; at −20°, 60–65%. At higher temperatures the yield was only 30%. The boiling points are 121° and 57°, respectively.

Mercury Recovery. The methods would be costly if the mercury could not be recovered and reworked. Details of a simple procedure for recovering the mercury by converting the mercuric bromide to the oxide and heating the oxide have been published.[41]

Addition of Hydrogen Fluoride to Unsaturated Compounds

ADDITION TO A TRIPLE BOND

Hydrogen fluoride reacts readily with alkynes.[18] The literature offers practically no details to cover the mode of operation, and most of the following observations are based upon the author's experience.

Acetylene and hydrogen fluoride react at room temperature to give vinyl fluoride and 1,1-difluoroethane. The claim [45] that mercuric ion is needed as a catalyst is apparently unfounded. The reactions are very violent and uneven. At low temperatures, there is a tendency for the reagents to accumulate, then suddenly to react with explosive violence. At higher temperatures, much resinification takes place. It is claimed [45] that aqueous as well as anhydrous hydrogen fluoride can bring about the reaction. Homologs of acetylene are more convenient to handle. They have been correctly reported [18] to yield pure 2,2-difluorides exclusively, as illustrated by the synthesis of $CH_3CF_2CH_3$, $C_2H_5CF_2CH_3$, $C_3H_7CF_2CH_3$, and $C_4H_9CF_2CH_3$, although details of the preparations were not given. The author's investigations lead to the recommendation of a reaction temperature of about −20°, continuous gentle agitation, and addition of the alkyne to liquefied hydrogen fluoride.

[45] Ger. pat., 621,977 [*Chem. Zentr.*, I, 1310 (1936)].

Reversing the order of addition, or using an ether as a solvent, causes a marked retardation of the reaction, with subsequent sudden, uncontrollable speed-up. Yields of about 80% are obtained and probably can be improved by devices to minimize the mechanical losses.[5a]

The addition of hydrogen fluoride to stearolic acid in methylene chloride solution to give 9,10-difluorostearic acid is cited in the patent literature.[45] This claim should be verified, as either 9,9- or 10,10-difluorostearic acid or a mixture is much more likely to be the reaction product.

ADDITION TO A DOUBLE BOND

Hydrogen fluoride reacts with olefins to yield monofluoroalkanes,[46, 47] but very few experimental details have been published. The reaction is reversible and is often accompanied by polymerization of the olefin, which is favored by excess hydrogen fluoride. The difficulties increase if the product is a secondary and especially a tertiary fluoride. Concentrated aqueous hydrofluoric acid does not react with olefins. The operation consists in feeding the olefin into liquefied hydrogen fluoride, under pressure if needed, with stirring or shaking. A successful method is to prepare the mixture at $-40°$ to $-60°$ in a metal container, then to allow gradual heating over a period of one to two hours to $75°$ or $90°$. The higher temperature favors the formation of primary fluorides but has an opposite effect on tertiary fluorides. Increased time of reaction always favors side reactions.

When hydrogen fluoride adds to an olefin, the fluorine becomes attached to the carbon with the least hydrogen. Ethylene yields ethyl fluoride; propylene yields isopropyl fluoride; cyclohexene gives cyclohexyl fluoride. Cyclopropane yields n-propyl fluoride when the reaction is conducted very slowly at $0°$, but if the temperature is not well regulated an isomerization takes place to yield isopropyl fluoride. The reactions are all non-catalytic and take place in paraffin or metal containers equally well. The yields are from 60 to 80%.[46]

Hydrogen fluoride adds easily to unsaturated fatty acids.[45, 48] The operation consists in passing hydrogen fluoride through a solution of the fatty acid in methylene chloride, chloroform, or carbon tetrachloride, at room temperature. Undecylenic acid, $C_{10}H_{19}CO_2H$, yields 10-fluoro-undecan-1-oic acid, $CH_3CHF(CH_2)_8CO_2H$. Oleic acid yields a fluorostearic acid of unknown structure, and it has not been established whether a single product or a mixture is formed. Hydrogen fluoride adds

[46] Grosse and Lind, *J. Org. Chem.*, **3**, 26 (1938).

[47] Grosse, Wacker, and Lind, *J. Phys. Chem.*, **44**, 275 (1940).

[48] Fr. pat., 799,432 (1936) [*C. A.*, **30**, 7585 (1936)].

to oleyl alcohol to give a fluorostearyl alcohol of unknown structure. It adds to ketene to form acetyl fluoride, and to cyanic acid in ether solution cooled to $-78°$ to form carbamyl fluoride, $FCONH_2$.[49] Unpublished observations indicate that hydrogen fluoride adds with difficulty to $CH_3CH=CBr_2$, more readily to $CH_3CH=CCl_2$, and rapidly and quantitatively to $CH_3CH=CClF$ and $CH_3CH=CF_2$. In all cases, a 1,1,1-trihalopropane results exclusively.[5a]

A mixture of $CH_2=CClCH_2Cl$ and hydrogen fluoride forms $CH_3CClFCH_2Cl$.[50] The operation consists merely in mixing the reagents at low temperature in a steel container, sealing, letting stand overnight at room temperature, cooling, pouring onto cracked ice, washing, and distilling. A conversion of about 50% is observed, and the balance of the chloroölefin is recovered. If the operation is altered by keeping the container overnight at 40°, the reaction proceeds to completion, and if excess hydrogen fluoride is present $CH_3CF_2CH_2Cl$ appears as a by-product (about 25%); the latter is formed by loss of hydrogen chloride from the primary product and subsequent addition of hydrogen fluoride. A similar reaction is observed when 2-chloro-2-butene is treated with hydrogen fluoride. The primary reaction product is the expected $CH_3CH_2CClFCH_3$, and the secondary product is $CH_3CH_2CF_2CH_3$.[5a]

No addition has been observed in the case of $CHCl=CHCl$, $CHCl=CCl_2$, or $CCl_2=CCl_2$. Preliminary studies have indicated that $CH_3CCl=CH_2$ gives mostly $CH_3CF_2CH_3$, together with some $CH_3CCl_2CH_3$. The hydrofluorination of $CH_3CH=CHCl$ (or of $CH_3CH=CHBr$) fails to give the expected addition product but yields an appreciable amount of $C_3H_6Cl_2$ (or $C_3H_6Br_2$, apparently the 1,2-dihalopropane in both cases) and a large amount of polymeric material. Isocrotylchloride, $(CH_3)_2C=CHCl$, and methallyl chloride, $CH_2=C(CH_3)CH_2Cl$, yield the same addition product. It must therefore be $(CH_3)_2CFCH_2Cl$. Addition also takes place with allyl chloride, but the position of the fluorine atom has not yet been ascertained.[5a]

Experimental Procedures

Ethyl Fluoride.[46] Ethylene from a storage tank is forced intermittently into an Allegheny metal autoclave which contains 200 g. of hydrogen fluoride. The autoclave is equipped with a stirrer which is operated during the addition, and the temperature is kept at 90° throughout the addition. After 85 g. of ethylene has been introduced, stirring

[49] Linhard and Betz, *Ber.*, **73**, 177 (1940).
[50] Henne and Haeckl, *J. Am. Chem. Soc.*, **63**, 2692 (1941).

is continued for another hour; then the mass is cooled with solid carbon dioxide and allowed to distil through water. The crude ethyl fluoride, obtained in 81% yield, is passed through a soda-lime tube, then rectified, b.p. −37.7°.

Isopropyl Fluoride.[46] The procedure is the same as for ethyl fluoride except that the temperature is kept at 0°, and the ratio of hydrogen fluoride to propylene is held to 1.08. The yield is 61%; isopropyl fluoride boils at −10.1°.

Cyclohexyl Fluoride.[46] In a copper container fitted with inlet, outlet, and stirrer is placed 200 g. of anhydrous hydrogen fluoride. After cooling to −35°, 400 g. of precooled cyclohexene is added dropwise over a period of seventy-five minutes. The reaction mixture is poured into a copper beaker filled with cracked ice, stirred, decanted, dried, and distilled under 300 mm. pressure (b.p. 71–71.4°). The yield is 60%; at 10° it is only 54%.

2,2-Difluoropropane ($CH_3CF_2CH_3$).[5a] The vapor of 1 mole of propyne (b.p. −23.3°) is introduced into 4 moles of liquefied hydrogen fluoride in a metal container held at −23° by means of a carbon tetrachloride bath to which enough solid carbon dioxide has been added to keep it mushy. Care is exercised to prevent the escape of any vapors. The reaction occurs at once. After completion of the addition, the reaction mixture is allowed to warm, and the vapors are passed through water and then condensed in a receiver cooled with solid carbon dioxide. The distillation of the condensate yields 54 g. (64%) of 2,2-difluoroethane, $CH_3CF_2CH_3$, b.p. 0°. Lower reaction temperatures retard the addition, whereas higher temperatures favor polymerization.

Direct Fluorination and Addition of Fluorine

The direct action of fluorine, first reported by Moissan,[51] has been used to replace hydrogen, to replace another halogen, or to add to a double bond. In very few cases, however, has the reaction been sufficiently well controlled to offer a practical method of preparation of organic fluorides. In all cases, several reaction products have been obtained. The procedure has always been performed on a very small scale, and only recently has it been improved to the point where it is not dangerous when the proper precautions are taken. The method has possibilities which still await technical improvements.

Most organic compounds burn or explode when brought in contact with fluorine. When the reaction is carried out in a solvent which is immune to fluorine or reacts only slowly with it, care must be taken not

[51] Moissan, "Le fluor et ses composés," G. Steinheil, Paris, 1900.

to allow the fluorine to accumulate in the solvent. Many accidents have occurred when mixtures of fluorine and an inert gas (usually nitrogen) were passed through a solution of an organic compound in carbon tetrachloride or difluorodichloromethane. These accidents were caused by the fact that fluorine dissolved, while the diluent passed through the solution unabsorbed. For this mode of operation, the best solvents are the fluorinated refrigerants available commercially (CCl_2F_2 and $C_2F_4Cl_2$) or liquefied hydrogen fluoride.[52]

The interaction of fluorine with an organic compound liberates a quantity of energy which is frequently of the order of magnitude of, or greater than, the energy which binds the carbon atoms in chains. It is estimated [53] that the addition of fluorine to a double bond liberates 102 calories per mole, whereas chlorine liberates only 30 calories. Careful control of the temperature throughout the reacting masses is therefore essential. Even in the most favorable cases, much decomposition occurs and carbon tetrafluoride is frequently the main reaction product.[53-56]

The most satisfactory procedure for carrying out the reaction between fluorine and a gaseous compound consists in diluting both reagents with an inert gas, preferably nitrogen, and in bringing them together at the surface of a copper gauze, where a smooth reaction takes place.[53, 56-64] When fluorine is to react with a liquid compound, it is preferable to allow the reaction to take place at the surface of the liquid and in the vapor phase.[65, 66, 67]

The products obtained by the action of fluorine on a number of organic compounds are listed in Table III.

In a few isolated instances it has been possible to treat an unsaturated compound with a derivative capable of giving off free fluorine, namely, lead tetrafluoride or iodobenzenedifluoride, which are formed, respectively, from lead tetraacetate or iodosobenzene and hydrogen

[52] Calcott and Benning, U. S. pat., 2,013,030 (1935) [C. A., **29**, 6900 (1935)].
[53] Dimroth and Bockemuller, Ber., **64**, 516 (1931).
[54] Bigelow, Pearson, Cook, and Miller, J. Am. Chem. Soc., **55**, 4614 (1933).
[55] Bigelow and Pearson, J. Am. Chem. Soc., **56**, 2773 (1934).
[56] Miller, Calfee, and Bigelow, J. Am. Chem. Soc., **59**, 198 (1937).
[57] Calfee and Bigelow, J. Am. Chem. Soc., **59**, 2072 (1937).
[58] Fukuhara and Bigelow, J. Am. Chem. Soc., **60**, 427 (1933).
[59] Calfee, Fukuhara, and Bigelow, J. Am. Chem. Soc., **61**, 3552 (1939).
[60] Calfee, Fukuhara, Young, and Bigelow, J. Am. Chem. Soc., **62**, 267 (1940).
[61] Young, Fukuhara, and Bigelow, J. Am. Chem. Soc., **62**, 1171 (1940).
[62] Hadley and Bigelow, J. Am. Chem. Soc., **62**, 3302 (1940).
[63] Fukuhara and Bigelow, J. Am. Chem. Soc., **63**, 788 (1941).
[64] Fukuhara and Bigelow, J. Am. Chem. Soc., **63**, 2792 (1941).
[65] Fredenhagen and Cadenbach, Ber., **67**, 928 (1934).
[66] Bockemüller, Ann., **506**, 20 (1933).
[67] Miller, J. Am. Chem. Soc., **62**, 341 (1940).

TABLE III

PRODUCTS OBTAINED BY DIRECT ADDITION AND SUBSTITUTION OF FLUORINE

Starting Material	Products	Note	Reference
C	CF_4, C_2F_4, C_2F_6, C_3F_8	1, 2	68, 69, 70, 71
CH_4	CF_4, C_2F_4, C_2F_6, C_3F_8	1, 2	68, 69, 70, 71
C_2H_6	CF_4, C_2F_6, CH_2FCH_2F, CH_2FCHF_2, CHF_2CHF_2, CHF_2CF_3	1	57, 59, 61
C_2H_5Cl	CF_4, CF_3Cl, CF_2Cl_2, CF_3CF_2Cl, CHF_2CH_2Cl	1, 2	60
CH_3COCH_3	CF_3COCF_3, CH_2FCOCH_3, CH_3COF, $FOCCOF$, COF_2, CF_4		63
$CHCl_3$	CCl_3F, C_2Cl_6		67
C_2HCl_5	$CFCl_2CFCl_2$, C_2Cl_4, C_2HFCl_4, C_2Cl_6, C_4Cl_{10}		67
$CHCl_2CHCl_2$	$CHCl{=}CCl_2$, $CFCl_2CFCl_2$, $CHCl_2CFCl_2$, $CHCl_2CCl_3$		67
$CCl_2{=}CCl_2$	$CFCl_2CFCl_2$, $CFCl_2CCl_3$, $C_4F_2Cl_8$		67
$CHCl{=}CCl_2$	$CHFClCFCl_2$, $CFCl{=}CCl_2$, $CHFClCCl_3$, $CHCl_2CFCl_2$, $C_4H_2Cl_6$, $C_4H_2Cl_8$		67
C_6Cl_6	$C_6Cl_6F_6$		55, 56, 58
n-$C_{16}H_{34}$	$CH_2FCHF(CH_2)_{13}CH_3$		66
$CH_3CH{=}CHCO_2H$	$CH_3CHFCHFCO_2H$	3	66

1. CF_4 is the major product.
2. Higher members of the series are also produced.
3. The product is a mixture of two diastereoisomeric pairs.

[68] Moissan, *Compt. rend.*, **110**, 276 (1890).
[69] Lebeau and Damiens, *Compt. rend.*, **162**, 1340 (1926).
[70] Ruff and Keim, *Z. anorg. allgem. Chem.*, **192**, 249 (1930).
[71] Simons and Block, *J. Am. Chem. Soc.*, **59**, 1407 (1937); **61**, 2964 (1939).

fluoride.[53, 72] 1,1-Diphenylethylene yields a difluoride; anthracene gives rise to a mixture of 9-fluoroanthracene and 9,10-difluoroanthracene. It is claimed [72] that small amounts of hydrogen fluoride or silicon tetrafluoride are needed to cause the reaction of aryl iodofluorides and olefins.

Direct fluorination requires equipment seldom available in the laboratory but easily constructed. A variety of fluorine generators have been proposed,[73-77] all involving the electrolysis of an acid salt of potassium

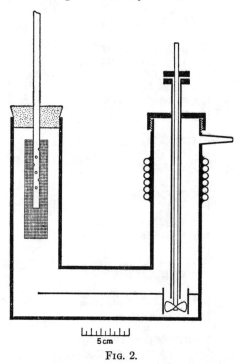

5 cm

FIG. 2.

fluoride. They all have about the same efficiency and differ only in details of construction.[78] They have been made of magnesium, aluminum, Monel metal, and stainless steel. For laboratory purposes copper is both convenient and inexpensive. A laboratory generator which has been found satisfactory over a long period of operation has been described.[79]

[72] Bockemüller, *Ber.*, **64**, 522 (1931).
[73] Simons, *J. Am. Chem. Soc.*, **46**, 2175 (1924).
[74] Schumb and Gamble, *J. Am. Chem. Soc.*, **52**, 4302 (1930).
[75] Dennis, Veeder, and Rochow, *J. Am. Chem. Soc.*, **53**, 3263 (1931).
[76] Dennis and Rochow, *J. Am. Chem. Soc.*, **56**, 879 (1934).
[77] Miller and Bigelow, *J. Am. Chem. Soc.*, **58**, 1585 (1936).
[78] Simons, *Inorg. Syntheses*, **I**, 134 (1940).
[79] Henne, *J. Am. Chem. Soc.*, **60**, 96 (1938).

Various mechanical means of providing a constantly renewed surface have been proposed,[65, 66] of which the following one is simple and efficient.[67] The apparatus shown in Fig. 2 is constructed from brass tubing with silver soldered joints. One arm of the U-shaped vessel is closed by a rubber stopper which supports the fluorine inlet tube, as indicated in the drawing. The rubber stopper is protected on the inside by a covering of thin copper foil, and, in case of a too sudden reaction, functions as a safety valve. In use, the vessel is filled up to the horizontal division. The stirrer then acts as a pump to force a rapid countercurrent flow of liquid along the horizontal section which divides the lower part of the vessel. Fluorine is passed in through a roll of copper gauze, and temperature control is obtained by surrounding the reaction vessel with a suitable bath.

EXPERIMENTAL PROCEDURE

Fluorination of Pentachloroethane.[67] Pentachloroethane, heated to 90° in the apparatus described in the preceding paragraph, is subjected for ten hours to the action of fluorine. From 350 g. of material, 297 g. of reaction product (partly crystallized at 0°) is obtained. Preliminary distillation yields the following fractions: (1) 7.6 g., 88–100°; (2) 28.5 g., 100–130°; (3) 57.4 g., 130–140° (solid); (4) 11.8 g., 140–148°; (5) 12.9 g., 148–156°; (6) 91.6 g., 156–159°; (7) 45.2 g., oily semi-solid residue. By repeated fractionation the following products are isolated: 5 g. of CCl_2FCCl_2F; 15.6 g. of $CCl_2{=}CCl_2$; 83.1 g. of $CHCl_2CCl_2F$; 93.4 g. of $CHCl_2CCl_3$; 28.5 g. of CCl_3CCl_3; 2 g. of C_4Cl_{10}.

Replacement of the Hydroxyl Group of Alcohols

The interaction of an alcohol and hydrogen fluoride gives an alkyl fluoride,[80] but the reaction is reversible. When the acid and the alcohol are merely heated together, the equilibrium mixture usually contains less than 40% of alkyl fluoride. It is impracticable to remove the organic fluoride from the equilibrium mixture (except for the first few homologs); the organic fluorides boil at lower temperatures than the alcohols, but higher than hydrogen fluoride. It is also impracticable to remove the water, because the agents capable of fixing the water promote the decomposition of the fluoride into a mixture of olefin and hydrogen fluoride. The fact that water is formed necessitates platinum equipment. Other metals are always sufficiently corroded to produce salts which catalyze the decomposition of the alkyl fluorides. Glass equip-

[80] Meslans, *Compt. rend.*, **115**, 1080 (1892) ; *Ann. chim.*, [7] **1**, 346 (1894).

ment cannot be employed. The methods claimed in the patent literature for the synthesis of alkyl fluorides from alcohols have many disadvantages. Since it is now possible to add hydrogen fluoride efficiently to olefins, the conversion of alcohols to alkyl fluorides is of interest only in a few special cases.

Synthesis of Fluorides Other than Hydrocarbon Derivatives

In general, it is difficult to introduce fluorine into a molecule containing oxygen. Direct fluorination of oxygen compounds has been tried repeatedly, but usually has yielded indefinite fluorine-containing derivatives in which the location of the fluorine was not ascertained. Only recently has acetone been transformed into monofluoro- and hexafluoroacetone in experiments explicitly described.[63] When replacement of halogen or addition of hydrogen fluoride is attempted, enough water is usually formed to stop the reaction or alter its course.

Acids. Partly fluorinated acetic acids have been synthesized by interchange of halogens between halogenated acetic acids and mercurous fluoride. Examples are CCl_2FCO_2H,[23] $CClF_2CO_2H$,[81] $CHFICO_2H$,[82] CBr_2FCO_2H,[83] and $CBrF_2CO_2H$.[84] The synthesis of trifluoroacetic acid [85] has been performed by oxidation of benzotrifluoride or its *meta*-amino derivative in chromic anhydride-sulfuric acid mixture, with a yield of about 50%. It has been obtained also in a 90% yield by oxidation of $CF_3CCl=CCl_2$ with alkaline permanganate.[5a] Anhydrides, esters, and amides have been obtained from the acids by the usual procedures. Trifluoroacetoacetic acid [86] and its esters have been obtained from trifluoroacetic esters by ester condensations. The electrolysis of sodium trifluoroacetate yields hexafluoroethane,[87] an example of an unusually efficient Kolbe reaction.

Aldehydes. Fluorinated aldehydes are unknown. It has been observed that the reduction of a fluoro acid yields the alcohol directly, and also that the oxidation of a fluoro alcohol does not stop short of the acid.[88]

Alcohols. Trifluoroethanol has been obtained by catalytic reduction of trifluoroacetic anhydride on platinum black.[88] This reaction, which

[81] Swarts, *Chem. Zentr.*, I, 1237 (1906); II, 581 (1907); *Bull. acad. roy. Belg.*, **1907**, 339.
[82] Swarts, *Chem. Zentr.*, I, 13 (1903).
[83] Swarts, *Bull. acad. roy. Belg.*, **1898**, 319.
[84] Swarts, *Chem. Zentr.*, II, 710 (1903).
[85] Swarts, *Bull. acad. roy. Belg.*, **8**, 343 (1922).
[86] Swarts, *Bull. acad. roy. Belg.*, **1926**, 689, 721.
[87] Swarts, *Bull. soc. chim. Belg.*, **42**, 102 (1933).
[88] Swarts, *Bull. soc. chim. Belg.*, **43**, 471 (1934).

was performed by Swarts, has never been successfully duplicated despite the attempts with a variety of catalysts and conditions. It must be concluded that Swarts used a particularly suitable catalyst which, unfortunately, was not described. Trifluoroisopropyl alcohol [89] has been obtained by the reduction of 1,1,1-trifluoroacetone,[90] which had been obtained from trifluoroacetoacetic ester.[86] Fluoroethanol [12] has been made by saponification of its acetate, which was obtained from the acetate of bromoethanol and silver or mercury fluoride. Difluoroethanol [91] has been obtained from CHF_2CH_2I and mercuric oxide in water at 140° in sealed tubes. The reaction of two molecules of methylmagnesium bromide with an ester of trifluoroacetic acid has been used for the synthesis of tertiary trifluorobutyl alcohol, $CF_3(CH_3)_2COH$.[92]

Ethers. Fluoro ethers have been obtained either by replacement, such as the formation of CF_3OCH_3 from the trichloro derivative,[93] or by the action of alcoholic potassium hydroxide upon a polyhalide. Examples are $CHBrFCF_2OCH_3$ from $CHBrFCF_2Br$,[94] and $CH_2FCF_2OCH_3$ from CH_2FCF_2Br and methanolic potassium hydroxide.[94] It is to be noted that the use of alcohols with longer chains minimizes the importance of the ether formation and favors the elimination of one molecule of halogen acid, with consequent formation of an olefin.

Ketones. Fluoro ketones have been obtained from fluoro acetoacetates and sulfuric acid.[86] Examples are CF_3COCH_3 and CHF_2COCH_3. They have also been obtained by halogen interchange, such as CH_2FCOCH_3 from CH_2ICOCH_3 and thallium fluoride.[95]

Amines. The synthesis of fluorinated ethyl amines has been accomplished [96] by heating CHF_2CH_2I to 130° in a sealed tube with concentrated aqueous ammonia; a mixture of the primary amine, $CHF_2CH_2NH_2$, secondary amine, $(CHF_2CH_2)_2NH$, and tertiary amine, $(CHF_2CH_2)_3N$, is obtained.

[89] Swarts, *Bull. sci. acad. roy. Belg.*, **1927**, 179.
[90] Swarts, *Bull. acad. roy. Belg.*, **1927**, 175.
[91] Swarts, *Bull. soc. chim. Belg.*, **1902** (731).
[92] Swarts, *Bull. soc. chim. Belg.*, **1927**, 195; **1929**, 108.
[93] Booth and Burchfield, *J. Am. Chem. Soc.*, **57**, 2070 (1935).
[94] Swarts, *Bull. acad. roy. Belg.*, **1911**, 563.
[95] Ray, *Nature*, **132**, 749 (1933).
[96] Swarts, *Bull. acad. roy. Belg.*, **1904**, 762.

TABLE IV

ALIPHATIC FLUORINE COMPOUNDS *

Formula	Structure	Physical Properties	Preparation (yield, remarks)	Reference †
$(CF)_x$		Explosive crystals	Graphite + F_2, 280° and 25 mm.	97
$CFBr_3$		B.p. 107°	CBr_4 + SbF_3 + Br_2, 4 hr., 110–120°; CBr_4 + AgF, 50–60°	98
$CFCl_3$		B.p. 23.8°, $d^{17}1.4944$, $n^{18}1.3865$	CCl_4 + SbF_3 + $SbCl_5$	23, 24
CFN		Sublimes at −72°	ICN + AgF at 220° (25%)	99
CF_2Br_2		M.p. below −80°, b.p. 245°	CBr_4 + AgF at 140–150°	98
CF_2Cl_2		M.p. −160°, b.p. −29.8°	CCl_4 + SbF_2 + $SbCl_5$	24, 81, 100
CF_2O		M.p. −114°, b.p. −83°	F_2 + $COCl_2$ over CaF_2 at 2000°; CF_4 + CO in arc; CH_3COCH_3 + F_2; CH_3CH_2OH + F_2	101, 102, 103
CF_3Cl		M.p. −181°, b.p. −81.1°	CCl_4 + F_2 + As(54%); CCl_2F_2 in arc; C_2H_5Cl + F_2; CCl_2F_2 + F_2 (best yield)	60, 101, 102, 103
CF_4		M.p. −183.6°, b.p. −128°	C + F_2 (55%); CCl_4 + F_2(74%); $CHCl_3$ + F_2; CH_4 + F_2	51, 70, 71, 104, 105
$CHFBrCl$		B.p. 38°, $d^{16}1.9058$	$CHClBr_2$ + SbF_3 + Br_2 at 60°	23
$CHFBr_2$		B.p. 65°, $d^{20}2.4256$	$CHBr_3$ + SbF_3 + Br_2 at 110–120°	106
$CHFCl_2$		B.p. 89°, $d^{0}1.4216$	$CHCl_3$ + SbF_3 + Br_2	23, 24, 25, 26
$CHFI_2$		M.p. −34.5°, b.p. 100°	CHI_3 + HgF + CaF_2	107
$CHFO$	HCOF	B.p. −26°, $d^{30}1.195$, $d^{26}1.160$, $d^{0}1.099$	HCO_2H + C_6H_5COCl + KF (16%)	5
CHF_2Br		B.p. −14.5°, $d^{18}1.55$	$CHBr_3$ + SbF_3 + Br_2 at 110–120°	40, 106
CHF_2Cl		M.p. −146°, b.p. −40.8°	$CHCl_3$ + SbF_3 + $SbCl_5$	24, 26

Formula	Structure	Constants	Preparation	References
CHF_2I		M.p. $-122°$, b.p. $21.6°$	$CHI_3 + HgF + CaF_2$ at $80-150°$; $CHI_3 + IF_5$	101, 107
CHF_3		M.p. $-163°$, b.p. $-82.2°$	$CHF_2Br + HgF_2$; $CHI_3 + HgF + CaF_2$	40, 101, 107
CH_2FBr		B.p. $18-20°$	$CHBr_2F + Zn + C_2H_5OH \rightarrow CH_2FBr + CH_3F$	106
CH_2FCl		B.p. $-9.0°$	$CH_3F + Cl_2$; $CH_2Cl_2 + SbF_3 + SbCl_5$	26, 108
CH_2FI		B.p. $53.4°$, $d^{20}1.366$, $n^{20}1.491$	$CH_2I_2 + HgF$ at $120°$	109
CH_2FNO	H_2NCOF	M.p. $46.7°$	Cyanic acid + HF in ether (very violent)	49
CH_2F_2		B.p. $-51.6°$	$CH_2Cl_2 + SbF_3 + SbCl_5$; $CH_2Cl_2 + AgF$ at $180°$	20, 26
CH_3F		M.p. $-141.8°$, b.p. $-78.2°$	$CH_3I + HgF$; $CH_3SO_4K + KF$ at $160-200°$	3, 4, 42, 110
CH_3FO_2S	CH_3SO_2F	B.p. $124.2°$, $n^{20}1.3596$	$CH_3SO_2Cl + ZnF_2$	111
CH_3FO_3S	FSO_3CH_3	B.p. $92°$, $d^{16}1.427$	$CH_3OH + HFSO_3$	112
C_2FBr_2ClO	$CClBr_2COF$	B.p. $114°$	$CBr_2ClCOCl + SbF_3 + Br_2$ at $100°$	113
$C_2FBr_2Cl_3$	$CCl_2BrCClFBr$	M.p. $122.5°$	$CCl_2{=}CClF + Br_2$	27
C_2FBr_3	$CFBr{=}CBr_2$	B.p. $147.3°$, $d^{20}2.6659$, $n^{20}1.54821$	$CHFBrCBr_3 + KOH$	114
C_2FBr_5		M.p. $176°$	$CBr_2{=}CBrF + Br_2$	114
C_2FCl_3	$CClF{=}CCl_2$	M.p. $-82°$, b.p. $72.1°$, $d^{20}1.5541$, $n^{20}1.4360$	$CCl_3CCl_2F + Zn$	27
C_2FCl_3O	$CFCl_2COCl$	B.p. $75°$	$(CCl_3CO)_2O + SbF_3 + Br_2$ at $90-100°$; $CFCl_2CO_2H + PCl_5$ (violent)	23
C_2FCl_5		M.p. $101.3°$, b.p. $137.9°$	$C_2Cl_6 + SBF_3 + Cl_2$	27
C_2F_2BrClO	$CFClBrCOF$	B.p. $51°$	$CClBr_2COCl + SbF_3 + Br_2$ at $100°$	113
$C_2F_2Br_2$	$CF_2{=}CBr_2$		$CHBr_2CF_2OC_2H_5 + CH_3CO_2K + K_2CO_3$	94
	$CFBr{=}CFBr$	B.p. $70.5°$	$CHBrFCBr_2F + NaOC_2H_5$	115
$C_2F_2Br_2Cl_2$	$CClFBrCClFBr$	M.p. $32.9°$, b.p. $139.9°$	$CClF{=}CClF + Br_2$	116
	CCl_2BrCF_2Br	M.p. $45.5°$, b.p. $138.9°$	$CF_2{=}CCl_2 + Br_2$	116

* Preparations reported after January 1, 1941, are not included.
† References 97-153 appear on pp. 92-93.

TABLE IV—*Continued*

ALIPHATIC FLUORINE COMPOUNDS

Formula	Structure	Physical Properties	Preparation (yield, remarks)	Reference [*]
$C_2F_2Br_2O$	$CFBr_2COF$	B.p. 75.5°	$CBr_3COCl + SbF_3 + Br_2$ at 130°	117
$C_2F_2Br_4$	CBr_2FCBr_2F	M.p. 62.5°, b.p. 186.5°	$CFBr{=}CFBr + Br_2$	117
	CBr_3CBrF_2	M.p. 99°, b.p. 185°	$CBr_2{=}CF_2 + Br_2$	94
$C_2F_2Cl_2$	$CClF{=}CClF$, *trans*	M.p. -110.3°, b.p. 22.0°, $d^0 1.4936$, $n^0 1.3798$	$CCl_2FCCl_2F + Zn$	27
	$CClF{=}CClF$, *cis*	M.p. -130.5°, b.p. 21.1°, $d^0 1.4950$, $n^0 1.3777$	$CCl_2FCCl_2F + Zn$	27
	$CF_2{=}CCl_2$	M.p. -115°, b.p. 18.9°	$CCl_3CF_2Cl + Zn$	116
$C_2F_2Cl_2O$	$CFCl_2COF$	B.p. 31°	$(CCl_3CO)_2O + SbF_3 + Br_2$ at 95°	23
	$CF_2ClCOCl$	B.p. 34°	$CHF_2CH_2OH + Cl_2$ in sunlight	23
$C_2F_2Cl_4$	$CFCl_2CFCl_2$	M.p. 24.65°, b.p. 92.8°, $d^{25} 1.6447$, $n^{25} 1.4130$	$C_2Cl_6 + SbF_3 + SbCl_5$	27
	CF_2ClCCl_3	M.p. 40.6°, b.p. 91°	$CHCl_2CHF_2 + Cl_2$	116
C_2F_3Br	$CF_2{=}CFBr$	B.p. -2.5°, $d^{18} 1.89$	$CFBr_2CF_2Br + Zn$	118
$C_2F_3Br_2Cl$	$CClFBrCF_2Br$	B.p. 92.9°, $d^{20} 2.2318$, $n^{20} 1.4272$	$CClF{=}CF_2 + Br_2$	27
$C_2F_3Br_3$	$CFBr_2CBrF_2$	B.p. 117°, $d^7 2.5666$, $n^7 1.4666$	$CFBr{=}CF_2 + Br_2$	118
C_2F_3Cl	$CClF{=}CF_2$	M.p. -157.9°, b.p. -27°	$CF_2ClCFCl_2 + Zn$	27
$C_2F_3Cl_3$	CCl_2FCClF_2	M.p. -36.4°, b.p. 47.7°, $d^{25} 1.5635$, $n^{25} 1.35572$	$C_2Cl_6 + SbF_3Cl_2$	27
	CF_3CCl_3	M.p. 14.2°, b.p. 45.9°, $d^{20} 1.5790$, $n^{20} 1.3610$	$CH_3CF_3 + Cl_2$	116
C_2F_3N	CF_3CN	B.p. -61°	$CF_3CONH_2 + P_2O_5$	85
C_2F_4	$CF_2{=}CF_2$	M.p. -144°, b.p. -78.4°	$CF_2ClCF_2Cl + Zn$	27

				Ref.
$C_2F_4Br_2$	CF_2BrCF_2Br	M.p. $-112°$, b.p. $46.4°$, $d^{25}2.149$	$C_2F_4 + Br_2$	27
$C_2F_4Cl_2$	CF_2ClCF_2Cl	M.p. $-94°$, b.p. $3.8°$, $d^0 1.5312$, $n^0 1.3073$	$C_2Cl_6 + SbF_3Cl_2$	27
	CF_3CFCl_2	B.p. about $-2°$	By-product of preceding	27
$C_2F_2O_2$	$(COF)_2$	B.p. $26°$	$CH_3COCH_3 + F_2$	63
C_2F_4O	CF_3COF	B.p. $-59°$	CF_3CO_2Na at $340°$	85
C_2ClF_5		M.p. $-106°$, b.p. $-38°$	$C_2Cl_6 + SbF_2Cl_2$; $C_2H_5Cl + F_2$	27, 62
C_2F_6		M.p. $-106°$, b.p. $-79°$	Electrolysis of CF_3CO_2Na; $C_2H_4 + F_2$	57, 87
$C_2F_6N_2$	$CF_3N{=}NCF_3$	M.p. $-133°$	$AgCN + F_2$	119
$C_2HFBrClO$	$CHFBrCOCl$	B.p. $98°$, $d^{15}1.879$	$CHFBrCO_2H + PCl_5$	82
$C_2HFBrClO_2$	$CFClBrCO_2H$	M.p. $-5°$, b.p. $182°$	$CFClBrCO_2C_2H_5 + KOH$	113
C_2HFBr_2	$CBrF{=}CHBr$	B.p. $88.8°$, $d^{17}2.2898$	$CBr_2FCH_2Br + KOH$	94
C_2HFBr_2	$CHF{=}CBr_2$	B.p. $90.3°$, $d^{17}2.2908$, $n^{17}1.4954$	$CHF_2CHBr_2 + NaOC_2H_5$; $CHFBrCHBr_2 + KOH$	114
$C_2HFBr_2Cl_2$	$CHClBrCClFBr$	B.p. $163.5°$, $d^{23}2.2833$, $n^{23}1.5160$	$CHCl{=}CClF + Br_2$	28
	$CCl_2BrCHFBr$	B.p. $163.5°$, $d^{23}2.1301$	$CCl_2{=}CHF + Br_2$	82
C_2HFBr_2O	$CHBr_2COF$	B.p. $112.5°$, $d^{10}2.3314$	$CBrF{=}CHBr + (O)$	114
	$CHFBrCOBr$	M.p. $26.5°$, b.p. $198°$	$CBrF{=}CHF + (O)$	82
$C_2HFBr_2O_2$	$CFBr_2CO_2H$	B.p. $211°$, $d^{17}2.9094$	$CBrF{=}CBrF + (O)$	83
C_2HFBr_4	CBr_2FCHBr_2	B.p. $204°$, $d^{16}1.9386$, $n^{16}1.59707$	$CBr_2CHBr_2 + SbF_3 + Br_2$	94
	CBr_3CHBrF		$CBr_2{=}CHF + Br_2$	94
C_2HFCl_2	$CCl_2{=}CHF$	M.p. $-108.8°$, b.p. $37.3°$, $d^{20}1.3833$, $n^{20}1.40364$	$CHClFCCl_3 + Zn$	28
C_2HFCl_2	$CHCl{=}CClF$	B.p. $35.1°$, $d^{16}1.4032$, $n^{16}1.372$	$CHCl_2CCl_2F + Zn$	28
C_2HFCl_2O	$CHCl_2COF$	B.p. $70.5°$, $d^{17}1.4802$, $n^{17}1.3961$	$CHCl_2COCl + SbF_3Cl_2$	12
$C_2HFCl_2O_2$	$CFCl_2CO_2H$	M.p. $-20°$, b.p. $162.5°$	$CFCl_2COCl + H_2O$	23
C_2HFCl_4	$CHClFCCl_3$	M.p. $-95.4°$, b.p. $116.7°$, $d^{20}1.6253$, $n^{20}1.4525$	$CHF{=}CCl_2 + Cl_2$	28

* References 97–153 appear on pp. 92–93.

TABLE IV—*Continued*

ALIPHATIC FLUORINE COMPOUNDS

Formula	Structure	Physical Properties	Preparation (yield, remarks)	Reference *
	$CHCl_2CCl_2F$	M.p. $-82.6°$, b.p. $116.6°$, $d^{20}1.6223$, $n^{20}1.4487$	$CHCl_2CCl_3 + SbF_3Cl_2$	28
C_2HF_2Br	$CF_2{=}CHBr$	B.p. $6.2°$, $d^01.82$	$CBrF_2CH_2Br + CH_3CO_2K + K_2CO_3$	94
	$CHF{=}CBrF$	B.p. $19.6°$, $d^01.8337$, $n^01.3846$	$CHBrFCBr_2F + Zn$	83
$C_2HF_2BrO_2$	CF_2BrCO_2H	M.p. $40°$, b.p. $145{-}160°$	$CHF_2CO_2H + Br_2$ at $160°$	84
$C_2HF_2Br_2Cl$	$CHClBrCF_2Br$	B.p. $118.7°$, $d^{25}2.2319$, $n^{25}1.4611$	$CHCl{=}CF_2 + Br_2$	28
$C_2HF_2Br_3$	$CFBr_2CHFBr$	B.p. $146°$, $d^{20}2.6028$, $n^{17}1.5078$	$CBr_3CHFBr + SbF_3 + Br_2$	117
	$CHBr_2CBrF_2$	B.p. $143.5°$, $d^{17}2.6130$, $n^{17}1.5025$	$CF_2{=}CHBr + Br_2$	94
C_2HF_2Cl	$CHCl{=}CF_2$	B.p. $2.4°$	$CHCl_2CClF_2 + Zn$	28
C_2HF_2ClO	CHF_2COCl	B.p. $25°$	$CHF_2CO_2H + PCl_5$	84
$C_2HF_2ClO_2$	CF_2ClCO_2H	M.p. $22.9°$, b.p. $121.5°$	$CHF_2CO_2H + Cl_2$	81
$C_2HF_2Cl_3$	$CHCl_2CClF_2$	B.p. $71.9°$, $d^{25}1.54472$, $n^{25}1.3889$	$C_2HCl_5 + SbF_3Cl_2$	28
	$CHClFCCl_2F$	B.p. $72.5°$, $d^{25}1.5492$, $n^{25}1.3916$	$CHCl_2CCl_3 + SbF_3 + Cl_2$	28
	CHF_2CCl_3	B.p. $73.0°$, $d^{20}1.5661$, $n^{20}1.3979$	$CHCl_2CHF_2 + Cl_2$	28
C_2HF_2N	CHF_2CN	B.p. $22.8{-}23.4°$	$CHF_2CONH_2 + P_2O_5$	120
C_2HF_3	$CHF{=}CF_2$	B.p. $-51°$, $d^{78}1.26$	$CF_2BrCHFBr + Zn$	118
$C_2HF_3Br_2$	$CBrF_2CHBrF$	B.p. $76.5°$, $d^{10}2.2713$, $n^{10}1.4171$	$CBr_3CHFBr + SbF_3 + Br_2$	117, 118
C_2HF_3Cl	$CHClFCClF_2$	B.p. $28°$, $d^{10}1.496$, $n^{20}1.327$	$CHCl_2CClF_2 + SbF_3Cl_2$	28
$C_2HF_3O_2$	CF_3CO_2H	M.p. $-15.5°$, b.p. $72.4°$	Oxidation of trifluorotoluidine	85
C_2HF_4Cl	CHF_2CF_2Cl	B.p. $-12°$	By-product of preparation of $CHCl_2CCl_2F$	28
C_2HF_5		M.p. $-103°$, b.p. $-48.5°$	$F_2 + C_2H_6$	61
C_2HF_6N	CF_3NHCF_3	M.p. $-130°$	By-product of ICN + PF_5	119

Formula	Structure	Properties	Preparation	Ref.
C_2H_2FBr	$CH_2{=}CFBr$	B.p. 12.5° or 6.8° or 30–35°	$CHBrFCH_2Br + CH_3CO_2K + K_2CO_3$ at 60°; $CFBr_2CH_2Br + Zn$	12, 94
	$CHF{=}CHBr$	B.p. 36° or 39.6°, $d^{15}1.7097$ or 1.7566, $n^{15}1.4063$ or 1.4204	$CHF_2CHBr_2 + Zn$	114, 117
$C_2H_2FBrClNO$	$CFClBrCONH_2$	M.p. 131.5°	From the acid	82
$C_2H_2FBrCl_2$	$CHClBrCHClF$	B.p. 124.7–125.1°, $d^{20}1.932$, $n^{20}1.4776$	$CHClBrCHClBr + SbF_3 + Br_2$	36
$C_2H_2FBrO_2$	CH_2BrCCl_2F	B.p. 110.8°, $d^{25}1.8672$, $n^{25}1.4626$	$CH_2BrCCl_2Br + HgF_2$	5a
	$CHFBrCO_2H$	M.p. 49°, b.p. 183°	$CHFBrCOBr + ice$	82
$C_2H_2FBr_2NO$	$CFBr_2CONH_2$	M.p. 136°	$CFBr_2CO_2C_2H_5 +$ concentrated aqueous NH_3	117
$C_2H_2FBr_3$	$CHBr_2CHFBr$	B.p. 174°, $d^{17}2.6709$, $n^{18}1.5638$	$CHBr_2CHBr_2 + HgF_2$	38
	CH_2BrCBr_2F	B.p. 163°, $d^{17}2.6054$, $n^{17}1.54321$	$CBr_3CH_2Br + SbF_3 + Br_2$	121
C_2H_2FCl	$CH_2{=}CClF$	B.p. −25.5°	$CH_2BrCCl_2F + Zn$	5a
	$CHF{=}CHCl$	B.p. 10–11°	$CHF_2CHCl_2 + Zn$; $CHClFCHCl_2 + Zn$	82
$C_2H_2FCl_2NO$	$CFCl_2CONH_2$	M.p. 126.5°, b.p. 215°	$Ester + NH_4OH$	23
$C_2H_2FCl_3$	CH_2ClCCl_2F	M.p. −104.7°, b.p. 88.8°, $d^{20}1.4921$, $n^{20}1.4248$	$CH_2ClCCl_3 + SbF_3 + SbCl_5$	29
	$CHCl_2CHFCl$	B.p. 102°, $d^{17}1.5497$, $n^{17}1.5492$	$CHCl_2CHCl_2 + SbF_3 + SbCl_5$	82
$C_2H_2FIO_2$	$CHIFCO_2H$	M.p. 74°	$CHBrFCO_2C_2H_5 + KI$ and saponify	82
C_2H_2FN	CH_2FCN	B.p. 82°, $d^{16}1.0730$	$CH_2FCONH_2 + P_2O_5$	85
$C_2H_2F_2$	$CH_2{=}CF_2$	B.p. −83°	$CHF_2CH_2Br + NaOC_2H_5$; $CH_2BrCHF_2Br + Zn$	122, 5a
$C_2H_2F_2BrCl$	$CHClBrCHF_2$	B.p. 82.4°, $d^{20}1.879$, $n^{20}1.4173$	$CHClBrCHClBr + SbF_3 + Br_2$	36
$C_2H_2F_2Br_2$	CHF_2CHBr_2	B.p. 107.5°, $d^{20}2.3120$, $n^{20}1.46880$	$CHBr_2CHBr_2 + HgF_2$	39
	CF_2BrCH_2Br	M.p. −58°, b.p. 93°, $d^{17}2.24223$, $n^{17}1.44815$	$CBr_3CH_2Br + SbF_3 + Br_2$	94, 121
$C_2H_2F_2ClNO$	$CF_2ClCONH_2$	M.p. 78.5°, b.p. 93°/18 mm.	$Ester + NH_3$	81
$C_2H_2F_2Cl_2$	CHF_2CHCl_2	B.p. 60°, $d^{25}1.473$, $n^{25}1.3690$	$CHCl_2CHCl_2 + SbF_3 + SbCl_5$	82

TABLE IV—Continued
ALIPHATIC FLUORINE COMPOUNDS

Formula	Structure	Physical Properties	Preparation (yield, remarks)	Reference *
	$CH_2ClCClF_2$	M.p. $-101.2°$, b.p. $46.8°$, $d^{20}1.4163$, $n^{20}1.36193$	$CH_2ClCCl_3 + SbF_3 + SbCl_5$	29
$C_2H_2F_2O_2$	CHF_2CO_2H	M.p. $35°$, b.p. $134.2°$	$CHF_2CH_2OH + CrO_3$	122
$C_2H_2F_3Br$	CH_2FCF_2Br	B.p. $250°$	$CBrF_2CH_2Br + AgF$	94
	CF_3CH_2Br	B.p. $26.5°$, $d^{17.5}1.8383$	$CF_3CH_2OH + PBr_5$	123
	CHF_2CHFBr	B.p. $41°$, $d^{10}1.874$, $n^{10}1.36175$	$CHBr_2CHBr_2 + HgF_2$	36
$C_2H_2F_3Cl$	CHF_2CHFCl	B.p. $17°$, $d^{10}1.365$	$CHCl_2CHCl_2 + SbF_3 + SbCl_5$	82
	CF_3CH_2Cl	B.p. $6.1°$, $d^01.389$, $n^01.3090$	$CHCl_2CHCl_2 + SbF_3Cl_2$	36
$C_2H_2F_3NO$	CF_3CONH_2	M.p. $74.8°$, b.p. $162.5°$	Ester $+ NH_4OH$ (48%)	85
$C_2H_2F_4$	CHF_2CHF_2	B.p. $-23°$	$CHBr_2CHF_2 + HgF_2$	36
C_2H_3F	$CH_2{=}CHF$	M.p. $-160.5°$, b.p. $-72.2°$, $d^{72}0.853$	$C_2H_2 + HF$	124
C_2H_3FBrCl	$CHClFCH_2Br$	M.p. $-67.7°$, b.p. $96.6°$, $d^{20}1.8291$, $n^{20}1.4546$	$CHClBrCH_2Br + SbF_3 + Br_2$	36
C_2H_3FBrNO	$CHFBrCONH_2$	M.p. $44°$	Ester $+ 20\%$ NH_4OH	82
$C_2H_3FBr_2$	CH_2FCHBr_2	B.p. $117.5°$, $n^{20}1.50084$	By-product from $CH_2BrCHBr_2 + SbF_3 + Br_2$	125
	$CHFBrCH_2Br$	M.p. $-54°$, b.p. $122°$, $d^{10}2.26333$, $n^{20}1.51759$	$CHBr_2CH_2Br + SbF_3 + Br_2$ or HgF_2	39, 125
$C_2H_3FCl_2$	CH_3CCl_2F	B.p. $31.7°$, $d^51.2673$, $n^51.38679$	$CH_3CCl_3 + SbF_3 + SbF_3Cl_2$	21
	$CHClFCH_2Cl$	B.p. $73.9°$, $d^{20}1.3814$, $n^{20}1.41132$	$CH_2ClCHCl_2 + HgF_2$	21
C_2H_3FINO	$CHIFCONH_2$	M.p. $92.5°$	Ester $+ NH_3$	82
C_2H_3FO	CH_3COF	B.p. $20.5°$, $d^01.0369$	$CH_3COCl + ZnF_2$ or $(CH_3CO)_2O + HF$	2, 43

Molecular formula	Structure	Physical constants	Preparation	References[*]
C₂H₃FO₂	CH₂FCO₂H	M.p. 33°, b.p. 165°	Ester + soda	113
	FCO₂CH₃	B.p. 40°, d^{33}1.06	ClCO₂CH₃ + TlF in the cold	1
C₂H₃F₂Br	CHF₂CH₂Br	M.p. −74.5°, b.p. 57.3°, d^{18}1.82445, n^{10}1.39400	CHBr₂CH₂Br + HgF₂	39
C₂H₃F₂Cl	CH₃CClF₂	B.p. −9.6°	CH₃CCl₃ + SbF₃ + SbF₃Cl₂	21
	CHF₂CH₂Cl	B.p. 35.1°, d^{15}1.312, n^{15}1.3528	CHCl₂CH₂Cl + HgF₂	21
C₂H₃F₂ClO	CF₂ClOCH₃ †	M.p. −105°, b.p. 55.3°	CCl₃OCH₃ † + SbF₃	68
C₂H₃F₂I	CHF₂CH₂I	B.p. 89.5°, d^{12}2.2433, n^{12}1.4681	CHF₂CH₂Br + KI	93
C₂H₃F₂NO	CHF₂CONH₂	M.p. 51.8°, b.p. 108°/35 mm.	Ester + NH₃	84
C₂H₃F₃	CHF₂CH₂F	M.p. −84°, b.p. 5°	CHF₂CH₂I + HgF₂	21
	CH₃CF₃	M.p. −107°, b.p. −46.7°	CH₃CCl₃ + SbF₃ + SbF₃Cl₂	21
C₂H₃F₃O	CF₃OCH₃ †	M.p. −96°, b.p. 30°	CCl₃OCH₃ † + SbF₃	93
	CF₃CH₂OH	M.p. −43.5°, b.p. 74.5°, d^{21}1.3739, n^{22}1.2907	(CF₃CO)₂O + H₂ + Pt	88
C₂H₄FBr	CH₂BrCH₂F	B.p. 71.5°, d^{25}1.7044, n^{25}1.42261	CH₂BrCH₂Br + HgF₂	21
C₂H₄FCl	CH₃CHClF	B.p. 15.5°	CH₃CCl₃ + SbF₃ + SbF₃Cl₂	21
C₂H₄FClSO₂	CH₃CHClSO₂F	B.p. 138°, n^{20}1.4070	From the sulfonyl chlorides	111
C₂H₄FI	CH₂FCH₂I	B.p. 98–102°	CH₂ICH₂I + HgF₂	21
C₂H₄FNO	CH₂FCONH₂	M.p. 108°	From ester and ammonia	113
C₂H₄F₂	CH₃CHF₂	B.p. −24.7°	CH₃CHCl₂ + SbF₂ + SbF₃ + SbF₃Cl₂	21
	CH₂FCH₂F	B.p. 10–11°	CH₂BrCH₂Br + HgF₂	21
C₂H₄F₂N₂O₂	CHF₂CH₂NHNO₂	M.p. 19.6°, b.p. 111°	Difluoroethylurethan + HNO₃	96
C₂H₄F₂O	CHF₂CH₂OH	M.p. 28.2°, b.p. 96°, d^{17}1.3084	CHF₂CH₂Br + HgO	91
C₂H₅F		M.p. −143.2°, b.p. −37.1°	C₂H₅Br + HgF₂	39
C₂H₅FO	CH₂FCH₂OH	M.p. −26.45°, b.p. 103.4°	Fluoroethyl acetate + conc. HCl	121
C₂H₅SO₂F		B.p. 134°, n^{20}1.3757	C₂H₅SO₂Cl + 70% KF	111
C₂H₅SO₃F		B.p. 113°, d1.310	HFSO₃ + (C₂F₅)₂O	112
C₂H₅F₂N	CHF₂CH₂NH₂	B.p. 67.5°, d1.17576, n1.34701	CHF₂CH₂Br + NH₃	96
C₃FCl₇	CCl₃CCl₂CCl₂F	M.p. 97°, b.p. 237°	C₃Cl₈ + SbF₃ + SbF₃Cl₂	30

* References 97–153 appear on pp. 92–93.
† The product may have been another isomer; the structure of the trichloromethyl ether was not proved.

TABLE IV—*Continued*

ALIPHATIC FLUORINE COMPOUNDS

Formula	Structure	Physical Properties	Preparation (yield, remarks)	Reference *
$C_3F_2Cl_6$	$CCl_3CCl_2CClF_2$	M.p. 51°, b.p. 193.4°	$CHCl_2CCl_2CClF_2 + Cl_2$	30
	$CCl_2FCCl_2CCl_2F$	M.p. 298°, b.p. 194.2°	$C_3Cl_8 + SbF_3 + SbF_3Cl_2$	30
	$CCl_3CF_2CCl_3$	M.p. $-12.9°$, b.p. 194.4°, $d^{20}1.8105$, $n^{20}1.47996$	$CH_3CF_2CH_3 + Cl_2$	20, 33
$C_3F_3Cl_5$	$CCl_3CF_2CCl_2F$	B.p. 154.5°, $d^{20}1.7590$, $n^{20}1.4394$	$CCl_3CF_2CCl_3 + SbF_3Cl_2$	19, 30
	$CCl_3CClFCClF_2$	M.p. $-15°$, b.p. 153.4°, $d^{20}1.7702$, $n^{20}1.4392$	$CHCl_2CClFCClF_2 + Cl_2$	31
	$CCl_2FCCl_2CClF_2$	M.p. $-4.9°$, b.p. 152.3°, $d^{20}1.7702$, $n^{20}1.43959$	$C_3Cl_8 + SbF_3Cl_2$	30, 31
$C_3F_4Br_2Cl_2$	$CClFBrCFBrCClF_2$	M.p. 35.5–37°, b.p. 154°	$Br_2 + CClF=CFCClF_2$	5a
$C_3F_4Cl_2$	$CClF=CFCClF_2$	B.p. 43.5°, $d^{10}1.555$	$CCl_2FCClFCClF_2 + Zn$	5a
$C_3F_4Cl_4$	$CCl_3CF_2CF_2Cl$	B.p. 112.3°, $d^{20}1.6992$, $n^{20}1.3961$	$Cl_2 + CH_2ClCF_2CF_2Cl$	33
	$CCl_2FCClFCClF_2$	M.p. $-58°$, b.p. 112.5°, $d^{20}1.7185$, $n^{20}1.3960$	$CCl_3CClFCClF_2 + SbF_3Cl_2$	5a
	$CClF_2CCl_2CClF_2$	M.p. $-42.9°$, b.p. 112.0°, $d^{20}1.7199$, $n^{20}1.3958$	$C_3Cl_8 + SbF_3Cl_2$	31
	$CCl_3CClFCF_3$	M.p. 12°, b.p. 112.5°, $d^{20}1.7254$, $n^{20}1.4002$	$CCl_2=CFCF_3 + Cl_2$	5a
	$CCl_2FCCl_2CF_3$	M.p. 41°, b.p. 112.5°	$CCl_3CCl_2CF_3 + SbF_3Cl_2$	5a
C_3F_6O	CF_3COCF_3	M.p. $-129°$, b.p. $-28°$	$CH_3COCH_3 + F_2$	63
C_3F_8		M.p. $-183°$, b.p. $-36°$	$C_2H_6 + F_2$; $C + F_2$	62, 71, 101
C_3HFCl_6	$CCl_3CHClCCl_2F$	B.p. 207°, $d^{20}1.76188$, $n^{20}1.50105$	$CCl_3CHClCCl_3 + SbF_3 + SbCl_5$	30

Formula	Compound	Physical constants	Preparation	References*
$C_3HF_2Cl_5$	$CCl_2FCCl_2CHCl_2$	B.p. $210°$, $d^{20}1.77384$, $n^{20}1.50311$	$CHCl_2CCl_2CCl_3 + SbF_3 + SbCl_5$	30
	$CHCl_2CCl_2CClF_2$	B.p. $168.4°$, $d^{20}1.73162$, $n^{20}1.46241$	$CHCl_2CCl_2CCl_3 + SbF_3 + SbCl_5$	30
	$CCl_2FCHClCCl_2F$	B.p. $167.4°$, $d^{20}1.71720$, $n^{20}1.45972$	$CCl_3CHClCCl_3 + SbF_3 + SbCl_5$	30
	$CHCl_2CF_2CCl_3$	B.p. $174°$, $d^{20}1.7557$, $n^{20}1.4641$	$Cl_2 + CH_2ClCF_2CCl_3$ or $CH_3CF_2CCl_2CH_3$	19, 33
$C_3HF_3Cl_4$	$CCl_2FCHClCClF_2$	B.p. $128.7°$, $d^{20}1.6747$, $n^{20}1.41569$	$CCl_3CHClCCl_3 + SbF_3 + SbF_3Cl_2$	31
	$CHCl_2CClFCClF_2$	B.p. $129.8°$, $d^{20}1.69124$, $n^{20}1.41967$	$CHCl_2CCl_2CCl_3 + SbF_3 + SbF_3Cl_2$	30, 31
$C_3HF_4Cl_3$	$CHCl_2CF_2CF_2Cl$	B.p. $91.8°$, $d^{20}1.5877$, $n^{20}1.3750$	$Cl_2 + CH_2ClCF_2CF_2Cl$	33
	$CClF_2CHClCClF_2$	B.p. $88°$	$CCl_3CHClCCl_3 + SbF_3 + SbF_3Cl_2$	31
	$CHClFCClFCClF_2$	B.p. $89.6{-}90°$, $d^{20}1.6368$, $n^{20}1.37613$	$CHCl_2CClFCClF_2 + SbF_3Cl_2$	31
$C_3H_2F_2Cl_4$	$CH_2ClCF_2CCl_3$	B.p. $150.8°$, $d^{20}1.6404$, $n^{20}1.4409$	$CH_3CF_2CH_3 + Cl_2$	33
$C_3H_2F_3Cl_3$	$CH_2ClCF_2CCl_2F$	B.p. $108.3°$, $d^{20}1.5813$, $n^{20}1.3914$	$CH_2ClCF_2CCl_3 + SbF_3Cl_2$	33
$C_3H_2F_4Cl_2$	$CH_2ClCF_2CClF_2$	B.p. $67.9°$, $d^{20}1.5225$, $n^{20}1.3464$	$CH_2ClCF_2CCl_3 + SbF_3Cl_2$	33
$C_3H_3F_2Cl_3$	$CH_3CF_2CCl_3$	M.p. $49°$, b.p. $102°$	$CH_3CF_2CH_3 + Cl_2$	19, 33
$C_3H_3F_3Cl_2$	$CH_3CF_2CCl_2F$	B.p. $60°$, $d^{20}1.4175$, $n^{20}1.3534$	$CH_3CF_2CCl_3 + SbF_3Cl_2$	19, 33
$C_3H_3F_3O$	CF_3COCH_3	B.p. $21.9°$, $d^{0}1.282$	$CF_3COCH_2CO_2C_2H_5 + 10\% \, H_2SO_4$	89
$C_3H_4FCl_3$	$CH_2ClCClFCH_2Cl$	B.p. $130°$, $d^{20}1.4376$, $n^{20}1.4470$	$CH_2ClCCl_2CH_2Cl + HgF_2$	5a
$C_3H_4F_2Cl_2$	$CH_2ClCF_2CH_2Cl$	B.p. $96°$, $d^{20}1.4143$, $n^{20}1.3960$	$CH_2ClCCl_2CH_2Cl + HgF_2$	5a
	$CH_3CF_2CHCl_2$	B.p. $79°$, $d^{20}1.3666$, $n^{20}1.38327$	$CH_3CF_2CH_3 + Cl_2$	19, 33
$C_3H_4F_2Cl_2O$	$CHCl_2CF_2OCH_3$	B.p. $104°$, $d1.414$, $n^{17}1.3387$	$CHCl_2CF_2Cl + KOH + CH_3OH$	126
$C_3H_4F_2O$	CHF_2COCH_3	B.p. $46.6°$, $d^{20}1.1644$, $n^{20}1.32802$	$CHF_2COCH_2CO_2C_2H_5 + 10\% \, H_2SO_4$	127
$C_3H_4F_3Br$	$CF_3CHBrCH_3$	B.p. $49°$, $d^{15}1.633$	$CF_3CHOHCH_3 + PBr_3 + Br_2$	92
$C_3H_4F_3NO$	$CF_3(CH_3)C{=}NOH$	B.p. $103°$, $d^{10}1.3042$	From CF_3COCH_3	90
C_3H_5F	$CH_2{=}CHCH_2F$	Liquid at $-3°$	$CH_2{=}CHCH_2I + AgF$	6
C_3H_5FBrCl	$CH_3CFClCH_2Br$	B.p. $110{-}112°$, $d^{20}1.6475$, $n^{20}1.45503$	$CH_3CClBrCH_2Br + SbF_3 + Br_2$	19
$C_3H_5FBr_2$	$CH_2BrCHBrCH_2F$	B.p. $158{-}159°$, $d^{18}2.09$	$CH_2{=}CHCH_2F + Br_2$	128
$C_3H_5FCl_2$	$CH_2ClCHClCH_2F$	B.p. $118{-}119°$, $d^{18}1.327$	$CH_2{=}CHCH_2F + Cl_2$	128
C_3H_5COF	CH_3CH_2COF	B.p. $44°$, $d^{15}0.972$	$CH_3CH_2COCl + ZnF_2$; $(CH_3CH_2CO)_2O + HF$	2, 43

* References 97–153 appear on pp. 92–93.

TABLE IV—*Continued*

ALIPHATIC FLUORINE COMPOUNDS

Formula	Structure	Physical Properties	Preparation (yield, remarks)	Reference*
C_3H_5FO	CH_2FCOCH_3	B.p. 72° or 78°	$CH_2ICOCH_3 + TlF$; $CH_2BrCOCH_3 +$ TlF; $CH_3COCH_3 + F_2$	95, 111
$C_3H_5FO_2$	$CH_2FCO_2CH_3$	B.p. 104°, $d^{15}1.1613$	$CH_2ICO_2CH_3 + AgF$ or TlF	95, 113
	$FCO_2C_2H_5$	B.p. 57°	$ClCO_2C_2H_5 + TlF$	95
$C_3H_5F_2Br$	$CH_3CF_2CH_2Br$	B.p. 76.2°, $d^{20}1.6102$ or 1.38860	$SbF_3 + CH_3CClBrCH_2Br$	19
$C_3H_5F_2Cl$	$CH_3CF_2CH_2Cl$	B.p. 55.1°, $d^{20}1.2023$, $n^{20}1.3506$	$Cl_2 + CH_3CF_2CH_3$	19, 33
$C_3H_5F_3O$	$CH_2FCF_2OCH_3$	B.p. 45°	$CH_2FCF_2Br + NaOCH_3$	94
	$CF_3CHOHCH_3$	B.p. 77.4°, $d^{15}1.2799$, $n^{15}1.31720$	$CF_3COCH_3 + H_2$	90
C_3H_6FCl	$CH_3CFClCH_3$	B.p. 35.2°, $d^{10}1.0072$, $n^{10}1.35856$	$CH_3CCl_2CH_3 + SbF_3$	19
$C_3H_6F_2$	$CH_3CH_2CHF_2$	B.p. 7–8°	$CH_3CH_2CHCl_2 + HgF_2$	20
	$CH_3CF_2CH_3$	B.p. $-0.5°$, $d^0 0.9205$, $n^{-42.5}1.3118$	$CH_3CCl_2CH_3 + SbF_3$	19
$C_3H_6F_2O$	$CHF_2CH_2OCH_3$	B.p. 47°	$CHF_2CH_2Br + KOH + CH_3OH$	94
C_3H_7F	$CH_3CH_2CH_2F$	M.p. $-150°$, b.p. $-32°$	$C_3H_7I + AgF$	129
	CH_3CHFCH_3	M.p. $-133°$, b.p. $-94°$	$CH_2{=}CHCH_3 + HF$	46
$C_4F_2Cl_8$	$CCl_2FCCl_2CCl_2CCl_2F$	M.p. 4°, b.p. 152°/20 mm., $d^{20}1.9272$, $n^{20}1.5256$	$C_2Cl_4 + F_2$	67
	$CCl_3CF_2C_2Cl_5$	M.p. $-2°$, b.p. 108°/2 mm., $d^{20}1.8994$, $n^{20}1.5139$	$CH_3CF_2C_2H_5 + Cl_2$	20
$C_4F_6O_3$	$(CF_3CO)_2O$	M.p. $-65°$, b.p. 40°	$CF_3CO_2H + P_2O_5$	88
C_4F_{10}		M.p. $-84.5°$, b.p. 4°	$C + F_2$	71
$C_4H_2F_2Cl_6$		M.p. 55–56°	$CHCl{=}CCl_2 + F_2$	67
$C_4H_2F_6O_2$	$CF_3CO_2CH_2CF_3$	M.p. $-65.5°$, b.p. 55°, $d^{18}1.4725$, $n^{18}1.2812$	$(CF_3CO)_2O + H_2 + Pt$	88

Formula	Structure	Properties	Method	Ref.
$C_4H_3F_3O_3$	$CF_3COCH_2CO_2H$	M.p. 72.8°, b.p. 79°/8 mm:	Hydrolysis of ester with HCl	86
$C_4H_4F_2O_3$	$(CH_2FCO)_2O$	Semi-solid	$CH_2FCO_2H + P_2O_5$	130
$C_4H_5FBrClO_2$	$CFClBrCO_2C_2H_5$	B.p. 151°, $d^{21}1.61289$, $n^{20}1.4357$	$CClBrCO_2C_2H_5 + AgF$	113
$C_4H_5FBr_2O_2$	$CFBr_2CO_2C_2H_5$	B.p. 173°, $d^{12}1.7851$, $d^{30}1.77097$	$CBr_3CO_2C_2H_5 + AgF$	117
$C_4H_5FCl_2O_2$	$CFCl_2CO_2C_2H_5$	B.p. 130°, $d^{14}1.3313$, $n^{17}1.4072$	$CCl_2FCOF + C_2H_5OH$	23
$C_4H_5F_2ClO_2$	$CF_2ClCO_2C_2H_5$	B.p. 97°, $d^{23}1.252$	$CF_2ClCOCl + C_2H_5OH$	81
$C_4H_5F_2Cl_3$		M.p. 58-60°	$CH_3C(CH_3)C_2H_5 + Cl_2$	20
$C_4H_5F_3$	$CF_3(CH_3)C{=}CH_2$	B.p. 6.4°, $d^5 1.045$	$CF_3C(CH_3)OHCH_3 + PBr_5$	92
$C_4H_5F_3Br_2$	$CF_3C(CH_3)BrCH_2Br$	M.p. $-54°$, b.p. 138°, $d^{15}1.9825$, $n^{15}1.4410$	$CF_3C(CH_3)OHCH_3 + PBr_5$	92
$C_4H_5F_3N_2O$	$CF_3C({=}NH)CH_2{-}CONH_2$	M.p. 137°		86
$C_4H_5F_3O_2$	$CH_3CO_2CH_2CF_3$	B.p. 77.85°, $d^{16}1.32058$	$CF_3CH_2OH + CH_3COCl$	88
	$CF_3CO_2C_2H_5$	B.p. 61.7°, $d^{16}1.1953$	From acid	85
$C_4H_6FBrO_2$	$CHFBrCO_2C_2H_5$	B.p. 154°, $d^{17}1.5587$	Acid halide $+ C_2H_5OH$	82
$C_4H_6FIO_2$	$CHFICO_2C_2H_5$	B.p. 180°, $d^{11}1.6716$	$CHBrFCO_2Et + CaI_2$	82
$C_4H_6F_2Br_2O$	$CHBr_2CF_2OC_2H_5$	B.p. 67°/25 mm, $d^{17}1.9158$	$CF_2BrCHBr_2 + KOH + C_2H_5OH$	94
$C_4H_6F_2Cl_2O$	$CHCl_2CF_2OC_2H_5$	B.p. 120°, $d^{20}1.330$, $n^{20}1.3949$	$CHCl_2CF_2Cl + KOH + C_2H_5OH$	126
$C_4H_6F_2O_2$	$CHF_2CO_2C_2H_5$	B.p. 99.2°, $d^{17}1.1800$	Acid $+ C_2H_5OH$	84
	$CH_3CO_2CH_2CHF_2$	B.p. 106°, $d^{15}1.1781$	$CH_3COCl + CHF_2CH_2OH$	84
$C_4H_6F_3Br$	$CF_3CH(CH_3)CH_2Br$	M.p. 81°, b.p. 100-112°/13 mm.	Crotonic acid $+ F_2$	66
		B.p. 79.81°, $d^{17}1.550$	$CF_3C(CH_3){=}CH_2 + HBr$	92
$C_4H_6F_3BrO$	$CBrF_2CHFOC_2H_5$	B.p. 106°, $d^{10}1.6121$, $n^{10}1.3794$	$CBrF_2CHBrF + NaOC_2H_5$	131
$C_4H_6F_4N_2O$	$(CHF_2CH_2)_2NNO$	B.p. 179°, $d^{16}1.4490$	$(CHF_2CH_2)_2NH + HNO_2$	96
$C_4H_7FBr_2O$	$CHBr_2CHFOC_2H_5$	B.p. 150-160°	By-products of oxidation of $CBr_2{=}CHF$	12
$C_4H_7FCl_2O$	$CHCl_2CHFOC_2H_5$	B.p. 121°, $d^{25}1.214$	$CHClFCHCl_2 + NaOC_2H_5$	12
$C_4H_7FO_2$	$CH_2FCH_2OCOCH_3$	B.p. 119.3° or 45.5°/27 mm., $d^{20}1.0986$, $n^{10}1.37792$	Bromoacetate $+ AgF$ or HgF	132

* References 97-153 appear on pp. 92-93.

TABLE IV—*Continued*

ALIPHATIC FLUORINE COMPOUNDS

Formula	Structure	Physical Properties	Preparation (yield, remarks)	Reference *
$C_4H_7FO_2$	$CH_3(CH_2F)CHCO_2H$	B.p. 80–82°/13 mm.	Isobutyric acid + F_2	66
	$CH_2FCO_2C_2H_5$	B.p. 120° or 126°, $d^{20}1.0926$, $n^{20}1.37665$	$CH_2ClCOC_2H_5$ + KF. $BrCH_2CO_2C_2H_5$ + TlF	82, 133
$C_4H_7F_2BrO$	$CH_2BrCF_2OC_2H_5$	B.p. 114–115°	$CBrF_2CH_2Br$ + $NaOC_2H_5$	94
$C_4H_7F_3N_2O_2$	$CF_3C(ONH_4)=CHCO-NH_2$	M.p. 97°	NH_3 + $CF_3COCH_2CO_2C_2H_5$	86
$C_4H_7F_3O$	$CF_3C(CH_3)_2OH$	M.p. 20.75°, b.p. 81.6°, $d^{22}1.1903$	CF_3CO_2R + $2CH_3MgI$	92
$C_4H_7F_4N$	$(CHF_2CH_2)_2NH$	B.p. 124.4°, $d^{16}1.30412$	CHF_2CH_2Br + NH_3	96
C_4H_8FI		B.p. 50°, $d1.74$, $n^{15}1.49$	$CH_2CBrICH_2CH_3$ + HF	134
$C_4H_8F_2$	$CH_3CF_2C_2H_5$	B.p. 30.8°, $d^{10}0.9164$, $n^{10}1.31862$	$CH_3CCl_2C_2H_5$ + SbF_3	20
$C_4H_8F_2O$	$C_2H_5OCH_2CHF_2$	B.p. 66.5°, $d^{15}1.039$	CHF_2CH_2Br + KOC_2H_5	135
C_4H_9F	$C_3H_7CH_2F$	B.p. 32°, $d^{16}0.7824$, $n^{15}1.3419$	C_4H_9I + HgF	136
	$CH_3CHFC_2H_5$	B.p. 25.2°, $d^{0}0.7884$, $n^{12}1.3366$	HF + butene	47
	$(CH_3)_2CHCH_2F$	Liquid at +16°	$(CH_3)_2CHCH_2I$ + AgF	137
	$(CH_3)_3CF$	M.p. −77°, b.p. 12.1°, $d^{12}0.7527$, $n^{12}1.3241$	HF + isobutylene	47
$C_5F_2Cl_{10}$	$CCl_3CF_2C_3Cl_7$	M.p. 10–15°	$CH_3CF_2C_3H_7$ + Cl_2	20
C_5F_{12}		M.p. −10°, b.p. 30°	C + F_2	71
$C_5H_7F_2Cl_2$		M.p. 52°	$CH_3CF_2C_3H_7$ + Cl_2	20
$C_5H_7F_3O_2$	$CH_3(CF_3)CHOCOCH_3$	B.p. 85.6°/75 mm, $d^{15}1.1823$, $n^{15}1.3314$	$CF_3CHOHCH_3$ + CH_3COCl	92
$C_5H_7F_3N_2O_3$	Allophanate of $CF_3CHOHCH_3$	M.p. 160°		92

Formula	Compound	Properties	Method	Ref.
$C_5H_9FBr_2O$	$C_2H_5OCH_2CBrFCH_2Br$	B.p. 188°	$C_2H_5OCH_2CF{=}CH_2 + Br_2$	138
C_5H_9FO	$CH_2{=}CFCH_2OC_2H_5$	B.p. 77.5°, $d^{15}0.9166$, $n^{15}1.3790$	$C_2H_5OCH_2CHFCH_2Br + NaOCH_3$	138
$C_5H_9FO_2$	$CH_3CHFCO_2C_2H_5$	B.p. 138.41°	$CH_3CHBrCO_2C_2H_5 + AgF + CaF_2$	66
$C_5H_9F_2NO_2$	$CHF_2CH_2NHCO_2C_2H_5$	M.p. 37.6°, b.p. 185°	Difluoroethylamine + ethylchlorocarbamate	96
$C_5H_{10}FBrO$	$C_2H_5OCH_2CHFCH_2Br$	B.p. 157°	$C_2H_5OCH_2CHBrCH_2Br + HgF$ or AgF	138
$C_5H_{10}F_2$	$CH_3CF_2C_3H_7$	B.p. 59.8°, $d^{20}0.8958$, $n^{20}1.3357$	$CH_3CCl_2C_3H_7 + SbF_3$	20
$C_5H_{10}F_2O$	$C_2H_5OCH_2CHFCH_2F$	B.p. 114.5°	$C_2H_5OCH_2CHBrCH_2Br + AgF$ or HgF	138
$C_5H_{11}F$	$CH_3(CH_2)_4F$	M.p. $-80°$, b.p. 62.8°, $d^{20}0.7880$	$C_5H_{11}Br + HgF$	139
	$(CH_3)_2CH(CH_2)_2F$	B.p. 53.5°	$iso\text{-}C_5H_{11}Br + HgF$	139
	$CH_3CHFC_3H_7$	B.p. 50°	$CH_3CHIC_3H_7 + AgF$	140
	$CH_2FC(CH_3)C_2H_5$	B.p. 55.9°	Bromide + AgF in acetonitrile	141
	$C_2H_5C(CH_3)_2F$	M.p. $-121°$, b.p. 44.8°, $d^{40}0.7535$, $n^{44}1.3375$	$(CH_3)_2C{=}CHCH_3 + HF$	47
C_6F_{14}		M.p. $-4°$, or glass, b.p. 51° or 60°	$C + F_2$	71
$C_6H_7F_3O_3$	$CF_3COCH_2CO_2C_2H_5$	M.p. $-39°$, b.p. 131.5°	$CF_3CO_2C_2H_5 + CH_3CO_2C_2H_5 + NaOC_2H_5$	86
$C_6H_8F_2O_3$	$CHF_2COCH_2CO_2C_2H_5$	B.p. 70°/28 mm, b.p. 160°, $d^{20}1.2418$, $n^{20}1.4059$	$CHF_2CO_2H + CH_3CO_2C_2H_5 + NaOC_2H_5$	127
$C_6H_8F_3NO_2$	$CF_3C{=}NHCH_2CO_2{-}C_2H_5$	M.p. 25.2°, b.p. 157°/145 mm.	$CF_3C(ONH_4){=}CHCO_2C_2H_5$ at 100°	86
$C_6H_9F_3O_2$	$CF_3CO_2C_4H_9$	B.p. 100.2°, $d^{22}1.0268$, $n^{21}1.353$	$CF_3COCl + NaOC_4H_9$	5a
$C_6H_9F_6O_4P$	$(CHF_2CH_2)_3PO_4$	B.p. 253-255°	$CHF_2CH_2OH + P + Br_2$	142
$C_6H_{10}FClO_4$	d-Glucosyl fluoride-6-chlorhydrin	Dec. 138°, $[\alpha]_D^{20}88.8$ in water	Na in CH_3OH + aceto-1-fluoro-d-glucose-6-chlorhydrin	143
$C_6H_{10}F_2Cl_2O$	$CHCl_2CF_2OC_4H_9\text{-}sec$	B.p. 154°, $d^{20}1.215$, $n^{18}1.4051$	$CHCl_2CF_2Cl + KOH + sec$-butyl alcohol	126
$C_6H_{11}FO_5$	d-Glucosyl fluoride	M.p. 118-125°, $[\alpha]_D^{18}96.7°$ in H_2O	Saponification of acetofluoroglucose by 1% CH_3ONa in abs. CH_3OH	144, 145
$C_6H_{12}F_2$	$CH_3CF_2C_4H_9$	B.p. 86.6°, $d^{20}0.8919$, $n^{20}1.3538$	$CH{=}CC_4H_9 + HF$	18
$C_6H_{12}F_2$	$C_2H_5CF_2C_3H_7$	B.p. 86.8°, $d^{20}0.9024$, $n^{20}1.3553$	$CH_3C{=}CC_3H_7 + HF$	18

* References 97–153 appear on pp. 92–93.

TABLE IV—*Continued*

ALIPHATIC FLUORINE COMPOUNDS

Formula	Structure	Physical Properties	Preparation (yield, remarks)	Reference *
$C_6H_{13}F$	Normal	B.p. 93.5°, $d^{20}0.8002$, $n^{20}1.3748$	$C_6H_{13}Br + HgF$	136
	2-Fluorohexane	B.p. 69-72°	Iodide + HgF	140
	2-(or 3)-Fluorohexane	B.p. 86.3°, $d^{20}0.7916$, $n^{20}1.3693$	By-product of preparation of $C_6H_{11}F$	136
	2-(or 3)-Fluorohexane	M.p. −104°, b.p. 82.6°, $d^0 0.819$, $n^{26}1.3683$	sec-Hexyl iodide + Ag_2SiF_6	146
$C_6H_{13}FO_2$	$CH_2FCH(OC_2H_5)_2$	B.p. 60°/25 mm.	Bromoacetal + TlF	147
$C_7H_9F_3O_4$	$CF_3C_4H_7(CO_2H)_2$ Trifluoromethyl adipic acid		By-product of nitration of $C_6H_5CF_3$	85
$C_7H_{11}F_3O_2$	$CF_3COOC_5H_{11}$-iso	B.p. 119.5°, $d^{15}1.0834$, $n^{15}1.3530$	CF_3CO_2H + isoamyl alcohol	90
$C_7H_{14}F_2$	$CHF_2C_6H_{13}$	B.p. 119.7°, $d^{20}0.8959$, $n^{20}1.37098$	$C_6H_{13}CHCl_2 + HgF_2$	20
	$CH_3CF_2C_5H_{11}$	B.p. 112.4°, $d^{20}0.8889$, $n^{20}1.3658$	$CH{\equiv}CC_5H_{11} + HF$	18
$C_7H_{15}F$	Normal	M.p. −73°, b.p. 119.2°, $d^{21}0.8039$, $n^{21}1.3855$	Bromide + HgF	139
$C_8H_{17}F$	$CH_3(CH_2)_5CHFCH_3$	B.p. 139.3°	Iodide + AgF (violent)	139
	Normal	B.p. 142.5°, $d^0 0.798$	Iodide + AgF	139
$C_{10}H_{21}F$	Normal	B.p. 183.5°, $d^{10}0.792$	Bromide + AgF	139
$C_{11}H_{16}FO_7$	Fluorotriacetyl-l-arabinose	M.p. 117-118°, $[\alpha]_D^{20}138.02°$ in CHCl₃	Corresponding acetyl derivative + HF	148
$C_{12}H_{16}FClO_7$	Aceto-1-fluoro-d-glucose-6-chlorhydrin	M.p. 151-152°, $[\alpha]_D^{20}106.95°$ in CHCl₃		143
$C_{12}H_{17}FO_8$	2-Fluorotriacetylfructose	M.p. 134-135°, $[\alpha]_D^{20} -128.8°$	HF and fructosepentaacetate	149
$C_{12}H_{21}FO_{10}$	α-Lactosyl fluoride	$[\alpha]_D^{15}83.2°$ in water	Heptaacetylfluorolactose + Na in CH₃OH	150
	Gentiobiosyl fluoride	$[\alpha]_D^{20}33.47°$ in water [sinters 180°]	NH₃ in CH₃OH on 6-(tetraacetyl-β-glucosido)-2,3,5-tribenzoyl glucosyl fluoride	144

$C_{13}H_{19}FO_8$	(2-Fluoro-3-methyl-triacetylfructose)	M.p. 113.4°, $[\alpha]_D^{20} -88.7°$	HF + 3-methylfructose	149
	1-Methyl-2-fluorotri-acetylfructose	M.p. 94°, $[\alpha]_D^{20} -116.3°$	Methylation of 2-fluorotriacetyl fructose	149
	α-Acetofluoroglucose	M.p. 98°, $[\alpha]_D^{18} 21.9°$ in CHCl₃	AgF in CH₃CN on α-acetobromoglucose	150
	Fluorotetraacetylglucose	M.p. 108°, $[\alpha]_D^{20} 90.08°$ in CHCl₃	Acyl derivative with HF	151
	Fluorototetraacetylfructose	M.p. 112°, $[\alpha]_D^{20} -90.43°$ in CHCl₃	Pentaacetylfructose and HF	151
$C_{16}H_{21}FO_{11}$	Fluoroacetyltetra-acetylglucose	M.p. 119-120°, $[\alpha]_D^{20} 92.27°$	Tetraacetylglucose + ZnCl₂ + fluoroacetic anhydride	130
$C_{16}H_{32}F_2$		B.p. 103°/0.2 mm.	Hexadecene + F₂	66
$C_{16}H_{33}F$	Cetyl fluoride	Solid room temp., b.p. 287°, b.p. 181°/24 mm., $d^{17}0.809$	By-product of $C_8H_{17}I$ + AgF	139
$C_{16}H_{33}F$		M.p. 7°, b.p. 104-112°/0.2 mm.	Hexadecane + F₂ + CO₂	66
$C_{18}H_{34}F_2O_2$		M.p. 70-74°	Stearolic acid and HF in CH₂Cl₂	152
$C_{18}H_{34}F_2O_2$		M.p. 81°	Oleic acid + F₂	66
$C_{18}H_{35}FO_2$	Monofluorostearic acid	M.p. 68°	Oleic acid + HF	153, 5a
$C_{25}H_{25}FO_5$	6-Triphenylmethylglu-cosyl fluoride	M.p. 140°, $[\alpha]_D^{14} 58.4°$ in C₅H₅N	Ph₃CCl in C₅H₅N + d-glucosyl fluoride	144
$C_{26}H_{35}FO_{17}$	Fluoroheptaacetylcellu-lose	M.p. 187°, $[\alpha]_D^{20} 30.03°$	Acetyl derivative + HF	151
$C_{31}H_{30}FO_8$	Triacetyl derivative of 6-triphenylmethyl-glucosyl fluoride	M.p. 147-148°, $[\alpha]_D^{20} 119.6°$	By acetylation in C₅H₅N	144
$C_{34}H_{27}FO_9$	Tetrabenzoyl-d-glucosyl fluoride	M.p. 110-112°, $[\alpha]_D^{22} 110°$ in C₅H₅N	By benzoylation in C₅H₅N	144
$C_{41}H_{41}FO_{17}$	6-Tetraacetyl-β-gluco-sido-2,3,5-tribenzoyl-glucosyl fluoride	M.p. 195-196°, $[\alpha]_D^{20} 15°$		144

* References 97–153 appear on pp. 92–93.

REFERENCES TO TABLE

[97] Ruff, Bretschneider, and Ebert, Z. anorg. allgem. Chem., **217**, 1 (1934).
[98] Rathsburg, Ber., **51**, 669 (1918).
[99] Cossuth, Z. anorg. allgem. Chem., **201**, 75 (1931).
[100] Plank and Seger, Z. ges. Kälte-Ind., **46**, 41 (1939).
[101] Simons, Bond, and McArthur, J. Am. Chem. Soc., **62**, 3477 (1940).
[102] Ruff and Keim, Z. anorg. allgem. Chem., **201**, 245 (1931).
[103] Thornton, Burg, and Schlessinger, J. Am. Chem. Soc., **55**, 3177 (1933).
[104] Ruff and Keim, Z. anorg. allgem. Chem., **201**, 255 (1931).
[105] Lebeau and Damiens, Compt. rend., **182**, 1340 (1926); **191**, 939 (1930).
[106] Swarts, Bull. acad. roy. Belg., **1910**, 113.
[107] Ruff, Bretschneider, Luchsinger, and Miltschitzky, Ber., **69**, 299 (1936).
[108] Collie, J. Chem. Soc., **55**, 111 (1889).
[109] Van Arkel and Zanetsky, Rec. trav. chim., **56**, 167 (1937).
[110] Moles and Batuecas, J. chim. phys., **17**, 537 (1919); **18**, 353 (1920).
[111] Davies and Dick, J. Chem. Soc., I, 483 (1932).
[112] Meyer and Schramm, Z. anorg. allgem. Chem., **206**, 24 (1932).
[113] Swarts, Bull. soc. chim. [3] **15**, 1134 (1896).
[114] Swarts, Bull. acad. roy. Belg., [3] **33**, 471 (1897).
[115] Swarts, Bull. acad. roy. Belg., **1897**, 317.
[116] Henne and Wiest, J. Am. Chem. Soc., **62**, 2051 (1940).
[117] Swarts, Chem. Zentr., II, 1099 (1897); II, 702 (1898).
[118] Swarts, Chem. Zentr., II, 281 (1899).
[119] Ruff and Willenberg, Ber., **73**, 724 (1940).
[120] Swarts, Bull. soc. chim. Belg., **31**, 364 (1924).
[121] Swarts, J. chim. phys., **20**, 30 (1923).
[122] Swarts, Chem. Zentr., II, 804 (1901).
[123] Swarts, Compt. rend., **197**, 1261 (1933).
[124] Ger. pat., 641,878 (1937) [C. A., **31**, 5809 (1937)].
[125] Swarts, Bull. acad. roy. Belg., **1909**, 728.
[126] Brit. pat., 523,449 (1940) [C. A., **35**, 6265 (1941)].
[127] Désirant, Bull. acad. roy. Belg., [5] **15**, 966 (1929).
[128] Meslans, Ann. chim., [7] **1**, 382 (1894).
[129] Meslans, Compt. rend., **108**, 352 (1889).
[130] Brauns, J. Am. Chem. Soc., **47**, 1285 (1925).
[131] Swarts, Bull. acad. roy. Belg., **1899**, 357.
[132] Swarts, Bull. acad. roy. Belg., **1914**, 7.
[133] Ray, J. Indian Chem. Soc., **13**, 427 (1936).
[134] Petrob, J. Gen. Chem. U.S.S.R., **4**, 1458 (1934).
[135] Swarts, Bull. acad. roy. Belg., **1901**, 393, 400.
[136] Desreux, Bull. soc. chim. Belg., **44**, 1 (1935).
[137] Young, J. Chem. Soc., **39**, 489 (1881).
[138] Swarts, Bull. soc. chim., **25**, 103 (1919).
[139] Swarts, Bull. acad. roy. Belg., **1921**, 302, 442.
[140] Bergmann, Polanyi, and Szabo, Trans. Faraday Soc., **32**, 843 (1936).
[141] Brauns, J. Am. Chem. Soc., **56**, 1421 (1934).
[142] Swarts, Rec. trav. chim., **28**, 166 (1909).
[143] Helferich and Bredereck, Ber., **60**, 1995 (1927).
[144] Helferich, Bauerlein, Wiegand, Ann., **447**, 27 (1926).
[145] Helferich and Peters, Ann., **494**, 101 (1932).
[146] Paterno and Spallino, Atti acad. Lincei, [2] **16**, 160 (1907).
[147] Ray, Goswami, and Ray, J. Indian Chem. Soc., **12**, 93 (1935).
[148] Brauns, J. Am. Chem. Soc., **46**, 1484 (1924).

[149] Brauns, *Bur. Standards J. Research*, **6**, 449–456 (1931).
[150] Helferich and Gootz, *Ber.*, **62**, 2505 (1929).
[151] Brauns, *J. Am. Chem. Soc.*, **45**, 833 (1923).
[152] Ger. pat., 621,977 (1935) [*C. A.*, **30**, 2314 (1936)].
[153] Fr. pat., 799,432 (1936) [*C. A.*, **30**, 7585 (1936)].

CHAPTER 3

THE CANNIZZARO REACTION

T. A. GEISSMAN

University of California, Los Angeles

CONTENTS

INTRODUCTION

The reaction in which two aldehyde groups are transformed into the corresponding hydroxyl and carboxyl functions, existing separately or in combination as an ester, has been termed the Cannizzaro reaction. Although this name has been applied at various times to the reactions brought about by a variety of agents, it will be restricted, in the present discussion, to the dismutation of two similar aldehyde groups into the corresponding alcohol and carboxylic salt functions by means of aqueous or alcoholic alkali. The conversion of benzaldehyde into a mixture of benzyl alcohol and sodium benzoate is an example.

Dismutations of the same type, but involving two unlike aldehyde molecules, will be classed as "crossed" Cannizzaro reactions. The reduction of benzaldehyde to benzyl alcohol by means of formaldehyde and alkali is an example.

The most commonly employed procedure for carrying out the reaction consists in shaking or stirring the aldehyde with strong (50%) alkali, in aqueous or alcoholic solution, without heating. Other reagents which can be employed to bring about the dismutation include alkali amides in liquid ammonia, alkali alkoxides in alcohol solution, and alkoxides of metals such as aluminum or magnesium in alcohol solution or in suspension in inert solvents.[1, 2, 3, 4, 5]

Oxidation-reduction reactions similar to the Cannizzaro process are brought about in the living cell by certain enzyme systems. Numerous examples [6, 7, 8, 9, 10] of these have been studied *in vitro* by the aid of tissue preparations, and certain of them [6] suggest possible application in preparative methods. The dismutation of aldehydes in basic or neutral solution also has been effected by catalytic metals, such as nickel and platinum.[11, 12] It seems likely that there is a closer analogy between

[1] Meisenheimer, *Ann.*, **442**, 180 (1925).

[2] Marshall, *J. Chem. Soc.*, **127**, 2184 (1925).

[3] Tishchenko, *Ber.*, **20**, 246 (1887); *J. prakt. Chem.*, **86**, 322 (1912).

[4] Child and Adkins, *J. Am. Chem. Soc.*, **45**, 3013 (1923); **47**, 798 (1925).

[5] Claisen, *Ber.*, **20**, 646 (1887).

[6] Parnas, *Biochem. Z.*, **28**, 298 (1910).

[7] Josephson and von Euler, *Z. physiol. Chem.*, **135**, 49 (1924).

[8] Schweiger and Geilinger, *Mitt. Lebensm. Hyg.*, **15**, 41 (1924).

[9] Kuhn and Hecksher, *Z. physiol. Chem.*, **160**, 116 (1926).

[10] Abderhalden and Wertheimer, *Arch. ges. Physiol. (Pflügers)*, **198**, 415 (1923) [*C. A.*, **17**, 2294 (1923)].

[11] Delepine and Horeau, (a) *Compt. rend.*, **204**, 1605 (1937); (b) *Bull. soc. chim.*, [5] **4**, 31, 1525 (1937).

[12] Levene and Christman, *J. Biol. Chem.*, **120**, 575 (1937).

these enzyme and catalytic reactions than between either of them and the true Cannizzaro reaction.

MECHANISM OF THE REACTION

A number of mechanisms have been suggested for the Cannizzaro reaction.[13, 14, 15] One mechanism, based upon a proposal by Lock,[15] who patterned his suggestion after those put forward by Grignard and Fluchaire [16] and by Fredenhagen and Bonhoeffer,[17] is the following.

$$RCHO + OH^- \rightleftharpoons RCH \overset{\displaystyle O^-}{\underset{\displaystyle OH}{<}}$$

$$RCH \overset{\displaystyle O^-}{\underset{\displaystyle OH}{<}} + RCHO \rightleftharpoons \underset{\displaystyle OH\ \ O^-}{RCHOCHR}$$

$$\underset{\displaystyle OH\ \ O^-}{RCHOCHR} \rightarrow \underset{\displaystyle O}{RCH_2O\overset{\displaystyle \|}{C}R} + OH^- \rightleftharpoons \underset{\displaystyle O^-}{RCH_2O\overset{\displaystyle OH}{C}R}$$

$$\underset{\displaystyle O^-}{RCH_2O\overset{\displaystyle OH}{C}R} \rightarrow RCH_2OH + RCO_2^-$$

This mechanism adequately coördinates the well-known variations of base-induced dismutations of aldehydes into a general picture and makes it unnecessary to suppose that different bases act in different ways. The formation of esters when an aldehyde is treated with an alkoxide follows the same scheme, with OR^- in place of OH^-, and takes into account the ester interchanges which have been observed to occur. The transformation of benzaldehyde into benzamide and benzyl alcohol by the action of sodamide [18] proceeds analogously, amide-ester interchange brought about by the amide ion being the last step.

[13] Hammett, "Physical Organic Chemistry," p. 350, McGraw-Hill, New York, 1940.
[14] Eistert, "Tautomerie und Mesomerie," p. 116, Enke, Stuttgart, 1938.
[15] Eitel and Lock, *Monatsh.*, **72**, 392 (1939).
[16] Grignard and Fluchaire, *Ann. chim.*, [10] **9**, 5 (1928).
[17] Fredenhagen and Bonhoeffer, *Z. physik. Chem.*, **A181**, 379 (1938).
[18] Haller and Bauer, *Ann. chim. phys.* **16**, 145 (1909).

It would be a consequence of this mechanism that under certain conditions an ester might be isolated as one of the products of the reaction. Such is found to be the case. Thus, Lachman [19] has shown that benzyl benzoate can be isolated in the reaction between benzaldehyde and aqueous sodium hydroxide if precautions are taken to avoid high temperature and an excess of alkali.

The view that the first step in the reaction proceeds by an initial coordination of the base (e.g., OH^-) with the aldehyde carbonyl group is supported by the investigations of Lock,[15] Molt,[20] Weissberger and Haase,[21] and Bailar, Barney, and Miller [21a] on the effect of substituents upon the rate of the reaction. Electron-attracting groups (e.g., halogen, $-NO_2$) increase the rate, and electron-repelling substituents (e.g., $-OCH_3$, $-CH_3$, and particularly those groups such as $-O^-$ and NR_2 which can furnish electrons directly to the carbonyl carbon atom) decrease the rate.

It has been shown [17] that the alcohol which is formed when the reaction is carried out in heavy water contains no deuterium in the $-CH_2-$ group. This is evidence for the view that the transfer of the hydrogen atom takes place intramolecularly without interchange with the solvent.

It has been shown by Kharasch and Foy [22] and confirmed by Urushibara and Takebayashi [23] that the presence of peroxides markedly accelerates the heterogeneous Cannizzaro reaction. Highly purified benzaldehyde undergoes dismutation to the extent of only 2–4% under conditions which result in 25–80% reaction with "ordinary" benzaldehyde. 5-Bromofurfural dismutates only slowly with 30% sodium hydroxide in ether, but the reaction is accelerated markedly by the addition of a trace of hydrogen peroxide.[24] Various explanations have been advanced to account for the effect of peroxides,[25, 25a] but the problem is still obscure.

SCOPE OF THE REACTION

The Cannizzaro reaction is characteristic of aldehydes which have no hydrogen on the α-carbon atom, such as aromatic and many heterocyclic aldehydes, properly substituted aliphatic aldehydes, and formalde-

[19] Lachman, J. Am. Chem. Soc., 45, 2356 (1923).

[20] Molt, Rec. trav. chim., 56, 232 (1937).

[21] Weissberger and Haase, J. Chem. Soc., 1934, 535.

[21a] Bailar, Barney, and Miller, J. Am. Chem. Soc., 58, 2110 (1936).

[22] Kharasch and Foy, J. Am. Chem. Soc., 57, 1510 (1935).

[23] Urushibara and Takebayashi, Bull. Chem. Soc. Japan, 12, 328 (1937) [C. A., 31, 7394 (1937)].

[24] Chute, Orchard, and Wright, J. Org. Chem., 6, 157 (1941).

[25] Lock, Monatsh., 72, 410 (1939).

[25a] Weiss, Trans. Faraday Soc., 37, 782 (1941).

hyde. It has been observed with aldehydes which have α-hydrogen atoms, although generally under conditions quite dissimilar to those employed with aldehydes of the first class. For example, isobutyralde-hyde is reported to undergo quantitative conversion into isobutyric acid and isobutyl alcohol when heated with barium hydroxide solution at 150° in a sealed tube.[26] There are reports that aldehydes containing two hydrogen atoms on the α-carbon atom undergo the Cannizzaro reaction,[27, 28] but the results are inconclusive. In some cases workers unable to repeat earlier experiments [26, 29] attributed the previous results to impurities in the reactants (e.g., methylethylacetaldehyde in isovaler-aldehyde). In another case [28] the extent of the supposed Cannizzaro reaction was deduced only from a decrease in the alkali concentration as the reaction between acetaldehyde and alkali was followed by titration.

The Cannizzaro reaction often occurs indirectly when aldehydes containing α-hydrogen atoms are treated with alkali. The first products usually are those formed by aldol condensation, and these may undergo Cannizzaro reactions of either the normal or crossed variety.

Aliphatic Aldehydes

Aldehydes without α-Hydrogen Atoms. Formaldehyde, the simplest member of this class, undergoes the Cannizzaro reaction to yield methyl alcohol and formic acid.[30, 31] Glyoxylic acid disproportionates in a normal manner to yield glycolic and oxalic acids.[32, 33] α-Ketoaldehydes and glyoxal undergo intramolecular dismutation under the influence of alkali, a reaction analogous to both the Cannizzaro reaction and the benzilic acid rearrangement of α-diketones:

$$\text{RCOCHO} + \text{NaOH} \rightarrow \underset{\underset{\text{OH}}{|}}{\text{RCHCOONa}}$$

The readiness with which higher aldehydes undergo the Cannizzaro reaction and the extent of the reaction vary with the nature of the groups present on the α-carbon atom. For example, hydroxypivalalde-hyde, $HOCH_2C(CH_3)_2CHO$, upon treatment with 50% aqueous potassium hydroxide at room temperature is converted quantitatively into

[26] Lederer, *Monatsh.*, **22**, 536 (1901).
[27] Rosinger, *Monatsh.*, **22**, 545 (1901).
[28] Hammarsten, *Ann.*, **420**, 262 (1920); **421**, 293 (1920).
[29] Neustadter, *Monatsh.*, **27**, 879 (1906).
[30] Lieben, *Monatsh.*, **22**, 302 (1901).
[31] Delepine, *Bull. soc. chim.*, [3] **17**, 938 (1897).
[32] Debus, *J. Chem. Soc.*, **85**, 1391 (1904); *Ann.*, **338**, 336, 346 (1904).
[33] Böttinger, *Ber.*, **13**, 1932 (1880).

β,β-dimethyltrimethyleneglycol and hydroxypivalic acid.[34] Pivalaldehyde is only slightly affected by 50% aqueous alkali, but when treated with 50% alcoholic potassium hydroxide it yields 50–60% of neopentyl alcohol and pivalic acid.[35, 36] This apparently greater reactivity of the hydroxyaldehyde is to be attributed at least in part to its greater solubility in 50% aqueous alkali. α-Hydroxyisobutyraldehyde undergoes smooth dismutation with dilute sodium or potassium hydroxide (3–10%) to yield isobutylene glycol and α-hydroxyisobutyric acid.[37, 38] The same products can be obtained from α-bromoisobutyraldehyde, hydrolysis to the hydroxyaldehyde preceding the dismutation.

Certain aliphatic aldehydes which have no hydrogen atoms on the α-carbon atom undergo cleavage under the influence of alkali. The conversion of a trihaloacetaldehyde to the haloform and the alkali formate is the best-known example. Triphenylacetaldehyde undergoes a similar cleavage, yielding triphenylmethane and the alkali formate.[38a] Aldehydes in which the α-carbon atom is part of an ethylenic or acetylenic system do not give the normal Cannizzaro reaction; their behavior is discussed on p. 102.

The most useful examples of the Cannizzaro reaction as applied to aliphatic aldehydes are those involving β-hydroxyaldehydes formed by aldol condensation of aldehydes which have α-hydrogen atoms or of these aldehydes with formaldehyde. Since, in these reactions, the β-hydroxyaldehyde is not isolated, examples will be classified under the headings of the reactants which serve as the actual starting materials.

Aldehydes with One α-Hydrogen Atom. Aldehydes of the type RR'CHCHO under suitable conditions [39] (Table I) can be made to condense smoothly to the aldols. Under other conditions the aldol condensation may be the first step, followed by a crossed Cannizzaro reaction between the aldol and the original aldehyde. The products of this reaction are the glycol formed by reduction of the aldol and the acid formed by oxidation of the original aldehyde.[29, 39, 40, 41]

$$
\begin{array}{ccc}
& \overset{R}{\underset{|}{}} & \overset{R}{\underset{|}{}} \\
2\text{RCHCHO} \rightarrow \text{RCHCH}-\text{CCHO} & \xrightarrow{\text{R(R')CHCHO}} & \text{RCHCH}-\text{CCH}_2\text{OH} + \text{RCHCO}_2\text{H} \\
\underset{R'}{|} \quad\quad \underset{R'}{|} \; \underset{\text{OH}}{|} \; \underset{R'}{|} & & \underset{R'}{|} \; \underset{\text{OH}}{|} \; \underset{R'}{|} \quad\quad \underset{R'}{|} \\
& \text{Aldol} & \text{Glycol} \quad\quad\quad \text{Acid}
\end{array}
$$

[34] Wessely, *Monatsh.*, **22**, 66 (1901).

[35] Hinterberger, dissertation, Vienna, 1923.

[36] Conant, Webb, and Mendum, *J. Am. Chem. Soc.*, **51**, 1246 (1929).

[37] Franke, *Monatsh.*, **21**, 1122 (1900).

[38] Danilov and Danilova, *Ber.*, **67**, 24 (1934).

[38a] Danilov, *J. Russ. Phys. Chem. Soc.*, **49**, 282 (1917) [*C. A.*, **18**, 1488 (1924)].

[39] Herrmann, *Monatsh.*, **25**, 188 (1904).

[40] Fossek, *Monatsh.*, **2**, 614 (1881); **4**, 663 (1883).

[41] Franke and Kohn, *Monatsh.*, **19**, 354 (1898).

TABLE I

R	R′	Base	Conditions	Products (yields)	Reference
CH_3	CH_3	Aq. K_2CO_3	Room temp.	Aldol only	41
CH_3	CH_3	Aq. KOH	Room temp.	Aldol, glycol, acid	41
CH_3	CH_3	NaOAc	100°	Glycol-i-butyrate	41
CH_3	CH_3	$Ca(OH)_2$	—	Aldol (40%), Glycol (10%), glycol isobutyrate (20%), acid (16%)	39
CH_3	CH_3	$Ca(OH)_2$	150°	Isobutyl alcohol (8%), glycol (18%), acid	39
CH_3	C_2H_5	1 N KOH	0–100°	Glycol (40%), acid (21%)	29

This reaction appears to be of limited usefulness as a preparative method. The fact that the ester is sometimes isolated [39, 41] is of interest in connection with the mechanism of the Cannizzaro reaction (p. 97).

Aldehydes with One α-Hydrogen Atom, in the Presence of Formaldehyde. Aldehydes of the type RR′CHCHO may condense with formaldehyde according to the following equation.

$$RR'CHCHO + H_2CO \xrightarrow{OH^-} \underset{R}{\overset{R'}{>}}C\underset{CH_2OH}{\overset{CHO}{<}}$$

The β-hydroxyaldehyde so formed may then undergo a crossed Cannizzaro reaction with formaldehyde to yield a β,β-disubstituted trimethylene glycol.

$$\underset{R}{\overset{R'}{>}}C\underset{CH_2OH}{\overset{CHO}{<}} + H_2CO \xrightarrow{OH^-} \underset{R}{\overset{R'}{>}}C\underset{CH_2OH}{\overset{CH_2OH}{<}} + HCO_2H$$

This reaction has been found to be a useful method of preparing β,β-disubstituted trimethylene glycols. Examples are given in Table II.

Aldehydes with Two α-Hydrogen Atoms, in the Presence of Formaldehyde. Aldehydes of the general type $RC(CH_2OH)_2CHO$ are formed by the condensation of formaldehyde with aldehydes having two α-hydrogen atoms.

$$RCH_2CHO + 2H_2CO \xrightarrow{OH^-} RC(CH_2OH)_2CHO$$

TABLE II

$RR'CHCHO + HCHO \rightarrow RR'C(CH_2OH)_2 + HCOOH$

R	R'	Amount of Aldehyde	HCHO	Base	Product	Yield	Reference
CH_3	CH_3	2 *	1 *	—	$(CH_3)_2C(CH_2OH)_2$	20–40%	42
CH_3	CH_3	1 *	2.08 *	12% alc. KOH	$(CH_3)_2C(CH_2OH)_2$	70%	43
CH_3	C_2H_5	48 g.	32.8 g. †	KOH 23 g.	$(CH_3)(C_2H_5)C(CH_2OH)_2$	77%	44
CH_3	C_3H_7	45 g.	17.9 g. †	KOH 16.8 g.	$(CH_3)(C_3H_7)C(CH_2OH)_2$	84%	44
CH_3	C_6H_5	100 g.	—	—	$(CH_3)(C_6H_5)C(CH_2OH)_2$	81%	44

* Parts by weight.
† Weight of formalin.

In the presence of excess formaldehyde a crossed Cannizzaro reaction ensues, leading to a trimethylol alkane.

$$RC(CH_2OH)_2CHO + H_2CO \xrightarrow{OH^-} RC(CH_2OH)_3 + HCO_2^-$$

In the special case of acetaldehyde the reaction is that used in the well-known method of preparing pentaerythritol.[45]

$$CH_3CHO + 4H_2CO + \tfrac{1}{2}Ca(OH)_2 \rightarrow C(CH_2OH)_4 + (HCO_2)Ca/2$$

Because of the technical importance of pentaerythritol, this reaction has been the subject of considerable investigation. The condensation is best effected by calcium hydroxide[46] in aqueous solution at moderate temperatures (15–90°), using an excess of formaldehyde over the ratio ($4CH_2O : 1CH_3CHO$) required by theory. A ratio of 5 : 1 has been found to give satisfactory yields (73.5%), a smaller proportion of formaldehyde causing the production of considerable amounts of the ether, $[C(CH_2OH)_3CH_2]_2O$.[47] In technical practice an excess of 40–60%

[42] Meyersburg, *Monatsh.*, **26**, 41 (1905).
[43] Fischer and Winter, *Monatsh.*, **21**, 301 (1900).
[44] Franke, *Monatsh.*, **34**, 1904 (1913).
[45] *Org. Syntheses*, Coll. Vol. I, 2nd ed., 425 (1941).
[46] Corbellini and Langini, *Giorn. chim. ind. applicata*, **15**, 53 (1933) [*C. A.*, **27**, 4526 (1933)].
[47] Friederich and Brünn, *Ber.*, **63B**, 2681 (1930).

of the lime required in the above equation generally is used,[48, 49, 50] although less than the stoichiometric amount of the base has been recommended in at least cne instance.[51] The use of promoters such as copper oxalate,[52] formamide,[52] and sugars [53] has been described, as has also the use of quaternary ammonium bases.[54]

The preparation of pentaerythritol in 56% yield on a laboratory scale has been described in *Organic Syntheses*.[45, 48] The modified procedure of Friederich and Brünn [47] gives better yields and is described in the experimental part (p. 111).

Propionaldehyde [55] and isovaleraldehyde [56] have been converted to the corresponding trimethylol derivatives, $CH_3C(CH_2OH)_3$ and $(CH_3)_2CHC(CH_2OH)_3$, by treatment with formalin and calcium hydroxide; although the yields are not specified they appear to be good. Phenylacetaldehyde [56] did not give the expected product.

The only useful Cannizzaro reactions involving the use of aldehydes having one or two α-hydrogen atoms are those already described, in which the aldehyde first undergoes an aldol condensation. The direct dismutation of aldehydes of these types has been carried out successfully only by means of enzyme systems or catalytic metals (p. 95). Such reactions do not represent the true Cannizzaro reaction and as yet have found little practical use. The smooth and practically quantitative dismutation of straight-chain aliphatic aldehydes of four to seven carbon atoms under the influence of the enzymes of hog-liver mash [6] suggests that practical applications of this method may be found.

α,β-**Unsaturated Aldehydes.** α,β-Unsaturated aldehydes do not undergo the normal Cannizzaro reaction, but dismutation of ethylenic aldehydes of this type may be brought about by other reagents, such as aluminum alkoxides, under conditions similar to those of the Tishchenko reaction.[57] The action of aqueous or alcoholic alkalies induces changes of another sort, leading to cleavage or condensation. In the presence of dilute alkali and formaldehyde, acrolein, crotonaldehyde,[47] and cinnamaldehyde [56] give pentaerythritol in good yields. The reaction involves the cleavage of the α,β-unsaturated aldehyde by a reversal of

[48] Backer and Schurink, *Rec. trav. chim.*, **50**, 921 (1931).

[49] T. R. Paterson, U. S. pat., 2,011,589 [*C. A.*, **29**, 6610 (1935)].

[50] T. Sakai, Jap. pat., 94,210 [*C. A.*, **27**, 2697 (1933)].

[51] Deutsche Gold und Silber-Scheideanstalt, Fr. pat., 744,397 [*C. A.*, **27**, 3953 (1933)].

[52] J. A. Wyler, U. S. pat., 2,206,379 [*C. A.*, **34**, 7301 (1940)]; U. S. pat., 2,240,734 [*C. A.*, **35**, 5135 (1941)].

[53] Kusin, *J. Gen. Chem.*, Ser. A, **5**, 1527 (1935) [*Chem. Zentr.*, I, 330 (1937)].

[54] J. A. Wyler, U. S. pat., 2,152,371 [*C. A.*, **33**, 5188 (1939)].

[55] Hasaens, *Ann.*, **276**, 76 (1893).

[56] van Marle and Tollens, *Ber.*, **36**, 1342 (1903).

[57] Endoh, *Rec. trav. chim.*, **44**, 866 (1925).

the aldol condensation, followed by the condensation of formaldehyde with the acetaldehyde so formed (p. 101).

$$CH_3CH{=}CHCHO + H_2O \overset{OH^-}{\rightleftharpoons} 2CH_3CHO \overset{HCHO}{\longrightarrow} C(CH_2OH)_4$$

Aldehydes containing the grouping $-C{\equiv}C{\cdot}CHO$ do not undergo dismutation when treated with alkali but are cleaved readily to yield the corresponding acetylene and formic acid. Propiolaldehyde and phenyl- and methyl-propiolaldehydes are cleaved smoothly in the following way.[58]

$$RC{\equiv}C{\cdot}CHO + NaOH \rightarrow RC{\equiv}CH + HCO_2Na \qquad (R{=}H, CH_3, C_6H_5)$$

Aromatic Aldehydes

The formation of benzoic acid when benzaldehyde is treated with aqueous alkali was first observed by Liebig and Wöhler.[59] Some years later Cannizzaro [60] recognized that benzyl alcohol is formed also. Later studies have shown that aromatic aldehydes which are not diortho-substituted generally react smoothly to give the corresponding aryl carbinols and aromatic acids in good yields. The usefulness of the reaction, which in the past has been employed largely as a route to the alcohol rather than the acid, is somewhat limited in practice by the modern developments in reduction procedures, by means of which an aldehyde may be converted into the desired alcohol with a possible yield of one mole per mole of aldehyde rather than the one-half mole attainable by the use of the Cannizzaro reaction. The crossed Cannizzaro reaction, in which the aldehyde is reduced not by another molecule of its kind but by one of formaldehyde, is, however, also capable of yielding the alcohol in amounts approaching one mole per mole of aldehyde, and is applicable to a wide variety of compounds.

The Cannizzaro and crossed Cannizzaro reactions can be carried out with a minimum expenditure of time and do not require elaborate equipment or special reagents. For the convenient reduction of an aldehyde which is inexpensive and readily obtainable, these procedures, especially the latter, are particularly suitable. Indeed, the reservation regarding cost and availability scarcely applies to the crossed reaction since it is convenient and affords excellent yields.

Monosubstituted Benzaldehydes (Table III). The smooth dismutation of monosubstituted benzaldehydes carrying non-functioning groups to give the corresponding benzyl alcohols and benzoic acids is a general

[58] Claisen, *Ber.*, **31**, 1023 (1898); **36**, 3664 (1903); **44**, 1166 (1911).
[59] Liebig and Wöhler, *Ann.*, **3**, 252 (1832).
[60] Cannizzaro, *Ann.*, **88**, 129 (1853).

reaction having no serious limitations. When the substituent is a functional group the Cannizzaro reaction proceeds normally except in a few special cases, namely, o- and p-hydroxybenzaldehyde and p-dimethylaminobenzaldehyde. It is probable that o- and p-amino- and alkylamino-benzaldehydes would also fail to undergo normal dismutation, but examples have not been described. It has been reported [61] that m-dimethylaminobenzaldehyde is unaffected by strong aqueous alkali.

TABLE III

$$2X \cdot C_6H_4 \cdot CHO + OH^- \rightarrow X \cdot C_6H_4 \cdot CH_2OH + X \cdot C_6H_4 \cdot COO^-$$

X=	Alkali *	Yield of		Reference
		$X \cdot C_6H_4CH_2OH$	$X \cdot C_6H_4COOH$	
4-CH₃	Alc. KOH	—	—	62
4-i-C₃H₇	Conc. alc. KOH	—	—	63
2-OCH₃	25% alc. KOH	—	—	64
2-OCH₃	Conc. KOH	—	76%	65
3-OCH₃	25% alc. KOH	—	—	64
4-OCH₃	25% alc. KOH	—	—	64
3-OCH₃	Conc. alc. KOH	—	94%	66
3-OH	50% KOH	90%	90%	67
3-Cl	50% KOH	92–97%	88%	68
3-Br	50% KOH	89%	90%	68
2-I	50% alc. KOH	90%	87.5%	68
4-I	50% alc. KOH	81%	84%	68
2-NO₂	35% NaOH	91%	91%	68
3-NO₂	35% NaOH	90%	90%	68
3-NO₂	14% KOH	—	—	69, 70
4-NO₂	15% NaOH	—	—	71
4-NO₂	35% NaOH	96%	90%	68

* Aqueous unless otherwise stated.

[61] Cocker, Harris, and Loach, *J. Chem. Soc.*, **1938, 751**.
[62] Cannizzaro, *Ann.*, **124**, 255 (1862).
[63] Kraut, *Ann.*, **92**, 66 (1854).
[64] Späth, *Monatsh.*, **34**, 1996 (1913).
[65] Stoermer, *Ber.*, **44**, 1850 (1911).
[66] Pschorr, *Ann.*, **391**, 43 (1912).
[67] Lock, *Ber.*, **62**, 1177 (1929).
[68] Lock, *Ber.*, **63**, 855 (1930).
[69] Becker, *Ber.*, **15**, 2090 (1882).
[70] Lock, *Ber.*, **66**, 1527 (1933).
[71] Basler, *Ber.*, **16**, 275 (1883).

Since it is highly probable that the Cannizzaro reaction proceeds by way of a step common to many addition reactions of the carbonyl group, namely, an initial attack upon the carbonyl carbon atom by a nucleophilic reagent (for example, a strong base), the failure of o- and p-hydroxybenzaldehydes to undergo dismutation is readily explicable. In the presence of alkali the anionic oxygen formed by ionization of the phenolic hydroxyl group could, by virtue of its strongly basic nature, contribute to the resonance structure:

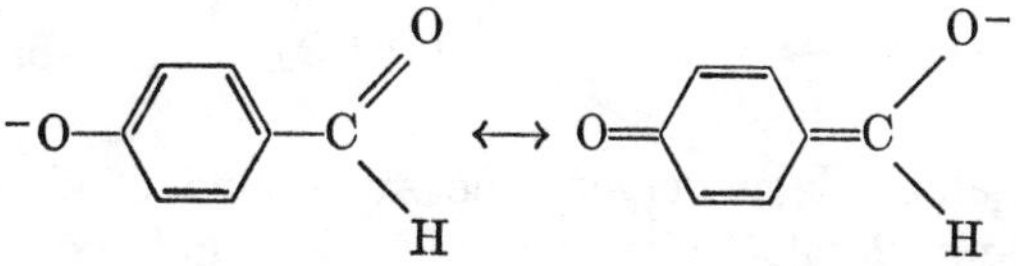

The effect may be considered a competition between one base (anionic oxygen) acting intramolecularly and another (hydroxyl ion) acting intermolecularly. The failure of p-dimethylaminobenzaldehyde to react can be ascribed to a similar contribution of an electron pair from the basic dimethylamino grouping. If the hydrogen atom of the hydroxyl group in o- or p-hydroxybenzaldehyde is replaced by a methyl group, then the Cannizzaro reaction can be effected. m-Hydroxybenzaldehyde reacts normally to give good yields of the dismutation products. There is no obvious explanation for the failure of m-dimethylaminobenzaldehyde to undergo the reaction.

All the nitrobenzaldehydes undergo normal dismutation under proper conditions. In general they require less concentrated alkali (15–35%) than most other aldehydes (50%) and more careful control of the temperature. Stronger alkali and higher temperatures lead to decreased yields of products difficult to purify and to the formation of side products such as azobenzenecarboxylic acids.[68]

An aldehyde which carries substituents sensitive to alkali may undergo other changes involving these groups. An example is found in o-acetylaminobenzaldehyde, which undergoes an intramolecular condensation leading to 2-hydroxyquinoline.[72]

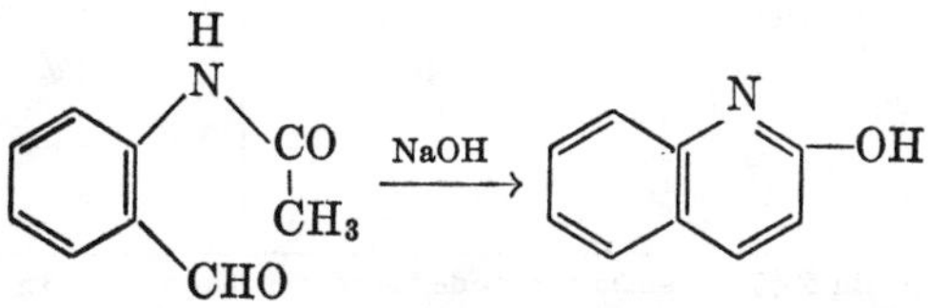

Disubstituted Benzaldehydes (Table IV). Benzaldehyde derivatives carrying two other substituents in the ring dismutate normally when at

[72] Camps, *Arch. Pharm.*, **237**, 682 (1899).

least one *ortho* position is open, except 2,4-dinitrobenzaldehyde and those compounds in which one of the substituents is a hydroxyl group *ortho* or *para* to the formyl group (see p. 104). When both *ortho* positions are filled with halogen or nitro groups the reaction of the aldehyde with alkali takes a different course; the formyl group is removed as formic acid and is replaced by a hydrogen atom.

$$X\text{-}C_6H_3(X)\text{-}CHO + OH^- \rightarrow X\text{-}C_6H_4\text{-}X + HCO_2^- \qquad (X=Br, Cl, I, NO_2)$$

2,4-Dinitrobenzaldehyde undergoes the same kind of change, but 2-nitro-4-halo- and 2-halo-4-nitrobenzaldehydes undergo normal dismutation. A free hydroxyl group *ortho* or *para* to the formyl group interferes with both the cleavage and the dismutation reactions. The effect of two *ortho* alkyl groups is not recorded. Examples of the cleavage

TABLE IV

$$X \cdot Y \cdot C_6H_3 \cdot CHO + OH^- \rightarrow X \cdot Y \cdot C_6H_3CH_2OH + X \cdot Y \cdot C_6H_3COO^-$$

X	Y	Yield of		Reference
		Alcohol	Acid	
2-Cl	5-Cl	90%	84%	70
3-Cl	5-Cl	90%	90%	73
3-OMe	5-OMe	88%	88%	73
2-I	3-OH	80%	80%	74
2-Cl	3-OMe	80%	80%	75
2-Br	5-OH	70%	80%	67
3-OH	4-OMe	86%	80%	67
2-NO$_2$	5-OH	70%	—	67
3-OH	4-OH	0 *	0 *	67
2-Cl	3-OH	87%	96%	76
3-OH	4-NO$_2$	39%	97%	67
3,4-Benzo(β-naphthaldehyde)	—	80%	82%	77

* After treatment with 50% potassium hydroxide for twenty-four hours, 95% of the aldehyde was recovered.

[73] Lock and Nottes, *Monatsh.*, **68**, 51 (1936).
[74] Lock and Nottes, *Monatsh.*, **67**, 320 (1936).
[75] Lock and Hoseaus, *Monatsh.*, **62**, 178 (1933).
[76] Lock and Hoseaus, *Monatsh.*, **55**, 307 (1930).
[77] Sah, *Rec. trav. chim.*, **59**, 461 (1940).

reaction for 2,6-dihalo-, 2,6-dinitro-, and 2,4-dinitro-benzaldehydes are not tabulated but may be found in the articles referred to in Table IV.

Tri- and Tetra-Substituted Benzaldehydes. No important deviation from the limitations discussed above are to be noted when further substituents are present, provided that at least one position *ortho* to the formyl group is open. When an *ortho* or *para* hydroxyl group is present neither dismutation nor cleavage occurs under the usual conditions of the reaction. An *ortho*-amino group acts similarly; 2,5-dichloro-6-aminobenzaldehyde was recovered after treatment with 50% KOH at 100° for four hours.[78]

Groups other than halogen or nitro in the two *ortho* positions also can influence the mode of reaction. For example, while opianic acid can be transformed in good yield into hemipinic acid and meconine,[79] pseudo-opianic acid loses the formyl group under the influence of strong alkali.[80]

CHO ⎯COOH OH⁻ ⟶ CH_2—O CO + COOH ⎯COOH

Opianic acid   Meconine   Hemipinic acid

(with OCH_3 substituents as shown)

COOH CHO OCH_3 OCH_3 OH⁻ ⟶ COOH OCH_3 OCH_3 + HCO_2^-

Pseudoöpianic acid

The reaction of hydrastinine with alkali is of special interest, since it leads to oxyhydrastinine and hydrohydrastinine.[81]

Hydrastinine OH⁻ ⟶ Oxyhydrastinine + Hydrohydrastinine

[78] Lock, *Ber.*, **68**, 1505 (1935).
[79] Beckett and Wright, *J. Chem. Soc.*, **29**, 281 (1876).
[80] Perkin, Jr., *J. Chem. Soc.*, **57**, 1054 (1890).
[81] McGeoch and Stevens, *J. Chem. Soc.*, **1934**, 1465.

Hydrohydrastinine does not arise by ring closure of the corresponding alcohol during the reaction, since the alcohol is stable to alkali under the conditions of the reaction. Further examples of the Cannizzaro reaction for polysubstituted benzaldehydes are given in Table V.

TABLE V

POLYSUBSTITUTED BENZALDEHYDES

Substituents	Yield of		Conditions	Reference
	Acid	Alcohol		
2,4-diBr-5-OCH₃	90%	95%	50% KOH; 60–70°; 4–5 hr.	75
2-Cl-3-OH-5-Br	80%	85%	50% KOH; 60–70°; 4–5 hr.	75
2-Cl-3-OCH₃-5-Br	90%	90%	50% KOH; 100°; 5 hr.	75
2-Br-3-OH-4-OCH₃	86%	80%	50% KOH; 100°; 30 hr.	82
2-Br-3,4-diOCH₃	92%	73%	50% KOH; 100°; 15 hr.	82
2-Br-3,5-diOCH₃	85%	90%	50% KOH; 100°; 8 hr.	82
2-Cl-3,5-diOCH₃	87%	90%	50% KOH; 100°; 3 hr.	73

Aldehydes which are cleaved under the conditions of the reaction have been omitted, but pertinent references may be found in the literature cited.

Heterocyclic Aldehydes

The Cannizzaro reaction of heterocyclic aldehydes has been examined in a few cases only. Furfural,[83] α-thiophenealdehyde,[84] and α-pyridylaldehyde [85] undergo the reaction normally to give the expected products. 3-Formyl-1,2,5,6-tetrahydro-1-ethylpyridine resinifies upon treatment with potassium hydroxide,[86] a behavior consistent with the observation that it is structurally similar to an α,β-unsaturated alicyclic aldehyde. 3,4-Dibromothiophene-2,5-dialdehyde undergoes a complex series of reactions, involving both cleavage (loss of —CHO) and dismutation, when treated with alkali.[87] Of particular interest in this connection is the fact that under certain conditions the ester composed of the usual

[82] Lock, Monatsh., 64, 341 (1934).
[83] Org. Syntheses, Coll. Vol. I, 2nd ed., 276 (1941).
[84] Biedermann, Ber., 19, 636 (1886).
[85] Harries and Lenart, Ann., 410, 107 (1915).
[86] Wohl and Losanitsch, Ber., 38, 4170 (1906).
[87] Steinkopf and Eger, Ann., 533, 270 (1938).

dismutation products could be isolated. α-Pyrrolaldehyde appears to be stable to alkali.[88]

The Crossed Cannizzaro Reaction

Examples of this reaction have long been known, and several have been discussed above (pp. 99–102). Applications of the method to aldehydes of the aromatic series have been reported more recently. Nenitzescu and Gavât [89] observed that equimolal mixtures of benzaldehyde or anisaldehyde with formaldehyde led to the formation of both possible acids and alcohols, and that if formaldehyde was present in large excess the aromatic alcohol, and little of the corresponding acid, was formed. The procedure may therefore be looked upon as a method for reducing aromatic aldehydes. Davidson and Bogert [90] have worked out experimental conditions for carrying out the reduction of aldehydes by this means to give 85–90% yields of the alcohols.

Studies of the crossed Cannizzaro reaction have not embraced so wide a variety of structural modifications as the examples discussed above in connection with the normal dismutation. There is reason to believe,

TABLE VI

$$RCHO + H_2CO \xrightarrow{OH^-} RCH_2OH + HCOO^-$$

Aldehyde	Yield of Alcohol	Reference
Veratraldehyde	85–90%	90
Piperonaldehyde	85–90%	90
Anisaldehyde	85–90%	89, 90
Opianic acid	70–90%	91
Phthaldehydic acid	70–90%	91
Anisaldehyde	70–90%	91
Furfuraldehyde	70–90%	91
m-Nitrobenzaldehyde	—	89
p-Isopropylbenzaldehyde	42%	92
p-Phenylbenzaldehyde	—	93

[88] Fischer, Beller, and Stern, *Ber.*, **61**, 1074 (1928).

[89] Nenitzescu and Gavât, *Bul. Soc. Chim. România*, **16A**, 42 (1934) [*C. A.*, **30**, 5572 (1936)].

[90] Davidson and Bogert, *J. Am. Chem. Soc.*, **57**, 905 (1935).

[91] Rodinor and Fedorova, *J. Gen. Chem. U.S.S.R.*, **7**, 947 (1937) [*C. A.*, **31**, 5338 (1937)].

[92] Cooke, Gillespie, and Macbeth, *J. Chem. Soc.*, **1938**, 1825.

[93] Koelsch and Geissman, unpublished observation.

however, that certain of the influences of structure upon the course of the reaction will operate in the crossed reaction as well.

EXPERIMENTAL CONDITIONS

Concentration of Alkali

For aromatic aldehydes, 50% alkali (sodium or potassium hydroxide) is most generally used, except for nitrobenzaldehydes, where 15–35% alkali is sufficient to bring about the reaction and to control it so as to reduce the extent to which side products are formed. The use of less than about 50% alkali usually prolongs the time of the reaction and, since the products are not sensitive to the action of caustic, offers no advantages. Alcoholic potassium hydroxide (about 25%) has been employed with success for the dismutation of methoxybenzaldehydes but appears to offer no particular advantages since o-methoxybenzaldehyde is converted into the alcohol in excellent yield by the action of concentrated aqueous potassium hydroxide. Alcoholic alkali may be preferred for difficultly soluble aldehydes.

Solvents

Except as noted above, aqueous alkali alone is usually a sufficient solvent (or diluent); vigorous shaking to form an emulsion of the aldehyde in the caustic solution is recommended. The use of alcohol or other solvent inert to the alkali may aid either in solution or dispersion of the aldehyde and is sometimes advantageous. The crossed Cannizzaro reaction is carried out in methyl alcoholic solution.

Temperature

Often a spontaneous rise in temperature is observed when the aldehyde and alkali are shaken together. This may be moderated by cooling under the tap; careful temperature control is seldom necessary. With aldehydes which react slowly the reaction mixture may be heated on the water bath until the reaction is complete (as noted by the disappearance of the characteristic aldehyde odor).

Nitrobenzaldehydes react vigorously with 35% alkali, and if the temperature is not controlled the reaction may proceed past the initial stage and lead to the formation of the corresponding nitrobenzoic acid and azobenzene carboxylic acid, none of the nitrobenzyl alcohol being obtained. At 45°, yields of the normal dismutation products are excellent.

EXPERIMENTAL PROCEDURES

The Cannizzaro reaction with benzaldehyde is described in a number of manuals of organic laboratory practice. The preparation of penta-erythritol (p. 101) and the conversion of furfural into furfuryl alcohol and furoic acid are described in *Organic Syntheses*.[33] Below are a few typical examples of the reaction covering a number of the modifications discussed in the foregoing pages.

2-Methyl-2-ethylpropane-1,3-diol.[42] To a mixture of 46 g. of methyl-ethylacetaldehyde and 82 g. of formalin (40%) is added with cooling a 12% alcoholic solution of potassium hydroxide containing 23 g. of potassium hydroxide. After twelve hours the excess alkali is neutralized by passing in carbon dioxide, and most of the alcohol is removed by dis-tillation. The aqueous residue is extracted thoroughly with ether, and after removal of the ether the product is distilled. The yield of the glycol, b.p. 218–220°, is nearly the theoretical amount. It melts at 42°.

Isobutylene Glycol and α-Hydroxybutyric Acid.[37] To 16.3 g. of α-hydroxyisobutyraldehyde is added dropwise 40 cc. of 10% aqueous sodium hydroxide. The resulting solution is warmed on the water bath to complete the reaction, cooled, and extracted with ether. Removal of the ether leaves the glycol as a honey-colored oil which is purified by dis-tillation (b.p. 177–179°).

The alkaline solution remaining after extraction of the glycol is acidi-fied and extracted with ether. The ether is removed, leaving the acid as a crystalline residue (6.7 g.; 70%). After purification of the acid by dis-tillation it melts at 80° (corr.).

The same products are obtained if α-bromoisobutyraldehyde (31 g.) is used, a preliminary treatment with 87.3 cc. of 10% NaOH in the cold being followed by further treatment with 40 cc. of 10% NaOH as described above.

Pentaerythritol.[47] To a mixture of 18.5 g. of calcium hydroxide and 75 g. of formaldehyde in 500 cc. of water is slowly added 22 g. of acetalde-hyde. The temperature of the mixture is maintained at 15° during the addition of the acetaldehyde and then gradually raised to 45°. The calcium is precipitated with oxalic acid, the calcium oxalate removed by filtration, and the filtrate evaporated to dryness under reduced pressure. The residue is taken up in 200 cc. of hot ethanol, and the resulting solu-tion allowed to cool. The pentaerythritol which separates weighs 50 g. (73.5% of the theoretical amount) and melts at 258°. Pure penta-erythritol melts at 260°.[45]

m-**Hydroxybenzyl Alcohol and *m*-Hydroxybenzoic Acid.**[67] To a solu-tion of 25 g. of sodium hydroxide in 25 cc. of water is added 12.2 g. of *m*-hydroxybenzaldehyde. The aldehyde dissolves slowly, and the mixture becomes warm; the mixture is warmed to 50–60°, and rapid solution of the aldehyde takes place. After one hour at 50–60° the solution is acidified with dilute hydrochloric acid, saturated with sodium bicarbonate, and extracted with ether. From the ether solution is obtained 5.8 g. (93.6%) of *m*-hydroxybenzyl alcohol, m.p. 68°; after one recrystallization from benzene the m.p. is 73° (corr.).

The residual solution is acidified and extracted with ether; removal of the ether and recrystallization of the residue from water affords 6.5 g. (94.2%) of *m*-hydroxybenzoic acid, m.p. 202° (corr.).

_m_-Bromobenzyl Alcohol and _m_-Bromobenzoic Acid.[68] The following procedure is applicable to monohalogen-substituted benzaldehydes in general:

m-Bromobenzaldehyde is added slowly to an excess (5–7 moles) of 50% aqueous potassium hydroxide, the mixture warming slightly. After all the aldehyde has been added the mixture is warmed on the water bath until the aldehyde odor has disappeared (one hour). With certain halobenzaldehydes the addition of a small amount of ethanol hastens the reaction. After dilution of the reaction mixture with water the *m*-bromobenzyl alcohol is extracted with ether. Removal of the ether and distillation of the product yields 89% of the alcohol, b.p. 128°/10 mm. The alkaline solution is acidified and the *m*-bromobenzoic acid collected. The yield of acid (m.p. 155°) is 96%.

_o_-Methoxybenzyl Alcohol.[65] A mixture of 140 g. of *o*-methoxybenzaldehyde with a solution of 126 g. of potassium hydroxide in 60 g. of water is shaken until a stable emulsion has formed. The temperature rise which occurs on shaking the mixture is moderated by cooling in running water. After standing at 30° for two days the mixture is diluted with much water and the product is extracted with ether. Any unchanged aldehyde is removed by washing the ether solution with sodium bisulfite solution, and, after drying, the ether is removed, and the product is distilled. The yield of *o*-methoxybenzyl alcohol boiling at 245–255° (or 119°/8 mm.) is 54 g. (cf. Späth, reference 64).

_o_-Nitrobenzyl Alcohol and _o_-Nitrobenzoic Acid.[68] To 30.2 g. of *o*-nitrobenzaldehyde is added in one portion 60 g. of 35% aqueous sodium hydroxide solution. After the mixture has been shaken for a short time it becomes more fluid but then solidifies completely at a time when the temperature has reached 45°. At this point the mixture is diluted with much water and yields *o*-nitrobenzyl alcohol upon extraction with ether. The yield of pure material, m.p. 74° after one recrystallization from 50% alcohol, is 13.9 g. (91%). Acidification of the alkaline solution after removal of the *o*-nitrobenzyl alcohol yields *o*-nitrobenzoic acid. The yield of pure acid, m.p. 146° after recrystallization from water, is 15.2 g. (96%).

A similar procedure is followed with the *m*- and *p*-nitrobenzaldehydes, comparable yields being obtained.

The Crossed Cannizzaro Reaction.[90,] *   Into a 2-l. three-necked flask fitted with a dropping funnel, mercury-sealed stirrer, and reflux condenser are introduced one mole of the aromatic aldehyde, 700 cc. of methanol, and 100 cc. (1.3 moles) of formalin. The solution is heated to 65°, and the flask is surrounded by cold water while a solution of 120 g. of sodium hydroxide or 168 g. (3 moles) of potassium hydroxide in 120 cc. of water is added rapidly, the temperature being maintained at 65–75°. The mixture is then heated at 75° for forty minutes and finally refluxed for twenty minutes. The solution is cooled, diluted with 300 cc. of water, the oily layer separated, and the aqueous layer extracted with four 150-cc. portions of benzene. The combined oil and benzene extracts are dried, the benzene removed, and the product distilled under reduced pressure. The yields are 85–95%.

Acidification of the alkaline solution yields 2–5% of the aromatic acid.

* The preparation of *p*-tolyl carbinol by the crossed Cannizzaro reaction is described in *Organic Syntheses, Coll. Vol.* **2**, 590 (1943).

CHAPTER 4

THE FORMATION OF CYCLIC KETONES BY INTRAMOLECULAR ACYLATION

William S. Johnson

The University of Wisconsin

CONTENTS

INTRODUCTION

The cyclizations of γ-phenylbutyric acid (I) to tetralone-1 (II) and of β-phenylpropionic acid (III) to hydrindone-1 (IV) exemplify a type of intramolecular acylation which has served as an important tool in the synthesis of polycyclic hydroaromatic and aromatic compounds.[1, 2, 3]

Such ring closures have been effected by a variety of methods generally involving either the direct cyclodehydration of the acids or the cyclodehydrohalogenation of the acid chlorides by an intramolecular Friedel-

[1] Linstead, *Ann. Repts. Chem. Soc.*, **33**, 336 (1936).

[2] Springall, *Ann. Repts. Chem. Soc.*, **36**, 301 (1939).

[3] Fieser, "Chemistry of Natural Products Related to Phenanthrene," 2nd ed., Reinhold Publishing Corp., 1937.

Crafts reaction.[4] This chapter presents a discussion of these methods and the various problems involved in the formation of cyclic ketones by the ring closure of aryl-substituted aliphatic acids.[4a]

The structural aspects which determine the inherent capability of these acids to undergo ring closure, and which consequently control the course of the cyclization, are: (a) the size of the ring formed; (b) the reactivity of the aromatic nucleus, including the effect of substituent groups; (c) steric considerations other than ring size.

In addition, the reagent and reaction conditions are sometimes critical and may have an extrinsic and secondary effect on the course of ring closure.

THE SIZE OF THE RING

In a study of the fundamental structural problems involved in ring closure by intramolecular acylation, v. Braun and his collaborators found that the susceptibility of an acid to cyclization depends upon the size of the ring to be formed. The tendency toward formation of rings of various sizes is as follows: six > five > seven > others. This order may not be preserved unless comparisons are made on ring closures into nuclei which are similarly activated.

The fact that *six-membered rings are formed in preference to five-membered ones* was demonstrated by the cyclization of α-benzyl-γ-phenylbutyric acid (V) to 2-benzyltetralone-1 (VI).[5, 6]

---

[4] Thomas, "Anhydrous Aluminum Chloride in Organic Chemistry," pp. 394–428, Reinhold Publishing Corp., 1941.

[4a] Formation of anthraquinones from o-benzoylbenzoic acids, of anthrones and anthranols from o-benzylbenzoic acids, of fluorenones from o-carboxybiphenyls, of naphthols from γ-phenylcrotonic acids, or of indones from allo-cinnamic acids represents analogous reactions which are not discussed in this chapter. Acids containing nitrogen, oxygen, or sulfur in the side chain, leading to heterocyclic ketones on cyclization, also are not considered in this chapter; a treatment of this subject may be found elsewhere (reference 4). Ring closure into a non-aromatic nucleus containing an ethylenic bond has been applied successfully but is not within the scope of this chapter; this reaction has been covered by reviews through 1939 (references 1 and 2).

[5] v. Braun, *Ber.*, **61**, 441 (1928).

[6] Leuchs, *Ber.*, **61**, 144 (1928).

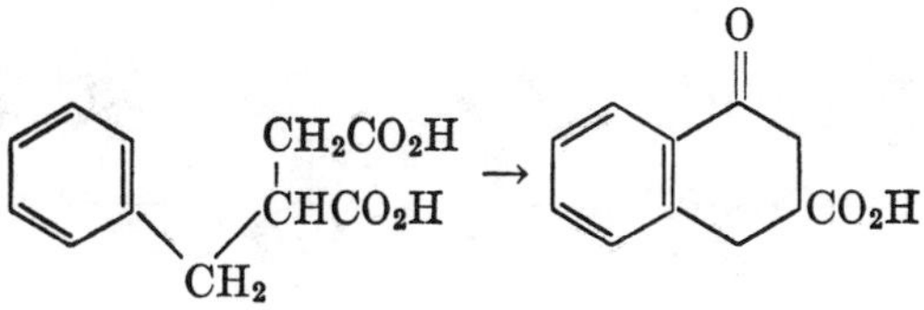

VII → VIII

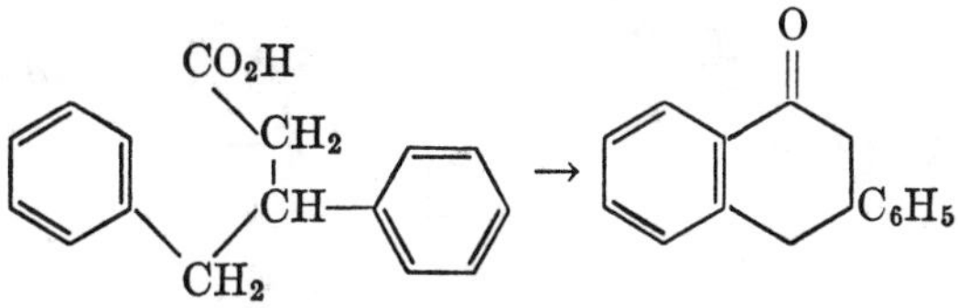

IX → X

None of the isomeric hydrindone was obtained. Further substantiation was found in the conversion of benzylsuccinic acid (VII) into 3-carboxytetralone-1 (VIII) as the only product of cyclization which could be isolated.[5] β,γ-Diphenylbutyric acid (IX), which has the structural possibility of cyclizing to 3-benzylhydrindone-1, gave only the product (X) of six-membered ring closure.[7] In all cases the cyclizations were accomplished by the Friedel-Crafts method (p. 130), and the structures of the resulting ketones were proved. This preference regarding ring size is illustrated also by the cyclization of β,β'-diphenyladipic acid to a chrysene derivative,[8] and by the formation of 3-carboxy-4-phenyltetralone-1 upon ring closure of diphenylmethylsuccinic acid.[9]

Cyclization to form a *five- rather than a seven-membered ring* is always realized provided that both modes of ring closure are subject to the same intrinsic cyclizing influence. This predilection for five-ring formation was inferred from the observation [10] that benzosuberone (XII) was obtained repeatedly in yields of approximately 20% from δ-phenylvaleric acid (XI), under the same conditions with which hydrindone-1 and also tetralone-1 were prepared in 70–80% yields.

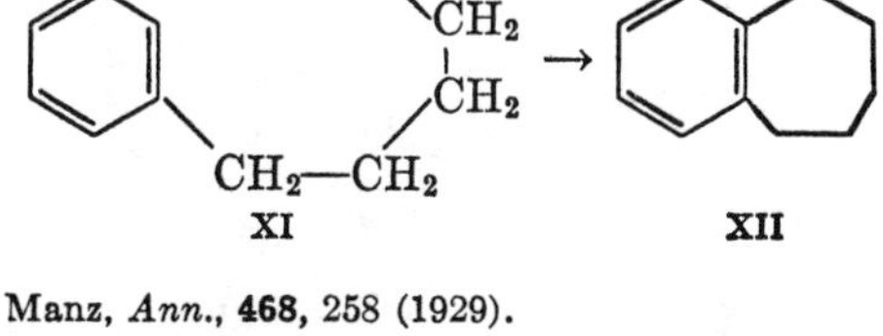

XI → XII

[7] v. Braun and Manz, *Ann.*, **468**, 258 (1929).
[8] v. Braun and Irmisch, *Ber.*, **64**, 2461 (1931).
[9] Hewett, *J. Chem. Soc.*, **1936**, 596.
[10] v. Braun and Rath, *Ber.*, **60**, 1182 (1927).

Proof of the premise was found in the cyclization [7] of α-benzyl-δ-phenyl-valeric acid (XIII) and of α-benzylglutaric acid (XV) which gave the hydrindone derivatives XIV and XVI, respectively, and none of the isomeric benzosuberones. The formation of 4-phenylhydrindone-1 from β-2-biphenylpropionic acid afforded further substantiation, since the acid has the structural possibility of cyclizing to a seven-membered ring ketone.

The formation of a *six-* *in preference to a seven-membered ring* follows as a corollary from the above considerations. Experimental foundation, moreover, was afforded by examination of the ring closure of β-benzyl-adipic acid (XVII), which was found to yield only the tetralone deriva-tive XVIII.[11]

No examples have been found in which either an eight-membered ring or a four- or three-membered ring has been formed by intramolecular acylation. The failure of phenylacetyl chloride and benzoyl chloride to cyclize under the conditions of the Friedel-Crafts reaction has been reported.[12]

INFLUENCE OF THE REACTIVITY OF THE AROMATIC NUCLEUS

Ortho and *Para* Directing Groups. In general the common rules of orientation regarding intermolecular acylation can be extended to the

[11] v. Braun, Bayer, and Cassel, *Ber.*, **60,** 2602 (1927).
[12] Wedekind, *Ann.*, **323**, 246 (1902).

intramolecular reaction.   Thus as *ortho* and *para* directing groups enhance intermolecular acylation, so ring closures are preferably directed to one of these positions rather than into an unsubstituted nucleus. This has been substantiated [13] in the ring closure of β-*m*-tolylhydrocinnamic acid (XIX).   The product of reaction, obtained in 60% yield, consisted solely of 5-methyl-3-phenylhydrindone-1 (XX), arising from acylation *para* to the methyl group.   No material was found which corresponded to cyclization into the unsubstituted nucleus.   A similar result was observed in the ring closure of α-benzyl-β-*m*-tolylpropionic acid (XXI).   The hydrindone XXII, formed in 75% yield by substitution at the *para* position to the methyl group, was the only ketone encountered.

The powerful activating influence of the methoxyl group is indicated by the fact that γ-*m*-methoxyphenylbutyric acid (LIII, p. 125) can be cyclized under the mildest conditions in 96% yield.[14]   In the cyclization of γ-5-methoxy-1-naphthylbutyric acid (formula XCIV, p. 175), the course of the ring closure seemed to depend somewhat upon the reagent and conditions of the reaction, but the formation of the seven-membered ring ketone XCIII was definitely favored over the production of the phenanthrene derivative XCV.   The activating influence of the methoxyl group, therefore, seemed to offset in part the preference for the formation of a six-membered ring.

Cyclizations *meta* to an *ortho, para* directing substituent are known. For example, the 7-substituted tetralones XXIV were prepared [15] from the corresponding arylbutyric acids XXIII.

[13] v. Braun, Manz, and Reinsch, *Ann.*, **468**, 277 (1929).
[14] Bachmann and Thomas, *J. Am. Chem. Soc.*, **64**, 94 (1942).
[15] Krollpfeiffer and Schäfer, *Ber.*, **56**, 620 (1923).

$$R = CH_3, C_2H_5, OCH_3 \quad R = CH_3, C_2H_5, OCH_3$$

$$\text{XXIII} \qquad\qquad \text{XXIV}$$

Although there seems to be some question in regard to the influence exerted by an alkyl group thus situated,[15a] a more powerful directing substituent, such as the methoxyl group, appears to have a definite deactivating effect. Thus while γ-phenylbutyric acid (I) was cyclized by hydrogen fluoride (p. 157) to the extent of 92%,[16] the p-methoxy derivative XXIII (R = OCH$_3$) was converted by the same treatment to 7-methoxytetralone-1 (XXIV, R = OCH$_3$) in only 61.5% yield.[17] Similarly β-phenylpropionic acid (III) was cyclized by hydrogen fluoride in 73% yield,[16] while under the same conditions, ring closure of the p-methoxy derivative LXXXI (p. 157) took place only to the extent of 3%.[18] In addition, the comparison of yields is consistent with the premise that a six-membered ring is formed more readily than a five-membered one.

Meta **Directing Groups.** It is well known that groups which direct entering substituents to the *meta* position exert an inhibitory influence on intermolecular acylation. The common use of nitrobenzene as a solvent in the Friedel-Crafts reaction is made possible by the deactivating effect of the nitro group. The intramolecular reaction is similarly restrained by the presence of substituents which give *meta* orientation. Although β-o-nitrophenylpropionyl chloride (XXV) has been cyclized successfully with aluminum chloride to the hydrindone XXVI in 73% yield,[19] the p-nitro isomer failed to cyclize.[20]

[15a] The work of v. Braun and coworkers (reference 13) seemed to show that cyclization took place into an unsubstituted benzene nucleus rather than into the position *meta* to a methyl substituent. More recent work [Pfeiffer and Roos, *J. prakt. Chem.*, **159**, 13 (1941)] has shown, however, that some of v. Braun's assumptions are in error, and in at least one case opposite conclusions regarding the direction of cyclization were reached by sound methods.

[16] Fieser and Hershberg, *J. Am. Chem. Soc.*, **61**, 1272 (1939).

[17] Campbell and Todd, *J. Am. Chem. Soc.*, **64**, 928 (1942).

[18] Johnson and Shelberg, unpublished observation.

[19] Hoyer, *J prakt. Chem.*, **139**, 94 (1934).

[20] Ingold and Piggott, *J. Chem. Soc.*, **1923**, 1469.

XXV   XXVI

The product, which consisted mainly of starting material, contained, surprisingly, a small amount of β-p-nitrophenylpropionaldehyde (yield 15%). The resistance of some other acids to ring closure because of the presence of the nitro group has been recorded.[21] The carbonyl group seems to have less influence than the nitro group in hindering intramolecular acylation. Thus cyclization of the acid chloride of γ-phenylpimelic acid (XXVII) by the Friedel-Crafts method (p. 130) gave two products: the tetralonepropionic acid XXVIII and the diketone XXIX.[22, 23] The latter evidently arises from the cyclization of XXVIII, which involves acylation *meta* to the carbonyl group.

XXVII   XXVIII   XXIX

In the cyclization of β-phenyladipic acid (XXX), the main product was the keto acid XXXI, although a small amount of the diketone XXXII was produced.

XXX   XXXI   XXXII

[21] Gagnon and Hudon, *Trans. Roy. Soc. Canada*, III, **33**, 37 (1939) [*C. A.*, **34, 2837** (1940)].

[22] v. Braun and Weissbach, *Ber.*, **64**, 1785 (1931).

[23] Manske, *J. Am. Chem. Soc.*, **53**, 1104 (1931).

Examples of intramolecular acylation *ortho* to a carbonyl group are well known in the cyclization of *o*-benzoylbenzoic acids to anthraquinones. It is noteworthy that this type of ring closure requires more drastic cyclizing conditions than are necessary for the usual type of intramolecular acylation.

Polycyclic Nuclei. In general, arylpropionic and arylbutyric acids in which the aryl group is a polycyclic aromatic nucleus cyclize readily. Cyclization into the α-position of the naphthalene nucleus, for example, takes place more easily than into the benzene ring. The ring closure of the substituted naphthylpropionic acids XXXIII and XXXV proceeded smoothly.

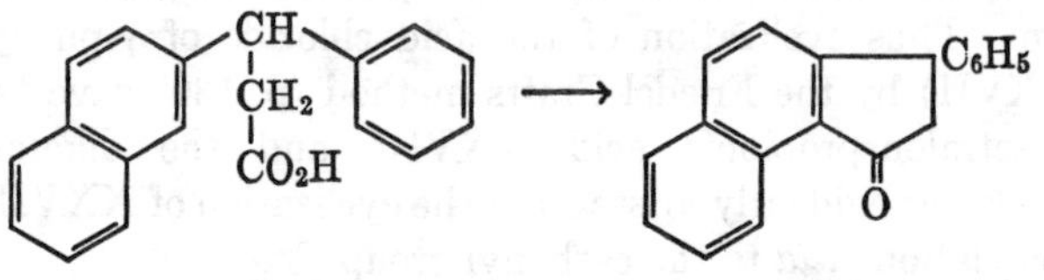

XXXIII   XXXIV

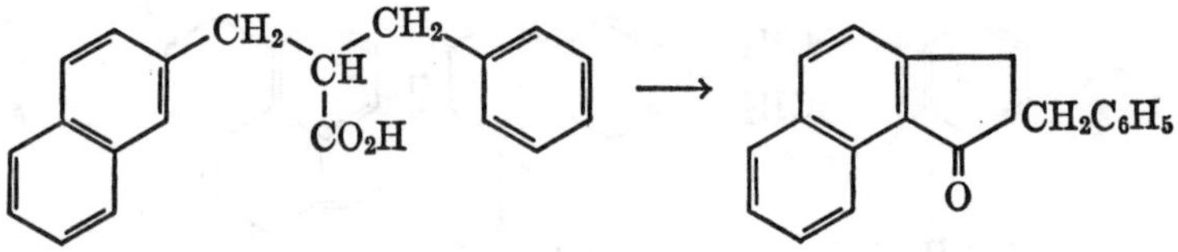

XXXV   XXXVI

The products, formed in yields above 70%, were the benzhydrindones XXXIV and XXXVI, respectively.[13] None of the isomeric ketones was found.

STERIC FACTORS OTHER THAN RING SIZE

The extraordinary difficulty experienced in preparing 5-methoxy-8-phenyltetralone-1 (XXXVIII) from γ-(4-methoxy-3-biphenyl)-butyric acid (XXXVII) possibly may be explained by the hindering effect of the phenyl substituent *ortho* to the point of ring closure. The necessity of the acylation occurring *meta* to the methoxyl group does not seem to account fully for the behavior because γ-*o*-methoxyphenylbutyric acid has been cyclized to 5-methoxytetralone-1 in fair yield[24] and other ring closures *meta* to the methoxyl group are known.[15, 25] Although XXXVII has been cyclized by means of hydrogen fluoride, the yield was very low.[16]

[24] Lockett and Short, *J. Chem. Soc.*, **1939**, 787.
[25] R. D. Haworth and Sheldrick, *J. Chem. Soc.*, **1934**, 1950.

Some of the other conventional methods of ring closure, moreover, failed to give any of the ketone XXXVIII.[26]

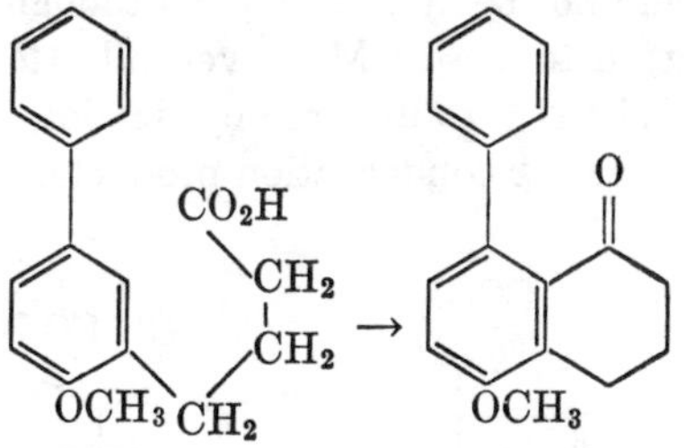

XXXVII   XXXVIII

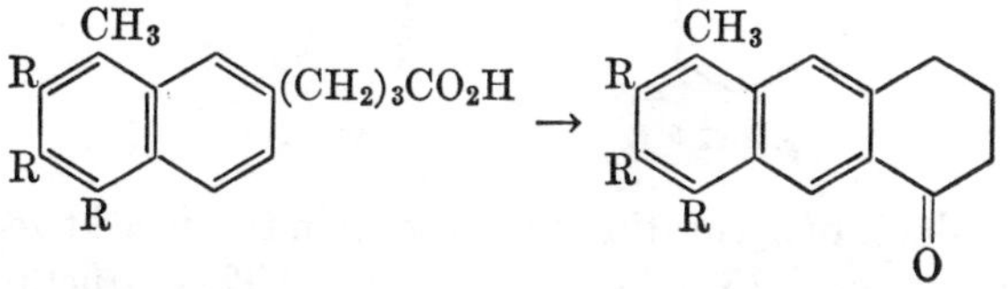

XXXIX (R = H)   XLI (R = H)
XL (R = CH₃)   XLII (R = CH₃)

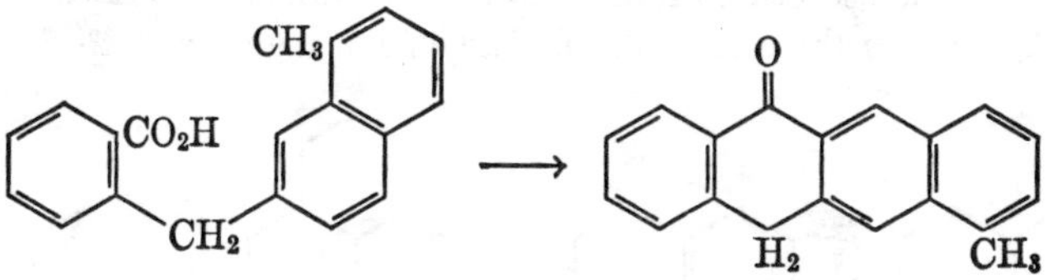

XLIII   XLIV

The only cases of cyclization of γ-2-naphthylbutyric acids in which the ring does not close into the reactive 1-position to form a phenanthrene derivative are those in which either this position is blocked or the 8-position is substituted. The latter clearly seems to be an example of hindrance. An illustration is afforded by the cyclization of γ-8-methyl-2-naphthylbutyric acid (XXXIX) to the linear anthracene derivative XLI instead of the expected ketotetrahydrophenanthrene.[25] The orientation influence of the methyl substituent would not be expected to affect the course of the reaction in such a manner. In like manner the tetramethyl derivative XL gave the product of linear ring closure XLII in good yield.[27] A similar abnormal course of cyclization [28] has been observed in the benzylbenzoic acid derivative, o-(8-methyl-2-naphthyl-methyl)-benzoic acid (XLIII) to give the linear benzanthrone XLIV.

[26] Fieser and Bradsher, J. Am. Chem. Soc., 58, 1738 (1936).
[27] Hewett, J. Chem. Soc., 1940, 293.
[28] Fieser and Hershberg, J. Am. Chem. Soc., 62, 49 (1940).

A different type of steric interference is revealed by the resistance to formation of certain types of polycyclic ring systems. The hydrindenyl-acetic acid XLV could not be cyclized,[29] even though the five-membered ring might be expected to close. Moreover, all attempts to induce the acids XLVI [30] and XLVII [31] to undergo cyclization resulted only in the formation of intermolecular condensation products.

XLV   XLVI   XLVII   XLVIII

All these products of cyclization would contain two fused five-membered rings mutually fused to a benzene nucleus. This structure, formula XLVIII, represents a highly strained system. On the other hand, the basic polycyclic structures represented by formulas XLIX through LII can be formed by the intramolecular acylation reaction.[10, 30, 32]

XLIX   L   LI   LII

DIRECTION OF RING CLOSURE

The Benzene Nucleus. The main problem in direction of cyclization is presented when both positions *ortho* to the acid side chain are available and ring closure into both would result in the formation of two isomeric ketones. In the benzene series the only acids having these structural properties are the *meta* substituted phenylbutyric and phenylpropionic acids, with which cyclization usually takes place at the position *para* to the substituent. Thus 6-methoxytetralone-1 (LIV) was obtained [14]

[29] v. Braun, Danziger, and Koehler, *Ber.*, **50**, 56 (1917).
[30] v. Braun and Rath, *Ber.*, **61**, 956 (1928).
[31] v. Braun and Anton, *Ber.*, **62**, 145 (1929).
[32] v. Braun and Reutter, *Ber.*, **59**, 1922 (1926).

in 96% yield from γ-m-methoxyphenylbutyric acid (LIII). Similar results were obtained with γ-m-tolylbutyric acid.[33] Occasionally a case may be found in which some of the isomeric ketone arising from *ortho* cyclization is formed, although in small proportion. For example,[20]

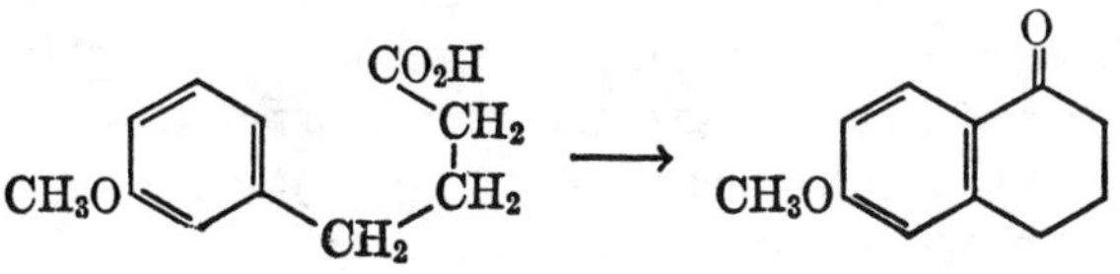

LIII   LIV

a small amount of 7-methoxyhydrindone-1 (LVII, R = CH_3) accompanied the main product LVI (R = CH_3) in the cyclization of m-methoxyhydrocinnamic acid (LV, R = CH_3). The free hydroxy acid LV (R = H) was shown to respond similarly to cyclization giving the ketones LVI (R = H) and LVII (R = H) in 80 and 14% yields, respectively.[34]

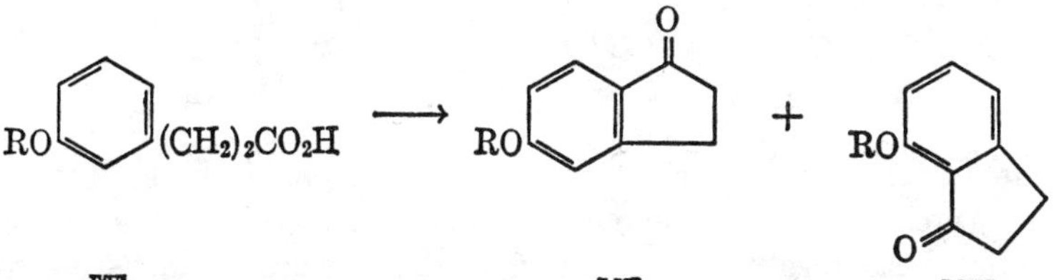

LV   LVI   LVII

The Naphthalene Nucleus. The cyclization of β-2-naphthylpropionic and γ-2-naphthylbutyric acids generally leads to angular ring closure into the reactive 1-position of the nucleus. The resulting ketones therefore have the basic structures LVIII and LIX, respectively. Examples may be found in Tables VI through XIII. Linear ring closure may be realized only under extraordinary circumstances (p. 123). The ring

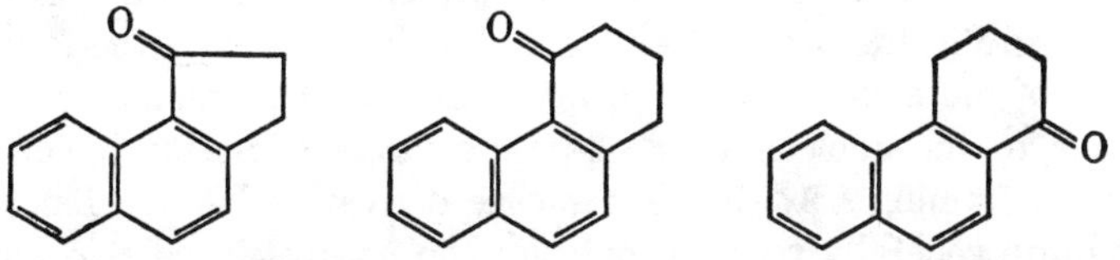

LVIII   LIX   LX

closure of γ-1-naphthylbutyric acids nearly always results in the formation of 1-ketotetrahydrophenanthrene (LX) derivatives which arise

---

[33] Fieser and Dunn, *J. Am. Chem. Soc.*, **58**, 572 (1936).
[34] Johnson and Anderson, unpublished observation.

from acylation at the adjacent 2-position of the nucleus. The alternative direction of cyclization is into the *peri* position, involving the formation of a seven-membered ring. The inherent resistance to this reaction may be overcome, in part, by the presence of activating groups appropriately situated (see p. 175, formulas XCIII through XCV). The *peri* ring closure is generally predominant, however, with β-1-naphthylpropionic acids.[35, 36, 37, 38, 39] The course of the reaction is probably decided by the preference of six- over five-membered ring formation, although doubtless the activities of the 8- and the 2-positions are not identical. In at least one instance [37] some of the five-membered ring product of 1,2-cyclization was formed. 4,5-Benzhydrindone-1 (LXIII) was isolated in 6% yield from the cyclization of β-1-naphthylpropionic acid (LXI) in addition to an 81% yield of 7-perinaphthanone (LXII).

LXI   LXII   +   LXIII

The Phenanthrene Nucleus. Of the higher polycyclic systems, the phenanthrene nucleus is the only one which has received much general attention with regard to cyclization of the aliphatic acid derivatives. The results of experiments on ring closure of the unsubstituted γ-phenanthrylbutyric and β-phenanthrylpropionic acids are summarized in Table I.

In the butyric acid series (column 2) no problem in direction of ring closure arises when the acid side chain is attached at the 1-, 4-, or 9-positions. Cyclization goes, respectively, to position 2 giving a chrysene derivative LXIV, to position 3 to form a 3,4-benzphenanthrene ketone LXXII, and to position 10 yielding the triphenylene derivative LXXIII. Ring closure in the opposite directions would necessitate the formation of rings of more than six members. When the butyric acid residue is attached to the nucleus at the 3-position, 3,2-cyclization seems to be preferred, forming a 1,2-benzanthracene derivative LXX. This seems to be quite generally true not only for the unsubstituted acid but also

[35] Cook and Hewett, *J. Chem. Soc.*, **1934**, 365.
[36] Darzens and Lévy, *Compt. rend.*, **201**, 902 (1935).
[37] Fieser and Gates, *J. Am. Chem. Soc.*, **62**, 2335 (1940).
[38] Fieser and Novello, *J. Am. Chem. Soc.*, **62**, 1855 (1940)
[39] Mayer and Sieglitz, *Ber.*, **55**, 1835 (1922).

TABLE 1

Products of Cyclization in the Phenanthrene Series

Position (x) of attachment of $-(CH_2)_n CO_2H$	From γ-x-Phenanthrylbutyric Acid	Reference	From β-x-Phenanthrylpropionic Acid	Reference
1	 LXIV	40, 41	 LXV and LXVI (predominant)	42
2	(See Table XIV) LXVII and LXVIII (ratio depends on method)	43	 LXIX	42; cf. 44

TABLE I—Continued

3	LXX	45, 46, 47, 48	LXXI	42; cf. 49
4	LXXII	50	Unknown	
9	LXXIII	51, 52	LXXIV and LXXV	42, 53

[40] Bachmann and Struve, *J. Org. Chem.*, **5**, 416 (1940).
[41] Hoch, *Compt. rend.*, **207**, 921 (1938).
[42] Bachmann and Kloetzel, *J. Am. Chem. Soc.*, **59**, 2207 (1937).
[43] Fieser and Johnson, *J. Am. Chem. Soc.*, **61**, 1647 (1939).
[44] Bergmann and Hillemann, *Ber.*, **66**, 1302 (1933).
[45] Bachmann and Bradbury, *J. Org. Chem.*, **2**, 175 (1937).
[46] R. D. Haworth and Mavin, *J. Chem. Soc.*, **1933**, 1012.
[47] Cook, *J. Chem. Soc.*, **1933**, 1592.
[48] Bachmann, *J. Org. Chem.*, **3**, 434 (1938).
[49] Hillemann, *Ber.*, **69**, 2610 (1936).
[50] Bachmann and Edgerton, *J. Am. Chem. Soc.*, **62**, 2970 (1940).
[51] E. Bergmann and Blum-Bergmann, *J. Am. Chem. Soc.*, **59**, 1441 (1937).
[52] Fieser and Joshel, *J. Am. Chem. Soc.*, **61**, 2958 (1939).
[53] Weizmann, E. Bergmann, and Berlin, *J. Am. Chem. Soc.*, **60**, 1331 (1938).

for acids containing substituents both on the side chain [54, 55, 56] and in the nucleus.[57] In one instance the isolation of a small but significant amount of the isomeric 3,4-benzphenanthrene derivative arising from 3,4-cyclization was reported.[56] Although cyclization of γ-2-phenanthrylbutyric acids generally seems to favor the formation of the chrysene structure, in the unsubstituted acid the ring may be induced to close either into the 3- or 1-position,[43] depending upon the experimental method used for cyclization (see p. 176). From this observation it appears that no valid generalization can be made regarding the proportion of isomers formed in any ring closure which has the inherent tendency to take place in two directions. A number of the following cyclizations fall into this category.

The cyclization of β-phenanthrylpropionic acids proceeded in two directions [42] when the acid side chain is located at the 1- or 9-position, giving mixtures of ketones LXV and LXVI from the 1- and LXXIV and LXXV from the 9-derivative. Cyclization of β-3-phenanthrylpropionic acid gave the 3,4-cyclopentenophenanthrene ketone (LXXI) in good yield. This tendency toward 3,4-cyclization also was realized with the β-methyl homolog.[49] Here, however, a small amount of the isomeric linear cyclization product was isolated also. In both examples the principal direction of ring closure is opposite to that which would be predicted on the basis of the behavior of γ-3-phenanthrylbutyric acid, which cyclizes almost exclusively to the 2-position. This should serve as a warning regarding the inadvisability of drawing conclusions from such analogies. A similar type of discrepancy was found in the 2-substituted propionic and butyric acid derivatives of 9,10-dihydrophenanthrene.[58] While the latter cyclized exclusively to the 3-position, almost one-fifth of the total ketone obtained from the propionic acid consisted of material formed by 2,1-cyclization.

Investigations on other polycyclic nuclei are not sufficiently extensive to warrant a discussion at this point. A number of individual cyclizations involving nuclei such as acenaphthene, fluorene, perinaphthane, anthracene, 1,2-benzanthracene, chrysene, pyrene, 3,4-benzpyrene, and others may be found in Tables IV through XIII. Some of these are considered in detail in the following pages.

[54] Bachmann and Chemerda, *J. Org. Chem.*, **6**, 36 (1941).
[55] Cook and Haslewood, *J. Chem. Soc.*, **1934**, 428.
[56] Cook and (Mrs.) A. M. Robinson, *J. Chem. Soc.*, **1938**, 505.
[57] Bachmann and Edgerton, *J. Am. Chem. Soc.*, **62**, 2550 (1940).
[58] Burger and Mosettig, *J. Am. Chem. Soc.*, **59**, 1302 (1937).

METHODS OF CYCLIZATION

Probably the two most generally useful methods for effecting intramolecular acylation are by the Friedel-Crafts type of reaction on the acid chloride and the action of anhydrous hydrogen fluoride on the free acid. In addition to these methods, cyclizations have been effected by the use of sulfuric acid and other reagents.

The Friedel-Crafts Method

Many acid chlorides can be induced easily to eliminate the elements of hydrogen chloride intramolecularly. Thus, in the preparation of the chlorides of γ-arylbutyric acids by warming with phosphorus pentachloride for a short period, in at least two instances cyclic ketones were obtained in addition to the acid chlorides.[59, 60] γ-6-Tetralylbutyric acid upon such treatment gave 40% of ketone, along with the expected acid chloride.[59] When heated at about 120° under diminished pressure, the acid chloride lost hydrogen chloride to an extent approximating completeness, so that the total yield of ketonic material was 83%. An extreme case is represented by the attempted conversion of β-(3,5-dimethylphenyl)-isovaleric acid into the acid chloride.[61] Only the product of cyclization, 3,3,5,7-tetramethylhydrindone-1, was obtained. Heating an acid chloride in the absence of a catalyst is a recognized method of cyclization (Table XIII). In general, however, the use of a Friedel-Crafts type of catalyst greatly facilitates ring closure.

From a general survey of the literature it appears that the most common causes of poor yields in the Friedel-Crafts cyclization of acid chlorides are (a) *reaction conditions which are too drastic*, and (b) *reagents of inadequate purity*. The optimum conditions are those which are mild but still sufficient to complete cyclization. An apparent necessity for heating the reaction mixture in order to induce cyclization may be due, in part, to insufficient purity of reagents. The vital effect of the presence of impurities on the Friedel-Crafts reaction is fairly well known,[62, 63] but the advantage of mild conditions has not been generally appreciated.

The disadvantage of heating Friedel-Crafts acylation reaction mixtures as long as hydrogen chloride is evolved has been demonstrated in the acetylation of benzene to acetophenone.[63] An increase in the reaction

[59] Schroeter, *Ber.*, **57**, 2003 (1924).

[60] Schroeter, *Ber.*, **57**, 2025 (1924).

[61] Smith and Spillane, *J. Am. Chem. Soc.*, **65**, 202 (1943).

[62] Calloway, *Chem. Revs.*, **17**, 327 (1935).

[63] Calloway and Green, *J. Am. Chem. Soc.*, **59**, 809 (1937).

time resulted in a decrease in yield and increase in formation of high-boiling oxygen-containing substances and tars.   Dypnone, $C_6H_5C(CH_3)$=$CHCOC_6H_5$, formed by condensation of two molecules of acetophenone was the chief by-product and became essentially the main product when the ketone was present in greater molar quantities than the aluminum chloride.   In the reaction of acetyl chloride and toluene under the influence of a variety of catalysts, it was shown [64] in several instances that a rapid decrease in yield resulted as the reaction time was increased.

Similarly, low yields of hydrindone-1 (LXXVII) were obtained from β-phenylpropionyl chloride (LXXVI) and aluminum chloride when the reaction mixture was heated too long.[65]   A high-boiling oily substance was the main product, which has been shown [66] to contain some hydrindenylidenehydrindone-1 (LXXVIII).   The chlorine-containing compound $C_{18}H_{15}OCl$ isolated by Kipping [65] may therefore be the product formed by addition of hydrogen chloride to LXXVIII.

LXXVI   LXXVII   LXXVIII

On the other hand, in the preparation of hydrindone-1 from pure instead of crude β-phenylpropionyl chloride, the reactivity was so increased that only a few minutes' heating was required to bring about ring closure in markedly improved yields.[67]   With pure aluminum chloride, also, the cyclization was completed in a few seconds and the yield still further improved to 90%.[20]

The conditions just discussed apply, in general, in the cyclization of arylbutyric and arylpropionic acids by the Friedel-Crafts method. Although other factors may enter, it is significant that a higher incidence of good yields is found under milder reaction conditions.   This may be seen by arranging the results of a cyclization in the order of increasing yields as in Tables II, III, and IV.

In Table II experiments on the formation of hydrindone-1 from β-phenylpropionic acid by various methods have been listed according to increasing yields.   Six examples (4, 7, 8, 9, 10, 11) of the Friedel-Crafts

[64] Dermer, Wilson, Johnson, and Dermer, *J. Am. Chem. Soc.*, **63**, 2881 (1941).
[65] Kipping, *J. Chem. Soc.*, **1894**, 480.
[66] Johnson and Helms, unpublished observation.
[67] Ingold and Thorpe, *J. Chem. Soc.*, **1919**, 143.

ring closure may be found. It is apparent that excellent yields (examples 9 and 10) were obtained when the reaction mixture was heated for only a short period or not at all. Repetition of example 4 by other investigators [68] gave similar results (50–55% yields of hydrindone-1), but by operating in the cold (example 8), consistent yields of 80% were obtained. The superior yield reported in 11 was obtained by a procedure which seems to warrant further investigation. The reaction was conducted in an inverse manner in that the acid chloride was added to the mixture of aluminum chloride in petroleum ether. The condensing agent thus was always present in excess, a condition which might serve as an explanation of the success of the cyclization, in light of the observation [63] that the formation of undesired bimolecular ketone condensation products is inhibited by the presence of aluminum chloride in excess of one mole. The inverse Friedel-Crafts technique has been used in a few other instances (Table VII, examples marked with "a"), and the yields are generally good.

The better yields (Table III, examples 6 and 7) of tetralone-1 obtained by the action of aluminum chloride on γ-phenylbutyryl chloride also involve the use of milder reaction conditions. The technique of heating until the evolution of hydrogen chloride ceased resulted in very poor yields (examples 1 and 2).

In the cyclization of γ-3-pyrenylbutyric acid (Table IV) the higher yields obtained by the Friedel-Crafts reaction (examples 7 and 8) again involved the use of mild conditions. Even with the mild condensing agent, stannic chloride, it was found unnecessary to heat the reaction mixture in order to obtain 96% yields (example 8).

A comparison of yields of some other cyclizations found in Table V affords further evidence in favor of the superiority of mild reaction conditions.

The catalysts or condensing agents which have been employed most frequently for intramolecular acylation by the Friedel-Crafts method are aluminum chloride and the less active stannic chloride. Mention of the use of the intermediately active ferric chloride may be found,[12] but the generality of this procedure has not been demonstrated.

The most common solvents are benzene and carbon disulfide. Others such as petroleum ether and sym-tetrachloroethane also have been employed successfully. Nitrobenzene has served as a unique solvent in conjunction with aluminum chloride, since a complex is formed reducing the activity of the catalyst.

For the preparation of the acid chloride from the free acid, *phosphorus pentachloride* and *thionyl chloride* have been used most frequently.

[68] Haller and Bauer, *Ann. chim.*, **16**, 340 (1921).

TABLE II

CYCLIZATION OF β-PHENYLPROPIONIC ACID TO HYDRINDONE-1

Example	Condensing Agent	Solvent	Conditions	Yield	Reference
1	Concentrated sulfuric acid		Warm	0%	69
2	Concentrated sulfuric acid		130° for 15 minutes	10%	70
3	5% Fuming sulfuric acid		140° for 5 minutes	27%	71
4	(a) Aluminum chloride	60–70° petroleum ether	Heat 20–30 minutes	55–60%*	65 72
5	Hydrogen fluoride		26 hours at 20°	73%	16
6	Chloroacetic anhydride	Anisole	170° for 48 hours	74%	73
7	(a) Aluminum chloride	Petroleum ether	Heat only a few minutes	75% *	67
8	(a) Aluminum chloride	Petroleum ether	Cold	80%	68
9	(a) Aluminum chloride	Petroleum ether	(b) Reaction over in a few seconds	90% *	20
10	(a) Aluminum chloride	Benzene	(c) (d) Cold	90% *	74
11	(a) Aluminum chloride	60–70° petroleum ether	(d) Warmed until complex dissolved	95% *	75

* Yield based on acid chloride.

(a) Friedel-Crafts reaction on the acid chloride.

(b) Procedure same as in example 7, except that purer acid chloride was used. A noticeable increase in the rate of reaction was thus brought about.

(c) Reaction was vigorous in the cold.

(d) The reaction was run inversely in that the acid chloride was added to the mixture of aluminum chloride in petroleum ether.

[69] Miller and Rohde, *Ber.*, **23**, 1887 (1890).

[70] Speight, Stevenson, and Thorpe, *J. Chem. Soc.*, **1924**, 2185.

[71] Price and Lewis, *J. Am. Chem. Soc.*, **61**, 2553 (1939).

[72] Revis and Kipping, *J. Chem. Soc.*, **1897**, 238.

[73] Unger, *Ann.*, **504**, 267 (1933).

[74] Amagat, *Bull. soc. chim.*, [4]**41**, 940 (1927).

[75] Thiele and Wanscheidt, *Ann.*, **376**, 269 (1910).

TABLE III

CYCLIZATION OF γ-PHENYLBUTYRIC ACID TO TETRALONE-1

Example	Condensing Agent	Solvent	Conditions	Yield	Reference
1	(a) Aluminum chloride	70–80° petroleum ether	Heat until all hydrogen chloride is evolved	10% *	76
2	(a) Aluminum chloride	100–110° petroleum ether	Heat until all hydrogen chloride is evolved	(b) 10% *	77
3	° 95% Sulfuric acid		100° for 1 hour	27%	35
4	Concentrated sulfuric acid		Water bath (3.5 hours)	49%	78
5	Concentrated sulfuric acid		Water bath (3 hours)	50%	15
6	(a) Aluminum chloride	Benzene	(c) Cold	70% *	74
7	(a) Aluminum chloride	Carbon disulfide	Warm for 10 minutes	74–91%	79
8	Hydrogen fluoride		16 hours at room temperature	92%	16

* Yield based on acid chloride.

(a) Friedel-Crafts reaction on the acid chloride.
(b) Kipping suggests that the by-product is of the hydrindylidenehydrindone type.
(c) Allowed to stand until the evolution of hydrogen chloride became vigorous; then hydrolyzed.

[76] Mayer and Stamm, Ber., **56**, 1424 (1923).
[77] Kipping and Hill, J. Chem. Soc., **1899**, 144.
[78] Horne and Shriner, J. Am. Chem. Soc., **55**, 4652 (1933).
[79] Martin and Fieser, Org. Syntheses, Coll. Vol. **2**, 569 (1943).

TABLE IV

CYCLIZATION OF γ-3-PYRENYLBUTYRIC ACID TO 4'-KETO-1',2',3',4'-TETRAHYDRO-3,4-BENZPYRENE

Example	Condensing Agent	Solvent	Conditions	Yield	Reference
1	P_2O_5, 80% H_2SO_4, $POCl_3$, $AlCl_3$ (a)			All failed	80
2	Zinc chloride		Fuse at 180° for 1 hour	16%	80
3	Stannic chloride		Fuse at 115–120° for 1 hour	19%	80
4	Stannic chloride		Fuse at 110–112° for 1 hour	37%	81
5	(b) Aluminum chloride	Benzene	8 hours at room temperature	56%	82
6	(a) Stannic chloride	Carbon disulfide	3 hours at 0°; 3 hours refluxing	80–85%	83 84
7	(b) Stannic chloride	Benzene	4 hours at room temperature; 4 hours refluxing	85–95%	38
8	(b) Stannic chloride	Benzene	8 hours at room temperature	96%	85

(a) Friedel-Crafts reaction on the acid chloride.
(b) Same as (a) except that reaction was carried out in the presence of the phosphorus compounds remaining after the formation of the acid chloride with phosphorus pentachloride.

[80] Cook and Hewett, *J. Chem. Soc.*, **1933**, 398.
[81] Winterstein, Vetter, and Schön, *Ber.*, **68**, 1079 (1935).
[82] Vollmann, Becker, Corell, and Streeck, *Ann.*, **531**, 1 (1937).
[83] Fieser and Fieser, *J. Am. Chem. Soc.*, **57**, 782 (1935).
[84] Fieser, Hershberg, Long, and Newman, *J. Am. Chem. Soc.*, **59**, 475 (1937).
[85] Bachmann, Carmack, and Safir, *J. Am. Chem. Soc.*, **63**, 1682 (1941).

Phosphorus trichloride also has been employed, but this reagent has serious disadvantages.[86] Purification of the acid chloride by distillation or crystallization is generally unsatisfactory. Both techniques are likely to be wasteful, and few of the polycyclic acid chlorides can be distilled even under reduced pressure without considerable decomposition. It has been found generally expedient to treat the acid in such a manner that the by-products on formation of the chloride are readily removed, thus excluding all material which might interfere with the cyclization. Procedures involving the use of phosphorus pentachloride and thionyl chloride are described in the following discussions of stannic and aluminum chloride in cyclizations.

STANNIC CHLORIDE

Stannic chloride has been shown to be generally effective in the Friedel-Crafts reaction in bringing about ring closures into polycyclic nuclei. Of thirty-eight acid chlorides which have been cyclized (Table VI), twenty-one were converted to the ketones in yields of 90% or over. In six instances (Tables IV and V) the acid chlorides had previously been cyclized with aluminum chloride, and in all but one (example 5, Table V) the yields were definitely better with stannic chloride. The milder condensing agent, however, appears to be less satisfactory for more difficult ring closures. Thus no ketone could be obtained from β-p-methoxyphenylpropionyl chloride and stannic chloride by procedures similar to those described below.[18] With the aluminum chloride method, however, consistently good yields (86%) of LXXXII (p. 157) resulted.

With Phosphorus Pentachloride. One of the simplest and most satisfactory procedures [38] consists in treating the acid to be cyclized first with one equivalent of phosphorus pentachloride in benzene, then with stannic chloride (Table VI, examples with asterisks). The following procedure for the cyclization of γ-1-naphthylbutyric acid serves as a representative example of this method.

Procedure I.[87] 1-Keto-1,2,3,4-tetrahydrophenanthrene.[88] To a mixture of 69.5 g. (0.324 mole) of γ-1-naphthylbutyric acid in 300 cc. of thiophene-free benzene (dried over sodium) contained in a 1-l. round-bottomed flask is added 74 g. (0.355 mole) of powdered phosphorus pentachloride in portions with swirling and cooling in ice water. The

---

[86] Borsche and Eberlein, *Ber.*, **47**, 1460 (1914).

[87] Recommended for polynuclear and other acids having a strong cyclization susceptibility.

[88] A. L. Wilds, private communication; see Wilds, *J. Am. Chem. Soc.*, **64**, 1421 (1942).

flask is protected from moisture by a calcium chloride tube which is removed only during the addition of reagents. Heat and hydrogen chloride are evolved during the vigorous reaction, and after standing at room temperature for an hour nearly all the acid and phosphorus pentachloride are in solution. The mixture is warmed on the steam bath for about five minutes, in order to ensure complete reaction, and then is chilled until the benzene shows signs of beginning to solidify. At this point a solution of 80 cc. (about 0.7 mole) of anhydrous stannic chloride in 80 cc. of dry thiophene-free benzene is added rapidly with swirling or mechanical stirring, whereupon an orange-yellow complex separates. After standing for fifteen minutes in ice water the mixture is hydrolyzed by the addition of ice followed by 250 cc. of concentrated hydrochloric acid. A small amount of ether (about 25 cc.) is added to hasten the hydrolysis of the stannic chloride addition complex (which is soluble in ether), and the mixture is shaken until all the complex is dissolved. After separation, the organic layer is washed with several portions of 5% hydrochloric acid, water, 5% aqueous sodium hydroxide, and finally again with water. After evaporation of the solvent the residue is crystallized (distillation for purification is unnecessary) from methanol, giving 56.5 g. of colorless ketone, m.p. 94–95°. A second crop from the filtrate amounts to 4.2 g. of material of the same melting point. The total yield is 95%.

The time and temperature of the action of the stannic chloride have been varied. In the cyclization [54] of β-methyl-γ-3-phenanthrylbutyric acid (5-g. run), even when the hydrolysis of the complex was effected immediately after the addition of the stannic chloride, the yield of ketone was 97%. Other acids, however, may be converted completely to the ketone only after several hours at the stannic chloride stage.[38, 85, 89] Thus in the cyclization of γ-3-pyrenylbutyric acid (Table IV), the best yields (example 8) were obtained when the suspension of solid complex was stirred for eight to nine hours at room temperature. The procedure was essentially the same as Procedure I, except that a three-necked flask fitted with a mercury-sealed stirrer was employed.

With Thionyl Chloride. Although thionyl chloride has been more widely used in the preparation of acid chlorides for cyclization with both stannic and aluminum chloride, it is perhaps less generally advantageous than phosphorus pentachloride. If it is desired to obtain the acid chloride essentially free of by-products, thionyl chloride presents some advantage in that these by-products of the reaction are gaseous and therefore may be eliminated readily. Since, moreover, the reagent has a

[89] Fieser and Heymann, J. Am. Chem. Soc., **63**, 2333 (1941).

boiling point of 79°, it can be removed readily when used in excess. On the other hand, a number of instances are on record [48, 83, 84, 90, 91, 92] describing a deleterious action of thionyl chloride. Among these are six examples in which the use of the reagent directly upon the acid resulted in the formation of tarry decomposition products. In one case [48] the difficulty was eliminated by employing ether as a solvent, and in three others [83, 90, 91] it was found necessary also to use thionyl chloride of a high degree of purity.[79] The treatment of γ-3-pyrenylbutyric acid with thionyl chloride was found to require exceptional care. In addition to the above precautions the mixture could not be heated much above 40° during removal of the ether without decomposition.[84] When thionyl chloride is used in conjunction with stannic chloride it is usually necessary to remove the thionyl chloride completely before cyclization.[54, 84] Even a trace of the reagent which is often almost impossible to remove without spoiling the acid chloride may cause a noticeable decrease in the yield of ketone. Thus in the cyclization of β-methyl-γ-3-phenanthrylbutyric acid it was found that, even after taking the usual precautions in removing the last traces of ether and thionyl chloride, the yield was 86% as compared to 97% obtained by the phosphorus pentachloride method.[54] In the same work a similar result was noted with γ-3-phenanthrylvaleric acid. Commercial thionyl chloride may also promote undesirable side reactions to give sulfur-containing material,[93] or, without the introduction of pyridine in more than catalytic amounts, it may fail to give good yields of acid chlorides.[94]

In spite of the many disadvantages, thionyl chloride has been used with considerable success in numerous cyclizations. A generally effective procedure for preparing the acid chloride involves the treatment of a dry ethereal solution of the acid with an excess of thionyl chloride and a drop or two of pyridine as a catalyst.[90] By this method, in conjunction with stannic chloride and benzene for the cyclization, excellent yields of ketones (Table VI, examples without asterisks) were obtained. The ring closure of γ-1-naphthylbutyric acid affords a typical illustration of the procedure.

Procedure II.[87, 95]   1-Keto-1,2,3,4-tetrahydrophenanthrene.[95a]   In a 125-cc. suction flask with a calcium chloride tube attached to the side

[90] Fieser and Peters, *J. Am. Chem. Soc.*, **54**, 4373 (1932).

[91] Fieser and Snow, *J. Am. Chem. Soc.*, **60**, 176 (1938).

[92] Koelsch, *J. Am. Chem. Soc.*, **55**, 3885 (1933).

[93] Fieser and Desreux, *J. Am. Chem. Soc.*, **60**, 2255 (1938).

[94] Carré and Libermann, *Compt. rend.*, **199**, 1422 (1934).

[95] Bachmann and Wilds, *J. Am. Chem. Soc.*, **62**, 2084 (1940).

[95a] Private communication. An expanded description of the procedure of Bachmann and Wilds (reference 95).

arm is placed 25 cc. of dry ether containing 2 drops of pyridine. To the cooled mixture are added 8 cc. (about 0.1 mole) of commercial thionyl chloride and then 13 g. (0.06 mole) of γ-1-naphthylbutyric acid. The flask is stoppered and allowed to stand in the hood at room temperature for one-half hour with occasional swirling. A piece of porous plate is introduced, and the mixture is warmed for ten minutes on the steam bath in order to complete the reaction. The drying tube is then removed and suction (water pump) gradually applied to remove all the ether and excess thionyl chloride. The temperature should not be permitted to exceed 40°. After a few minutes at the full pressure of the water pump about 5 cc. of dry benzene is added and the process repeated. The last traces of volatile substances may be removed by reducing the pressure to about 1 mm. with the vacuum pump for about five minutes. The acid chloride, which remains as an oil, is transferred into a 200-cc. round-bottomed flask with the aid of 60 cc. of dry, thiophene-free benzene. As in Procedure I the mixture is chilled, 15 cc. (0.13 mole) of stannic chloride in 15 cc. of benzene is added, and after being swirled for five to ten minutes at 5° the mixture is hydrolyzed (using 50 cc. of concentrated hydrochloric acid) and worked up as in Procedure I. It is advisable to distil (a two-bulb type flask [96] is satisfactory) the crude ketone under reduced pressure (1–2 mm.) before recrystallizing from methanol. The yield of material m.p. 94–96° is 11.0–11.2 g. (92–94%).

A list of ketones which have been prepared by the Friedel-Crafts stannic chloride method may be found in Table VI. Yields marked by an asterisk were obtained from acid chlorides prepared by the phosphorus pentachloride procedure; all others were obtained from acid chlorides prepared from thionyl chloride.

[96] Fieser, "Experiments in Organic Chemistry," 2nd ed., pp. 250 and 318, D. C. Heath and Co., 1941.

TABLE V

COMPARISON OF YIELDS WITH ALUMINUM AND STANNIC CHLORIDE
IN THE FRIEDEL-CRAFTS METHOD

Acid	Condensing Agent and Medium	Conditions	Yields of Ketones	Reference
1	(a) Aluminum chloride in benzene	Several hours at room temperature; 1.5 hours reflux	77%	97
	(b) Stannic chloride in benzene	1 hour cold	90%	54
2	(b) Aluminum chloride in sym-tetrachloroethane	16 hours at 0°	86%	98
	(b) Stannic chloride in benzene	1 minute cold	92%	99
3	(a) Aluminum chloride in benzene	6 hours at room temperature	72%	56
	(a) Stannic chloride in benzene	13 hours at room temperature	81%	89
4	(a) Aluminum chloride in benzene	12 hours at room temperature, 2.5 hours reflux	(c) 81%	100
	(b) Stannic chloride in benzene	5 minutes cold	92–94%	95
5	(b) Aluminum chloride in nitrobenzene	24 hours at 0°	74%	42
	(b) Stannic chloride in carbon disulfide	1.5 hours reflux	(d) 54%	

(a) Acid chloride formed with phosphorus pentachloride; phosphorus compounds not removed before addition of condensing agent.

(b) Acid chloride formed with thionyl chloride.

(c) Crude distilled ketone.

(d) About 17% of unreacted acid was recovered. The yield based upon acid which reacted was 65%.

[97] Fieser and Johnson, J. Am. Chem. Soc., 61, 168 (1939).

[98] Kon and F. C. J. Ruzicka, J. Chem. Soc., 1936, 187.

[99] Bachmann and Holmes, J. Am. Chem. Soc., 62, 2750 (1940).

[100] Drake and McVey, J. Org. Chem., 4, 464 (1939).

TABLE VI

<small>CYCLIZATIONS BY THE FRIEDEL-CRAFTS STANNIC CHLORIDE METHOD</small>

Ring System of Ketones Prepared	Yields	Reference
Naphthalene		
	96% *	14
Phenanthrene		
	92–94% *	88, 95
9-ethyl	77%	101
7-methoxy	90–95%	102
9-methoxy	92%	99
2-methyl	95%	103
4-methyl	91%	104
	88%	104
6-ethyl	80% *	104
4,5-Methylenephenanthrene		
	92% *	105
6-ethyl	60%	106
Cyclopentenophenanthrene		
	54%	42
Example 5, Table V	54%	42

TABLE VI—*Continued*

CYCLIZATIONS BY THE FRIEDEL-CRAFTS STANNIC CHLORIDE METHOD

Ring System of Ketones Prepared	Yields	Reference
1,2-*Benzanthracene*		
Example 1, Table V	90%	54
Example 3, Table V	74–80%	89
	91%	48
7-methyl	97% *	54
8-methyl	88% *	54
1'-methyl	89%	57
3,4-*Benzphenanthrene*		
	96%	50
Chrysene		
	74%	107
3-methyl	64%	40
2-methyl	86%	107
1-methyl	72%	40
7,8,9,10-tetrahydro	68%	40
	92%	40
11-methyl	91%	57

TABLE VI—*Continued*

CYCLIZATIONS BY THE FRIEDEL-CRAFTS STANNIC CHLORIDE METHOD

Ring System of Ketones Prepared	Yields	Reference
Pyrene		
	90%	50
Triphenylene		
	95%	101
Cholanthrene		
	93%	48
4-methyl	92% *	108
5-methyl	80% *	108
7-methyl	97% *	109a
3,4-Benzpyrene		
	96% *	85
3'-methyl	74% *	110
2'-methyl	90% *	110
1'-methyl	73% *	110

TABLE VI—*Continued*

CYCLIZATIONS BY THE FRIEDEL-CRAFTS STANNIC CHLORIDE METHOD

Ring System of Ketones Prepared	Yields	Reference
4′,5-Dimethylene-3,4-benzpyrene	98% *	111

* Prepared by the phosphorus pentachloride method; those without asterisk were made with thionyl chloride.

ALUMINUM CHLORIDE

The examples of intramolecular acylation by the use of aluminum chloride in the Friedel-Crafts reaction occur in the literature so frequently that no attempt has been made here to enumerate all of them. Table VII includes several different types of arylpropionic and arylbutyric acids which have been cyclized by this method.

The reaction conditions generally seem to be more critical with aluminum chloride than with stannic chloride. Yields, perhaps as a result, are more often hard to duplicate. These facts are doubtless due in part to the greater reactivity of aluminum chloride and to the difficulty commonly experienced in obtaining samples of this reagent which do not vary in catalytic effect. A pronounced influence of the grade of the aluminum chloride already has been mentioned.

In five out of six ring closures, better yields were obtained with stannic chloride than with aluminum chloride. The greater activity of the latter reagent was apparently not necessary in these instances. There

[101] Bachmann and Struve, *J. Org. Chem.*, **4**, 472 (1939).
[102] Bachmann, Cole, and Wilds, *J. Am. Chem. Soc.*, **62**, 824 (1940).
[103] Burnop, Elliott, and Linstead, *J. Chem. Soc.*, **1940**, 727.
[104] Bachmann and Edgerton, *J. Am. Chem. Soc.*, **62**, 2219 (1940).
[105] Bachmann and Sheehan, *J. Am. Chem. Soc.*, **63**, 204 (1941).
[106] Bachmann and Sheehan, *J. Am. Chem. Soc.*, **63**, 2598 (1941).
[107] Bachmann and Struve, *J. Org. Chem.*, **4**, 456 (1939).
[108] Bachmann and Chemerda, *J. Org. Chem.*, **6**, 50 (1941).
[109] (a) Bachmann and Safir, *J. Am. Chem. Soc.*, **63**, 855 (1941); (b) *ibid.*, 2601.
[110] Bachmann and Carmack, *J. Am. Chem. Soc.*, **63**, 2494 (1941).
[111] Bachmann and Carmack, *J. Am. Chem. Soc.*, **63**, 1685 (1941).

seems to be, however, a definite use for aluminum chloride where cyclization is difficult. The application of the method is discussed below without reference to such distinctions.

With Phosphorus Pentachloride. The method already described for the use of stannic chloride in conjunction with phosphorus pentachloride in benzene is a modification of the older aluminum chloride method (Table VII, examples marked by "*k*"). Nitrobenzene also has been used as the solvent (examples marked by "*k*" and "*f*"). The technique is essentially the same as that described in Procedure I except that efficient stirring (the Hershberg wire stirrer [112] is highly satisfactory) generally is necessary while the aluminum chloride is added in portions with cooling. An excellent method of introducing the reagent slowly without exposure to the atmosphere has been described.[113] The aluminum chloride is placed in an Erlenmeyer flask fitted to one of the apertures of a three-necked flask by means of a section of rubber tubing of large diameter. The intermittent addition is accomplished by raising the containing flask, which can be cut off from the system at any time by kinking the rubber tube.

There is some indication that the phosphorus oxychloride formed in the preparation of the acid chloride interferes with the cyclization when aluminum chloride is used. Thus, the cyclization of α,γ-diphenylbutyric acid was effected in 94% yield only after the volatile phosphorus compounds had been removed from the reaction mixture; otherwise the yield was only 77%.[114] By removing the phosphorus oxychloride under reduced pressure before introduction of the aluminum chloride,[114, 115, 116] seven acids have been cyclized in yields of 85% or better. No single set of directions can be given which is entirely general. The following description of the cyclization of α,γ-diphenylbutyric acid is a typical example of the form of procedure. The critical phase of the reaction is during the aluminum chloride treatment; the *optimum time and temperature may vary for each acid.*

Procedure III. 2-Phenyltetralone-1.[116a] In a 500-cc. round-bottomed flask fitted with a calcium chloride tube are placed 83 g. (0.4 mole) of phosphorus pentachloride and 100 cc. of benzene (which has been dried over sodium). To this is added in portions with swirling

[112] Hershberg, *Ind. Eng. Chem., Anal. Ed.*, **8**, 313 (1936).

[113] Fieser, "Experiments in Organic Chemistry," 2nd ed., p. 311, D. C. Heath and Co., 1941.

[114] Newman, *J. Am. Chem. Soc.*, **62**, 870 (1940).

[115] Newman, *J. Am. Chem. Soc.*, **60**, 2947 (1938).

[116] Newman, *J. Am. Chem. Soc.*, **62**, 2295 (1940).

[116a] Private communication. An expanded description of the procedure of M. S. Newman (references 114 and 115).

a suspension of 91 g. (0.38 mole) of α,γ-diphenylbutyric acid in 200 cc. of dry benzene.[116b] After the vigorous reaction subsides and the reactants are nearly completely dissolved, the mixture is heated for a few minutes on a steam bath.   A condenser and receiver are then set for reduced-pressure distillation, and all the volatile material is removed at the water pump at 100° or less to avoid discoloration of the acid chloride.   The residual oily acid chloride is transferred with 380 cc. of dry thiophene-free benzene into a 1-l. three-necked flask equipped with a condenser (calcium chloride tube), a mercury-sealed wire stirrer,[112] and a rubber-tubed addition flask (p. 145) containing 53 g. (0.4 mole) of aluminum chloride.   (The reaction temperature is more readily controlled with lumpy aluminum chloride than with finely powdered grades.)   The aluminum chloride is added to the stirred solution at room temperature over a period of one-half hour (external cooling is sometimes necessary). The mixture is then heated for one-half hour each at 40° and 60°.   After cooling to room temperature during an additional half-hour period, the mixture is poured onto ice and hydrochloric acid, and about 100 cc. of ether is added to aid in the separation of the layers.   The organic solution is washed successively with dilute hydrochloric acid, water, dilute sodium hydroxide solution, water, and finally with saturated salt solution.   After filtering by gravity through a dry filter paper containing some anhydrous sodium sulfate, the solution is concentrated and the product purified by distillation at reduced pressure as in Procedure II. The yield of colorless ketone is 74–75.5 g. (92–94%), m.p. 76–77°.

Other solvents such as carbon disulfide [48, 109, 117] and sym-tetrachloroethane [118] have been found successful in the cyclization stage.   Another method of separating the phosphorus compounds is by the use of petroleum ether, in which the acid chloride, but not the phosphorus oxychloride, is soluble.[119]

With Thionyl Chloride.   A good procedure for the cyclization of γ-phenylbutyric acid to tetralone-1 is described in *Organic Syntheses*.[79] The acid is treated with thionyl chloride, the excess of which is removed under reduced pressure; carbon disulfide is added, then aluminum chloride, and the mixture is heated for a short period.   This description may be considered a general procedure, although the reaction time and temperature may have to be altered and mechanical stirring may be required.

[116b] The acid is added to the phosphorus pentachloride so that the latter will always be present in excess, thus avoiding anhydride formation according to the reaction $RCOOH + RCOCl \rightarrow (RCO)_2O + HCl$.

[117] Fieser and Bowen, *J. Am. Chem. Soc.*, **62**, 2103 (1940).

[118] Newman and Joshel, *J. Am. Chem. Soc.*, **60**, 485 (1938).

[119] Perkin and Robinson, *J. Chem. Soc.*, **1907**, 1073.

A more generally useful procedure may be developed by preparing the acid chloride according to Procedure II and conducting the cyclization as in Procedure III.

Directions for using nitrobenzene as the cyclizing solvent have been described in detail.[90] The manipulation may be facilitated by the fact that aluminum chloride is soluble in nitrobenzene and can therefore be added in solution. The average yield of ketone on ring closure of γ-3-acenaphthylbutyric acid by this method was 74%.

Cyclization of Anhydrides. Instead of the acid chloride, an intramolecular anhydride of the type LXXIX may be used for cyclization by the Friedel-Crafts reaction (Table VII, examples marked by "h"). This resembles the intermolecular acylation with succinic anhydride, and a similar procedure is generally followed. The product of ring closure is a keto acid LXXX. Nitrobenzene [9, 56, 120] is a generally effective solvent for the reaction; sym-tetrachloroethane also may be used.[121]

LXXIX → LXXX

[120] Haworth and Sheldrick, *J. Chem. Soc.*, **1935**, 636.
[121] Newman and Joshel, *J. Am. Chem Soc.*, **62**, 972 (1940)

TABLE VII

SOME CYCLIZATIONS BY THE FRIEDEL-CRAFTS ALUMINUM CHLORIDE METHOD

Acids Submitted to Cyclization	Yields of Ketones	Reference
BENZENE DERIVATIVES		
β-Phenylpropionic acid	55–60%	65
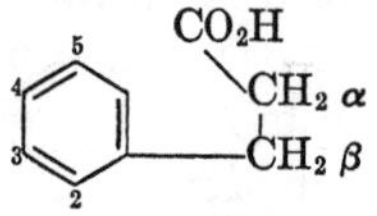	75%	67
	80%	68
	90%	20
	(a) 90%	74
	(a) 95%	75
(See Table II, p. 133)		
β-acetic acid	80%	22
β-(9-anthrone-10-yl)-	75%	122
α-benzyl-3-methyl-	75%	13
2-bromo-	(b) *	123
	70% *	124
2-bromo-5-t-butyl- ⎤ mixture	74% *	91
5-bromo-2-t-butyl- ⎦		
2-bromo-α,5-dimethyl- ⎤ mixture	95% *	125
5-bromo-α,2-dimethyl- ⎦		
2-bromo-5-isopropyl- ⎤ mixture	64–82%	126
5-bromo-2-isopropyl- ⎦		
2-bromo-5-methyl- ⎤ mixture	94% *	127
5-bromo-2-methyl- ⎦		
2-chloro-	90%	128
	93% *	129
2-chloro-5-methoxy-	65%	128
2-chloro-β-methyl-	76%	128
2-chloro-3-methyl-	90–95%	128
2-chloro-4-methyl-	(c)(d) 95% *	117
2-chloro-5-methyl-	—	128
2,3-dichloro-	—	128
2,5-dichloro-	85%	128
2,3-dichloro-β-methyl-	66%	128
2,5-dichloro-β-methyl-	70%	128
α,α-diethyl-	—	130
3,4-dimethoxy-	(e) 6–28%	119
α,α-dimethyl-	80%	68
2,4-dimethyl-	—	131
2,5-dimethyl-	—	131
2,6-dimethyl-	—	131
α,α-diphenyl-	80%	68
β,β-diphenyl-	96% *	132
5-isopropyl-α,2-dimethyl-	82% *	133

The structure depicted in the table:

CO$_2$H
CH$_2$ α
CH$_2$ β

(benzene ring with positions labeled 2, 3, 4, 5)

TABLE VII—*Continued*

SOME CYCLIZATIONS BY THE FRIEDEL-CRAFTS ALUMINUM CHLORIDE METHOD

Acids Submitted to Cyclization	Yields of Ketones	Reference
3-methoxy-	—	20
	(a) 35%	134
4-methoxy-	(f) 20%	135
	86%	18
3-methoxy-4-methyl-	(d) 42% *	136
4-methoxy-α-methyl-	—	137
α-methyl-	70–80%	138
	82%	139
3-methyl-β-phenyl-	60%	13
β-methyl-α-phenyl-	—	140
3,4-methylene dihydroxy-	(e) 15%	119
2-nitro-	(g) 73%	19
α-phenyl-	—	137
β-phenyl-	—	137
2-phenyl-	—	7
β-o-tolyl-	80%	13; cf. 15a
β-p-tolyl-	70%	13, 141
2,3,5-trichloro-	75%	128
2,3,5-trichloro-β-methyl-	66%	128
α-p-xylyl	70%	13
α-CH₂CH₂CO₂H	(f)(h) 30%	7
α-CH₂CH₂CH₂C₆H₅	60%	7
γ-Phenylbutyric acid	10%	76
	10%	77
	70%	74
	74–91% *	79

(See Table III, p. 134)		
γ-acetic acid	Some (i)	22, 23
β-anisyl-4-methoxy-γ-acetic acid	(j) 80%	142
α-benzyl-	60%	5, 6
α-bromo-	80%	143
4-bromo-	77–84% *	144
β-carboxy-	60–65%	5
β-carboxy-3,4-dimethoxy-γ-(3,4-dimethoxy-phenyl)-	(f)(h) 91% *	120
β-carboxy-γ-phenyl-	(f)(h) 72%	9

TABLE VII—*Continued*

SOME CYCLIZATIONS BY THE FRIEDEL–CRAFTS ALUMINUM CHLORIDE METHOD

Acids Submitted to Cyclization	Yields of Ketones	Reference
α,β-dimethyl-	81%	145
	—	146
α,2-dimethyl-	90%	147
α,4-dimethyl-	92.5%	146
	75%	76
β,γ-dimethyl-	—	146
β,4-dimethyl-	90%	146
	72%	76
γ,2-dimethyl-	89% *	148
γ,4-dimethyl-	(a) 94%	149
	76%	76
	—	146
2,3-dimethyl-	—	150
2,4-dimethyl-	(a) 92.5%	151
	85–90%	146
α,2-dimethyl-5-isopropyl-	(f) —	152
β,2-dimethyl-5-isopropyl-	(a) 94%	153
α,4-dimethyl-2-methoxy-	—	154
α,4-dimethyl-3-methoxy-	—	154
α,β-diphenyl-	58% *	155
4-ethyl-	87% *	104
α-ethyl-2-methyl-	(a) 94%	156
β-ethyl-2-methyl-	(a) >100%	156
4-isopropyl-	(a) 59% *	157
5-isopropyl-2-methyl-	80%	158
4-methoxy-	(j) 83% *	25
2-methoxy-α,4,5-trimethyl-	—	154
2-methoxy-β,γ,3-trimethyl-	—	154
4-methoxy-β,2,3-trimethyl-	—	154
α-methyl-	75%	145
	70%	76
β-methyl-	73% *	159
	48%	160
γ-methyl-	70%	76
2-methyl-	(a) 82%	156
3-methyl-	81% *	33
4-methyl-	90%	150, 161
	72%	76
β-methyl-α-o-tolyl-	92% *	116

TABLE VII—*Continued*

SOME CYCLIZATIONS BY THE FRIEDEL-CRAFTS ALUMINUM CHLORIDE METHOD

Acids Submitted to Cyclization	Yields of Ketones	Reference
4-methyl-β-*p*-tolyl-γ-acetic acid	(*i*) 43% *	162
3,4-methylenedihydroxy-	—	163
α-phenyl-	(*c*) 94% *	114, 115
	(*k*) 78% *	140
β-phenyl-	75%	7
β-phenyl-γ-acetic acid	(*l*) 33–45%	8
γ-phenyl-β-acetic acid	(*c*)(*i*) 52% *	118
β,γ,2,4-tetramethyl-	—	164
β,γ,2,5-tetramethyl-	—	164
γ-*p*-tolyl-	70%	13; cf. 15a
α,β,2-trimethyl-	80%	165
α,β,4-trimethyl-	—	146
α,γ,4-trimethyl-	—	146
α,2,3-trimethyl-	(*a*) 95%	164
α,2,4-trimethyl-	90%	164
β,γ,2-trimethyl-	92%	146
β,γ,4-trimethyl-	—	146
γ,2,4-trimethyl-	(*a*) 82%	151
γ,2,5-trimethyl-	—	146
β-$CH_2CH_2CO_2H$	55%	11
γ-$CH_2CH_2CO_2H$	17%; (*i*) 45%	22
	53%; (*i*) 6%	23
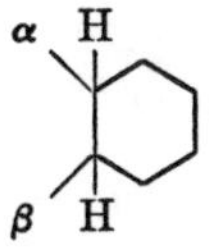 *trans*	58% *	166
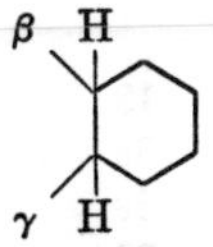 *cis* or *trans*	58% *	166
δ-*Phenylvaleric acid*	(*m*) 20%	10
	(*m*)(*d*) 30–40%	167
	(*m*) 45%	168
	(*m*) 50%	169
3,4-methylene dihydroxy-	(*m*) —	163

HYDRINDENE DERIVATIVES

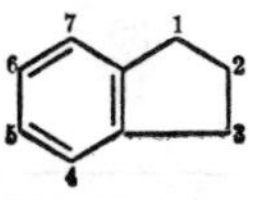

TABLE VII—*Continued*

SOME CYCLIZATIONS BY THE FRIEDEL-CRAFTS ALUMINUM CHLORIDE METHOD

Acids Submitted to Cyclization	Yields of Ketones	Reference
β-1-*Hydrindylpropionic acid*	20–36%	32
γ-1-*Hydrindylbutyric acid*	(*m*) 15%	10
γ-5-*Hydrindylbutyric acid*	83% *	170
NAPHTHALENE DERIVATIVES		
1-*Naphthylacetic acid*	—	171
4-bromo-	(*f*) —	39
2-ethyl-	85% *	106
α-ethyl-2-phenyl-1,2,3,4-tetrahydro-	(*c*)(*n*)	114
α-methyl-2-phenyl-1,2,3,4-tetrahydro-	(*c*)(*n*)	114
α-phenyl-	(*k*) 69%	172
2-phenyl-1,2,3,4-tetrahydro-	(*c*) 81% *	115
1,2,3,4-tetrahydro-	40%	32
2-*Naphthylacetic acid*		
1-phenyl-1,2,3,4-tetrahydro-	70% *	9
β-1-*Naphthylpropionic acid*		
CH₂CH₂CO₂H	(*o*) 34%	39
α-benzyl-	(*f*) 70%	13
4-bromo-	(*p*)	39
α-ethyl-	(*q*)	39
4-methoxy-	(*p*)	39
2-methoxy-β-phenyl-	(*k*) 88% *	173
2-methyl-	(*a*) 72% *	174
1,2,3,4-tetrahydro-	35–45%	32
β-2-*Naphthylpropionic acid*	(*r*)	39
α-benzyl-	(*f*) 70%	13
1-bromo-	(*r*)	39
α-ethyl-	—	39
β-phenyl-	—	13

TABLE VII—*Continued*

SOME CYCLIZATIONS BY THE FRIEDEL-CRAFTS ALUMINUM CHLORIDE METHOD

Acids Submitted to Cyclization	Yields of Ketones	Reference
γ-1-*Naphthylbutyric acid*		
$CH_2CH_2CH_2CO_2H$		
	(k) 81% *	100
4-methoxy-	(j) 86% *	98
5-methoxy-	(o)(m) 41% *	98
6-methyl-	(k) 76% *	175
α-n-propyl-	82%	176
1,2,3,4-tetrahydro-	(m) 12%	10
γ-2-*Naphthylbutyric acid*		
β,γ-dimethyl-6-methoxy-	(j) 30% *	177
8-methyl-	(j) 16% *	25
7-methyl-γ-isopropyl-	(k) 74% *	175
ACENAPHTHENE DERIVATIVES		
β-7-*Acenaphthylpropionic acid*		
8a, 1,2,3-tetrahydro-	65%	30
γ-1-*Acenaphthylbutyric acid*	(f) 73%	90
γ-3-*Acenaphthylbutyric acid*	(f) 87%	178
FLUORENE DERIVATIVES		
β-9-*Fluorylpropionic acid*	33%	31
γ-2-*Fluorylbutyric acid*	(k) 78% *	92
PERINAPHTHANE DERIVATIVES		

TABLE VII—*Continued*

SOME CYCLIZATIONS BY THE FRIEDEL-CRAFTS ALUMINUM CHLORIDE METHOD

Acids Submitted to Cyclization	Yields of Ketones	Reference
Perinaphthane-7-acetic acid 9a, 1,2,3-tetrahydro-	60%	30
β-7-Perinaphthanepropionic acid 9a, 1,2,3-tetrahydro-	75%	30

PHENANTHRENE DERIVATIVES

Acids Submitted to Cyclization	Yields of Ketones	Reference
β-1-Phenanthrylpropionic acid	$(f)(s)$ 31% *	42
β-2-Phenanthrylpropionic acid		
9,10-dihydro-	$(k)(t)$ 97% *	58
β-methyl-	(f) 69%	44; cf. 179
β-3-Phenanthrylpropionic acid	(f) 74% *	42
β,1-dimethyl-7-isopropyl-	(k) 32% *	180; cf. 181
β-methyl-	$(f)(t)$ 95% *	49
β-9-Phenanthrylpropionic acid	$(f)(t)$ 81% *	42
γ-2-Phenanthrylbutyric acid	$(f)(k)(u)$ 57% *	43
	$(k)(u)$ 53% *	43
9,10-dihydro-	(k) 77% *	97
γ-3-Phenanthrylbutyric acid		
α-carboxy-γ-methyl-	$(f)(h)$ 65%	56
1-methyl-7-isopropyl-	(k) 35%	182; cf. 181
γ-4-Phenanthrylbutyric acid 1,10-dimethylene-5,6,7,8-tetrahydro-	(f) 62% *	90
ANTHRACENE DERIVATIVES *γ-2-Anthrylbutyric acid*	(k) 72% *	56
BENZANTHRACENE DERIVATIVES 1,2-*Benzanthracene-5-acetic acid*	(c) 74% *	48

TABLE VII—*Continued*

SOME CYCLIZATIONS BY THE FRIEDEL-CRAFTS ALUMINUM CHLORIDE METHOD

Acids Submitted to Cyclization	Yields of Ketones	Reference
CHRYSENE DERIVATIVES 11-*Methyl-1,2,3,4-tetrahydrochrysene-1-acetic acid*	(c) 82% *	109b
PYRENE DERIVATIVES γ-3-*Pyrenylbutyric acid*	(k) 56% *	82

* Yields marked by an asterisk were calculated from the acid. Most of the others were based upon the acid chloride.

(a) Inverse type Friedel-Crafts reaction.
(b) Yield "almost quantitative."
(c) Phosphorus oxychloride removed at reduced pressure.
(d) Yield calculated from acid consumed.
(e) Phosphorus oxychloride separated with petroleum ether.
(f) Nitrobenzene solvent.
(g) After six hours' boiling in carbon disulfide, 20% unchanged acid recovered.
(h) Cyclic anhydride used instead of acid chloride.
(i) Double cyclization.
(j) *sym*-Tetrachloroethane solvent.
(k) Phosphorus oxychloride not removed.
(l) Yield for *meso* form; diketone also prepared from *racemic* but no yield given.
(m) Seven-membered ring formed.
(n) Yield above 85% * (private communication).
(o) *Peri* ring closure.
(p) Abnormal reaction; group lost.
(q) Crude oily product in good yield.
(r) Yield poor.
(s) Mixture of isomers; cyclized to 2-position, 2.2% yield; cyclized to 10-position, 29% yield.
(t) Crude neutral fraction; mixture of ketones from cyclization in both directions.
(u) Mixture of isomers (see p. 177).

[122] Gagnon and Gravel, *Can. J. Research*, **8**, 600 (1933) [*C. A.*, **27**, 5321 (1933)].
[123] Hoyer, *J. prakt. Chem.*, **139**, 242 (1934).
[124] Fieser and Seligman, *J. Am. Chem. Soc.*, **57**, 2174 (1935).
[125] Bruce and Fieser, *J. Am. Chem. Soc.*, **59**, 479 (1937).
[126] Bruce and Todd, *J. Am. Chem. Soc.*, **61**, 157 (1939).
[127] Fieser and Seligman, *J. Am. Chem. Soc.*, **57**, 942 (1935).
[128] Mayer, Philipps, Ruppert, and Schmitt, *Ber.*, **61**, 1966 (1928).
[129] Fieser and Hershberg, *J. Am. Chem. Soc.*, **59**, 394 (1937).
[130] Haller and Bauer, *Compt. rend.*, **150**, 1472 (1910).
[131] Bachmann, Cook, Hewett, and Iball, *J. Chem. Soc.*, **1936,** 54
[132] Koelsch and Le Claire, *J. Org. Chem.*, **6**, 516 (1941).
[133] Whittleston, *J. Am. Chem. Soc.*, **59**, 825 (1937).
[134] Brand and Horn, *J. prakt. Chem.*, **115**, 351 (1927).
[135] Chakravarti and Swaminathan, *J. Ind. Chem. Soc.*, **11**, 101 (1934).
[136] Fieser and Lothrop, *J. Am. Chem. Soc.*, **58**, 2050 (1936).
[137] v. Auwers and Auffenberg, *Ber.*, **52**, 92 (1919).

[138] Kipping and Clarke, *J. Chem. Soc.*, **1903**, 913.
[139] Cook, Hewett, Mayneord, and Roe, *J. Chem. Soc.*, **1934**, 1727.
[140] Plentl and Bogert, *J. Am. Chem. Soc.*, **63**, 989 (1941).
[141] Pfeiffer and Roos, *J. prakt. Chem.*, **159**, 13 (1941).
[142] Ramage and Robinson, *J. Chem. Soc.*, **1933**, 607.
[143] Bergs, *Ber.*, **63**, 1285 (1930).
[144] Fieser and Seligman, *J. Am. Chem. Soc.*, **60**, 170 (1938).
[145] Schroeter, Lichtenstadt, and Irineu, *Ber.*, **51**, 1587 (1918)
[146] Ruzicka and Ehmann, *Helv. Chim. Acta*, **15**, 140 (1932).
[147] Ruzicka and Hosking, *Helv. Chim. Acta*, **13**, 1402 (1930).
[148] Linstead, Millidge, Thomas, and Walpole, *J. Chem. Soc.*, **1937**, 1146.
[149] Rupe and Schütz, *Helv. Chim. Acta*, **9**, 992 (1926).
[150] Ruzicka and Mörgeli, *Helv. Chim. Acta*, **19**, 377 (1936).
[151] Heilbron and Wilkinson, *J. Chem. Soc.*, **1930**, 2537.
[152] Plattner and Magyar, *Helv. Chim. Acta*, **24**, 1163 (1941).
[153] Rapson and Short, *J. Chem. Soc.*, **1933**, 128.
[154] Ruzicka, Hösli, and Hofmann, *Helv. Chim. Acta*, **19**, 370 (1936).
[155] Crawford, *J. Am. Chem. Soc.*, **61**, 608 (1939).
[156] Harvey, Heilbron, and Wilkinson, *J. Chem. Soc.*, **1930**, 423.
[157] Ruzicka and Stoll, *Helv. Chim. Acta*, **5**, 923 (1922).
[158] Ruzicka and Mingazzini, *Helv. Chim. Acta*, **5**, 710 (1922).
[159] Bachmann and Struve, *J. Am. Chem. Soc.*, **62**, 1618 (1940).
[160] Weygand and Schröder, *Ber.*, **74B**, 1844 (1941).
[161] Ruzicka and Waldmann, *Helv. Chim. Acta*, **15**, 907 (1932).
[162] Ramage, *J. Chem. Soc.*, **1938**, 397.
[163] Borsche, *Ber.*, **44**, 2942 (1911).
[164] Ruzicka, Ehmann, and Mörgeli, *Helv. Chim. Acta*, **16**, 314 (1933).
[165] Wilkinson, *J. Chem. Soc.*, **1931**, 1333.
[166] Cook, Hewett, and Lawrence, *J. Chem. Soc.*, **1936**, 71.
[167] Kipping and Hunter, *J. Chem. Soc.*, **1901**, 602.
[168] Ramart and Hoch, *Bull. soc. chim.*, [5] **5**, 848 (1938).
[169] Borsche and Roth, *Ber.*, **54**, 174 (1921).
[170] Fieser and Seligman, *J. Am. Chem. Soc.*, **59**, 883 (1937).
[171] Ger. pat., 230,237 (1910 [*Chem. Zentr.*, I, 359 (1911)]).
[172] Koelsch and Richter, *J. Am. Chem. Soc.*, **59**, 2165 (1937).
[173] Koelsch, *J. Am. Chem. Soc.*, **58**, 1326 (1936).
[174] Klyne and Robinson, *J. Chem. Soc.*, **1938**, 1991.
[175] Orcutt and Bogert, *J. Am. Chem. Soc.*, **63**, 127 (1941).
[176] Kon, Narracott and Reid, *J. Chem. Soc.*, **1938**, 778.
[177] R. D. Haworth and Sheldrick, *J. Chem. Soc.*, **1934**, 864.
[178] Fieser and Peters, *J. Am. Chem. Soc.*, **54**, 4347 (1932).
[179] Hillemann, *Ber.*, **68**, 102 (1935).
[180] Adelson and Bogert, *J. Am. Chem. Soc.*, **59**, 399 (1937).
[181] Fieser and Clapp, *J. Am. Chem. Soc.*, **63**, 319 (1941).
[182] Adelson and Bogert, *J. Am. Chem. Soc.*, **59**, 1776 (1937); see reference 181 regarding structure.

The Hydrogen Fluoride Method

In 1939 it was observed [16] that anhydrous liquid hydrogen fluoride is an excellent agent for effecting intramolecular acylation of aryl substituted aliphatic acids. Since that time a number of cyclizations have been performed with this reagent (Table VIII).

The general procedure consists in allowing a solution of the acid in hydrogen fluoride to stand for a few hours in an open vessel at room temperature. The excellence of the method lies in the simplicity of manipulation and in the consistently good yields. The examples in Table VIII include the cyclizations of a number of different types of arylbutyric and arylpropionic acids. Of the twenty-nine ring closures, nineteen were accomplished in yields of 87% or better. The unique cyclizing power of hydrogen fluoride is shown with γ-(4-methoxy-3-biphenyl)-butyric acid (formula XXXVII). Ring closure was realized, if only to the extent of 16%, whereas other methods, including the Friedel-Crafts, were unsuccessful.[26] In contrast, β-p-methoxyphenyl-propionic acid (LXXXI) was cyclized in only 3% yield by hydrogen fluoride; 94% of unchanged acid was recovered.[18] Although the yield could be raised to 36% by operating under pressure, the Friedel-Crafts method gave consistently good yields (86%) of LXXXII. (It is significant that in spite of the low cyclization susceptibility of LXXXI no intermolecular acylation occurred, although benzene was used as the solvent.)

LXXXI → LXXXII

The success of hydrogen fluoride as a cyclizing agent may be attributed in part to the fact that it manifests only a comparatively slight tendency to promote ketonic condensations and other undesirable side reactions. It has been shown [34] that in the cyclization of m-hydroxy-hydrocinnamic acid (LV, R = H) the unprotected phenolic residue offers no complication with hydrogen fluoride; the total yield of phenolic ketones (LVI and LVII, R = H) was 94%. β-1-Naphthylpropionic acid (LXI) cyclized [37] with hydrogen fluoride to give perinaphthanone-7 (LXII) in excellent yield. Other methods [35, 36, 39] always gave considerable amounts of the dehydrogenation product, perinaphthenone. Hydrindone-1, which seems to have a strong tendency to undergo self-condensation, was prepared in satisfactory yield (Table II) using hydrogen fluoride, although better yields have been obtained by the Friedel-Crafts method (Table II, examples 8, 9, 10, 11). The cyclization of γ-phenylbutyric acid to tetralone-1 (Table III) is perhaps best effected by this new method.

General Procedure. Liquid hydrogen fluoride (b.p. 19.4°) containing only 0.1–0.2% of water is available commercially in steel cylinders. It is highly corrosive to tissue,[182a] and the vapors are very toxic. Consequently, it should be handled with care; goggles and rubber gloves must be worn. With heed to these precautions hydrogen fluoride can be handled safely and easily.

The reactions may be carried out in the hood in an open container without provision for reflux. Platinum vessels appear to be most satisfactory, although copper flasks also may be used.[183] The vessel containing the acid to be cyclized is tared on a rough balance in the hood and filled with 7 to 30 parts (based on the weight of acid) of hydrogen fluoride from the inverted tank through a copper tube. If the tank is previously chilled to about 5°, fuming will be reduced. If the acid does not dissolve at once, the mixture should be stirred occasionally with a metal spatula. If the acid is extraordinarily insoluble it may be necessary to employ mechanical stirring. A colored soluble complex almost always is formed, and the reaction is often complete in ten to twenty minutes. It is usually expedient to allow the mixture to stand at room temperature for several hours so that most of the excess reagent will evaporate. This process may be hastened in a current of air, or by heating gently on a steam bath; or the solution may be poured into a beaker containing ice and the product quickly collected by suction filtration or by ether or benzene extraction followed immediately by a washing with soda solution. (This latter manipulation is not recommended for large-scale runs.) The ketone may then be purified in the customary manner. The cyclization of γ-(9,10-dihydro-2-phenanthryl)-butyric acid [184] serves as a typical illustration of the procedure.

Procedure IV. 8-Keto-3,4,5,6,7,8-hexahydro-1,2-benzanthracene.[184a] Into a platinum vessel containing 7.1 g. of γ-(9,10-dihydro-2-phenanthryl)-butyric acid is poured approximately 100 g. of liquid hydrogen fluoride. The acid dissolves readily on swirling, and the colored solution

---

[182a] When spilled on the skin hydrogen fluoride produces severe burns which become apparent only through pain several hours later. Parts that have been in contact with the reagent should be washed immediately with water and then treated with a paste of magnesia, water, and glycerol.

[183] Fieser, "Experiments in Organic Chemistry," 2nd ed., p. 388, D. C. Heath and Co., 1941.

[184] Fieser and Johnson, *J. Am. Chem. Soc.*, **62**, 575 (1940).

[184a] An expanded description of the procedure of Fieser and Johnson (reference 184).

is allowed to stand at room temperature for about two hours. The reagent is then largely removed with a stream of air and the residue neutralized with sodium carbonate solution and extracted with benzene. This is washed with water, shaken with a little anhydrous sodium sulfate, and concentrated to remove the benzene. The residual oil is distilled under reduced pressure as in Procedure II, giving 6.2 g. (94%) of nearly colorless ketone. A single crystallization from ligroin (b.p. 60–80°) yields 5.92 g. (89.5%) of pure ketone, m.p. 89.5–90.5°, remelting [184b] at 96.5–97.5°.

As much as 67 g. of γ-2-naphthylbutyric acid, using 500 g. of hydrogen fluoride, has been cyclized at one time.[185] The yield of pure ketone was 94%. The method also is applicable to the cyclization of o-benzylbenzoic acids to anthrones.[129]

[184b] The double melting point corresponds to two polymorphic forms (reference 97).
[185] Adkins and Lohr, unpublished observation

TABLE VIII

CYCLIZATIONS WITH HYDROGEN FLUORIDE

Ring System of Ketones Prepared	Yields	Reference
Hydrindene		
	73%	16
5-hydroxy	80% ⎱ 94%	34
7-hydroxy	14% ⎰	
6-methoxy	(a) 3%	18
	(b) 36%	
Naphthalene		
	92%	16
3-acetic acid-4-phenyl	89%	121
7-methoxy	(c) 61.5%	17
5-methoxy-8-phenyl	(d) 16%	16
Perinaphthane		
	(e) 81%	37
9-methyl	96%	38
Phenanthrene		
	94%	185
2,3-dimethyl	(f) 89%	186
8-CH$_2$CH$_2$-9	88%	16

TABLE VIII—*Continued*

CYCLIZATIONS WITH HYDROGEN FLUORIDE

Ring System of Ketones Prepared	Yields	Reference
	94%	185
1-methyl	93%	187
2,3-dimethyl	91%	186
Benzfluorene		
	91%	188
Pyrene		
	31%	186
1,2-Benzanthracene		
	(*g*) 74–81%	89
	78%	43
5-methyl	82%	43
3,4-dihydro	90%	184
3,4-dihydro-3′-isopropyl-10-methyl	93%	181
Triphenylene		
	87%	52

TABLE VIII—*Continued*

CYCLIZATIONS WITH HYDROGEN FLUORIDE

Ring System of Ketones Prepared	Yields	Reference
4-methyl	88%	52
2-methyl	93%	52
2,3-dimethyl	(f) 71%	186
4,5-*Methylenechrysene*		
	95%	189
	90%	189
3,4-*Benzpyrene*		
	70%	89

(a) Acid recovered unchanged, 94%.

(b) Reaction conducted in closed container under pressure for five days; 57% acid recovered.

(c) Unchanged acid amounted to 34%.

(d) Friedel-Crafts and sulfuric acid methods failed to give any ketone (reference 26).

(e) Small amount (6%) of 4,5-benzhydrindone-1 was isolated, total yield of ketone 87%.

(f) Mixture of diastereoisomers.

(g) Lower yield on larger runs.

The Sulfuric Acid Method

It has been known for some time [190] that sulfuric acid can be used as an agent for dehydrating γ-arylbutyric and β-arylpropionic acids to

[186] Fieser and Daudt, *J. Am. Chem. Soc.*, **63**, 782 (1941).

[187] Johnson and Goldman, unpublished observation.

[188] Lothrop and Coffman, *J. Am. Chem. Soc.*, **63**, 2564 (1941).

[189] Fieser and Cason, *J. Am. Chem. Soc.*, **62**, 1293 (1940).

[190] An early instance has been reported by Reimer, *Ber.*, **14**, 1802 (1881), and Roser, *Ann.*, **247**, 152 (1888).

cyclic ketones. The method usually gives at least some of the cyclized material, although the reaction conditions may sometimes be quite critical. A simple procedure which has been followed frequently consists in dissolving the acid to be cyclized in 4 to 10 parts of 80–98% sulfuric acid and warming the mixture on the steam bath for one-half to three hours. Occasionally the introduction of some fuming sulfuric acid [71] or temperatures over 100° [70] may prove efficacious.

The yields by the sulfuric acid method generally are lower than by the Friedel-Crafts or hydrogen fluoride methods. The examples in support of this are so numerous that no attempt is made to cite them all (see Table IX). A collection of typical cyclizations with sulfuric acid is given in Table X.

One of the disadvantages of sulfuric acid as an acylating agent is its strong tendency to promote ketone condensation reactions. Early attempts to cyclize β-phenylpropionic acid, for example, resulted only in the formation of hydrindenylidenehydrindone (LXXVIII) and truxene. [65] These substances were shown to be the result of the di- and tri-molecular condensation of hydrindone. Although it has since been possible to obtain hydrindone in 27% yield by the sulfuric acid method, [71] the conditions appear to be extremely critical. A further difficulty rests in the tendency of the reagent to sulfonate, particularly the uncyclized acid. Thus a monosulfonic acid of γ-2,4-dimethylphenylbutyric acid was isolated [15] from the water-soluble fraction produced on cyclization. The yields of ketone were only 10–15%. Extensive sulfonation may occur when highly activated nuclei are involved. Thus an attempt [15] to cyclize γ-p-methoxyphenylbutyric acid with concentrated sulfuric acid failed; no ketone was produced, and only a sulfonic acid was obtained. Successful cyclization, however, was realized with the Friedel-Crafts method.

There seems to be some indication that α-substituted γ-arylbutyric acids can be cyclized by sulfuric acid in better yields than the unsubstituted acids. Thus, whereas γ-phenylbutyric acid has not been cyclized in yields exceeding 50% with sulfuric acid (Table III), the α-methyl and α-ethyl homologs have been converted to the tetralones in 98% and 86% yields respectively. [191] Similarly α-methyl-γ-1-naphthylbutyric acid was cyclized in 91% yield, [192] although in the case of the unsubstituted acid yields over 75% [193] could not be obtained. This peculiarity may be explained by the fact that ring closure of acids containing a substituent in the α-position gives rise to ketones lacking the usual reactive methyl-

[191] Brunner and Grof, *Monatsh.*, **64**, 76 (1934).
[192] Bachmann and Wilds, unpublished observation.
[193] Haworth, *J. Chem. Soc.*, **1932**, 1125.

ene group. The possibility of interfering ketone condensations of the type discussed above is therefore eliminated. Being a structural feature this is true regardless of the method of cyclization. It may be presumed, therefore, that the conditions for cyclizing α-substituted acids by any method are in general less critical than for acids retaining both α-hydrogen atoms.

For the sulfuric acid method of cyclization there is no single procedure which is entirely general, because the concentration of the acid, and the reaction time and temperature, may be critical. The method of R. D. Haworth [193] has been used in the ring closure of a large number of acids, but the description serves only to indicate the form of procedure. In order to obtain optimum yields, it may be necessary to alter the conditions and concentrations.

Procedure V. Ring Closure with Sulfuric Acid.[193] For the conversion of γ-arylbutyric acids into cyclic ketones, the finely powdered acid (1 part) is added gradually with stirring to a mixture of concentrated sulfuric acid (3 volumes) and water (1 volume). After one hour's heating on the water bath the colored solution is cooled, diluted with water by pouring onto ice, and extracted with ether. The extract is washed with water, which removes traces of colored sulfonation product, then with dilute aqueous ammonia, and dried over anhydrous potassium carbonate; the solvent is removed, the residue distilled under reduced pressure, and the distillate crystallized from a suitable solvent.

An interesting application of sulfuric acid cyclization was reported [194] in which β-benzylglutaric acid (LXXXIII) was cyclized to the keto acid LXXXIV by the action of concentrated sulfuric acid at room temperature. The yield of crude material was 88%. This seems to be a

LXXXIII   LXXXIV

LXXXV

[194] Stevenson and Thorpe, *J. Chem. Soc.*, **1922**, 1717.

general reaction for dicarboxylic acids which are capable of forming cyclic anhydrides. 3-Carboxytetralone-1 (LXXX) was thus obtained from benzylsuccinic acid.[195] A similar type of cyclization was reported [196] in the case of the tricarboxylic acid LXXXV. The ring was closed by the action of concentrated sulfuric acid at 0° for forty minutes, but the yield was not recorded.

TABLE IX

COMPARISON OF YIELDS OBTAINED BY THE SULFURIC ACID AND
FRIEDEL-CRAFTS METHODS

Acids Submitted to Cyclization	Best Yields of Ketones			
	Sulfuric Acid	Reference	Friedel-Crafts	Reference
β-Phenylpropionic acid (a)	27%	71	95%	75
γ-Phenylbutyric acid (b)	50%	15, 78	74–91%	79
γ-m-Methoxyphenylbutyric acid	79%	197	96%	14
γ-p-Ethylphenylbutyric acid	50–55%	15	87%	104
α,β,γ-Triphenylbutyric acid	25%	155	58%	155
γ-1-Naphthylbutyric acid (c)	70–75%	193	81–94%	95, 100
γ-2-Naphthylbutyric acid	70–75%	193	90%	104
γ-2-Phenanthrylbutyric acid (d)	44%	43	80–91%	43
γ-(9,10-Dihydro-2-phenanthryl)-butyric acid (c)	30%	58	77–90%	54, 97
γ-3-Pyrenylbutyric acid (e)	0%	80	85–96%	38, 85
1,2-Benzanthracene-5-acetic acid	0%	48	74%	48
β,γ-Dianisyladipic acid	0%	142	80%	142

(a) See Table II.
(b) See Table III.
(c) See Table V.
(d) See Table XIV.
(e) See Table IV.

[195] Attwood, Stevenson, and Thorpe, J. Chem. Soc., **1923**, 1755.
[196] Robinson and Thompson, J. Chem. Soc., **1938**, 2009.
[197] Rapson and Robinson, J. Chem. Soc., **1935**, 1285.

TABLE X

Some Cyclizations with Sulfuric Acid

Acids Submitted to Cyclization	Yields of Ketones	Reference
β-Phenylpropionic acid		
	10%	70
	27%	71
2-bromo-	10%	198
3-bromo-	40–50%	69
4-bromo-	—	69
β-carboxy-	22%	70
β-carboxy-α-phenyl-	(a) —	190
3-chloro-	55–60%	69
4-chloro-	—	198
3-chloro-α-methyl-	63%	69
2-chloro-5-methyl- ⎫ mixture	(b) 56%	199
5-chloro-2-methyl- ⎭		
4-iodo-	—	198
α-methyl-	60%	69
β-methyl-	—	70
2-methyl-	25%	200
3-methyl-	—	69
4-methyl-	—	69
α-phenyl-	30%	201
β-CH₂COOH	49%	70
γ-Phenylbutyric acid		
	27%	35
	49%	78
	50%	15
β-carboxy-	(c) —	195
β,β-dicarboxy-	(c) —	195
3,4-dimethoxy-	(d) 82%	202
3,4-dimethoxy-α-phenyl-	(e) 72%	203
3,4-dimethoxy-α,β-dimethyl-	—	202
3,4-dimethoxy-β-methyl-	70%	204
2,4-dimethyl-	10–15%	15
3,4-dimethyl-	—	15
α,β-diphenyl-	25%	155
3-ethoxy-	70%	205
α-ethyl-	86%	191
4-ethyl-	50–55%	15
5-ethyl-4-methoxy-2-methyl-	94%	206
3-methoxy-	79%	197
α-methyl-	98%	191
4-methyl-	80%	15
α-phenyl-	(f) 57%	155

TABLE X—*Continued*

SOME CYCLIZATIONS WITH SULFURIC ACID

Acids Submitted to Cyclization	Yields of Ketones	Reference
β-phenyl-γ-CH₂CO₂H { meso / racemic	78% 68% } (a)(g)	142
α-CHCH₂CO₂H CH₂CH₂CO₂H	(c) —	196
trans- / *cis-*	(c) 68% (c)(h) 60%	166 166
	—	207
β-CH₂CO₂H	(c) 88%	194
γ-1-*Naphthylbutyric acid* 	70–75%	193
α,β-cyclopentano-	(i)	208
α,α-dimethyl-	82%	209
α,4-dimethyl-	85%	210
α,5-dimethyl-	—	211
γ,5-dimethyl-	—	210
α-ethyl-	(j) 60%	210
6-methoxy-	(k) 84%	212
α-methyl-	70%	193
	91%	192
4-methyl-	65%	211
5-methyl-	70%	210
α,α,4-trimethyl-	89%	209
γ-2-*Naphthylbutyric acid* 	70–75%	193

TABLE X—*Continued*

SOME CYCLIZATIONS WITH SULFURIC ACID

Acids Submitted to Cyclization	Yields of Ketones	Reference
α,α-dimethyl-	80%	209
α,γ-dimethyl-	—	210
α,6-dimethyl-	60%	210
γ,6-dimethyl-	—	213
β,6-dimethyl-	50%	210
6,7-dimethyl-	80%	210
γ-ethyl-6-methyl-	50%	214
γ-ethyl-6-isopropyl-	60%	214
6-isopropyl-	75%	210
α-methyl-	70%	193
β-methyl-	(j) 25%	210
6-methyl-	—	213
γ-methyl-6-isopropyl-	—	213
5,6,7,8-tetrahydro-	75%	15
5,6,7,8-tetramethyl-	69%	27
α,β,γ-trimethyl-	—	27
β,γ,6-trimethyl-	70%	215
α,γ,6-trimethyl-	—	215
γ,6,7-trimethyl-	—	215
1,2-*Dihydrophenanthryl-4-acetic acid*	40%	35
γ-2-*Phenanthrylbutyric acid*	60%	46
9,10-dihydro-	30%	58
γ-3-*Phenanthrylbutyric acid*	40%	46
4b,5,6,7,8,8a,9,10-octahydro-	77%	216
γ-9-*Phenanthrylbutyric acid*		
1,2,3,4,5,6,7,8-octahydro-	75%	217
1,2-*Benzanthracene-5-acetic acid*		
1',2',3',4',1,2,3,4,5,6,7,8-dodecahydro-	69%	216
γ-1-*Pyrenylbutyric acid*		
3,4,5,8,9,10-hexahydro-	29%	80
1'-*Naphthylmethyl-2-benzoic acid*		

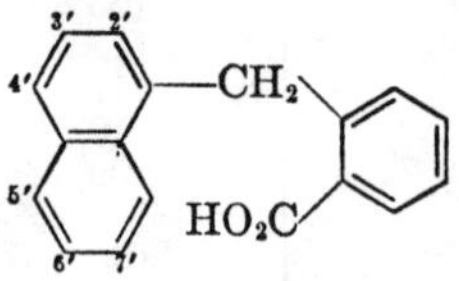	(l) 97%	218
2',7'-dimethoxy-	(l) 97%	218

(a) Double cyclization.
(b) Mixture.
(c) Heating unnecessary.
(d) Crude ketone.
(e) Pure ketone.
(f) Sulfuric-acetic acid mixture used for cyclization.

(g) Dimethyl ester used for cyclization.
(h) Mixture of *cis* and *trans* isomers.
(i) Variable results.
(j) Yield based on keto acid.
(k) 9% acid recovered.
(l) Seven-membered ring produced.

[*References to table on next page.*]

Other Methods

The extent of consideration given to the methods of cyclization discussed below is not intended to be an indication of the relative merits of the methods but is necessarily limited by the available experimental data.

Stannic Chloride on the Free Acid. Ring closure by heating the free acid with stannic chloride at 100–120° has been shown to be successful on several types of acids.[35, 47, 55, 56, 80, 139, 219] These and some other acids which have been cyclized by this method may be found in Table XI. In four instances (items 3, 7, 14, 17) stannic chloride treatment gave better results than sulfuric acid. Eleven of the acids in Table XI (items 3, 5, 8, 9, 10, 12, 13, 14, 16, 17, 18) have been cyclized also by the Friedel-Crafts method on the acid chloride. With seven acids (3, 6, 8, 9, 12, 14, 17) the yields were better, while with four (5, 10, 16, 18) they were lower, than with stannic chloride. Except for one (18) of these latter acids, however, there seems to be some question as to whether the optimum conditions for the Friedel-Crafts reaction were employed. Of the acids (4, 6, 12) which have since been cyclized with hydrogen fluoride, considerable improvement in yields was realized.

It may be suggested tentatively that ring closure by the action of stannic chloride on the free acid is generally inferior to both the Friedel-Crafts and hydrogen fluoride methods. Some advantages seem to be afforded, however, by the simplicity of manipulation.

[198] Miersch, *Ber.*, **25**, 2109 (1892).

[199] Fieser and Seligman, *J. Am. Chem. Soc.*, **58**, 2482 (1936).

[200] Young, *Ber.*, **25**, 2102 (1892).

[201] Miller and Rohde, *Ber.*, **25**, 2095 (1892).

[202] Haworth and Mavin, *J. Chem. Soc.*, **1932**, 1485.

[203] Robinson and Young, *J. Chem. Soc.*, **1935**, 1414.

[204] Haworth and Atkinson, *J. Chem. Soc.*, **1938**, 797.

[205] Peak, Robinson, and Walker, *J. Chem. Soc.*, **1936**, 752.

[206] Harland and Robertson, *J. Chem. Soc.*, **1939**, 937.

[207] Bluminfeld, *Ber.*, **74B**, 524 (1941).

[208] E. Bergmann and Blum-Bergmann, *J. Am. Chem. Soc.*, **59**, 1572 (1937).

[209] Sengupta, *J. prakt. Chem.*, **152**, 9 (1939).

[210] Haworth, Mavin, and Sheldrick, *J. Chem. Soc.*, **1934**, 454.

[211] Haworth and Mavin, *J. Chem. Soc.*, **1932**, 2720.

[212] Haberland, *Ber.*, **69**, 1380 (1936).

[213] Haworth, Letsky, and Mavin, *J. Chem. Soc.*, **1932**, 1784.

[214] Haworth, *J. Chem. Soc.*, **1932**, 2717.

[215] Haworth and Bolam, *J. Chem. Soc.*, **1932**, 2248.

[216] Cook and Haslewood, *J. Chem. Soc.*, **1935**, 767.

[217] van de Kamp, Burger, and Mosettig, *J. Am. Chem. Soc.*, **60**, 1321 (1938).

[218] Fieser, *J. Am. Chem. Soc.*, **55**, 4977 (1933).

[219] Cook and Hewett, *J. Chem. Soc.*, **1933**, 1098.

Phosphorus Pentoxide. The direct dehydration of arylbutyric and arylpropionic acids has been accomplished in some instances with phosphorus pentoxide in organic solvents such as benzene or toluene (Table XII). The procedure involves treating the solution of the acid with 1 to 10 parts of powdered phosphorus pentoxide and boiling the suspension for one to three hours with mechanical stirring. The addition of a portion of Filter-Cel equal in weight to the amount of acid being cyclized may improve the reaction by holding in suspension the phosphoric anhydride, which otherwise tends to form a sticky coagulum.[192] After the reaction is terminated, the excess phosphorus pentoxide usually is decomposed with dilute alkali and the product purified in the customary manner. The method appears fairly general and has the advantage over sulfuric acid in that no substitution reactions comparable to sulfonation can take place. On the other hand, the strong dehydrating action of phosphoric anhydride readily promotes further ketone condensations. Thus, phosphorus pentoxide reacted exothermically with β-phenylpropionic acid[220] to form truxene in about 40% yield. No hydrindone-1 was obtained.

A modification of the phosphorus pentoxide method involves the use of syrupy phosphoric acid.[221] This affords the advantage of a homogeneous reaction mixture, but there is no indication that the method is an improvement, since so little experimental work is available.

Miscellaneous Methods and Reagents. Some other methods of cyclization may be mentioned, although the generality of the procedures hardly has been demonstrated. The technique of *heating the free acid chloride* under reduced pressure already has been mentioned. The yields are generally inferior, and often the method may fail because the acid chloride either decomposes or distils unchanged. Some of the acids which have been cyclized by this method may be found in Table XIII. Ring closure by heating the free acid has been accomplished but appears to be of no practical value. Thus, 7-hydroxy-hydrindone-1 was prepared in 3% yield by slow distillation of *m*-hydroxyhydrocinnamic acid at atmospheric pressure.[222]

By boiling a solution of α-*p*-anisyl-γ-3-methoxyphenylbutyric acid (LXXXVI) in *phosphorus oxychloride* for five minutes, the cyclic ketone (LXXXVII) was formed in 73% yield;[222a] unchanged acid amounting to 16% was recovered. This same method applied to the trimethoxy acid

[220] Kipping, *J. Chem. Soc.*, **1894**, 269.

[221] Koebner and Robinson, *J. Chem. Soc.*, **1938**, 1994.

[222] Knake and Salkowski, *Ber.*, **49**, 2103 (1916).

[222a] Dodds, Goldberg, Lawson, and Robinson, *Proc. Roy. Soc.* (*London*), **B127**, 140 (1939); Goldberg and Robinson, *J. Chem. Soc.*, **1941**, 575.

LXXXVIII gave the tetralone derivative LXXXIX in 99% yield. A modification of the phosphorus oxychloride method was used to cyclize

LXXXVI (R = H)
LXXXVIII (R = CH₃O)

LXXXVII (R = H)
LXXXIX (R = CH₃O)

γ-2-methoxyphenylbutyric acid in 55% yield. sym-Tetrachloroethane was used as the solvent, and the mixture was boiled for two and one-half hours.[24] This was an improvement over the phosphorus pentoxide method which gave a yield of 16%.

The excellent method for cyclizing o-benzylbenzoic acids to anthranol acetates, by heating the acid in a mixture of *acetic acid and anhydride with zinc chloride* as a catalyst,[223] has been used also in the preparation of cyclic ketones of the tetralone type. In this way γ-3-acenaphthylbutyric acid has been cyclized in 78% yield;[224] γ-2-phenanthrylbutyric acid [43] and the 9,10-dihydro derivative [97] in 51% and 59% yields respectively; and α,β-dimethyl-γ-2-naphthylbutyric acid in 90% yield.[186]

Another reagent, *fused zinc chloride*, which has been more commonly used for the ring closure of o-benzylbenzoic acids, was applied to the cyclization of γ-3-pyrenylbutyric acid (Table IV, example 2). The reaction was carried out at 180°, and the yield was 16%.

An interesting ring closure has been described in an attempt to effect an acylation of anisole with β-phenylpropionic acid in the presence of chloroacetic anhydride.[73] Only intramolecular acylation occurred, giving hydrindone-1; the yield after heating for forty-eight hours at 170° was 74%. 3,3-Diphenylhydrindone-1 was similarly prepared in 67% yield. This further stresses the preference for intra- over inter-molecular acylation.

[223] Fieser and Hershberg, *J. Am. Chem. Soc.*, **59**, 1028 (1937).
[224] Fieser and Hershberg, *J. Am. Chem. Soc.*, **60**, 1893 (1938).

TABLE XI

SOME CYCLIZATIONS WITH STANNIC CHLORIDE ON THE FREE ACIDS

Acids Submitted to Cyclization	Yields of Ketones	Reference
β-Phenylpropionic acid		
1. α,5-dimethyl-2-isopropyl-	(a) 69%	139
2. 5-methyl-2-isopropyl-	(b) 90%	139
γ-Phenylbutyric acid		
3. 3-methoxy-	85–90%	225
4. *β-1-Naphthylpropionic acid*	(c) 45%	35
5. *β-2-Naphthylpropionic acid*	32%	219
6. *γ-1-Naphthylbutyric acid*	70%	226
7. α,β-cyclopentano-	(d) 13%	208
8. 5-methoxy-	(e) 40%	98
9. 6-methoxy-	68%	227
	70%	226
γ-2-Naphthylbutyric acid		
10. β,γ-dimethyl-6-methoxy-	72%	177
11. 6-methoxy-5-methyl-	34–77%	228
12. *γ-2-Anthrylbutyric acid*	65%	56
13. *γ-1-Phenanthrylbutyric acid*	—	41
14. *γ-3-Phenanthrylbutyric acid*	75%	45, 47
15. α-methyl-	29%	55
16. 1-methyl-7-isopropyl-	49%	182; cf. 181
17. *γ-3-Pyrenylbutyric acid*	37%	81
18. α-methyl-	80%	81

(a) Cyclization process repeated twice on recovered acid.

(b) Calculated from acid consumed (about one-half).

(c) Ring closure in two directions to give mainly perinaphthenone resulting from dehydrogenation of the normal cyclization product perinaphthanone, and a small amount of 4,5-benzhydrindone-1.

(d) Toluene used as a solvent.

(e) Abnormal cyclization; gives variable results (see p. 175).

[225] Peak and Robinson, *J. Chem. Soc.*, **1937**, 1581.

[226] Hoch, *Bull. soc. chim.* [5] **5**, 264 (1938).

[227] Butenandt and Schramm, *Ber.*, **68**, 2083 (1935).

[228] Hill, Short, and Higginbottom, *J. Chem. Soc.*, **1936**, 317.

TABLE XII

Some Cyclizations with Phosphorus Pentoxide

Acids Submitted to Cyclization	Yields of Ketones	Reference
β-*Phenylpropionic acid*		
3,4-dimethoxy-	82%	119
2,5-dimethoxy-	(a) 82%	229
3,4-methylenedihydroxy-	87%	119
γ-*Phenylbutyric acid*		
4-methoxy-	61%	230
2-methoxy-	16%	24
δ-*Phenylvaleric acid*	(b) 10%	86
3,4-methylenedihydroxy-	(b) 19%	86
γ-1-*Naphthylbutyric acid*		
α,β-cyclopentano-	11%	208
5-methoxy-	47%	24
7-methoxy-	83%	230
α-methyl-6-methoxy-	86%	103
γ-2-*Naphthylbutyric acid*	(c)(d) 86%	192
6-s-butyl-γ-methyl-	—	231a
3,7-dimethoxy-	30%	231b
6-ethyl-γ-methyl-	—	231a
3-methoxy-	—	232
6-methoxy-γ-methyl-	80%	233
[structure: cyclopentanone ring with O, β H, γ H]	(e) 63%	221
6-methoxy-	(e) 19%	221
β-9-*Phenanthrylpropionic acid*	32%	53
γ-9-*Phenanthrylbutyric acid*	68%	51
1,2-*Benzanthracene-5-acetic acid*		
2-methyl-1,2,3,4-tetrahydro-	51%	208

(a) Crude yield.
(b) As the semicarbazone.
(c) Yield based on acid consumed (about nine-tenths).
(d) Filter-Cel used in cyclization.
(e) Syrupy phosphoric acid used in cyclization.

[229] Arnold and Zaugg, *J. Am. Chem. Soc.*, **63**, 1317 (1941).
[230] Plimmer, Short, and Hill, *J. Chem. Soc.*, **1938**, 694.
[231] (a) Ruzicka and Kaufmann, *Helv. Chim. Acta*, **24**, 939 (1941); (b) Haberland and Siegert, *Ber.*, **71**, 2619 (1938).
[232] Haberland and Kleinert, *Ber.*, **71**, 470 (1938).
[233] Short, Stromberg, and Wiles, *J. Chem. Soc.*, **1936**, 319.

TABLE XIII

Some Cyclizations by Heating the Free Acid Chlorides

Acids Submitted to Cyclization	Yields of Ketones	Reference
β-*Phenylpropionic acid*		
3,4-methylenedihydroxy-	(a) —	86
γ-*Phenylbutyric acid*		
α-benzyl-	(b) 60%	6
2,4-dimethyl-	(b) 40%	15
3,4-methylenedihydroxy-	(a) —	86
δ-*Phenylvaleric acid*	Failed	86
3,4-methylenedihydroxy-	(a) 55%	86
γ-1-*Naphthylbutyric acid*	(c)(b) 65%	234
4-methoxy-6-methyl-	(d) 50%	161
4-methoxy-5,6,7,8-tetrahydro-	—	234
5,6,7,8-tetrahydro-	88%	60
γ-2-*Naphthylbutyric acid*	(b) 67%	234
	(d) —	235
5,6,7,8-tetrahydro-	(b)(e) 83%	59

(a) Phosphorus trichloride used to form the acid chloride.
(b) Phosphorus pentachloride used to form the acid chloride.
(c) Twelve per cent acid recovered.
(d) Thionyl chloride used to form the acid chloride.
(e) Mixture of ketones (see p. 175).

THE INFLUENCE OF THE METHOD ON THE DIRECTION OF CYCLIZATION

In an acylation reaction which gives a mixture of isomeric ketones, the proportion of these isomers can sometimes be altered more or less by changing (a) the *solvent*, (b) the *temperature*, and (c) the entire *method* of acylation. To what extent the proportion of products may be altered, if at all, by such experimental changes cannot be predicted.

The influence of the above factors on the course of the reaction has been demonstrated for intermolecular acylation. Changing the *solvent* from benzene to nitrobenzene in the Friedel-Crafts acetylation of naphthalene makes it possible to obtain principally the β-isomer instead

[234] Schroeter, Müller, and Huang, *Ber.*, **62**, 645 (1929).
[235] Radcliffe, Sherwood, and Short, *J. Chem. Soc.*, **1931**, 2293.

of a mixture of the α- and β-substitution products.[236]   That a change in reaction *temperature* may influence the proportion of isomers was shown in the succinoylation of acenaphthene.[90]   Changing the *method* of acetylating acenaphthene from the Friedel-Crafts to the hydrogen fluoride technique was found to make possible the preparation of a new acetoacenaphthene in yields which can be accounted for only by a definite change in the proportion of isomers.[16, 237]

In the present problem of intramolecular acylation the conditions which have been most effective in altering the direction of ring closure have been those which involve different methods of cyclization.   The case of γ-5,6,7,8-tetrahydro-2-naphthylbutyric acid (XC) affords an example of the possibility of controlling, at least partially, the direction of ring closure by using different methods.   When the free acid chloride

$$\text{XCI} \xleftarrow{\text{H}_2\text{SO}_4} \quad (\text{CH}_2)_3\text{CO}_2\text{H} \xrightarrow{\text{PCl}_5} \quad + \quad$$

XC   XCI   XCII

was heated under reduced pressure, an 83% yield of a mixture of about equal quantities of 1-keto-1,2,3,4,5,6,7,8-octahydroanthracene (XCI) and 4-keto-1,2,3,4,5,6,7,8-octahydrophenanthrene (XCII) was obtained.[59]   On the other hand, when the acid (XC) was cyclized with warm concentrated sulfuric acid, a homogeneous product, which proved to be the ketoöctahydroanthracene XCI, resulted in 75% yield.[15]

Another instance of selective ring closure was reported [98] in the cyclization of γ-5-methoxy-1-naphthylbutyric acid (XCIV).   The

$$\xleftarrow[\text{AlCl}_3]{\text{SOCl}_2} \quad (\text{CH}_2)_3\text{CO}_2\text{H} \xrightarrow{\text{SnCl}_4} \quad + \text{ Some XCIII}$$

OCH₃   OCH₃   OCH₃
XCIII   XCIV   XCV

Friedel-Crafts reaction with aluminum chloride in *sym*-tetrachloroethane gave 7-keto-4-methoxyhomoperinaphthane (XCIII) in 41% yield.   Heating the free acid with stannic chloride, however, produced 1-keto-8-methoxy-1,2,3,4-tetrahydrophenanthrene (XCV) in 40% yield

[236] Rivkin, *J. Gen. Chem. U.S.S.R.*, **5**, 277 (1935).
[237] Fieser and Kilmer, *J. Am. Chem. Soc.*, **62**, 1354 (1940).

as the only product isolated.   The stannic chloride method upon repetition [238] proved to be unreliable as it gave the phenanthrene derivative less frequently than the product of *peri* ring closure.   The phosphorus pentoxide cyclization was shown also to give the seven-membered ring closure.[24, 239]

A striking example of selective orientation is illustrated by the cyclization of γ-2-phenanthrylbutyric acid (XCVI).   By the hydrogen

(74%)		(78%)
XCVIII	XCVI	XCVII

fluoride method, a high yield of ketone resulted consisting almost entirely of 8-keto-5,6,7,8-tetrahydro-1,2,-benzanthracene (XCVII), which was obtained pure in 78% yield.[43]   In contrast, the pure isomeric 4-keto-1,2,3,4-tetrahydrochrysene (XCVIII), was obtained in 74% yield by the Friedel-Crafts stannic chloride method,[107] and in 51% yield by the zinc chloride acetic acid-anhydride technique.[43]   When the ring was closed with sulfuric acid a mixture resulted from which only the chrysene derivative (XCVIII) could be isolated, and this in poor yield.

An apparent influence of the solvent was noted in the action of aluminum chloride on the chloride of XCVI, which gave mixtures of the two ketones in which the benzanthracene derivative (XCVII) predominated. This isomer constituted about two-thirds of the total using benzene as a solvent, and a still higher proportion (about nine-tenths) in nitrobenzene solution. A difference in reaction temperatures also may have influenced these ratios. That the temperature may affect the proportion of isomers is indicated by the fact that, when cyclization with stannic chloride was conducted at room temperature instead of in the cold, a mixture of ketones resulted instead of a single ketone.[107]

A summary of the results of the experiments on the cyclization of γ-2-phenanthrylbutyric acid may be found in Table XIV. The sharp contrast between the direction of ring closure with hydrogen fluoride (item 6) and with stannic chloride in the Friedel-Crafts reaction (item 1) is quite striking and of obvious practical significance. Some further indications that hydrogen fluoride has an unusual influence on the ori-

[238] Kon and Soper, *J. Chem. Soc.*, **1939**, 790.
[239] Hill, Short, and Stromberg, *J. Chem. Soc.*, **1937**, 1619.

entation in intramolecular acylation are given by the cyclization of α,β-dimethyl-γ-2-naphthylbutyric acid [186] and of γ-2-anthrylbutyric acid.[89] In both reactions there was a definite indication that some of the linear isomers were formed along with the normal products of ring closure. In the first this partial defiance of the normally strong tendency toward cyclization into the 1-position of the naphthalene nucleus seems to be significant.

TABLE XIV

CYCLIZATION OF γ-2-PHENANTHRYLBUTYRIC ACID

Method of Cyclization	Yield of Total Crude Ketone	Yield of Benzanthracene Ketone XCVII	Yield of Chrysene Ketone XCVIII
1. Friedel-Crafts—stannic chloride (thionyl chloride) method [107]	74% (m.p. 122–124°)		74% (m.p. 122–124°)
2. Friedel-Crafts—stannic chloride (phosphorus pentachloride) method [240]	80%	14% (m.p. 112–117°)	⨍58% (m.p. 124–125°)
3. Friedel-Crafts—aluminum chloride (phosphorus pentachloride) method [43]			
in benzene	91% (a)	35% (m.p. 115–116.5°)	17% (m.p. 122–125°)
in nitrobenzene	70% (m.p. 90–110°)	51% (m.p. 110–114°)	5% (m.p. 118–124°)
4. 85% Sulfuric acid [43]	44% (m.p. 90–112°)	(b)	23% (m.p. 123–125°)
5. Acetic acid-anhydride with zinc chloride [43]	62%		53% (m.p. 124–125°)
6. Hydrogen fluoride [43]	85% (m.p. 114–118°)	78% (m.p. 117–118°)	

(a) Crude distilled neutral oil.
(b) All attempts to isolate any of XCVII failed.

[240] Fieser and Johnson, unpublished observation.

CHAPTER 5

REDUCTION WITH ALUMINUM ALKOXIDES
(The Meerwein-Ponndorf-Verley Reduction)

A. L. WILDS

University of Wisconsin

CONTENTS

INTRODUCTION

In 1925 it was discovered independently by Verley [1] and by Meerwein and Schmidt [2] that an aldehyde can be reduced to the primary alcohol by treatment with aluminum ethoxide in the presence of ethanol. The reduction of the aldehyde occurs at the expense of an equivalent amount of ethanol which is oxidized to acetaldehyde.

$$RCHO + CH_3CH_2OH \underset{\longleftarrow}{\overset{Al(OC_2H_5)_3}{\longrightarrow}} RCH_2OH + CH_3CHO$$

The reaction is reversible, but the equilibrium can be shifted to the point of complete reduction by removal of the acetaldehyde with a stream of dry hydrogen or nitrogen. This has the additional advantage of preventing side reactions such as an aldol condensation between the original aldehyde and acetaldehyde. The method of reduction with aluminum ethoxide was found applicable to several aldehydes but to only a few ketones of special types.

In 1926 Ponndorf [3] reported that in independent work he also had evolved this new method of reducing aldehydes. He showed, further, that the reaction can be made more general by employing the aluminum derivatives of the more readily oxidizable secondary alcohols. By the use of aluminum isopropoxide, ketones as well as aldehydes could be reduced satisfactorily, the acetone formed being removed from the equilibrium mixture by slow distillation.

This mild and specific method of reducing carbonyl compounds became known as the Meerwein-Ponndorf-Verley reduction [4] and in the next decade was used successfully in a number of instances, particularly

[1] Verley, Bull. soc. chim., [4] 37, 537, 871 (1925); 41, 788 (1927).
[2] Meerwein and Schmidt, Ann., 444, 221 (1925).
[3] Ponndorf, Z. angew. Chem., 39, 138 (1926).
[4] Reviews of the Meerwein-Ponndorf-Verley reduction have been published by (a) Linstead, Ann. Repts. Chem. Soc. (London), 34, 228 (1937), and (b) Bersin, Angew. Chem., 53, 266 (1940).

with unsaturated aldehydes and ketones. Its general value, however, was not fully apparent until 1937, when Lund [5] applied the method to a variety of aldehydes and ketones and studied the scope and limitations of the reaction. He also developed a simple method for determining completeness of reduction, which consisted in testing the distillate for acetone with 2,4-dinitrophenylhydrazine.

The Nature of the Reaction

The reduction of aldehydes and ketones is carried out very easily. The carbonyl compound and aluminum isopropoxide, prepared from aluminum and isopropyl alcohol, are heated in boiling isopropyl alcohol solution with provision for slow distillation until no more acetone is formed. The general equation may be represented as follows.

$$\underset{R}{\overset{R'}{>}}C=O + \underset{\frac{Al}{3}-O}{\overset{H\quad CH_3}{>C<}}CH_3 \rightleftarrows \underset{R}{\overset{R'\quad H}{>C<}}O-\frac{Al}{3} + O=C\overset{CH_3}{<}CH_3$$

The reaction involves the transfer of one valence bond of the aluminum atom and one hydrogen atom from the alkoxide to the carbonyl compound. The exact mechanism of this transfer is unknown, although an intermediate aluminum derivative of a hemiacetal (I) has been postulated.[1, 2, 3] When isopropyl alcohol is the solvent the aluminum iso-

$$\underset{R}{\overset{R'\quad O-Al(OC_3H_7)_2}{>C}}\!\!-\!\!O\!\!-\!\!\underset{CH_3}{\overset{H\quad CH_3}{C<}}$$

$$I$$

propoxide may be considered a catalyst, since an exchange reaction of the solvent with the aluminum derivative of the reduction product regenerates the aluminum isopropoxide. However, it is usually preferable to employ enough of the reagent to accomplish the reduction directly. It has been shown that under the influence of light [6] or at temperatures of 200 to 300° [3] the equilibrium between the alcohol and the carbonyl compound is brought about slowly without a catalyst. At these high tem-

[5] Lund, *Ber.*, **70**, 1520 (1937); also *Kem. Maanedsblad*, **17**, 169 (1936) [*Chem. Zentr.* (I), 3480 (1937)].

[6] Ciamician and Silber, *Ber.*, **33**, 2911 (1900); **34**, 1530 (1901).

peratures ceric oxide [7] or sodium acetate [3] will accelerate the reaction. In the presence of the aluminum alkoxide the reaction occurs readily at temperatures of 20 to 80°, and as a result many undesirable side reactions are avoided.

The reaction between an aluminum alkoxide and a ketone can be reversed. This is the basis of the Oppenauer oxidation of a secondary alcohol to the ketone.[4b, 8] The aluminum derivative of the alcohol is prepared by means of aluminum t-butoxide and is oxidized with a large excess of acetone or cyclohexanone.

A polarographic study by Adkins and co-workers [9, 10] of the position of the equilibrium between various ketones and a single alcohol demonstrated the true equilibrium nature of the reaction; from the concentrations of ketones and alcohols at equilibrium the determination of the relative oxidation-reduction potentials of a number of ketone-alcohol systems was made possible.[10]

Advantages of Aluminum Isopropoxide over Other Alkoxides

Although a number of metals have been used as their alkoxides for the reduction reaction, including magnesium ethoxide,[2] chloromagnesium ethoxide,[2] iodo- and bromo-magnesium alkoxides,[11] and sodium,[1] stannic, or zirconium alkoxides,[12] up to the present the aluminum derivatives have been found to be the best reagents. They have the advantages of being much weaker condensing agents than sodium or magnesium alkoxides and of being soluble in both alcohols and hydrocarbons. The general superiority of aluminum isopropoxide over aluminum ethoxide for the reduction of ketones was recognized [1, 3] even before the work of Lund. In general, the isopropoxide induces a more rapid reaction, side reactions are reduced, and the yield of product is improved. It was only gradually appreciated that aluminum isopropoxide is equally suitable for the reduction of aldehydes and superior to the ethoxide for this purpose. Thus, in the reduction of butyraldehyde, crotonaldehyde, and benzaldehyde, yields of products are 20 to 25% higher with aluminum isopropoxide.[13] However, in specific cases yields of 85 to 100% have

[7] Milligan and Reid, J. Am. Chem. Soc., **44**, 202 (1922).

[8] Oppenauer, Rec. trav. chim., **56**, 137 (1937).

[9] Adkins and Cox, J. Am. Chem. Soc., **60**, 1151 (1938); **61**, 3364 (1939).

[10] Baker and Adkins, J. Am. Chem. Soc., **62**, 3305 (1940).

[11] Gomberg and Bachmann, J. Am. Chem. Soc., **52**, 4967 (1930); Shankland and Gomberg, ibid., **52**, 4973 (1930); Bachmann and Kloetzel, ibid., **59**, 2210 (1937).

[12] Meerwein, von Bock, Kirschnick, Lenz, and Migge, J. prakt. Chem., [2] **147**, 211 (1936).

[13] Young, Hartung, and Crossley, J. Am. Chem. Soc., **58**, 100 (1936).

been achieved with aluminum ethoxide, especially in the reduction of aromatic aldehydes.[2, 12, 14, 15, 16]

In general, the yields in aluminum isopropoxide reductions range from 80 to 100%. With a few low-boiling ketones difficulty may be experienced in separating the resulting alcohol from isopropyl alcohol; thus the yields of reduction products from diethyl ketone [5] and methoxyacetone [17] are reported to be 60% and 40%, respectively. Di-n-propyl ketone, on the other hand, gives a 92% yield of the carbinol.[5] As would be expected, side reactions are more significant and the yields are consequently lower when extremely sensitive compounds, such as unsaturated aldehydes and the carotenoids, are reduced.

The time required for a reduction varies greatly with the particular aldehyde or ketone; the aldehydes are usually more reactive. Quinone and cyclohexanone are reduced completely in a few minutes; camphor requires twelve to twenty-four hours. The rate of reduction also depends upon the amount of reducing agent used. The length of time required for a reaction, however, usually has little effect on the final yield, since removal of the acetone which is formed ensures complete reduction in any event. Reduction of aldehydes and ketones has been carried out successfully with quantities ranging from a few milligrams to more than 500 g.

THE SCOPE OF THE REACTION

The aluminum isopropoxide reduction has been carried out with aliphatic and aromatic aldehydes and ketones. Since the reducing agent is such a specific one, other groups susceptible of reduction are not affected. For example, carbon-carbon double bonds, including those α,β- to the carbonyl group, carboxylic esters, nitro groups, and reactive halogens * are not reduced by this reagent, in contrast to other reductions involving metals in acid or alkaline media, or even to catalytic hydrogenation in certain of these cases. Furthermore, the reduction of the carbonyl group does not stop at an intermediate stage; no pinacol formation has been observed, and pinacols are not reduced further by the reagent.[5] The possibility that the nitroso group may be reduced by aluminum alkoxides has been suggested,[5] but no details of such a reduction have been published.

---

* For certain exceptions see p. 193.

[14] Slotta and Lauersen, *J. prakt. Chem.*, [2] **139**, 220 (1934).

[15] Chalmers, *Org. Syntheses*, Coll. Vol. **2**, 598 (1943).

[16] Gardner and McDonnell, *J. Am. Chem. Soc.*, **63**, 2279 (1941).

[17] Adkins and Rossow, private communication.

Selective Reduction of Carbonyl Groups

Some efforts have been made to employ the aluminum isopropoxide reduction in such a way that only one of two or more carbonyl groups in the molecule would be reduced. Most of this work has been based upon the conversion of one of the carbonyl groups to an enol ether or acetal, thus protecting it from the action of the reducing agent. In this manner it was possible to reduce the dimethyl acetal of phenylglyoxal (II) [17] to the corresponding hydroxy acetal (III) in 55% yield. This type of protection also has been employed successfully in the sterol field. The α-

keto acetal (IV) was reduced to the corresponding hydroxy acetal (V).[18] After cleavage of the acetal linkage and conversion to the diacetate, the aldehyde (VI) was obtained in 68% over-all yield. The thioacetal [RCOCH(SC$_2$H$_5$)$_2$] corresponding to IV was resistant to reduction and could not be employed for this purpose.

The 3-enol ether (VIII) of 16-benzalandrostenedione (VII) was reduced selectively [19] to the carbinol (IX). After reduction the 3-keto group was regenerated by treatment of the enol ether with acid. Another

[18] Schindler, Frey, and Reichstein, *Helv. Chim. Acta*, **24**, 360 (1941).
[19] Stodola and Kendall, *J. Org. Chem.*, **6**, 839 (1941).

method for protecting one ketonic group while another is reduced has been applied to androstenedione (X).[20] This compound was converted into the 3-pinacol (XI) with sodium amalgam and then reduced by aluminum isopropoxide in 81% yield to the pinacol (XII) of testosterone. Treatment of the latter 1,2-glycol with lead tetraacetate regenerated the ketone group with cleavage of the molecule to give testosterone (XIII).

$$X \xrightarrow{\text{NaHg}_x} 2\left[XI\right] \xrightarrow{\text{Al(O-}i\text{-C}_3\text{H}_7)_3} 2\left[XII\right] \xrightarrow{\text{Pb(OAc)}_4} XIII$$

Two interesting examples of partial reduction without any protection of either carbonyl group have been described. A 70% yield of a mixture of cis- and trans-testosterone (XIII) was obtained by reduction of androstenedione (X) with aluminum t-butoxide in s-butyl alcohol.[21] The remainder of the material consisted of unreacted diketone as well as some of the corresponding diol. Several selective reductions have been successful with porphyrin derivatives.[22] When the reduction was carried out for a short time, only the aldehyde group in the methyl ester of meso-pyropheophorbide b (XIV) was reduced, and the ketone group in the molecule was unaffected. This selective reduction is reported to depend upon the use of pure aluminum in preparing the isopropoxide. Technical aluminum containing traces of copper and zinc brought about some reduction of the ketone group as well as the aldehyde group.

In view of these encouraging steps toward selective reduction of one carbonyl group in the presence of others, more work along these lines is desirable. It must be pointed out that the last two reductions were carried out with very special types of molecules, and that other examples

[20] N. V. Organon, Fr. pat., 842,940 (June 21, 1939) [Chem. Zentr. (I), 429 (1940)].
[21] Miescher and Fischer, Helv. Chim. Acta, 22, 158 (1939).
[22] Fischer, Mittenzwei, and Hevér, Ann., 545, 154 (1940).

of selectivity which have been found in these compounds cannot always be extended to simpler molecules. However, differences in the ease of reduction of various types of carbonyl groups undoubtedly exist, depend-

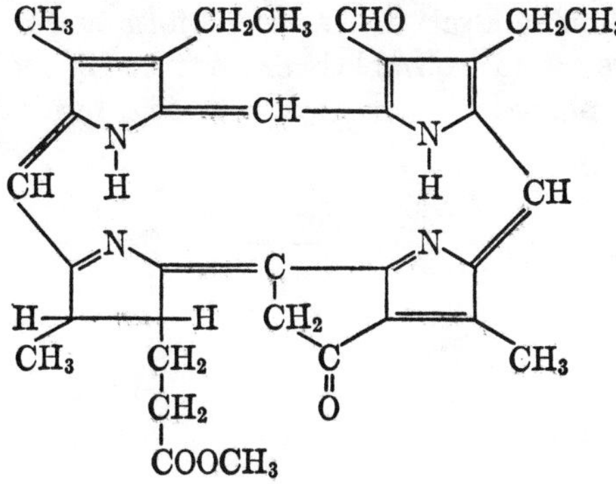

XIV

ing not only upon the speed of reduction but also upon the reduction potential. The oxidation-reduction series [9, 10] for various ketone-alcohol systems may give a clue to the direction in which progress may be made.

Stereochemical Configuration of the Reduction Products

In the reduction of an optically active ketone, the reaction results in the creation of an additional asymmetric center, and two diastereoisomers are possible. In many cases it has been found that both isomers are formed, often in comparable amounts. For example, reduction of camphor (XV) gives a mixture of borneol and isoborneol (XVI).[5] Numerous other examples may be noted in the tables at the end of this chapter. However, the reduction of benzil (XVII) or benzoin (XVIII) is reported to give 90% of *meso*-hydrobenzoin (XIX).[5]

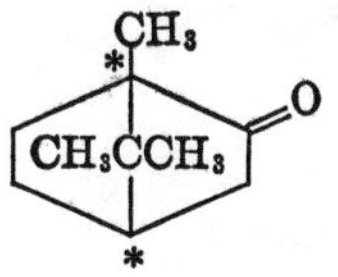

XV

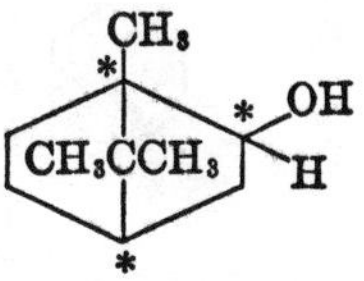

XVI

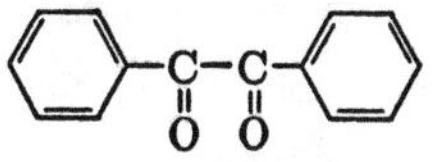

XVII

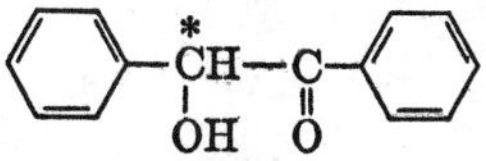

XVIII

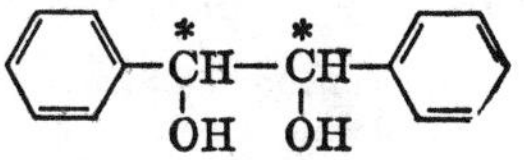

XIX

Limitations of the Method

With certain types of compounds this method of reduction fails. In general, β-keto esters (XX) and β-diketones which are capable of enolization form the aluminum salt of the enolic form and are not reduced.[5] However, if there are no enolizable hydrogens (XXI), reduction proceeds smoothly. If a phenolic ketone or a keto acid forms a salt which is

insoluble in the reaction medium, reduction may proceed slowly or not at all. If the salt is moderately soluble, or if the phenolic or acid group is converted to the ether or ester, reduction will occur.

4-Ketotetrahydrochrysene (XXII) does not undergo reduction[23] with aluminum isopropoxide in boiling isopropyl alcohol but can be reduced to the carbinol in 76% yield by substituting toluene as the solvent. Although no reduction of l-menthen-4-one-3 (XXIII) occurs in isopropyl alcohol solution,[24] substitution of the higher-boiling isobutyl alcohol results in an 84% yield of stereoisomeric carbinols.

Sabina ketone (XXIV)[25] and the esters of chelidonic acid (XXV)[5] are reported not to be reduced by aluminum isopropoxide in boiling isopropyl alcohol solution. Apparently no attempts have been made to

[23] Bachmann and Struve, *J. Org. Chem.*, **4**, 461 (1939).

[24] Malcolm and Read, *J. Chem. Soc.*, **1939**, 1037.

[25] Short and Read, *J. Chem. Soc.*, **1939**, 1415.

carry out these reductions with higher-boiling solvents. There are some indications that certain sterically hindered ketones may be resistant to aluminum isopropoxide reduction, but this is far from general. In the event of apparent failure of the method, it should be noted that other procedures, such as catalytic hydrogenation, often can be applied successfully.

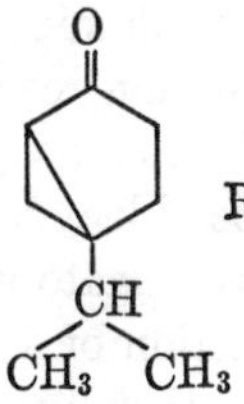

XXIV 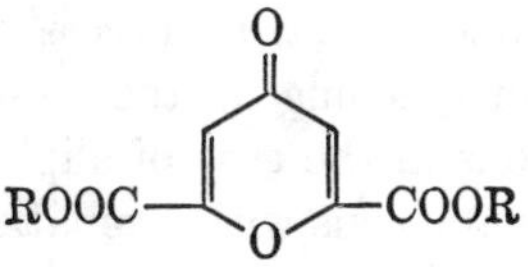   XXV

Side Reactions

Several different types of side reactions have been observed during aluminum isopropoxide reductions. These, however, are encountered only occasionally and usually are not a source of difficulty.

Condensation. Although aluminum alkoxides are effective in bringing about the mesityl oxide type condensation of ketones, as, for example, in the formation of dypnone (XXVII) from acetophenone (XXVI),[26] aluminum isopropoxide rarely induces this reaction to any significant degree in the reduction of ketones.

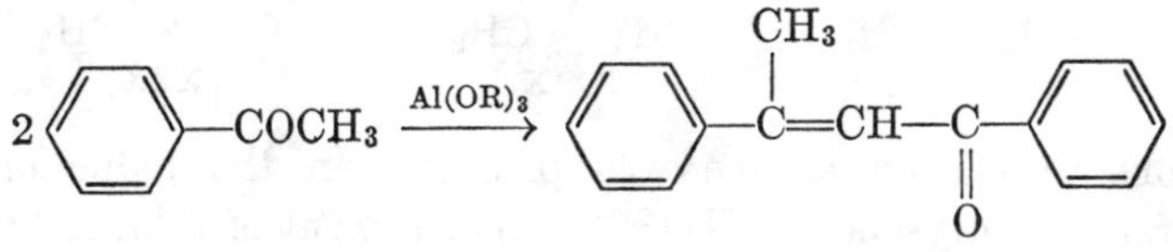

XXVI   XXVII

However, with cyclopentanone only a 33% yield of cyclopentanol was obtained, the remainder of the material probably having undergone the above-mentioned condensation.[5] As no appreciable condensation of this type occurs if dilute solution (approximately 0.05 molar) is used,[10] it seems possible that dilution may improve the yields with particularly sensitive ketones such as cyclopentanone.

With aldehydes, side reactions become more important. Aldol condensations often are possible not only between two molecules of the aldehyde but also between the aldehyde and acetone. The yields are often lower in the reduction of aldehydes if the acetone is not removed as it is formed.[13] Higher temperatures, for example, that of boiling

[26] Wayne and Adkins, *J. Am. Chem. Soc.*, **62**, 3401 (1940).

xylene as a solvent, increase the amount of polymerization and condensation of unsaturated aldehydes such as crotonaldehyde. In addition, the Tishchenko reaction can occur to produce the ester, $RCOOCH_2R$:[27]

$$2RCHO \xrightarrow{\text{Al(OR)}_3} RCOOCH_2R$$

This reaction occurs to a greater extent in benzene than in isopropyl alcohol.[13, 27a] It appears that an excess of aluminum isopropoxide has the desired effect of speeding up the reduction reaction and thus minimizing side reactions in the case of aliphatic aldehydes.[13] The excess, however, is disadvantageous with aromatic aldehydes (see p. 195).

Dehydration of the Alcohol. Several investigators have reported that dehydration sometimes accompanies reduction of a ketone and that an olefin is obtained as the major product. Usually, but not always, an abnormally high temperature was used to carry out the reduction. For example, d-pulegone (XXVIII) upon reduction at 120 to 170° for twenty hours gave over 40% of a mixture of menthadienes (XXX) and only 5 to 10% of the carbinols (XXIX).[28, 29, 30] Even under these drastic

conditions unreduced ketone was present. In the reduction of 4-ketotetrahydrochrysene (XXII)[23] the replacement of toluene by xylene as a solvent usually resulted in the formation of the hydrocarbon XXXII instead of the carbinol XXXI.

[27] Tishchenko, J. Russ. Phys. Chem. Soc., **38**, 355, 482 (1906) [Chem. Zentr., **77**, (II), 1309 1552 (1906)].

[27a] Child and Adkins, J. Am. Chem. Soc., **45**, 3013 (1923).

[28] Doeuvre and Perret, Bull. soc. chim., [5] **2**, 298 (1935).

[29] Grubb and Read, J. Chem. Soc., **1934**, 242.

[30] Short and Read, J. Chem. Soc., **1939**, 1306.

In both of the above cases the aluminum isopropoxide was prepared from aluminum metal amalgamated with a small amount of mercuric chloride, and was used without purification. Such an unpurified solution has been used successfully in many instances and excellent yields of the alcohol have been obtained. However, in these special cases in which the alcohols are sensitive to dehydration it is preferable to use distilled aluminum isopropoxide; inconsistent yields and an impure product were obtained when 4'-ketotetrahydro-3,4-benzpyrene (XXXIII) was reduced with unpurified reagent, but with distilled reagent the yield of the alcohol was always in the range 79–90%.[31]

XXXIII   XXXIV   XXXV

Migration of Double Bonds. It has been assumed by many workers that carbon-carbon double bonds are unaffected by aluminum isopropoxide. Although it is true that these double bonds are not reduced, yet in several instances reduction of an unsaturated ketone has resulted in a shift of the double bond as well as reduction of the carbonyl group. In the case of d-pulegone (XXVIII)[30] the small amount of alcoholic material which was obtained was not d-pulegol (XXXIV), but d-neo-isopulegol (XXIX). In addition, the unreduced ketonic material contained not only pulegone (XXVIII) but also isopulegone (XXXV). This involves migration of the double bond in the side chain from the α,β- to the β,γ-position, with respect to the carbonyl group. Several other examples of this type of double-bond migration have been observed in the sterols. In the reduction of ergostatrienone (XXXVI; R = C_9H_{17}),[32, 33] 80% of the product was the alloergosterol derivative (XXXVII; R = C_9H_{17}) and 20% was the ergosterol derivative (XXXVIII; R = C_9H_{17}), formed by a shift of one of the nuclear double bonds. Similar results were observed with $\Delta^{4, 7}$-dehydrocholestenone (XXXVI; R = C_8H_{17}).[34] However, with cholestenone (XXXIX) no double-bond migration occurred.[35]

[31] Bachmann, Carmack, and Safir, *J. Am. Chem. Soc.*, **63**, 1682 (1941).
[32] Heilbron, Kennedy, Spring, and Swain, *J. Chem. Soc.*, **1938**, 869.
[33] Windaus and Buchholz, *Ber.*, **71**, 576 (1938); **72**, 597 (1939).
[34] Windaus and Kaufmann, *Ann.*, **542**, 218 (1939).
[35] Schoenheimer and Evans, *J. Biol. Chem.*, **114**, 567 (1936).

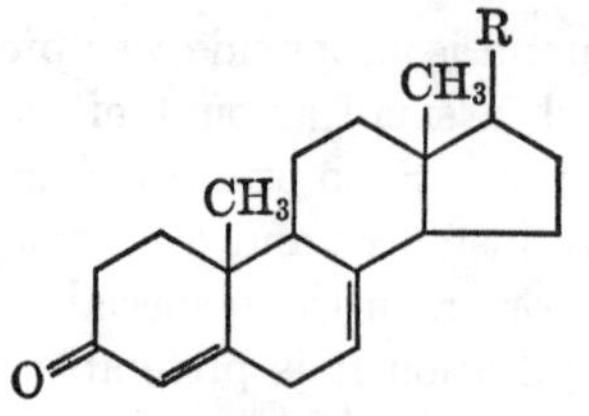

XXXVI

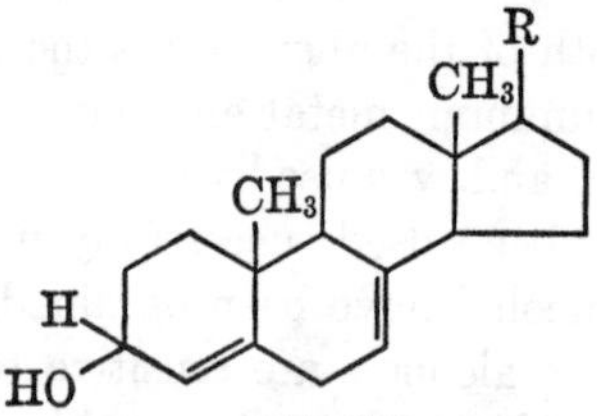

XXXVII

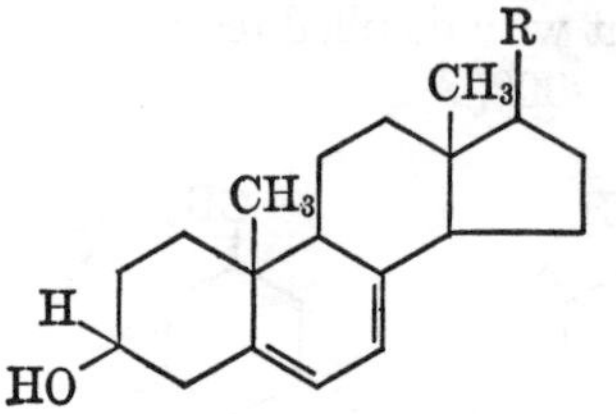

XXXVIII

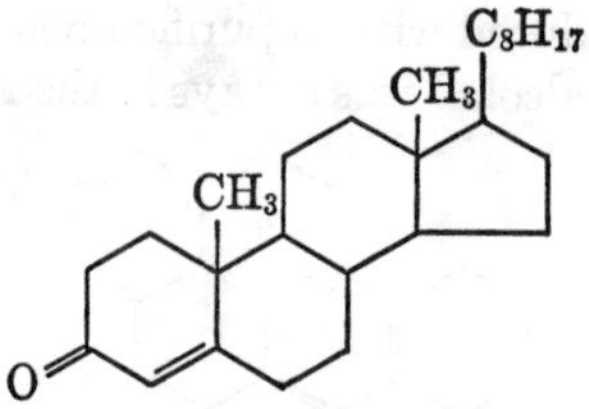

XXXIX

Ether Formation. It is reported that the reduction products of certain α,β-unsaturated ketones, for example, dibenzalacetone (XL), contained some of the isopropyl ethers of the carbinols.[5] Carbinols of this type are especially susceptible to ether formation; often recrystallization from an alcohol is sufficient to give the ether. However, ether formation is by no means the usual reaction with unsaturated ketones. Indeed, in most cases no ether was noted in the products. Even in the case of dibenzalacetone, the normal product, i.e., the carbinol, has been obtained in 58% yield.[36] 9,9-Dimethylanthrone-10 (XLI) gave 64% of a material corresponding in analysis to the isopropyl ether (XLII).[17] Similar observations of ether formation with α-halogen ketones will be discussed later. There appears to be no way of predicting with any degree of certainty when ether formation is likely, but it is not a common side reaction.

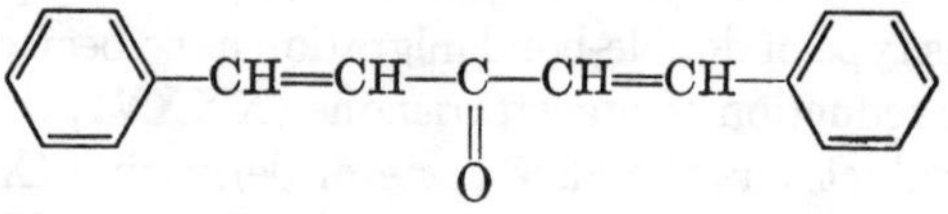

XL

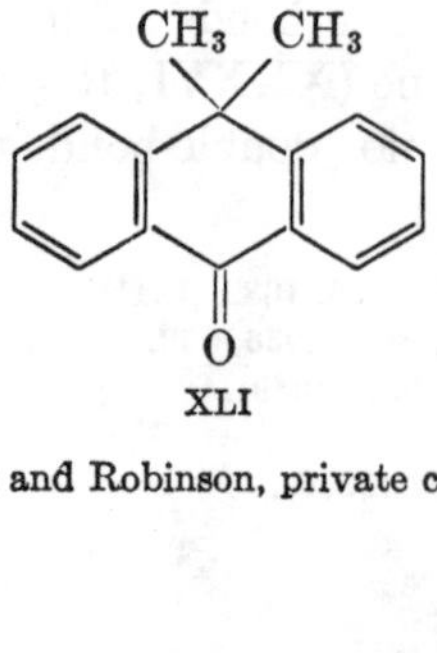

XLI

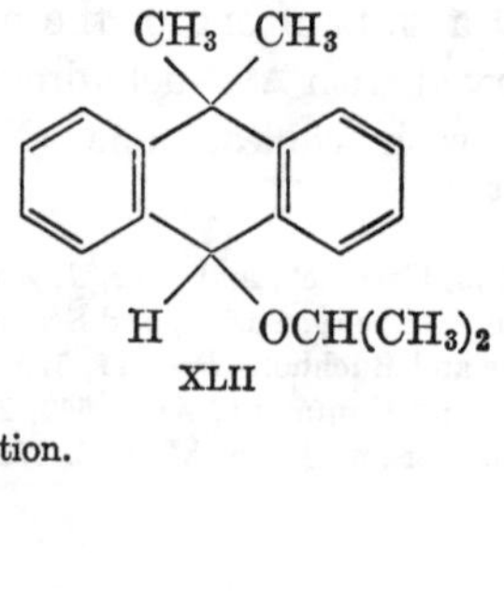

XLII

[36] Adkins and Robinson, private communication.

Further Reduction to a Hydrocarbon. In the reduction of benzophenone with aluminum ethoxide the formation of 7% of diphenylmethane was observed. When benzohydrol was treated with aluminum ethoxide under the same conditions, 28% reduction to diphenylmethane occurred.[12] In these reactions acetic acid, rather than acetaldehyde, was formed from the ethoxide. Aluminum isopropoxide does not give this type of undesirable reaction; with this reagent, pure benzohydrol is easily obtained in 100% yield from benzophenone.[5, 37] However, one case of reduction of a ketone to the hydrocarbon has been observed with aluminum isopropoxide.[17] When 9, 9-dimethylanthrone-10 (XLI) was reduced in xylene solution, rather than in isopropyl alcohol, to avoid formation of the ether (see p. 190), the hydrocarbon XLIII was formed in 65% yield. The reduction in either xylene or isopropyl alcohol was very slow, requiring two days for completion.

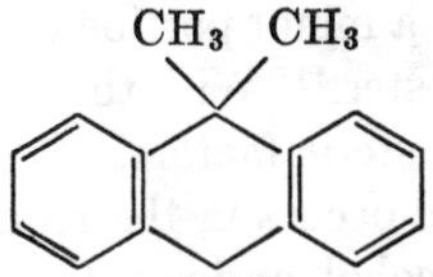

CH$_3$ CH$_3$

XLIII

Reduction of Keto Esters

Since aluminum alkoxides function effectively as catalysts for alcohol exchange in esters,[38, 39] reduction of keto esters by aluminum isopropoxide frequently yields the isopropyl ester of the hydroxy acid. Thus the reduction of the cyclopropane derivative XLIV gave the isopropyl ester of the reduced acid (XLV).[40] Similarly the substituted methyl β-keto ester (XLVI)[41] gave upon reduction the isopropyl esters of the stereoisomeric reduced acids (XLVII).

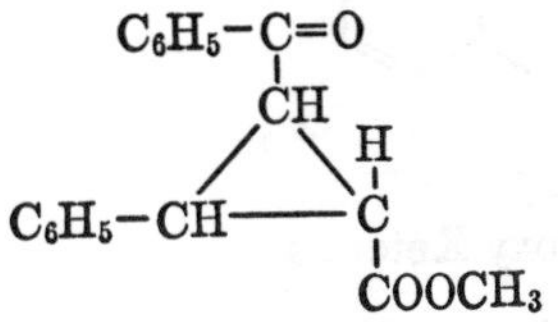

$C_6H_5-C=O$

C_6H_5-CHOH

CH

CH

H

H

C_6H_5-CH———C

C_6H_5-CH———C

COOCH$_3$

COOCH(CH$_3$)$_2$

XLIV

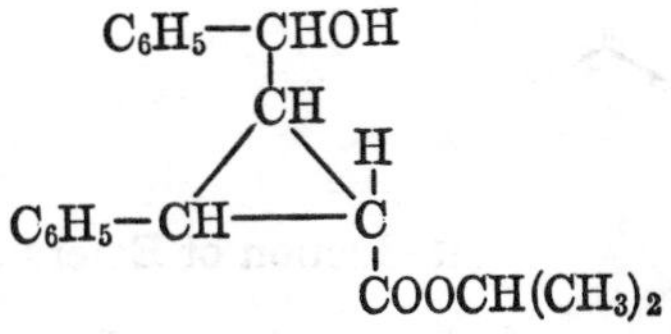

XLV

[37] Wilds, unpublished observations.
[38] Fehlandt and Adkins, *J. Am. Chem. Soc.*, **57**, 193 (1935).
[39] Baker, *J. Am. Chem. Soc.*, **60**, 2673 (1938).
[40] Schenk, *J. prakt. Chem.*, [2] **134**, 215 (1932).
[41] Bachmann and Wilds, unpublished observations.

XLVI   XLVII

γ-Keto esters, upon reduction, usually give rise to lactones of the hydroxy acids. The methyl ester of β-(2-naphthoyl)-propionic acid (XLVIII) was converted in almost quantitative yield [41] into the corresponding butyrolactone (XLIX). A similar reaction was found to occur when the carbon atoms between the ketone and ester groups were included as part of a ring. Methyl 1-ketotetrahydrophenanthrene-2-acetate (L) gave an 80% yield of the lactone (LI).[37] With the *cis* isomer of the cyclopropane derivative (XLIV) lactone formation occurred to the extent of 52%, only a minor portion of the reduced material being obtained as the isopropyl ester.[40] With the *trans* isomer (XLIV), lactone formation is prevented by steric factors. It should be pointed out that this formation of a lactone occurs in the reduction mixture in the presence of excess isopropyl alcohol, and not during the subsequent isolation and purification.

XLVIII   XLIX

L   LI

Reduction of Esters of Hydroxy Ketones

Because of the catalytic effect of aluminum alkoxides on alcohol exchange in esters, reduction of esters of hydroxy ketones usually is accompanied by cleavage of the ester group and the product is a glycol. Ether and acetal linkages are not affected. Thus, the reduction of the acetate (LII) gave a 94% yield of the glycol (LIII).[42]

[42] Schöpf, Brass, Jacobi, Jorde, Mocnik, Neuroth, and Salzer, *Ann.*, **544**, 42 (1940).

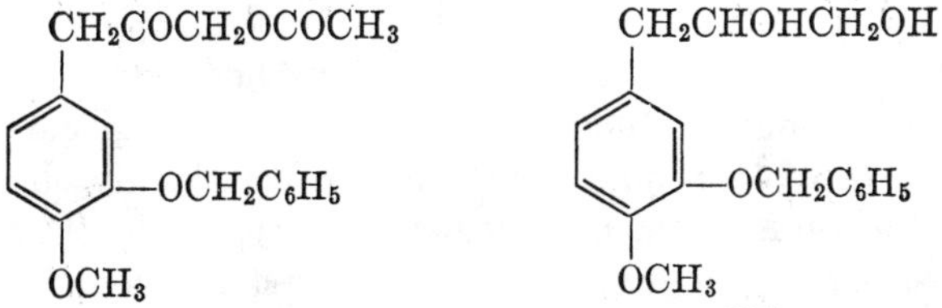

CH₂COCH₂OCOCH₃ structure and CH₂CHOHCH₂OH structure:

$CH_2COCH_2OCOCH_3$

(benzene ring)—$OCH_2C_6H_5$

OCH_3

LII

$CH_2CHOHCH_2OH$

(benzene ring)—$OCH_2C_6H_5$

OCH_3

LIII

Reduction of α-Bromoketones

Reduction of α-bromoacetophenone gave the corresponding bromo-hydrin in 85% yield.[5] Smooth reduction also occurred with chloral [2, 15] and bromal.[5] However, α-bromopropiophenone [43, 44] gave only 35 to 42% yields of the bromohydrin; the remainder of the product was halogen-free, consisting of a mixture of benzylmethylcarbinol and some ethers.

From α-bromoisobutyrophenone (LIV) [44, 45] very little bromohydrin (LV) was obtained with aluminum isopropoxide in boiling isopropyl alcohol. The main material was a mixture of the carbinols LX, LXI, and LXII and ethers derived from them. The occurrence of these products was explained by the formation of the oxide (LVI) from the intermediate bromohydrin. The oxide is capable of rearrangement, with or without the migration of a methyl or phenyl group, to give the carbonyl compounds LVII, LVIII, and LIX which would give rise to the carbinols through further reduction.

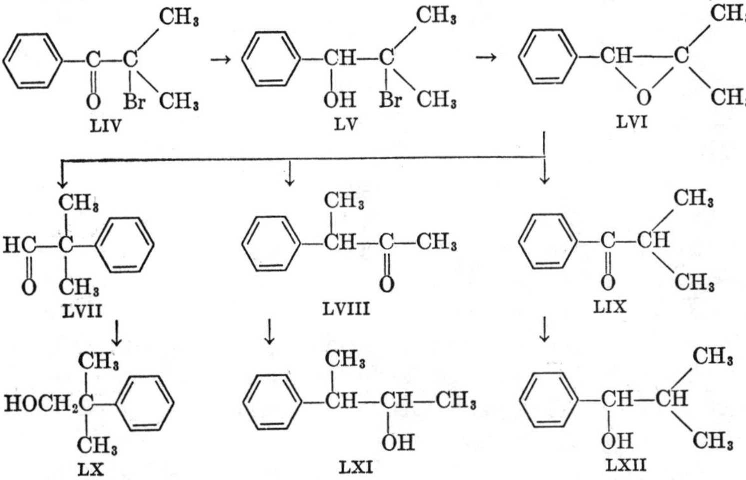

[43] Stevens, *J. Am. Chem. Soc.*, **60**, 3089 (1938).
[44] Stevens, Allenby, and DuBois, *J. Am. Chem. Soc.*, **62**, 1424 (1940).
[45] Stevens and Allenby, *J. Am. Chem. Soc.*, **62**, 3264 (1940).

Of these products the main one was the carbinol LXII. A similar oxide intermediate explains the formation of benzylmethylcarbinol from α-bromopropiophenone. In addition to the ethers corresponding to these carbinols, there was also obtained the monoether of a glycol. This may have been formed from the intermediate oxide (LVI) by the addition of isopropyl alcohol to the oxide ring, or by direct reaction of the bromohydrin (LV) with aluminum isopropoxide. Curiously enough, when the reduction was carried out at 33°, α-bromoisobutyrophenone gave a bromohydrocarbon as the main product.[44] This was shown to be LXIII accompanied by some of its allylic isomer (LXIV).

LXIII   LXIV   LXV

From 2-bromocyclohexanone (LXV), a 33% yield of cyclohexanol was obtained in addition to a 30% yield of bromohydrin.[46] This reaction may involve intermediates similar to those for α-bromoisobutyrophenone.

SELECTION OF EXPERIMENTAL CONDITIONS

Solvent and Temperature

For the reduction of *aldehydes*, anhydrous isopropyl alcohol is recommended as the solvent in order to avoid side reactions such as the Tishchenko reaction.[13] In those reductions for which aluminum ethoxide is satisfactory either ethyl or isopropyl alcohol may be employed as a solvent. For most aldehydes, the temperature of boiling isopropyl alcohol is satisfactory for rapid and complete reduction. Certain sensitive aldehydes or ketones may be reduced at room temperature by letting the mixture stand for several days. When aldehydes are reduced, a slow stream of dry nitrogen or hydrogen is frequently employed for reactions requiring long periods of time (including most of the aluminum ethoxide reductions), or when the reduction products are sensitive to air.

In the reduction of *ketones*, boiling isopropyl alcohol is generally satisfactory. In the few instances in which the temperature must be raised above this point to bring about reduction (that is, if no acetone has been detected after an hour of heating), dry toluene may be added and the isopropyl alcohol removed by distillation. If reduction still does not occur xylene may be substituted, but this is rarely necessary and may result in

[46] Winstein, *J. Am. Chem. Soc.*, **61**, 1610 (1939).

dehydration of the product. In general, if the reduction can be carried to completion in twelve to twenty-four hours in isopropyl alcohol it is usually undesirable to substitute a higher-boiling solvent, since the reaction is cleaner and side reactions are less likely to take place at the lower temperature.

Preparation and Amount of Aluminum Isopropoxide

The aluminum isopropoxide is prepared by dissolving cleaned amalgamated aluminum in anhydrous isopropyl alcohol. Although the resulting solution is dark because of suspended particles, in many cases it may be used for the reduction without purification.[5] This procedure is often convenient where single reductions are to be carried out with ketones which are known to be reduced satisfactorily in this manner (see tables at end of chapter). However, with aldehydes or ketones which are new or not readily available, or with those which are known to give anomalous results with unpurified reagent, it is advisable to use distilled aluminum isopropoxide, either as the solid or as a molar solution in isopropyl alcohol.

Although it appears that only a small amount of aluminum isopropoxide is required to catalyze the equilibrium between the alcohol and carbonyl compound, in practice it usually is desirable to employ an excess of the reagent. As the equation indicates, one mole of isopropoxide will reduce directly three moles of carbonyl compound.

$$3R_2C{=}O + Al\left[-OCH\begin{matrix} CH_3 \\ \diagup \\ \diagdown \\ CH_3 \end{matrix}\right]_3 \rightleftarrows (R_2CHO)_3Al + 3O{=}C(CH_3)_2$$

Actually, with *ketones* at least 100 to 200% excess of the reagent is desirable. With small runs of ketone (below 0.1 mole) it may even be well to use as much as three moles of isopropoxide (nine equivalents) to one mole of ketone. This has the advantage of shortening the time required for reduction. Results with 1-keto-1,2,3,4-tetrahydrophenanthrene (LXVI) illustrate this point.[41] With three moles (800% excess) of isopropoxide for one mole of the ketone, reduction was complete in forty-five minutes. When the reagent was decreased to two-thirds of one mole (100% excess) for one mole of the ketone, a six-hour period was required for complete reduction. However, irrespective of the amount of the reagent, the yield of the reduced carbinol was 100%.

On the other hand, with *aromatic aldehydes* it is preferable not to use excess reagent. Excellent yields (90–98%) in the reduction of piperonal

(LXVII) and benzyl isovanillin (LXVIII) have been obtained with less than one equivalent of aluminum isopropoxide.[47, 48] With benzaldehyde [13, 37] an excess of reagent gives only 55–65% yields of benzyl alcohol

LXVI   LXVII   LXVIII

with considerable benzyl benzoate resulting from the Tishchenko reaction. However, with only one-half an equivalent of reagent [37] an 89% yield of benzyl alcohol is obtained (Procedure II, p. 201).

Apparatus

The simplest type of apparatus, and one which is quite satisfactory except in the reduction of volatile ketones and aldehydes, consists of a round-bottomed flask equipped with a short reflux condenser (no water in the cooling jacket), attached at the top to another condenser set for distillation (see Procedure IV, p. 203). When the distillate no longer gives a test for acetone, the reduction is complete. If more than half of the solvent distils during the reaction it is advisable to add more isopropyl alcohol to maintain the volume. If a concentrated solution is to be avoided, a two-necked flask may be employed and fresh isopropyl alcohol added at the rate of removal by distillation.

More elaborate means have been described for removing the acetone by distillation with relatively little isopropyl alcohol. These include various columns such as a Vigreux [13] or a modified Widmer column.[10] They are to be recommended when the aldehyde or ketone boils within 50° of isopropyl alcohol, but are unnecessary under other circumstances. A reflux condenser maintained at constant temperature by boiling methanol has been suggested.[5] More convenient than this is the simple but effective partial condenser designed by Hahn.[49] An easily constructed modification is illustrated in Fig. 3 (adapted from *Organic Syntheses*).[50] The partial condenser is attached directly to the round-bottomed flask, and ethanol is placed in the inner condensing tube. The

[47] Schöpf and Salzer, *Ann.*, **544**, 14 (1940).
[48] Schöpf and Winterhalder, *Ann.*, **544**, 71 (1940).
[49] Hahn, *Ber.*, **43**, 420 (1910).
[50] Arndt, *Org. Syntheses*, **20**, 27 (1940).

top of this tube is connected to a small reflux condenser. The outside of the condenser below the side arm is wrapped with cloth or asbestos paper. The refluxing mixture boils the ethanol in the inner condensing tube, and most of the isopropyl alcohol is returned to the flask, while the lower-boiling acetone is permitted to distil. If several reductions are to be carried out this apparatus is highly recommended.

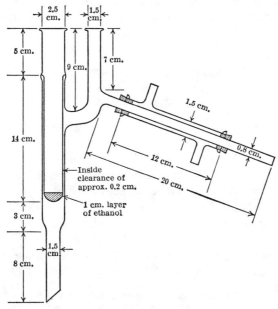

FIG. 3.

Instead of a steam bath or a water bath, an electrically heated oil bath is suitable. This permits easy regulation of the rate of distillation. However, the temperature of the bath should not exceed 95–100° when isopropyl alcohol is the solvent if possible dehydration of a sensitive alcohol is to be avoided. For this same reason, a burner, hot plate, or sand bath is not recommended for heating. Especially at the end of the reduction, superheating of the concentrated alkoxide solution may bring about dehydration or other decomposition of the product.

An apparatus suitable for micro quantities (5 to 50 mg.) has been described.[22]

Recovery of the Isopropyl Alcohol

Because of the low cost of isopropyl alcohol it is usually not economical to recover the solvent. However, if the isopropyl alcohol is to be recovered, caution must be exercised in working with it, particularly if it has been allowed to stand for several days. It is essential to test for the presence of peroxides, which form readily in the impure isopropyl alcohol-acetone mixture.[51, *] The literature records [52] a serious explosion during the distillation of a mixture of isopropyl alcohol and acetone (recovered from the reduction of crotonaldehyde) which had aged for a year. Any peroxides that are present can be removed conveniently by using stannous chloride [53] before drying and distilling the recovered isopropyl alcohol.[†]

EXPERIMENTAL PROCEDURES

Aluminum Isopropoxide [‡]

Twenty-seven grams (1 mole) of aluminum wire or foil which has just been cleaned with emery paper and wiped with a clean cloth (if turnings are employed, it may be necessary to clean, amalgamate, and dry them according to the procedure of Wislicenus)[54, 55] is placed in a 1-l. round-bottomed flask containing 300 cc. of anhydrous isopropyl alcohol (distilled from calcium oxide) and 0.5 g. of mercuric chloride. The flask is attached to an efficient reflux condenser, which is protected from moisture by a mercury trap or a calcium chloride drying tube, and the mixture is heated on the steam bath or a hot plate. When the liquid is boiling, 2 cc. of carbon tetrachloride, which is an effective catalyst for the

* To test for peroxides add 0.5 cc. of the isopropyl alcohol to 1 cc. of a 10% potassium iodide solution acidified with 0.5 cc. of dilute (1 : 5) hydrochloric acid. The test is positive if the yellow color of liberated iodine appears in one minute; it is still more sensitive if a few drops of 2% starch solution are added to this iodine solution to give the blue-black starch-iodine color.

† To remove the peroxides add 10 to 15 g. of solid stannous chloride for each liter of recovered isopropyl alcohol and reflux for one-half hour. A portion of the solution on cooling should no longer give a positive test with acidified potassium iodide even on the addition of starch solution. If any iodine is liberated additional 5-g. portions of stannous chloride should be added and refluxing continued until the test is completely negative. Calcium oxide is then added; the mixture is dried by refluxing for several hours and distilled. The first portion of the distillate is discarded until the test for acetone is negative (p. 200). Peroxides usually redevelop in this purified isopropyl alcohol in several days.

‡ Adapted (reference 37) from procedures by Lund (reference 5) and Young, Hartung, and Crossley (reference 13).

[51] For the formation of peroxides in pure isopropyl alcohol see Redemann, *J. Am. Chem. Soc.*, **64**, 3049 (1942). The possibility that the peroxide is trimolecular acetone peroxide has been pointed out by Acree and Haller, *ibid.*, **65**, 1652 (1943).

[52] Wagner-Jauregg, *Angew. Chem.*, **52**, 709 (1939).

[53] Stannous chloride has been used to remove peroxides from dioxane and ether, Fisher and Baxter, *Colo. School Mines Mag.*, **30**, 447 (1940)[*C. A.*, **34**, 8111 (1940)].

[54] Wislicenus and Kaufmann, *Ber.*, **28**, 1323 (1895).

[55] Adkins, *J. Am. Chem. Soc.*, **44**, 2178 (1922).

reaction of aluminum and dry alcohols,[41, 56, *] is added through the condenser, and heating is continued. The mixture turns gray, and in a few minutes a vigorous evolution of hydrogen begins. It is necessary to discontinue heating, and frequently the reaction must be moderated by cooling the flask in ice water. The mixture becomes black because of the presence of suspended particles. After the reaction has slackened, refluxing is resumed and is continued until all the aluminum has dissolved (six to twelve hours).

The hot solution is poured into a 500-cc. Claisen distilling flask attached to a water condenser with a 250-cc. suction flask as the receiver. A boiling-chip is added, and the flask is heated in an oil bath at 90° under slightly diminished pressure. When nearly all the isopropyl alcohol has been distilled, the bath temperature is raised to 170° and the pressure is lowered to the full vacuum of the water pump. As soon as the temperature of the distillate rises above 90° the distillation is stopped and the condenser is removed. A 500-cc. distilling flask, which now serves as the receiver, is attached directly to the Claisen flask (since air cooling is sufficient for condensation), and a fresh boiling-chip is added. The aluminum isopropoxide is distilled (oil-bath temperature, 180–190°) as a colorless, viscous liquid, b.p. 130–140°/7 mm. or 140–150°/12 mm.; yield 185–195 g. (90–95%).

The molten aluminum isopropoxide is poured into a wide-mouthed, glass-stoppered bottle, and the bottle is sealed with paraffin to exclude moisture. Although aluminum isopropoxide is a solid melting at 118° [55, 57] (125° [58]), it shows a great tendency to supercool, and it may solidify only after cooling at 0° for one or two days.

The reagent also is conveniently kept and used as an isopropyl alcohol solution. The molten alkoxide after distillation is weighed and dissolved in sufficient dry isopropyl alcohol to give a 1 M solution. This may be kept without deterioration in a glass-stoppered bottle sealed with paraffin. On standing the solution deposits large crystals of the alkoxide, but these redissolve slowly when the mixture is warmed to 60–70°.

For many purposes it is not necessary to distil the reagent; the dark solution which results after all the aluminum has reacted is used directly. In this case it is usually best to prepare just the amount needed for the reduction. The proportions of 1 g. of aluminum, 0.05 g. of mercuric chloride, 20 cc. of isopropyl alcohol, and 0.2 cc. of carbon tetrachloride

* Other catalysts which have been used include iodine (reference 28), copper bronze (reference 40), s-butyl alcohol (reference 28), or a small amount of an aluminum alkoxide (reference 13).

[56] Lund, Ber., 67, 936 (1934).
[57] Robinson and Peak, J. Phys. Chem., 39, 1128 (1935).
[58] Ulich and Nespital, Z. physik. Chem., A165, 298 (1933).

may be used. An equal volume of isopropyl alcohol is added with the ketone to the aluminum isopropoxide solution when the reduction is carried out.

Acetone Test Reagent (2,4-Dinitrophenylhydrazine) [5]

A 0.1% solution of the reagent is prepared by dissolving 0.12 g. of 2,4-dinitrophenylhydrazine in 25 cc. of distilled water and 21 cc. of concentrated hydrochloric acid by warming on the steam bath. The clear yellow solution is then cooled and diluted to 125 cc. with distilled water. For use, several drops of the reagent and a few drops of the acetone-isopropyl alcohol distillate are mixed in a small test tube. The presence of acetone is shown by the formation of a yellow cloudy suspension or precipitate of acetone 2,4-dinitrophenylhydrazone. The test is considered negative if no cloudiness forms within one-half minute when 3 cc. of the reagent is added to 5 drops of distillate. After a negative test is obtained, it is advisable to reflux the mixture for five to fifteen minutes with complete condensation and then to force over a few drops of distillate for another test. If no acetone is observed, reduction is complete. Otherwise the process is continued until no more acetone can be detected. This procedure indicates complete reduction even with ketones which are reduced very slowly.

The 2,4-dinitrophenylhydrazine test easily detects 1 part of acetone in 500 to 1000 parts of isopropyl alcohol. Since the reagent solution, even though kept in a stoppered bottle, may deteriorate in the course of several months, old solutions should be checked before use. For the use of the test with toluene instead of isopropyl alcohol see the note on p. 204.

Reduction of Aldehydes

For the reduction of volatile aliphatic aldehydes (b.p. below 150°) Procedure I, employing a Vigreux or a more efficient fractionating column, is recommended. For higher-boiling aliphatic aldehydes Procedure IV may be followed. With aromatic aldehydes, which readily undergo the Tishchenko reaction, an excess of aluminum isopropoxide is to be avoided and Procedure II should be used.

PROCEDURE I * (FOR VOLATILE ALIPHATIC ALDEHYDES AND KETONES)

Reduction of Crotonaldehyde. To the undistilled solution of aluminum isopropoxide, prepared as described above from 47 g. (1.74 moles)

* From the procedure of Young, Hartung, and Crossley (reference 13).

of aluminum and 500 cc. of isopropyl alcohol, are added 210 g. (3 moles) of crotonaldehyde and 1 l. of dry isopropyl alcohol. A 2-l. round-bottomed flask is used, equipped with an 80-cm. Vigreux column, the upper end of which is connected to a water condenser set for downward distillation. The mixture is heated with an oil bath, and the acetone slowly distils as it is formed. The temperature of the distillate is maintained at 60 to 70° (bath 110°), and when the distillate no longer gives a test for acetone (eight to nine hours) most of the remaining isopropyl alcohol is distilled under reduced pressure.*

The residue is cooled to 40° and slowly hydrolyzed (cooling as necessary) with 900 cc. of cold 6 N sulfuric acid, prepared from 145 cc. of concentrated sulfuric acid and 790 cc. of water. The oily layer is separated, washed once with water, and distilled at 60–70° while the pressure is lowered slowly from about 275 mm. to 65 mm. Finally the distillation is continued to 100° and 20 mm. This procedure permits separation of all the crotyl alcohol from the higher-boiling polymerization products. The aqueous layers are combined and distilled until the distillate no longer gives a test for unsaturation with a dilute solution of bromine in carbon tetrachloride. The distillate is then saturated with potassium carbonate, and the oily layer which separates is added to the product obtained by distillation of the oil.

After drying over 10 g. of anhydrous potassium carbonate, the oil is decanted and fractionated through an 80-cm. Vigreux column at atmospheric pressure. Crotyl alcohol distils at 117–122°/760 mm., weight 130 g. (60%). This material is 93% pure as determined by titration with bromine in carbon tetrachloride. If the crude crotyl alcohol is dried for several days before distillation the product is 97% pure. Refractionation through a 110-cm. bead column gives material boiling at 121.2°/760 mm. which is 99.1 to 99.7% pure.

PROCEDURE II † (FOR AROMATIC ALDEHYDES)

Reduction of Benzaldehyde with 0.5 Equivalent of Aluminum Isopropoxide. Use of the Hahn Condenser. In a 1-l. round-bottomed flask are placed 21 g. (0.2 mole) of benzaldehyde, 7 g. (0.034 mole) of distilled aluminum isopropoxide (or 34 cc. of a 1 M solution in isopropyl

---

* Reduced pressure should not be used when low-boiling ketones are reduced and only a small excess of aluminum isopropoxide is used, since some of the product may be liberated from its aluminum derivative and lost through an exchange with the excess isopropyl alcohol.

† Based (reference 37) upon the procedure of Schöpf and Salzer (reference 47) for piperonal.

alcohol), and 450 cc. of dry isopropyl alcohol. A Hahn partial condenser (or a reflux condenser or Vigreux column may be used), with a 1-cm. layer of ethanol in the inner condensing tube (p. 197), is attached, and the solution is heated on the steam bath. After six hours of slow distillation (2 to 6 drops per minute) the distillate may no longer give a direct test for acetone, but after five minutes of total reflux, followed by resumption of distillation, the first portion of the distillate usually contains acetone. (If the volume of the mixture should fall below 200 cc. during the reduction, it is advisable to add more isopropyl alcohol.) Heating is continued until the acetone test is completely negative, which requires about ten hours, the time depending to some extent upon the rate of distillation. A bent glass tube, attached to a water condenser set for distillation, is substituted for the Hahn condenser, and most of the remaining isopropyl alcohol is removed at atmospheric pressure. The cooled residue is hydrolyzed with cold, dilute hydrochloric acid prepared from 20 cc. of concentrated acid and 150 cc. of water, and the mixture is extracted with three 50-cc. portions of benzene. The combined extract is washed once with 50 cc. of water, and any suspended droplets of water are removed with 20 g. of anhydrous sodium sulfate.

The benzene is removed at atmospheric pressure, and the residue is distilled under reduced pressure from a 50-cc. Claisen flask. The fraction boiling at 89–91°/7 mm. consists of colorless benzyl alcohol; weight 19 g. (89%). A small amount of higher-boiling material, benzyl benzoate, remains in the flask (with a 200% excess of aluminum isopropoxide in 200 cc. of isopropyl alcohol, the yield dropped to 65% and a larger high-boiling fraction resulted).

PROCEDURE III. THE USE OF ALUMINUM ETHOXIDE

A procedure for the use of aluminum ethoxide in the reduction of chloral is described by Chalmers in *Organic Syntheses*.[15]

Reduction of Ketones

For the reduction of low-boiling ketones (below 150°), the procedure of Young, Hartung, and Crossley for crotonaldehyde (Procedure I) is recommended. A larger excess of aluminum isopropoxide may be desirable in small runs. For higher-boiling ketones, where there is no danger of loss of ketone with the distilling isopropyl alcohol, the following procedure is satisfactory.

PROCEDURE IV * (FOR KETONES BOILING ABOVE 175–200°)

Reduction of Benzophenone. In a 200-cc. round-bottomed flask are placed a solution of 20 g. (0.1 mole) of aluminum isopropoxide (unpurified reagent is also satisfactory for reduction of benzophenone and many other ketones) in 100 cc. of dry isopropyl alcohol (or 100 cc. of a 1 M solution in isopropyl alcohol) and 18.2 g. (0.1 mole) of benzophenone. A short (25-cm.) reflux condenser (a reflux condenser jacketed with boiling methanol [5] or a Hahn partial condenser may also be used) is attached to the flask, but no water is run through the cooling jacket. To the top of the condenser, by means of a short, bent glass tube and cork stoppers, is attached a small water-cooled condenser set for distillation. A boiling-chip is added, and the solution is refluxed on the steam bath at such a rate that 5 to 10 drops of distillate are collected per minute (a rate of 1 to 4 drops of distillate per minute is better for ketones which are reduced more slowly). In thirty to sixty minutes the acetone test becomes negative (if more than 50 or 60 cc. of isopropyl alcohol distils off, 20 cc. of dry isopropyl alcohol should be added to maintain the volume). Water is then passed through the upright condenser, and total reflux is maintained for five minutes. The water is again removed from the reflux condenser, and the first 5 drops of distillate is tested for acetone. If a positive test is obtained distillation is continued to remove the acetone, then the process is repeated. When a negative test is obtained, most of the excess isopropyl alcohol is removed under slightly reduced pressure. The cooled residue is hydrolyzed with cold, dilute hydrochloric acid (prepared from 35 cc. of concentrated acid and 175 cc. of water), and the cooled aqueous suspension is mixed well by swirling to complete the hydrolysis. The crystalline benzohydrol is filtered (it is necessary to extract with benzene or ether if unpurified aluminum isopropoxide has been used), washed well with cold dilute acid and water, and dried; weight 18.4 g. For purification the solid is dissolved in 50 cc. of hot (60–70°) petroleum ether. (If a clear solution does not result, 20 cc. of benzene should be added and the hot solution filtered.) Upon cooling, finally in ice, there is obtained 18.2 g. (99%) of colorless needles of benzohydrol melting at 67–69°. Usually the material in the filtrate is negligible unless benzene is used in the recrystallization.

* Developed (reference 37) from the procedure of Lund (reference 5).

PROCEDURE V * (FOR KETONES RESISTANT TO REDUCTION)

Reduction of 4-Keto-1,2,3,4-tetrahydrochrysene (XXII) in Toluene.
A solution of 8.2 g. (0.040 mole) of purified aluminum isopropoxide and
2.75 g. (0.011 mole) of 4-keto-1,2,3,4-tetrahydrochrysene in 25 cc. of
dry toluene is refluxed for four hours, in an oil bath. After the solution
has cooled slightly, 25 cc. of dry isopropyl alcohol is added to facilitate
removal of acetone, the water is removed from the reflux condenser, and
a water condenser set for downward distillation is attached to the top
by means of a short bent tube (a Hahn partial condenser with a 1-cm.
layer of isobutyl alcohol in the inner condensing tube may be used). The
mixture is heated at such a rate that slow distillation occurs (2 to 5 drops
per minute; the volume of solution should be maintained by further
addition of solvent as needed). When the test for acetone is completely
negative,[†] the toluene solution is cooled and the aluminum salt is decomposed with cold 10% sulfuric acid (from 5 cc. of concentrated sulfuric acid and 80 cc. of water). The product is separated with the
toluene, and the solution is washed with dilute aqueous ammonia and
water, and then evaporated at room temperature under a stream of air
(solutions of secondary alcohols which are susceptible to dehydration
should be evaporated at room temperature; a stream of air should not
be used with carbinols boiling below 200°). There is obtained 2.10 g.
(76%) of colorless 4-hydroxy-1,2,3,4-tetrahydrochrysene melting at
156–158°. Two recrystallizations from a mixture of benzene and petroleum ether bring the melting point to 160–162°.

Reduction of Acetals or Enol Ethers

Ketones containing these groups may be reduced according to the
procedures given above (Procedure I or IV, depending upon the vola-
tility of the compound). In order to avoid cleavage of the acetal or
enol ether linkage, acids should be avoided in working up the reaction
mixtures after reduction. Instead, excess sodium hydroxide solution
or a concentrated solution of sodium potassium tartrate [18] should be used
to dissolve the aluminum hydroxide.

---

* From the procedure of Bachmann and Struve (reference 23).

† The test for acetone requires slight modification for use with toluene. The following
test will easily detect 1 part of acetone in 300 parts of toluene. Five drops of the distillate
and 5 drops of water are shaken, then 2 cc. of 2,4-dinitrophenylhydrazine reagent solution
is added *without* shaking. The appearance of cloudiness in the aqueous layer indicates
acetone. Shaking the toluene-reagent mixture will clarify the cloudy suspension.

SURVEY OF ALUMINUM ALKOXIDE REDUCTIONS
REPORTED IN THE LITERATURE

The following tables are intended to include all the reductions with aluminum alkoxides which were reported prior to February, 1943, although some examples doubtless have been overlooked. Table I lists the reduction of aldehydes, which have been subdivided into: (a) aliphatic aldehydes and (b) alicyclic and aromatic aldehydes. Table II lists the reduction of ketones, which have been classified as: (a) saturated and unsaturated aliphatic ketones, (b) aromatic ketones, (c) alicyclic ketones, (d) unsaturated alicyclic and aromatic ketones, (e) α-halogen substituted ketones, (f) diketones, (g) protected diketones, (h) alcoholic and phenolic ketones (and ethers or esters of these), and (i) keto esters.

The yields that have been reported do not necessarily represent the highest that can be obtained, and it seems probable that some of the lower yields might be improved by making suitable modifications in the experimental procedure for the reduction and for the isolation of the product.

TABLE I

REDUCTION OF ALDEHYDES WITH ALUMINUM ALKOXIDES

Compound Reduced	Product Formed	Reagent and Solvent * R in Al(OR)$_3$	Yield	Reference
(a) Aliphatic Aldehydes				
Dichloroacetaldehyde	Dichloroethyl alcohol	i-C$_3$H$_7$(D)	60%	59
Chloral	Trichloroethyl alcohol	C$_2$H$_5$	85%	2, 15, 60
Bromal	Tribromoethyl alcohol	i-C$_3$H$_7$(C)	77–90%	5, 61
		C$_2$H$_5$	69%	2
Butyraldehyde	Butyl alcohol	i-C$_3$H$_7$ (benzene)	19–28%	13
		i-C$_3$H$_7$ (i-C$_3$H$_7$OH)	30–36%	13
		C$_2$H$_5$ (benzene)	6%	13
α,α,β-Trichlorobutyraldehyde	2,2,3-Trichlorobutanol-1	C$_2$H$_5$	92%	2
Aldol	1,3-Dihydroxybutane	C$_2$H$_5$ (25°)	30%	12
Crotonaldehyde	Crotyl alcohol	i-C$_3$H$_7$(U)	60–65%	12, 13
α-Chlorocrotonaldehyde	2-Chloro-2-butenol-1	C$_2$H$_5$	—	12
α-Bromocrotonaldehyde	2-Bromo-2-butenol-1	C$_2$H$_5$	—	12
2,4-Hexadienal-1	2,4-Hexadienol-1	i-C$_3$H$_7$(D)	64%	62
2,4,6-Octatrienal-1	2,4,6-Octatrienol-1	i-C$_3$H$_7$(D)	70%	62
2,4,6,8-Decatetraenal-1	2,4,6,8-Decatetraenol-1	i-C$_3$H$_7$(D)	—	62
Citral	Geraniol (24%) Nerol (44%)	i-C$_3$H$_7$ (U or D)	}83%	3, 63
Citronellal	Citronellol	i-C$_3$H$_7$(U)	32%	13
		C$_2$H$_5$	60%	1
Hydroxycitronellal	Hydroxycitronellol	C$_2$H$_5$	78%	[12
(b) Alicyclic and Aromatic Aldehydes				
Δ^3-Tetrahydrobenzaldehyde	Δ^3-Tetrahydrobenzyl alcohol	i-C$_3$H$_7$	—	64
Δ^3-6-Methyltetrahydrobenzaldehyde	Δ^3-6-Methyltetrahydrobenzyl alcohol	i-C$_3$H$_7$	—	64

NOTE: References 59–80 appear on p. 221.

* If no solvent is listed the alcohol corresponding to the alkoxide was used. C refers to clarified aluminum isopropoxide but not distilled; D, to distilled reagent; and U, to an untreated solution of the alkoxide (see p. 199).

TABLE I—*Continued*

REDUCTION OF ALDEHYDES WITH ALUMINUM ALKOXIDES

Compound Reduced	Product Formed	Reagent and Solvent * R in Al(OR)$_3$	Yield	Reference
Δ^3-3,4,6-Trimethyltetra-hydrobenzaldehyde	Δ^3-3,4,6-Trimethyltetra-hydrobenzyl alcohol	i-C$_3$H$_7$	—	64
Δ^3-2,2,4-Trimethyltetra-hydrobenzaldehyde	Δ^3-2,2,4-Trimethyltetra-hydrobenzyl alcohol	i-C$_3$H$_7$(D)	70%	65
Δ^3-2-Phenyltetrahydro-benzaldehyde	Δ^3-2-Phenyltetrahydro-benzyl alcohol	i-C$_3$H$_7$(D)	80%	66
Δ^3-6-Phenyl-3,4-dimeth-yltetrahydrobenzalde-hyde	Δ^3-6-Phenyl-3,4-dimeth-yltetrahydrobenzyl alcohol	i-C$_3$H$_7$	—	64
Cyclocitral	Cyclogeraniol	i-C$_3$H$_7$(D)	77–93%	67, 68
Axerophthal	Isomer of vitamin A (axerophthol)	i-C$_3$H$_7$(D)	—	69, 70
5,5,9-Trimethyl-5,6,7,8,9,-10-hexahydro-1-naph-thaldehyde	5,5,9-Trimethyl-5,6,7,8,-9,10-hexahydro-1-naph-thylmethanol	i-C$_3$H$_7$(D)	66%	71 (cf. 72)
Lupenal (a triterpene aldehyde)	Pseudolupenol	i-C$_3$H$_7$(D)	55%	73
Furfural	Furfuryl alcohol	C$_2$H$_5$ (25°)	88%	2
		i-C$_3$H$_7$ (82°)	75%	74
Benzaldehyde	Benzyl alcohol	i-C$_3$H$_7$(D)	89%	37
		i-C$_3$H$_7$ (benzene)	55%	13
		C$_2$H$_5$ (benzene)	28%	13
		C$_2$H$_5$	82–89%	2, 12
4-Chlorobenzaldehyde	4-Chlorobenzyl alcohol	C$_2$H$_5$(25°)	92%	2
4-Methoxybenzaldehyde	4-Methoxybenzyl alcohol	C$_2$H$_5$ (25°)	85%	2
3-Methoxy-6-bromoben-zaldehyde	3-Methoxy-6-bromoben-zyl alcohol	C$_2$H$_5$	88–100% (crude)	16
3,4-Methylenedioxyben-zaldehyde	3,4-Methylenedioxyben-zyl alcohol	i-C$_3$H$_7$(D)	90%	47
3-Benzyloxy-4-methoxy-benzaldehyde	3-Benzyloxy-4-methoxy-benzyl alcohol	i-C$_3$H$_7$(D)	93–98%	48
2-Nitrobenzaldehyde	2-Nitrobenzyl alcohol	i-C$_3$H$_7$(C)	92%	5
		C$_2$H$_5$	100%	14

NOTE: References 59–80 appear on p. 221.

* If no solvent is listed the alcohol corresponding to the alkoxide was used. C refers to clarified aluminum isopropoxide but not distilled; D, to distilled reagent; and U, to an untreated solution of the alkoxide (see p. 199).

TABLE I—*Continued*

REDUCTION OF ALDEHYDES WITH ALUMINUM ALKOXIDES

Compound Reduced	Product Formed	Reagent and Solvent * R in $Al(OR)_3$	Yield	Reference
4-Nitrobenzaldehyde	4-Nitrobenzyl alcohol	C_2H_5 (25°)	92%	2
2-Nitro-3,4-dimethoxy-benzaldehyde	2-Nitro-3,4-dimethoxy-benzyl alcohol	C_2H_5	92–97%	14
Cinnamaldehyde	Cinnamyl alcohol	i-C_3H_7	68–80%	13, 75
		C_2H_5	45–86%	1, 2, 3
		$C_6H_5CH_2$	80%	3, 63
α-Chlorocinnamaldehyde	α-Chlorocinnamyl alcohol	C_2H_5	—	12
α-Bromocinnamaldehyde	α-Bromocinnamyl alcohol	C_2H_5	—	12
2-, 3-, or 4-Nitrocinnamaldehyde	2, 3, or 4-Nitrocinnamyl alcohol	C_2H_5	—	12
α-Methylcinnamaldehyde	α-Methylcinnamyl alcohol	i-C_3H_7	—	44
11-Phenyl-2,4,6,8,10-undecapentaenal-1	11-Phenyl-2,4,6,8,10-undecapentaenol-1	i-C_3H_7(D)	90%	76
2-Styrylbenzaldehyde	2-Styrylbenzyl alcohol	i-C_3H_7	95%	77
2,3-Dimethyl-1-naphthaldehyde	2,3-Dimethyl-1-naphthylmethanol	i-C_3H_7	—	78
9-Fluorenealdehyde	9-Fluorylmethanol	i-C_3H_7(D)	50%	79
3-Pyrenealdehyde	3-Pyrenylmethanol	i-C_3H_7	54%	80
Methyl ester of meso-pyropheophorbide b	Methyl ester of meso-pyropheophorbide b-3-methanol (15 minutes) or	i-C_3H_7(C)	—	22
	Methyl ester of 9-hydroxydesoxo-meso-pyropheophorbide b-3-methanol (2 to 4 hours)	i-C_3H_7(C)	—	22
Methyl pheophorbide b	Methyl pheophorbide b-3-methanol	i-C_3H_7(C)	—	22
Trimethyl ester of rhodine g_7	Trimethyl ester of rhodine g_7-3-methanol	i-C_3H_7(C)	50%	22

NOTE: References 59–80 appear on p. 221.

* If no solvent is listed the alcohol corresponding to the alkoxide was used. C refers to clarified aluminum isopropoxide but not distilled; D, to distilled reagent; and U, to an untreated solution of the alkoxide (see p. 199).

TABLE II

REDUCTION OF KETONES WITH ALUMINUM ISOPROPOXIDE

Compound Reduced	Product Formed	Reagent and Solvent *	Yield	Reference
(a) Saturated and Unsaturated Aliphatic Ketones				
Diethyl ketone	Pentanol-3	C	60%	5
Di-n-propyl ketone	Heptanol-4	C	92%	5
Methyl nonyl ketone	Undecanol-2	U	—	1
3-Neopentyl-5,5-dimethylhexanone-2	3-Neopentyl-5,5-dimethylhexanol-2	D	63%	81
3-t-Butyl-3,5,5-trimethylhexanone-2	No reduction (4 hours)	—	0	82
Mesityl oxide	4-Methylpenten-3-ol-2	C	63%	5, 83
cis-Hepten-3-one-2 } trans-Hepten-3-one-2 }	Hepten-3-ol-2 (both gave same isomer)	—	24–26%	84
(b) Aromatic Ketones				
Acetophenone	α-Methylbenzyl alcohol	C	93%	5
4-Methylacetophenone	α,4-Dimethylbenzyl alcohol	D	52%	36
4-Bromoacetophenone	α-Methyl-4-bromobenzyl alcohol	D	86%	36
3-Nitroacetophenone	α-Methyl-3-nitrobenzyl alcohol	C	76%	5
4-Nitroacetophenone	α-Methyl-4-nitrobenzyl alcohol	D	74%	36
4-Acetylpyridine	Methyl-4-pyridylmethanol	D	75%	85
Benzophenone	Benzohydrol	C, D, U	99–100%	5, 37
4-Nitrobenzophenone	4-Nitrobenzohydrol	C	92%	5
Benzyl phenyl ketone	Benzylphenylmethanol	D	80–84%	17, 36
4-Propionylbiphenyl	Ethyl-4-biphenylmethanol	D	—	86
1-Acetylnaphthalene	Methyl-1-naphthylmethanol	C	95%	5
2-Acetylnaphthalene	Methyl-2-naphthylmethanol	C	90%	5

NOTE: References 81–158 appear on pp. 221–223.

* Unless otherwise stated, the reduction was carried out with aluminum isopropoxide in boiling isopropyl alcohol solution. C refers to clarified but undistilled aluminum isopropoxide; D, to distilled reagent; and U, to an untreated solution of the alkoxide (see p. 199).

TABLE II—*Continued*

REDUCTION OF KETONES WITH ALUMINUM ISOPROPOXIDE

Compound Reduced	Product Formed	Reagent and Solvent *	Yield	Reference
1-Propionylnaphthalene	Ethyl-1-naphthylmethanol	D	—	86
2-Propionylnaphthalene	Ethyl-2-naphthylmethanol	D	90% (crude)	86
1-Benzoylnaphthalene	Phenyl-1-naphthylmethanol	D	100%	36
2-Acetylfluorene	Methyl-2-fluorenylmethanol	D	78%	36
2-Acetylphenanthrene	Methyl-2-phenanthrylmethanol	U	95%	87
3-Acetylphenanthrene	Methyl-3-phenanthrylmethanol	U	90%	88
2-Phenanthreneacetone	1-(2'-Phenanthryl-) propanol-2	U, D	88%	89
9-Benzoylphenanthrene	Phenyl-9-phenanthrylmethanol	U	93%	90
2-Acetyldibenzothiophene	Methyl-2-dibenzothienylmethanol	U	68%	91
3-Acetylpyrene	Methyl-3-pyrenylmethanol	U	87%	80

(c) Alicyclic Ketones

Compound Reduced	Product Formed	Reagent and Solvent *	Yield	Reference
Cyclopentanone	Cyclopentanol	C	33%	5
Cyclohexanone	Cyclohexanol	C	95%	5
Methylcyclohexanones	Methylcyclohexanols	C	90–95%	5
4-Isopropylcyclohexanone	cis (5%) and trans (95%) 4-Isopropylcyclohexanols	U	—	92, 93
l-Menthone	l-Menthol and neomenthol	C, D	90–99%	5, 94
Sabina ketone	Little reduction	$(i\text{-}C_3H_7OH)$	—	25
Camphor	Borneol and isoborneol	C	100%	5
2-Morpholinomethylcyclohexanone	2-Morpholinomethylcyclohexanol	D	50%	95
4-Methyl-2-morpholinomethylcyclohexanone	4-Methyl-2-morpholinomethylcyclohexanol	D	83%	95

NOTE: References 81–158 appear on pp. 221–223.

* Unless otherwise stated, the reduction was carried out with aluminum isopropoxide in boiling isopropyl alcohol solution. C refers to clarified but undistilled aluminum isopropoxide; D, to distilled reagent; and U, to an untreated solution of the alkoxide (see p. 199).

TABLE II—*Continued*

REDUCTION OF KETONES WITH ALUMINUM ISOPROPOXIDE

Compound Reduced	Product Formed	Reagent and Solvent *	Yield	Reference
6-Methyl-2-morpholino-methylcyclohexanone	6-Methyl-2-morpholino-methylcyclohexanol	D	—	95
8-Methyl-2-hydrindanone	Stereoisomers of 8-methyl-2-hydrindanol	—	87%	96
1-Tetralone	1-Tetralol	D	86%	17
1-Decalone	1-Decalol	C	95%	5
9-Methyl-1-decalone	9-Methyl-1-decalol	D	90%	97
1-Ethyl-7-acenaphthenone	1-Ethyl-7-acenaphthenol	D	86%	98
Fluorenone	Fluorenol	C, D	85–89%	5, 10
3-Morpholinomethyl-4-chromanone	3-Morpholinomethyl-4-chromanol	D	40%	99
Xanthone	Xanthydrol	C	90%	5
9,9-Dimethylanthrone	Isopropyl ether of 9,9-dimethyl-10-hydroxy-9,10-dihydroanthracene	D (i-C$_3$H$_7$OH)	64%	17
	No reduction (10 hours)	D (benzene)	—	17
	9,9-Dimethyl-9,10-dihydroanthracene	D (xylene)	65%	17
1-Keto-1,2,3,4-tetrahydrophenanthrene	1-Hydroxy-1,2,3,4-tetrahydrophenanthrene	U	100%	41, 100
4-Keto-1,2,3,4-tetrahydrophenanthrene	4-Hydroxy-1,2,3,4-tetrahydrophenanthrene	U	96–98%	41, 100
4-Keto-2,3-dimethyl-1,2,3,4-tetrahydrophenanthrene	4-Hydroxy-2,3-dimethyl-1,2,3,4-tetrahydrophenanthrene	U	23%	101
cis-9-Keto-*asym*-octahydrophenanthrene	Mixture of 9-hydroxy-*asym*-octahydrophenanthrenes	—	—	102
9-Ketoperhydrophenanthrene	9-Hydroxyperhydrophenanthrene	—	84%	103
1-Keto-4,5-methylene-1,2,3,4-tetrahydrophenanthrene	1-Hydroxy-4,5-methylene-1,2,3,4-tetrahydrophenanthrene	D	87%	104
1-Keto-11-methyl-1,2,3,4-tetrahydrochrysene	1-Hydroxy-11-methyl-1,2,3,4-tetrahydrochrysene	D	82%	105

NOTE: References 81–158 appear on pp. 221–223.

* Unless otherwise stated, the reduction was carried out with aluminum isopropoxide in boiling isopropyl alcohol solution. C refers to clarified but undistilled aluminum isopropoxide; D, to distilled reagent; and U, to an untreated solution of the alkoxide (see p. 199).

TABLE II—*Continued*

REDUCTION OF KETONES WITH ALUMINUM ISOPROPOXIDE

Compound Reduced	Product Formed	Reagent and Solvent *	Yield	Reference
4-Keto-1,2,3,4-tetrahydrochrysene	4-Hydroxy-1,2,3,4-tetrahydrochrysene	U (i-C$_3$H$_7$OH)	0	23
		U (toluene)	76%	23
		U (xylene)	Dehydration	23
12-Keto-4,5-dimethyl-4b,5,6,10b,11,12-hexahydrochrysene	12-Hydroxy-4,5-dimethyl-4b,5,6,10b,11,12-hexahydrochrysene	U	—	106
7-Keto-4,5-methylene-7,8,9,10-tetrahydrochrysene	7-Hydroxy-4,5-methylene-7,8,9,10-tetrahydrochrysene	—	—	107
5-Keto-5,6,7,8-tetrahydro-1,2-benzanthracene	5-Hydroxy-5,6,7,8-tetrahydro-1,2-benzanthracene	U	99%	108
5-Keto-6-methyl-5,6,7,8-tetrahydro-1,2-benzanthracene	5-Hydroxy-6-methyl-5,6,7,8-tetrahydro-1,2-benzanthracene	U	>90%	88
5-Keto-7-methyl-5,6,7,8-tetrahydro-1,2-benzanthracene	5-Hydroxy-7-methyl-5,6,7,8-tetrahydro-1,2-benzanthracene	U	98%	88
5-Keto-8-methyl-5,6,7,8-tetrahydro-1,2-benzanthracene	5-Hydroxy-8-methyl-5,6,7,8-tetrahydro-1,2-benzanthracene	U	>79%	88
5-Keto-1'-methyl-5,6,7,8-tetrahydro-1,2-benzanthracene	5-Hydroxy-1'-methyl-5,6,7,8-tetrahydro-1,2-benzanthracene	D	93%	109
8-Keto-7-methyl-5,6,7,8-tetrahydro-1,2-benzanthracene	8-Hydroxy-7-methyl-5,6,7,8-tetrahydro-1,2-benzanthracene	U	>89%	88
10-Keto-5,6,7,8,8a,9,10,10a-octahydro-1,2-benzanthracene	10-Hydroxy-5,6,7,8,8a,9,10,10a-octahydro-1,2-benzanthracene	D	82%	110
4a'-Keto-5,6,7,8,8a,9,10,10a-octahydro-4,10-ace-1,2-benzanthracene	4a'-Hydroxy-5,6,7,8,8a,9,10,10a-octahydro-4,10-ace-1,2-benzanthracene	D	97%	110

NOTE: References 81–158 appear on pp. 221–223.

* Unless otherwise stated, the reduction was carried out with aluminum isopropoxide in boiling isopropyl alcohol solution. C refers to clarified but undistilled aluminum isopropoxide; D, to distilled reagent; and U, to an untreated solution of the alkoxide (see p. 199).

TABLE II—*Continued*

REDUCTION OF KETONES WITH ALUMINUM ISOPROPOXIDE

Compound Reduced	Product Formed	Reagent and Solvent *	Yield	Reference
4'-Keto-1',2',3',4'-tetra-hydro-3,4-benzpyrene	4'-Hydroxy-1',2',3',4'-tetrahydro-3,4-benz-pyrene	D	78–90%	31
4'-Keto-1'-methyl-1',2',-3',4'-tetrahydro-3,4-benzpyrene	4'-Hydroxy-1'-methyl-1',2',3',4'-tetrahydro-3,4-benzpyrene	C	91%	80
4'-Keto-2'-methyl-1',2',-3',4'-tetrahydro-3,4-benzpyrene	4'-Hydroxy-2'-methyl-1',-2',3',4'-tetrahydro-3,4-benzpyrene	C	100%	80
4'-Keto-3'-methyl-1',2',-3',4'-tetrahydro-3,4-benzpyrene	4'-Hydroxy-3'-methyl-1',2',3',4'-tetrahydro-3,-4-benzpyrene	C	94%	80
6'-Keto-4',5-dimethyl-ene-1',2',3',4'-tetrahy-dro-3,4-benzpyrene	6'-Hydroxy-4',5-dimeth-ylene-1',2',3',4'-tetra-hydro-3,4-benzpyrene	U	98%	111
7-Cholestanone	7-Cholestanol	—	—	112
Norlupanone	Norlupanol	D	16%	73

(d) Unsaturated Alicyclic and Aromatic Ketones

Cyclohexen-2-one-1	Cyclohexen-2-ol-1	U	49–74%	113, 114
4-Isopropylcyclohexen-2-one-1	4-Isopropylcyclohexen-2-ol-1	U	73–88%	92, 115
l-Menthen-4-one-3	*cis*- and *trans-l*-Menthen-4-ol-3	D (i-C_3H_7OH)	0	24
		D (i-C_4H_9OH)	84%	24
dl-Menthen-8-one-2	*dl*-Menthen-8-ol-2	—	—	116
l-Menthen-8-one-2	Stereoisomers of menthen-8-ol-2	D	94%	116
d-Menthen-4(8)-one-3	Menthadienes (43%) *d-neo*-menthen-8-ol-3 (5%)	U	48%	28, 29, 30
d-Menthadien-6,8-one-2	Stereoisomers of men-thadien-6,8-ol-2	D, U	65–79%	3, 63, 116, 117
4-Ketopinene	4-Hydroxypinene	—	—	118

NOTE: References 81–158 appear on pp. 221–223.

* Unless otherwise stated, the reduction was carried out with aluminum isopropoxide in boiling iso-propyl alcohol solution. C refers to clarified but undistilled aluminum isopropoxide; D, to distilled reagent; and U, to an untreated solution of the alkoxide (see p. 199).

TABLE II—*Continued*

REDUCTION OF KETONES WITH ALUMINUM ISOPROPOXIDE

Compound Reduced	Product Formed	Reagent and Solvent *	Yield	Reference
Axerophthylideneacetone	Axerophthylideneisopropyl alcohol	D	—	119, 120
Dihydrorhodoxanthin	Zeaxanthin	D	12%	121
Capsanthin	Capsanthol	D	23%	122
Benzalacetone	Methylstyrylmethanol	D	35%	36
Dibenzalacetone	Distyrylmethanol	C, D	58%	36 (5)
Dibenzalcyclopentanone Dibenzalcyclohexanone Dicinnamalacetone Cinnamalacetophenone	Difficult to isolate the pure reduced compounds	C	—	5
Benzaldesoxybenzoin	1,2,3-Triphenylallyl alcohol	D	91%	123, 124
Δ^8-1-Keto-5,10-dimethyl-3-isopropenyloctahydronaphthalene (eremophilone)	Δ^8-1-Hydroxy-5,10-dimethyl-3-isopropenyloctahydronaphthalene (eremophilol)	D	75% (crude)	125
3-Keto-1,2,3,9,10,10a-hexahydro-1,2-cyclopentanophenanthrene	3-Hydroxy-1,2,3,9,10,-10a-hexahydro-1,2-cyclopentanophenanthrene	D	80% (crude)	126
Androstadien-3,5-one-17	Androstadien-3,5-ol-17	D	35%	127
Cholesten-4-one-3	Cholesten-4-ol-3 and *epi*-cholesten-4-ol-3	D	52%	35
Cholesten-8-one-7	Cholesten-8-ol-7	D	44%	128
Cholestadien-4,7-one-3	Cholestadien-4,7-ol-3 (35%) *epi*-Cholestadien-4,7-ol-3 (49%) Cholestadien-5,7-ol-3 (15%) *epi*-Cholestadien-5,7-ol-3 (1%) (estimated ratios)	D	—	34
Ergosten-8(14)-one-3	Ergosten-8(14)-ol-3	—	—	129

NOTE: References 81–158 appear on pp. 221–223.

* Unless otherwise stated, the reduction was carried out with aluminum isopropoxide in boiling isopropyl alcohol solution. C refers to clarified but undistilled aluminum isopropoxide; D, to distilled reagent; and U, to an untreated solution of the alkoxide (see p. 199).

TABLE II—*Continued*

REDUCTION OF KETONES WITH ALUMINUM ISOPROPOXIDE

Compound Reduced	Product Formed	Reagent and Solvent *	Yield	Reference
Ergostatrien-4,7,22-one-3	Ergostatrien-4,7,22-ol-3 (45%) *epi*-Ergostatrien-4,7,22-ol-3 (35%) Ergostatrien-5,7,22-ol-3 (19%) *epi*-Ergostatrien-5,7,22-ol-3 (1%) (estimated ratios)	D	100%	32, 33, 129, 130
Ergostatetraen-4,7,9-(11),22-one-3	Mixture of ergostatetraenols-3	D	73%	32
Lumistatrienone-3	Mixture of lumistatrienols	D	—	32
Zymostenone	Zymostenol	—	—	131
4-Dehydrotigogenone-3	*epi*-4-Dehydrotigogenol-3	D	22%	132
Lanostenone	Lanosterol	D	—	133

(e) α-Halogen Substituted Ketones

Compound Reduced	Product Formed	Reagent and Solvent *	Yield	Reference
1,1,1-Trichloroacetone	1,1,1-Trichloropropanol-2	Al(OC$_2$H$_5$)$_3$	67%	2
α-Bromoacetophenone	2-Bromo-1-phenylethanol-1	C	85%	5
α,α,α-Trichloroacetophenone	2,2,2-Trichloro-1-phenylethanol-1	Al(OC$_2$H$_5$)$_3$	69%	2
α-Bromopropiophenone	2-Bromo-1-phenyl-propanol-1 (and other products—see p. 193)	U	35–42%	43, 44
α-Bromoisobutyrophenone	Little bromohydrin (see p. 193 for products)	U (100°)	—	44, 45
	1-Phenyl-2-methyl-3-bromopropene-1 (see p. 194)	U (33°)	42%	44
2-Bromocyclohexanone	2-Bromocyclohexanol (cyclohexanol 33%)	U	30%	46
2-Bromocholesten-4-one-3	Little bromine in product	U	—	44

NOTE: References 81–158 appear on pp. 221–223.

  * Unless otherwise stated, the reduction was carried out with aluminum isopropoxide in boiling isopropyl alcohol solution. C refers to clarified but undistilled aluminum isopropoxide; D, to distilled reagent; and U, to an untreated solution of the alkoxide (see p. 199).

TABLE II—*Continued*

REDUCTION OF KETONES WITH ALUMINUM ISOPROPOXIDE

Compound Reduced	Product Formed	Reagent and Solvent *	Yield	Reference
(f) Diketones				
Benzil	Mesohydrobenzoin	C	90%	5
1,4-Dibenzoylbutane	1,6-Diphenylhexane-diol-2,5	—	—	134
1,8-Dibenzoyloctane	1,10-Diphenyldecane-diol-2,9	—	—	134
1,16-Dibenzoylhexadecane	1,18-Diphenyloctadecane-diol-2,17	—	—	134
Quinone	Hydroquinone	C	100%	5
2-Methyl-2-phytyl-2,3-dihydro-1,4-naphthoquinone	2-Methyl-2-phytyl-1,2,-3,4-tetrahydro-1,4-naphthohydroquinone	U	94%	135
Androsten-4-dione-3,17	*cis-* and *trans-*Androsten-4-ol-17-one-3	$Al(O-t-C_4H_9)_3$ in $s-C_4H_9OH$	70%	21
(g) Protected Diketones				
Dimethylacetal of phenylglyoxal	Dimethylacetal of phenylglycollic aldehyde	D	55%	17
3-Enol ethyl ether of 16-benzalandrosten-4-dione-3,17	16-Benzalandrosten-4-ol-17-one-3 (isolated as acetate)	D	33%	19
21-Dimethylacetal of pregnen-5-ol-3-one-20-al-21	21-Dimethylacetal of pregnen-5-diol-3,20-al-21 (isolated as diacetate)	D	68%	18
(h) Alcoholic and Phenolic Ketones (and Ethers or Esters of These)				
Docosadien-1,21-ol-11-one-12	Docosadiene-1,21-diol-11,12 (α-isomer 22%, β-isomer 60%)	D	82%	136

NOTE: References 81–158 appear on pp. 221–223.

* Unless otherwise stated, the reduction was carried out with aluminum isopropoxide in boiling isopropyl alcohol solution. C refers to clarified but undistilled aluminum isopropoxide; D, to distilled reagent; and U, to an untreated solution of the alkoxide (see p. 199).

TABLE II—*Continued*

REDUCTION OF KETONES WITH ALUMINUM ISOPROPOXIDE

Compound Reduced	Product Formed	Reagent and Solvent *	Yield	Reference
Benzoin	Mesohydrobenzoin	C	90%	5
Androsten-4-ol-17-one-3	Stereoisomers of androstene-4-diol-3,17	D	95%	127, 137
3-Pinacol of androstene-4-dione-3,17	3-Pinacol of androsten-4-ol-17-one-3	D	81%	20
16-(1'-Methylpropylidene-)androsten-5-ol-3-one-17	16-(1'-Methylpropylidene-)androstene-5-diol-3,17 (isolated as diacetate)	D	38% (crude)	138
16-Benzylideneandrosten-5-ol-3-one-17	16-Benzylideneandrostene-5-diol-3,17	D	52% (crude)	138
Allopregnen-16-ol-3-one-20	Allopregnene-16-diol-3,-20	D	40%	139
Pregnadien-5,16-ol-3-one-20	Pregnadiene-5,16-diol-3,-20	D	—	139
Ox-norcafestadienone	Ox-norcafestadienol (isolated as acetate)	D	43%	140
4-(2'-Hydroxy-1'-naphthyl)-butanone-2	4-(2'-Hydroxy-1'-naphthyl)-butanol-2	D	69%	141
Equilenin	Stereoisomeric equilenin diols	U, D	92–100%	41, 142
Estrone	Stereoisomeric estradiols	D	"Good"	143
Estrone benzyl ether	3-Benzyl ether of estradiol	—	—	144
Methoxyacetone	1-Methoxypropanol-2	D	40%	17
α-Methoxyacetophenone	α-(Methoxymethyl-)benzyl alcohol	D	72%	17
2-Methoxyacetophenone	α-Methyl-2-methoxybenzyl alcohol	D	82%	36
3-Methoxyacetophenone	α-Methyl-3-methoxybenzyl alcohol	D	80%	36
4-Methoxyacetophenone	α-Methyl-4-methoxybenzyl alcohol	D	52%	36
3,5-Dimethoxyvalerophenone	n-Butyl-3,5-dimethoxyphenylmethanol	D	66%	36
2,5-Dimethoxypalmitophenone	Pentadecyl-2,5-dimethoxyphenylmethanol	D	—	145

NOTE: References 81–158 appear on pp. 221–223.

*.Unless otherwise stated, the reduction was carried out with aluminum isopropoxide in boiling isopropyl alcohol solution. C refers to clarified but undistilled aluminum isopropoxide; D, to distilled reagent; and U, to an untreated solution of the alkoxide (see p. 199).

TABLE II—*Continued*

REDUCTION OF KETONES WITH ALUMINUM ISOPROPOXIDE

Compound Reduced	Product Formed	Reagent and Solvent *	Yield	Reference
Benzoin methyl ether	Monomethyl ether of hydrobenzoin (stereoisomers)	D	83%	17
4-Phenoxypropiophenone	Ethyl-4-phenoxyphenylmethanol	D	—	86
4-(4′-Methoxyphenoxy-)propiophenone	Ethyl-4-(4′-methoxyphenoxy-)phenylmethanol	D	90%	86
3-Benzyloxy-4-methoxybenzyl acetoxymethyl ketone	3-Benzyloxy-4-methoxybenzylethylene glycol	D	94%	42
4-Propionyl-4′-methoxybiphenyl	Ethyl-4′-methoxy-4-biphenylmethanol	D	—	86
1-Propionyl-4-methoxynaphthalene	Ethyl-4-methoxy-1-naphthylmethanol	D	—	86
2-Propionyl-6-methoxynaphthalene	Ethyl-6-methoxy-2-naphthylmethanol	D	—	86
Estrone benzoate	3-Benzoate of estradiols	C, D	75%	5, 142
3,17-Diacetoxyandrosten-5-one-7	Androsten-5-triol-3,7,17	—	—	146
4,20-Diacetoxypregnanone-3	Pregnanetriol-3,4,20	—	—	147
3-Acetate 16-(ω-acetoxyisocaproate) of allopregnanediol-3,16-one-20	Allopregnanetriol-3,16,20	D	—	148
3-Acetate 16-(ω-acetoxyisocaproate) of pregnene-5-diol-3,16-one-20	Pregnene-5-triol-3,16,20	D	—	148
3-Acetoxycholesten-5-one-7	Stereoisomers of cholesten-5-diol-3,7	D	63%	149, 150
3-*epi*-Acetoxycholesten-5-one-7	Cholesten-5-diol-3-*epi*-7-α-(33%); 7-β (25%)	D	88%	130
7-Ketocampesteryl acetate	7-Hydroxycampesterol (isolated as the dibenzoate)	—	40%	151
3-Acetoxysitosten-5-one-7	Stereoisomers of sitosten-5-diol-3,7	D	93%	152

NOTE: References 81–158 appear on pp. 221–223.

* Unless otherwise stated, the reduction was carried out with aluminum isopropoxide in boiling isopropyl alcohol solution. C refers to clarified but undistilled aluminum isopropoxide; D, to distilled reagent; and U, to an untreated solution of the alkoxide (see p. 199).

TABLE II—*Continued*

REDUCTION OF KETONES WITH ALUMINUM ISOPROPOXIDE

Compound Reduced	Product Formed	Reagent and Solvent *	Yield	Reference
3-Acetoxystigmastadien-5,22-one-7	Stereoisomers of stigmastadien-5,22-diol-3,7	D	68%	153
Chlorogenone	Mixture of chlorogenin and β-chlorogenin	D	78% (crude)	154
Lupenalyl acetate	Lupenediol	D	33%	73
	(*i*) Keto Esters			
Ethyl trimethylpyruvate	Isopropyl trimethyllactate	D	65%	36
Ethyl 2-methylcyclohexanone-2-carboxylate	Isopropyl 2-methylcyclohexanol-2-carboxylate (plus some ethyl ester)	—	90%	155
Ethyl α-benzylideneacetoacetate	Ethyl α-benzylidene-β-hydroxybutyrate (?)	C	—	5
Ethyl β-benzoylpropionate	γ-Phenyl-γ-butyrolactone	D	75%	74
Ethyl α-phenyl-β-benzoylpropionate	α,γ-Diphenyl-γ-butyrolactone (after hydrolysis)	D	95%	156
Isopropyl benzophenone-4-carboxylate	Isopropyl benzohydrol-4-carboxylate	D	95%	36
Methyl 2-*cis*-phenyl-3-*cis*-benzoylcyclopropane-1-carboxylate	Lactone of 2-*cis*-phenyl-3-*cis*-phenylhydroxymethylcyclopropane-1-carboxylic acid (52%) (plus isopropyl ester of hydroxy acid)	U	>52%	40
Methyl 2-*trans*-phenyl-3-*cis*-benzoylcyclopropane-1-carboxylate	Lactone of hydroxy acid (19%) (plus isopropyl ester of hydroxy acid)	U	>19%	40
Methyl 2-*trans*-phenyl-3-*trans*-benzoylcyclopropane-1-carboxylate	Stereoisomeric mixture of isopropyl esters of hydroxy acid	U	82%	40
Methyl 2-*cis*-phenyl-3-*trans*-benzoylcyclopropane-1-carboxylate	Stereoisomeric mixture of isopropyl esters of hydroxy acid	U	—	40

NOTE: References 81–158 appear on pp. 221–223.

* Unless otherwise stated, the reduction was carried out with aluminum isopropoxide in boiling isopropyl alcohol solution. C refers to clarified but undistilled aluminum isopropoxide; D, to distilled reagent; and U, to an untreated solution of the alkoxide (see p. 199).

TABLE II—*Continued*

REDUCTION OF KETONES WITH ALUMINUM ISOPROPOXIDE

Compound Reduced	Product Formed	Reagent and Solvent *	Yield	Reference
Methyl β-(2-naphthoyl)-propionate	γ-(2-Naphthyl-)γ-butyrolactone	U	97%	41
Methyl fluorenone-2-carboxylate	Isopropyl fluorenol-2-carboxylate	D	85%	36
Isopropyl fluorenone-3-carboxylate	Isopropyl fluorenol-3-carboxylate	D	71%	36
Isopropyl anthraquinone-2-carboxylate	Isopropyl anthrahydroquinone-2-carboxylate	D	55%	74
Methyl 1-keto-1,2,3,4-tetrahydrophenanthrene-2-acetate	Lactone of 1-hydroxy-1,-2,3,4-tetrahydrophenanthrene-2-acetic acid	D	80%	37
Methyl 1-keto-2-methyl-1,2,3,4-tetrahydrophenanthrene-2-carboxylate	Isopropyl esters of stereoisomeric 1-hydroxy-2-methyl-1,2,3,4-tetrahydrophenanthrene-2-carboxylic acid (α-67%; β- 19%)	U	91%	41
Methyl 3-ketocholen-11-ate	Methyl 3-hydroxycholen-11-ate (after remethylation), α isomer = 46%, β isomer = 32%	D	78%	157
Methyl ester of Δ^5-7-ketocholenic acid	$\Delta^{5,7}$-Choladienic acid (after hydrolysis)	D	90%	158
Zinc complex of methylpheophorbide a	9-Hydroxydesoxomethylpheophorbide a	C	5%	22
Methylpyropheophorbide a	9-Hydroxydesoxomethylpyropheophorbide a	C	50%	22
Dimethyl ester of pheoporphyrin a_5	Dimethyl ester of 9-hydroxydesoxopheoporphyrin a_5	C	—	22
Trimethyl ester of 2,α-ketochloroporphyrin e_6	Trimethyl ester of 2,α-hydroxychloroporphyrin e_6	C	"Good"	22
Trimethyl ester of 2-desvinyl-2-acetyl-chlorin e_6	Trimethyl ester of 2,α-hydroxymesochlorin e_6	C	—	22

NOTE: References 81–158 appear on pp. 221–223.

* Unless otherwise stated, the reduction was carried out with aluminum isopropoxide in boiling isopropyl alcohol solution. C refers to clarified but undistilled aluminum isopropoxide; D, to distilled reagent; and U, to an untreated solution of the alkoxide (see p. 199).

TABLE II—*Continued*

REDUCTION OF KETONES WITH ALUMINUM ISOPROPOXIDE

Compound Reduced	Product Formed	Reagent and Solvent *	Yield	Reference
Dimethyl ester of 2,α-ketopheoporphyrin a_5	Dimethyl ester of 2,α-hydroxypheoporphyrin a_5 (main product)	C	—	22
Methyl ester of 2-desvinyl-2-acetyl-pheophorbide a	Methyl ester of 2,α-hydroxymesopheophorbide a (main product)	C	—	22

* Unless otherwise stated, the reduction was carried out with aluminum isopropoxide in boiling isopropyl alcohol solution. C refers to clarified but undistilled aluminum isopropoxide; D, to distilled reagent; and U, to an untreated solution of the alkoxide (see p. 199).

[59] E. E. Royals, private communication.
[60] Dworzak, *Monatsh.*, **47**, 11 (1926).
[61] I. G. Farbenindustrie A.-G., Ger. pat., 489,281 (Jan. 15, 1930) [*Chem. Zentr.* (I), 3104 (1930)].
[62] Reichstein, Ammann, and Trivelli, *Helv. Chim. Acta*, **15**, 261 (1932).
[63] Sachs, *Perfumers' J.*, **7**, No. 3, 11, 32 (1926) [*C. A.*, **20**, 2321 (1926)].
[64] French and Gallagher, *J. Am. Chem. Soc.*, **64**, 1498 (1942).
[65] Jitkow and Bogert, *J. Am. Chem. Soc.*, **63**, 1981 (1941).
[66] Blumenfeld, *Ber.*, **74**, 529 (1941).
[67] Kuhn and Hoffer, *Ber.*, **67**, 358 (1934).
[68] Kuhn and Wendt, *Ber.*, **69**, 1555 (1936).
[69] Haworth, Heilbron, Jones, Morrison, and Polya, *J. Chem. Soc.*, **1939**, 128.
[70] Krauze and Slobodin, *J. Gen. Chem. U.S.S.R.*, **10**, 907 (1940) [*C. A.*, **35**, 3237 (1941)].
[71] Batty, Heilbron, and Jones, *J. Chem. Soc.*, **1939**, 1556.
[72] Barraclough, Batty, Heilbron, and Jones, *J. Chem. Soc.*, **1939**, 1552.
[73] Jones and Meakins, *J. Chem. Soc.*, **1941**, 760.
[74] Adkins and Elofson, private communication.
[75] Ponndorf, Ger. pat., 535,954 (Oct. 17, 1931) [*Chem. Zentr.* (II), 2371 (1932)].
[76] Kuhn and Wallenfels, *Ber.*, **70**, 1333 (1937).
[77] Natelson and Gottfried, *J. Am. Chem. Soc.*, **64**, 2962 (1942).
[78] Fuson, Horning, Ward, Rowland, and Marsh, *J. Am. Chem. Soc.*, **64**, 32 (1942).
[79] Brown and Bluestein, *J. Am. Chem. Soc.*, **62**, 3256 (1940).
[80] Bachmann and Carmack, *J. Am. Chem. Soc.*, **63**, 2494 (1941).
[81] Whitmore and Lester, *J. Am. Chem. Soc.*, **64**, 1249 (1942).
[82] Whitmore and Randall, *J. Am. Chem. Soc.*, **64**, 1244 (1942).
[83] Kenyon and Young, *J. Chem. Soc.*, **1940**, 1549.
[84] Arcus and Kenyon, *J. Chem. Soc.*, **1938**, 698.
[85] Clemo and Hoggarth, *J. Chem. Soc.*, **1941**, 45.
[86] Campbell and Chattaway, *Proc. Roy. Soc. London*, **130B**, 435 (1942).
[87] Bachmann and Struve, *J. Org. Chem.*, **5**, 420 (1940).
[88] Bachmann and Chemerda, *J. Org. Chem.*, **6**, 36 (1941)
[89] Wilds, *J. Am. Chem. Soc.*, **64**, 1429 (1942).
[90] Bachmann and Osborn, *J. Org. Chem.*, **5**, 36 (1940).

[91] Burger and Bryant, *J. Am. Chem. Soc.*, **63**, 1057 (1941).
[92] Gillespie, Macbeth, and Swanson, *J. Chem. Soc.*, **1938**, 1820.
[93] Cooke, Gillespie, and Macbeth, *J. Chem. Soc.*, **1939**, 520.
[94] Zeitschel and Schmidt, *Ber.*, **59**, 2303 (1926); Zeitschel and Eck, *J. prakt. Chem.*, [2] **133**, 367 (1932).
[95] Harradence and Lions, *J. Proc. Roy. Soc. N. S. Wales*, **72**, 233 (1939).
[96] Burnop and Linstead, *J. Chem. Soc.*, **1940**, 726.
[97] Elliott and Linstead, *J. Chem. Soc.*, **1938**, 663.
[98] Bachmann and Sheehan, *J. Am. Chem. Soc.*, **63**, 2600 (1941).
[99] Harradence, Hughes, and Lions, *J. Proc. Roy. Soc. N. S. Wales*, **72**, 280 (1939).
[100] Bachmann and Edgerton, *J. Am. Chem. Soc.*, **62**, 2972 (1940).
[101] Fieser and Daudt, *J. Am. Chem. Soc.*, **63**, 786 (1941).
[102] Linstead, Whetstone, and Levine, *J. Am. Chem. Soc.*, **64**, 2020 (1942).
[103] Linstead and Walpole, *J. Chem. Soc.*, **1939**, 854.
[104] Bachmann and Sheehan, *J. Am. Chem. Soc.*, **63**, 205 (1941).
[105] Bachmann and Safir, *J. Am. Chem. Soc.*, **63**, 2601 (1941).
[106] Newman, *J. Am. Chem. Soc.*, **62**, 2300 (1940).
[107] Fieser and Cason, *J. Am. Chem. Soc.*, **62**, 1296 (1940).
[108] Bachmann, *J. Org. Chem.*, **3**, 439 (1938).
[109] Bachmann and Safir, *J. Am. Chem. Soc.*, **63**, 856 (1941).
[110] Fieser and Novello, *J. Am. Chem. Soc.*, **64**, 802 (1942).
[111] Bachmann and Carmack, *J. Am. Chem. Soc.*, **63**, 1687 (1941).
[112] Eck and Hollingsworth, *J. Am. Chem. Soc.*, **63**, 2989 (1941).
[113] Bartlett and Woods, *J. Am. Chem. Soc.*, **62**, 2936 (1940).
[114] Whitmore and Pedlow, *J. Am. Chem. Soc.*, **63**, 759 (1941).
[115] Gillespie and Macbeth, *J. Chem. Soc.*, **1939**, 1531.
[116] Johnston and Read, *J. Chem. Soc.*, **1934**, 233.
[117] Doeuvre, *Bull. soc. chim.*, [5] **1**, 201 (1934).
[118] Schmidt, Schulz, and Doll, *Ber. Schimmel & Co. Akt.-Ges.*, **1940**, 38 [*C. A.*, **37**, 363 (1943)].
[119] Karrer, Rüegger, and Geiger, *Helv. Chim. Acta*, **21**, 1173 (1938).
[120] Heilbron, Johnson, and Jones, *J. Chem. Soc.*, **1939**, 1563.
[121] Karrer and Solmssen, *Helv. Chim. Acta*, **18**, 479 (1935).
[122] Karrer and Hübner, *Helv. Chim. Acta*, **19**, 476 (1936).
[123] Bergmann, *J. Org. Chem.*, **6**, 547 (1941).
[124] Bergmann, Schapiro, and Eschinazi, *J. Am. Chem. Soc.*, **64**, 560 (1942).
[125] Gillam, Lynas-Gray, Penfold, and Simonsen, *J. Chem. Soc.*, **1941**, 66.
[126] Robinson and Slater, *J. Chem. Soc.*, **1941**, 379.
[127] Butenandt and Heusner, *Ber.*, **71**, 198 (1938).
[128] Eck and Hollingsworth, *J. Am. Chem. Soc.*, **64**, 142 (1942).
[129] Marker, Kamm, Laucius, and Oakwood, *J. Am. Chem. Soc.*, **59**, 1840 (1937).
[130] Windaus and Naggatz, *Ann.*, **542**, 204 (1939).
[131] Wieland, Rath, and Benend, *Ann.*, **548**, 19 (1941) [*C. A.*, **37**, 386 (1943)].
[132] Marker and Turner, *J. Am. Chem. Soc.*, **63**, 771 (1941).
[133] Bellamy and Dorée, *J. Chem. Soc.*, **1941**, 176.
[134] Schmidt and Grosser, *Ber.*, **75**, 826 (1942).
[135] Tishler, Fieser, and Wendler, *J. Am. Chem. Soc.*, **62**, 1989 (1940).
[136] Ruzicka, Plattner, and Widmer, *Helv. Chim. Acta*, **25**, 613 (1942).
[137] Butenandt, Tscherning, and Hanisch, *Ber.*, **68**, 2100 (1935).
[138] Stodola and Kendall, *J. Org. Chem.*, **7**, 338 (1942).
[139] Marker, Turner, Wagner, Ulshafer, Crooks, and Wittle, *J. Am. Chem. Soc.*, **63**, 781 (1941).
[140] Wettstein, Fritzsche, Hunziker, and Miescher, *Helv. Chim. Acta*, **24**, 349E (1941).
[141] McQuillin and Robinson, *J. Chem. Soc.*, **1941**, 589.
[142] Marker, *J. Am. Chem. Soc.*, **60**, 1897 (1938).
[143] Marker and Rohrmann, *J. Am. Chem. Soc.*, **60**, 2927 (1938)

[144] Chinoin, Fr. pat., 842,722 (June 19, 1939) [*C. A.*, **34**, 6022 (1940)].

[145] Cook, Heilbron, and Lewis, *J. Chem. Soc.*, **1942**, 661.

[146] Butenandt and Logemann, U. S. pat., 2,170,124 (Aug. 22, 1940) [*C. A.*, **34**, 1133 (1940)].

[147] Marker, Wittle, Plambeck, Rohrmann, Krueger, and Ulshafer, *J. Am. Chem. Soc.*, **61**, 3319 (1939).

[148] Marker, Turner, Wagner, Ulshafer, Crooks, and Wittle, *J. Am. Chem. Soc.*, **63**, 774 (1941).

[149] Windaus, Lettré, and Schenk, *Ann.*, **520**, 103 (1935).

[150] Wintersteiner and Ruigh, *J. Am. Chem. Soc.*, **64**, 2455 (1942).

[151] Ruigh, *J. Am. Chem. Soc.*, **64**, 1901 (1942).

[152] Wunderlich, *Z. physiol. Chem.*, **241**, 120 (1936).

[153] Linsert, *Z. physiol. Chem.*, **241**, 126 (1936).

[154] Marker, Turner, and Wittbecker, *J. Am. Chem. Soc.*, **64**, 221 (1942).

[155] Robinson and Walker, *J. Chem. Soc.*, **1937**, 64.

[156] Bergmann, Eschinazi, and Schapiro, *J. Am. Chem. Soc.*, **64**, 558 (1942).

[157] Press and Reichstein, *Helv. Chim. Acta*, **25**, 880 (1942).

[158] Dane and Wulle, *Z. physiol. Chem.*, **267**, 5 (1940).

CHAPTER 6

THE PREPARATION OF UNSYMMETRICAL BIARYLS BY THE DIAZO REACTION AND THE NITROSOACETYLAMINE REACTION

WERNER E. BACHMANN AND ROGER A. HOFFMAN

University of Michigan

CONTENTS

NATURE OF THE REACTIONS

The amino group of aromatic amines can be replaced by aryl groups with the formation of unsymmetrical biaryls by two general procedures: (1) by reaction of the aryldiazo hydroxide or acetate (obtainable from the diazotized amine) with aromatic compounds, and (2) by reaction of the nitrosoacetylamine (obtainable from the acetylated amine) with aromatic compounds. In general, the aromatic compound must be a liquid, for no solvent has been found which will not be attacked by the reactive intermediates which are formed in these reactions (p. 231). Both reactions owe their origin to Bamberger [1] and to Kühling,[2] but it remained for others to develop practical procedures for utilizing them.

Diazo Reaction. As developed by Gomberg and Bachmann,[3] the first method involves the following two steps (illustrated by the preparation of 4-bromobiphenyl).

1. Diazotization of an aromatic amine in the usual manner.

$$\text{Br}-\!\!\!\bigcirc\!\!\!-\text{NH}_2 + 2\text{HCl} + \text{NaNO}_2 \rightarrow \text{Br}-\!\!\!\bigcirc\!\!\!-\text{N}_2{}^+\text{Cl}^- + \text{NaCl} + 2\text{H}_2\text{O}$$

2. Conversion of the diazonium salt to the diazohydroxide by means of alkali in the presence of a liquid aromatic compound with which the

[1] Bamberger, Ber., **28**, 403 (1895); **30**, 366 (1897).
[2] Kühling, Ber., **28**, 41, 523 (1895); **29**, 165 (1896).
[3] Gomberg and Bachmann, J. Am. Chem. Soc., **46**, 2339 (1924).

diazohydroxide reacts. The overall reaction may be written in the following manner.

The second step is carried out by adding a 15–40% aqueous solution of sodium hydroxide dropwise to a well-stirred mixture of the cold diazonium salt solution and the aromatic liquid until a slight excess of alkali is present. This procedure avoids the isolation of the unstable, explosive diazohydroxides of Bamberger,[1] which are formed from the diazonium salt and the alkali. The diazohydroxide is extracted by the aromatic liquid as it is formed. The biaryl reaction takes place in the organic liquid and is complete when evolution of nitrogen ceases. In the example given, 4-bromobiphenyl is obtained in 35–46% yield.

A variation in the procedure for certain amines is to add the diazonium salt to sodium hydroxide in an amount sufficient to form the sodium diazotate. The biaryl compound is formed when the aqueous solution of the diazotate is stirred with an aromatic liquid.[4]

$$CH_3C_6H_4N_2{}^+Cl^- + 2NaOH \longrightarrow CH_3C_6H_4N{=}N{-}ONa + NaCl + H_2O$$

$$CH_3C_6H_4N{=}N{-}ONa + C_6H_6 \xrightarrow{H_2O} CH_3C_6H_4 \cdot C_6H_5 + N_2 + NaOH$$

In place of sodium hydroxide, sodium acetate may be added to the mixture of diazonium salt solution and the aromatic liquid.[5] Another variation, introduced by Hodgson and Marsden,[6] consists in converting the aryldiazonium chloride to a stabilized diazonium salt by treatment with naphthalene-1-sulfonic acid, naphthalene-1,5-disulfonic acid, or zinc chloride; the dried salt is then suspended in an aromatic liquid and treated with sodium acetate and acetic anhydride.

Nitrosoacetylamine Reaction. In this synthesis of unsymmetrical biaryls, developed by Grieve and Hey [7] and Heilbron [8] and collaborators, three steps are involved (illustrated by the preparation of 3-nitrobiphenyl).

[4] Gomberg and Pernert, *J. Am. Chem. Soc.*, **48**, 1372 (1926).

[5] Elks, Haworth, and Hey, *J. Chem. Soc.*, **1940**, 1285.

[6] Hodgson and Marsden, *J. Chem. Soc.*, **1940**, 208.

[7] Grieve and Hey, *J. Chem. Soc.*, **1934**, 1798.

[8] France, Heilbron, and Hey, *J. Chem. Soc.*, **1940**, 369. See also later references.

1. Acetylation of the amine.
2. Nitrosation of the acetylamine by means of N_2O_3* or NOCl.

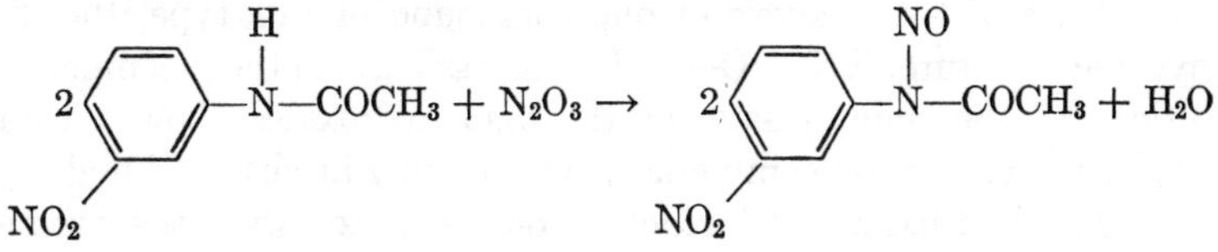

$$2 \; \text{(benzene ring, NO}_2\text{)}-\overset{H}{\underset{|}{N}}-COCH_3 + N_2O_3 \rightarrow 2 \; \text{(benzene ring, NO}_2\text{)}-\overset{NO}{\underset{|}{N}}-COCH_3 + H_2O$$

or,

$$\text{(benzene ring, NO}_2\text{)}-\overset{H}{\underset{|}{N}}-COCH_3 + NOCl + CH_3CO_2Na \rightarrow$$

$$\text{(benzene ring, NO}_2\text{)}-\overset{NO}{\underset{|}{N}}-COCH_3 + NaCl + CH_3CO_2H$$

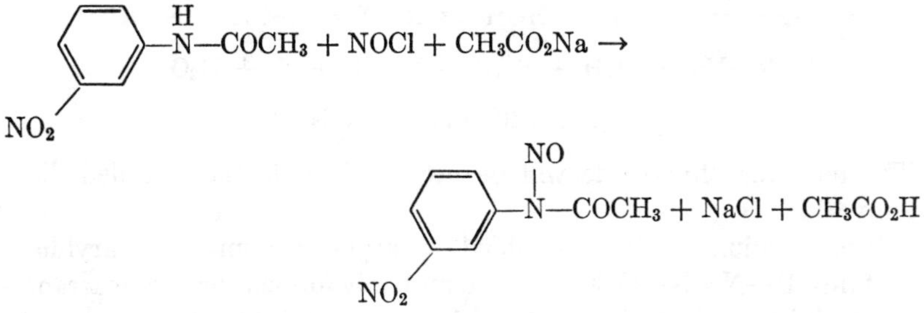

3. Reaction of the nitrosoacetylamine with a liquid aromatic compound.

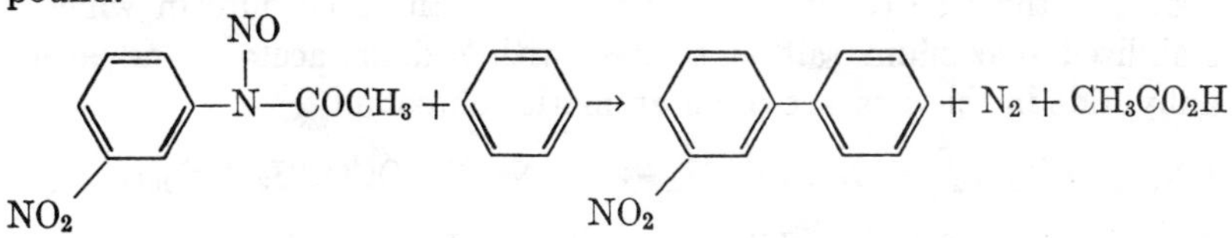

$$\text{(benzene ring, NO}_2\text{)}-\overset{NO}{\underset{|}{N}}-COCH_3 + \text{(benzene ring)} \rightarrow \text{(biphenyl, NO}_2\text{)} + N_2 + CH_3CO_2H$$

The nitrosation is carried out by passing nitrous fumes into an ice-cold solution or suspension of the acetylamine in acetic acid and acetic anhydride, or by adding a solution of nitrosyl chloride to the acetylamine and sodium acetate in acetic acid. The nitroso derivative is precipitated by pouring the solution into ice water and is extracted by the aromatic liquid or filtered and added to the liquid with which it reacts. In the example given, 3-nitrobiphenyl is obtained from *m*-nitroacetanilide in 63% yield.

MECHANISMS OF THE REACTIONS

When a dilute solution of sodium hydroxide is added gradually to a solution of an aryldiazonium salt, such as diazotized *p*-bromoaniline or *p*-nitroaniline, a yellow solid is precipitated. The same yellow solid can be obtained by adding an acid to the sodium diazotates, RN_2ONa, formed by addition of the diazonium salt to an excess of sodium hydroxide. These products, which are exceedingly unstable and explosive in the

---

* So-called nitrous fumes; a mixture of NO and NO_2 actually is used in the reaction.

dry or moist state, are the reactive intermediates in the diazo reaction and give biaryls when they come in contact with aromatic compounds. On the basis of the analysis of one compound of this type, the diazo anhydride structure, RN_2—O—N_2R, was assigned to these compounds.[1] Solutions of the sodium salts of the diazohydroxides show a similar behavior with aromatic compounds,[4] presumably in virtue of hydrolysis to the diazohydroxides and reaction of the latter with the aromatic compound.

$$R—N{=}N—ONa + HOH \rightleftarrows R—N{=}N—OH + NaOH$$

$$R—N{=}N—OH + R'H \rightarrow R—R' + N_2 + H_2O$$

$$(R \text{ and } R' = \text{aryl radicals})$$

The term diazohydroxide will be used to include the so-called diazo anhydrides.

When sodium acetate is added to aryldiazonium salts, aryldiazo acetates, R—N=N—$OCOCH_3$, are probably formed through rearrangement of the aryldiazonium salts initially produced, and they react in the same manner as the aryldiazo hydroxides. The aryldiazo acetates are probably the reactive intermediates also in the procedure in which a stabilized diazonium salt is treated with sodium acetate and acetic anhydride in the presence of an aromatic compound.

$$RN_2{}^+[SO_3C_{10}H_7]^- + NaOCOCH_3 \rightarrow R—N{=}N—OCOCH_3 + C_{10}H_7SO_3Na$$

The reaction of the aryldiazo acetates with aromatic compounds to give biaryls was utilized first by Kühling,[2] who treated a suspension of the potassium diazotate, RN_2OK, in the aromatic liquid with acetyl chloride.

The reactions involving the diazohydroxides, the diazoacetates, and the nitrosoacetylamines are closely related. Not only do these substances yield the same products when they react with aromatic compounds, but also they appear to react according to the same mechanism. This, perhaps, is not unexpected in view of the statements that nitrosoacetanilide is a tautomer of benzenediazoacetate.[9, 10, 11]

$$C_6H_5N(NO)COCH_3 \rightleftarrows C_6H_5N{=}N—OCOCH_3$$

Considerable evidence that all these reactions take place through a free radical mechanism has been accumulated.[12]   It is considered that

[9] Bamberger, Ber., 27, 914 (1894).

[10] v. Pechmann and Frobenius, Ber., 27, 651 (1894).

[11] Hantzsch and Wechsler, Ann., 325, 226 (1902).

[12] Discussions of the mechanisms of these reactions may be found in the excellent reviews of Hey and Waters, Chem. Revs., 21, 169 (1937), and of Hey, Ann. Repts., 37, 278 (1940).

free aryl radicals are produced by decomposition of the diazo compounds and of the nitrosoacetylamines, and that the radicals react with the second component to give the biaryl. Thus, in benzene, nitroso-*m*-nitroacetanilide decomposes into *m*-nitrophenyl and acetate radicals with evolution of nitrogen; the *m*-nitrophenyl radical reacts with benzene with elimination of a hydrogen atom and the formation of 3-nitrobiphenyl. The reactions are indicated in the following formulation, which shows also the probable fate of the acetate radical.

$$CH_3COO \cdot + H \cdot \rightarrow CH_3COOH$$
$$CH_3COO \cdot \rightarrow CH_3 \cdot + CO_2$$
$$CH_3 \cdot + H \cdot \rightarrow CH_4$$

In support of the free radical mechanism is the observation that the usual directive influences are not operative in these reactions. Substitution usually takes place *para* and *ortho* to the substituent in the benzene ring, irrespective of the nature of the groups. Even with nitrobenzene, *para* and *ortho* derivatives are formed. Thus, N-nitrosoacetanilide and nitrobenzene give 2- and 4-nitrobiphenyl.

Similarly, in the few reactions that have been carried out with benzaldehyde and benzonitrile, only the *para* isomer has been isolated from the reaction mixtures; with ethyl benzoate all three isomers were obtained. Another point of interest is that nitrobenzene is attacked more rapidly than toluene.

In the reactions with aliphatic hydrogen-containing compounds such as hexane, and halogen compounds such as carbon tetrachloride, hydrogen and halogen respectively are abstracted from these compounds; these are reactions characteristic of active free radicals.

$$Ar\cdot + RH \rightarrow ArH + R\cdot$$

$$Ar\cdot + RX \rightarrow ArX + R\cdot$$

(Ar· = free aryl radical; R = alkyl group; X = halogen)

Thus, N-nitrosoacetanilide yields benzene in hexane and chlorobenzene in carbon tetrachloride.

In support of the intermediate formation of the acetate radical from N-nitrosoacetanilide is the evolution of carbon dioxide during the reaction. Moreover, metals such as copper, zinc, lead, antimony, and iron are attacked when N-nitrosoacetanilide is allowed to decompose in a non-polar solvent such as carbon disulfide in the presence of the metals, a behavior similar to that of metals in contact with active free radicals in the Paneth test.

SCOPE AND LIMITATIONS OF THE REACTIONS

Types of Compounds Available through the Reactions

The two general reactions can be used to prepare a variety of compounds in which two aryl groups are linked. The unsymmetrical biaryls are of particular interest since they are not as accessible through other reactions as the symmetrical compounds. Some conception of the types of compounds available by replacement of the amino group of aromatic amines by aryl groups can be obtained from an examination of the following table, which shows the more important amines from which diazo

AMINES	COMPOUNDS USED FOR COUPLING
Aniline	Benzene
Halogenated anilines	Toluene
Nitroanilines	Nitrobenzene
Cyanoanilines	Methyl benzoate
Alkoxyanilines	Phenol ethers
C-Alkylanilines	Thiophene
Bromonitroanilines	Pyridine
Bromo-C-alkylanilines	
Anthranilic esters	
Aminophthalic esters	
Phenylenediamines	
Aminobiphenyls	
Benzidine	
Naphthylamines	

compounds or N-nitrosoacetyl derivatives have been prepared and some of the compounds which have been used for coupling. It is apparent that, by the proper combination of reagents, derivatives of biphenyl, the terphenyls, phenylnaphthalenes, phenylthiophenes, and phenylpyridines can be prepared.

With the diazohydroxides the yields usually lie between 15 and 35%, although in some instances they are much lower; with the nitrosoacetyl derivatives the yields are generally higher, lying between 40 and 70%. In some reactions in which the diazohydroxide fails to give the desired product, the nitrosoacetyl derivative may give it. Moreover, the modifications, such as the use of sodium acetate or the stabilized diazonium salts, occasionally serve to improve the yield in the diazo reaction. Even when the yields are low, these methods are often the only ones available for preparing substances of definite structure for purposes of identification.

A limitation of both methods is that the second component must be liquid at the temperature of the reaction, which is 5–10° for the diazohydroxide reaction and room temperature or slightly higher for the nitrosoacetylamine reaction. Experiments with solid reactants in solution have not been very successful, because of the difficulty of finding a suitable solvent. The solvent should be neutral and immiscible with water, have a high solvent action and reasonably low boiling point, and be inert to the free radicals which result from the diazo compound. The last qualification is the most difficult one to satisfy. Of the solvents which have been tried, carbon tetrachloride and chloroform appear to be the most suitable.[13] From diazotized aniline and biphenyl in these solvents, some p-terphenyl is obtained, and from diazotized p-nitroaniline and biphenyl a small amount of 4-nitro-4'-phenylbiphenyl is formed. In these reactions an appreciable amount of the aryl halide (chlorobenzene and p-nitrochlorobenzene) is produced as a by-product. In general, the yields of products obtained by coupling with reactants in solution are extremely low.

Derivatives of Biphenyl. By coupling diazo compounds and N-nitrosoacetyl derivatives obtained from substituted anilines with benzene, a large variety of biphenyl derivatives can be prepared in which only one of the rings is substituted. In this manner, the isomeric monosubstituted biphenyls, $RC_6H_4C_6H_5$, have been prepared in which $R = Br$, Cl, CH_3, OCH_3, NO_2, CN, etc. The *meta* derivatives, such as 3-bromobiphenyl (I), 3-nitrobiphenyl (II), and 3-cyanobiphenyl (III), are of particular interest because they cannot be prepared readily from biphenyl. The usefulness of the methods for the preparation of compounds of definite

[13] Grieve and Hey, *J. Chem. Soc.*, **1938**, 110.

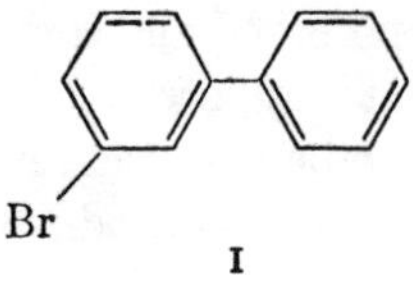

Br

I

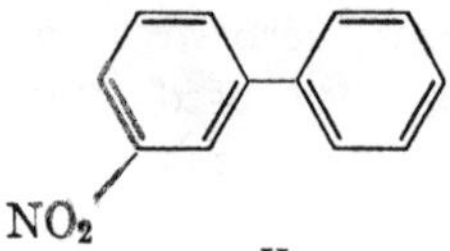

NO$_2$

II

CN

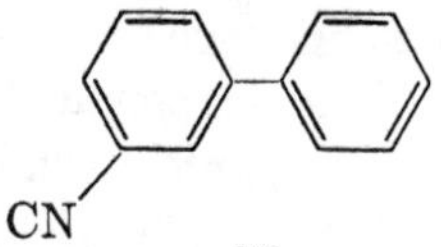

III

structure is illustrated by the following five isomeric bromomethylbiphenyls, which have been prepared from the corresponding bromotoluidines and benzene.

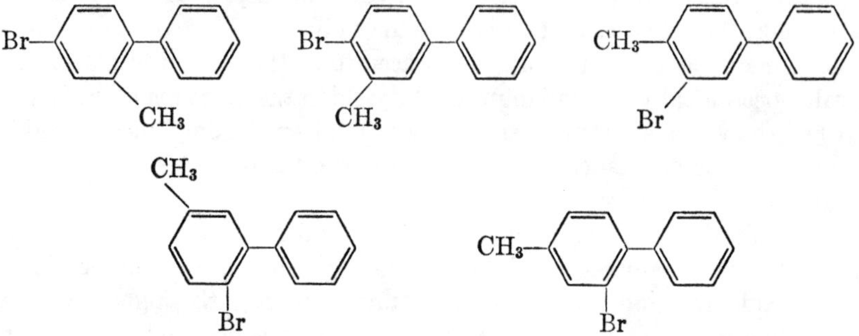

Br

CH$_3$

Br

CH$_3$

CH$_3$

Br

CH$_3$

Br

CH$_3$

Br

For the preparation of biphenyl compounds with substituents in only one ring, it is usually advisable to employ a substituted aniline and couple with benzene rather than to use aniline and couple with a benzene derivative, since with benzene only a single biaryl compound is produced. Thus, 4-methylbiphenyl can be isolated readily in pure form from the reaction between diazotized *p*-toluidine and benzene, but not from the mixture of 2- and 4-methylbiphenyl formed from diazotized aniline and toluene.

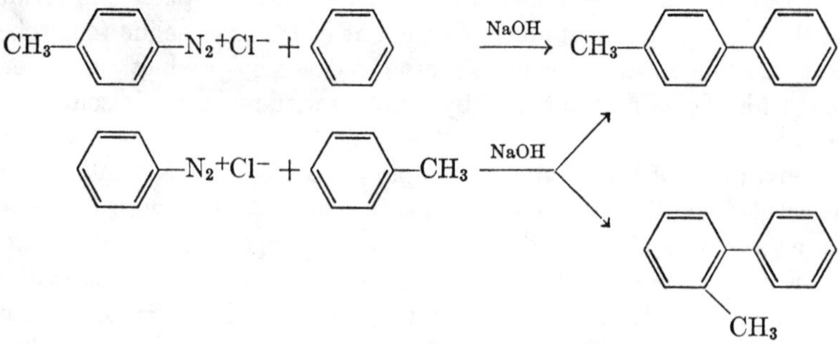

CH$_3$—⟨ ⟩—N$_2$$^+Cl^-$ + ⟨ ⟩ $\xrightarrow{\text{NaOH}}$ CH$_3$—⟨ ⟩—⟨ ⟩

⟨ ⟩—N$_2$$^+Cl^-$ + ⟨ ⟩—CH$_3$ $\xrightarrow{\text{NaOH}}$

CH$_3$

However, isolation of the product or products formed by coupling with nitrobenzene and certain other compounds has been successful. From nitrobenzene and diazotized aniline (in the form of the stabilized diazonium salt), 4-nitrobiphenyl is obtained in 33% yield, and from *o*-nitrotoluene and N-nitrosoacetanilide, 4-nitro-3-methylbiphenyl (IV) is obtained in 15% yield. It is of interest that in the latter reaction coupling takes place *para* to the nitro group rather than *para* to the methyl group. The structure of the compound follows from its formation from the nitrosoacetyl derivative of 3-methyl-4-nitroaniline and benzene.

C_6H_5—N(NO)COCH$_3$ + (o-NO$_2$, CH$_3$-phenyl) $\searrow$

$\nearrow$ (biphenyl)—NO$_2$, CH$_3$ IV

NO$_2$—(phenyl, CH$_3$)—N(NO)COCH$_3$ + C_6H_6 $\nearrow$

The stabilized diazonium salt procedure has given 3,4'-dinitrobiphenyl (V) in 54% yield from *m*-nitroaniline and nitrobenzene and 4,4'-dinitrobiphenyl (VI) in 69% yield from *p*-nitroaniline and nitrobenzene.

(biphenyl with NO$_2$ groups)—NO$_2$ V   NO$_2$—(biphenyl)—NO$_2$ VI

Alkoxy derivatives of biphenyl can be obtained either from alkoxy-anilines or by coupling with alkoxybenzenes. From diazotized *p*-bromo-aniline and anisole a 20% yield of 4-bromo-2'-methoxybiphenyl and a 7% yield of 4-bromo-4'-methoxybiphenyl are obtained. In connection with their studies on *Cannabis Indica*, Ghosh, Pascall, and Todd [14] prepared the highly substituted biphenyl compound, 2-cyano-5-methyl-2',5'-dimethoxy-4'-*n*-amylbiphenyl (VII), in 27% yield from the nitrosoacetyl derivative of 2-cyano-5-methylaniline and 2,5-dimethoxy-*n*-amylbenzene.

CH$_3$-(phenyl)—N(NO)COCH$_3$, CN + CH$_3$O-(phenyl)—C$_5$H$_{11}$-*n*, OCH$_3$ → CH$_3$ CH$_3$O-(biphenyl)—C$_5$H$_{11}$-*n*, CN OCH$_3$ VII

[14] Ghosh, Pascall, and Todd, *J. Chem. Soc.*, **1940**, 1118.

It is not possible to prepare biaryls containing a free carboxyl group directly by the diazo reaction. No biaryl is formed when (a) diazotized aniline and sodium benzoate, (b) diazotized anthranilic acid and aqueous sodium benzoate, or (c) diazotized anthranilic acid and benzene are used as components in the reaction.[13] On the other hand, the reaction proceeds normally if methyl benzoate is used in reaction (a) or when methyl anthranilate replaces the anthranilic acid in (b) and in (c). The success of the diazohydroxide reaction appears to lie in the ability of the non-aqueous liquid to extract the reactive diazo compound from the aqueous layer.[4] However, esters and nitriles can be prepared from esters of aromatic amino acids and cyanoanilines and also by coupling with esters of aromatic acids, and from the products the acids can be obtained by hydrolysis. By coupling N-nitrosoacetanilide with ethyl phthalate, ethyl 4-phenylphthalate (VIII) is formed in 37% yield.

The products obtained from esters of anthranilic acid and substituted anthranilic acids are of interest because fluorenones can be prepared from them. From diazotized methyl anthranilate and benzene, 2-carbomethoxybiphenyl is obtained in 24% yield. Hydrolysis affords 2-biphenylcarboxylic acid, which can be cyclized to fluorenone. By this procedure, a number of 2- and 3-substituted fluorenones have been prepared.[15] Thus, 3-chlorofluorenone was prepared from methyl 4-chloroanthranilate and benzene through the following steps.

[15] Heilbron, Hey, and Wilkinson, J. Chem. Soc., 1938, 113.

Fluorenonecarboxylic acids are accessible from the products formed by coupling diazotized esters of methyl 3-aminophthalic acids with benzene and benzene derivatives. From diazotized methyl 3-aminophthalate and benzene, methyl 3-phenylphthalate (IX) is obtained in 35% yield.

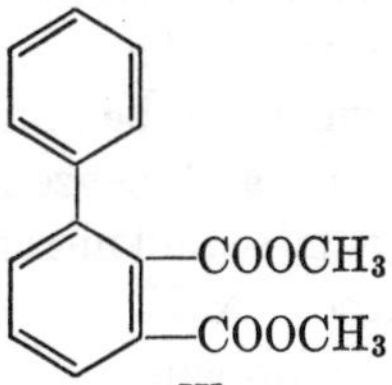

$$\text{—COOCH}_3$$
$$\text{—COOCH}_3$$
IX

Terphenyls and Derivatives. p-Terphenyl can be prepared satisfactorily in two ways: (a) from the nitrosoacetyl derivative of 4-aminobiphenyl, and (b) from the bis-nitrosoacetyl derivative of p-phenylenediamine. The yields by both routes are about the same (50–60%).

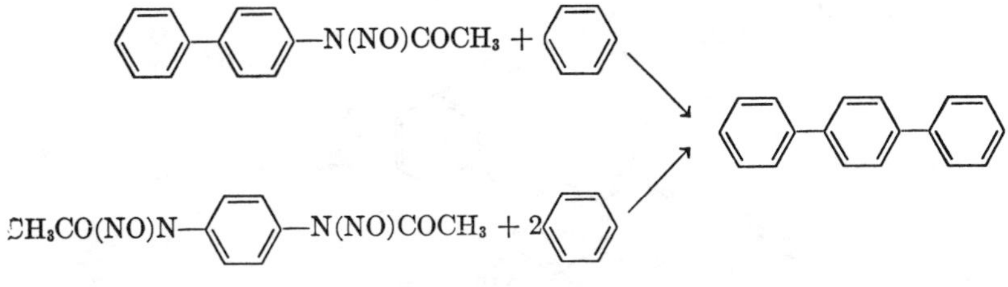

$$\text{—N(NO)COCH}_3 +$$

$$\text{CH}_3\text{CO(NO)N—}\quad\text{—N(NO)COCH}_3 + 2$$

m-Terphenyl can be prepared by analogous reactions from 3-aminobiphenyl and from m-phenylenediamine; the preparation of o-terphenyl by these methods has not been reported. Derivatives of m-terphenyl and p-terphenyl can be prepared from the substituted aminobiphenyls. When the diacetyl derivative of 3-nitro-1,4-phenylenediamine was treated with nitrous fumes, only a mononitroso derivative was formed, for the product obtained by treating the nitroso compound with benzene was 3-nitro-4-acetamidobiphenyl (X; 32% yield); the acetamido group *ortho* to the nitro group was not nitrosated. By coupling the bis-nitrosoacetyl derivative of benzidine with benzene, quaterphenyl (XI) is obtained in 17% yield.

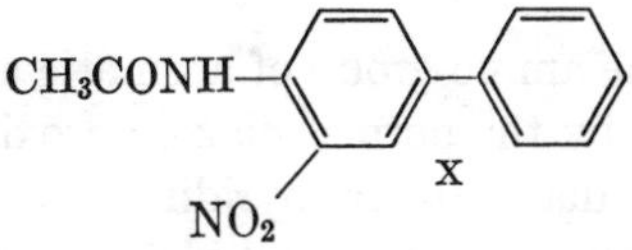

$$\text{CH}_3\text{CONH—}$$
X
$$\text{NO}_2$$

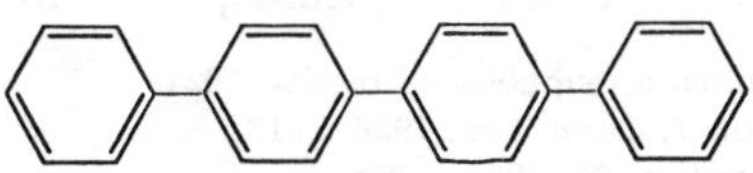

XI

Arylnaphthalenes. Arylnaphthalenes can be prepared by replacement of the amino group of naphthylamines by aryl groups. α-Phenylnaphthalene can be prepared satisfactorily only through the stabilized diazonium salt method, but β-phenylnaphthalene is obtained readily by several procedures. A considerable number of derivatives of β-phenylnaphthalene have been prepared. An example is 5-nitro-6-methoxy-2-phenylnaphthalene (XII), which can be obtained in 19% yield from the nitromethoxy-β-naphthylamine and benzene. From the reaction between diazotized β-naphthylamine and nitrobenzene and sodium acetate, β-(2-nitrophenyl)-naphthalene (XIII; 14%) and β-(4-nitrophenyl)-naphthalene (XIV; 26%) are formed.

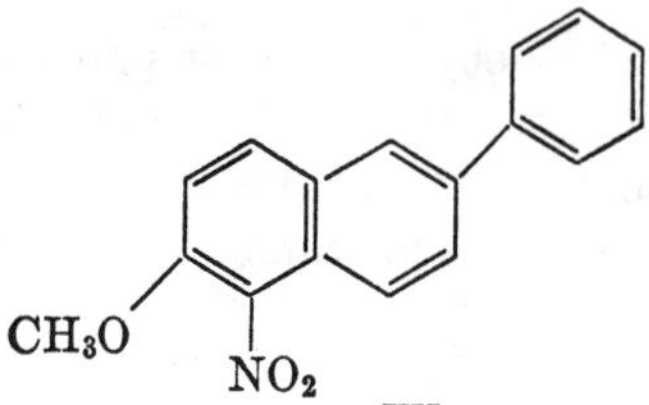

CH₃O NO₂   XII   XIII   NO₂

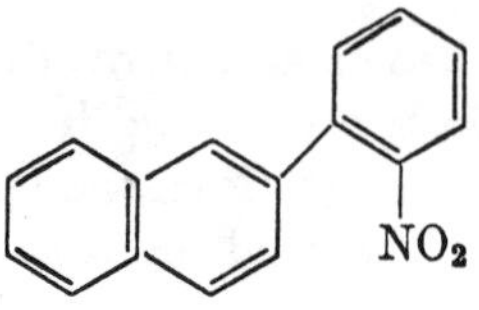

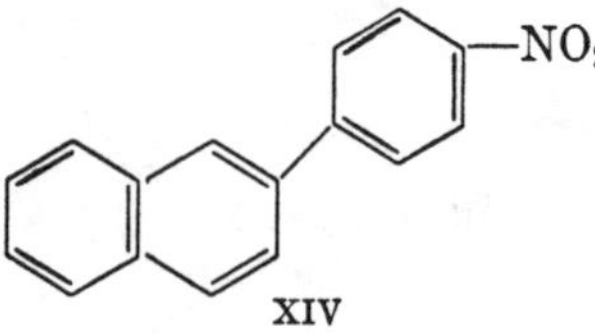

NO₂   XIV

Arylthiophenes. Thiophene couples with the diazohydroxides [3] and with N-nitrosoacetylamines [1] to give phenylthiophenes and derivatives. The position taken by the aryl groups in the thiophene nucleus has not been determined in all instances. The product obtained from diazotized m-cyanoaniline and thiophene [3] in 19% yield appears to be the α derivative (XV).[16]

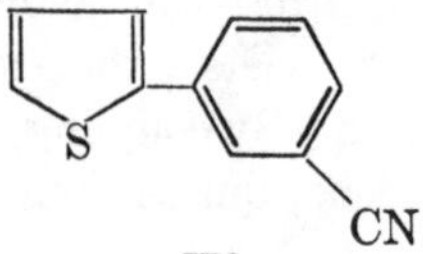

S   CN   XV

Arylpyridines. The amino group of aromatic amines can be replaced by the pyridyl group by the normal diazohydroxide reaction,[3] by treatment of the sodium diazotate in pyridine with acetyl chloride,[17] by adding the dry diazonium salt to pyridine,[18] and from the nitrosoacetyl

[16] Gomberg and Bachmann, unpublished results, 1924.
[17] Forsyth and Pyman, *J. Chem. Soc.*, **1926**, 2912.
[18] Möhlau and Berger, *Ber.*, **26**, 1994 (1893).

derivative and pyridine.[19] The best procedure is to add an aqueous solution of the diazonium salt to an excess of pyridine at temperatures ranging from 20° to 70°; the yields of products vary from 20 to 80%.[20] Apparently the pyridine plays the role of sodium hydroxide in liberating the reactive intermediate diazohydroxide, for, if the pyridine is added to the solution of the diazonium salt, no nitrogen is evolved until after one equivalent of pyridine has been introduced. A mixture of isomers results which can be separated either directly or through the picrates. From benzenediazonium chloride and pyridine a 40% yield of phenylpyridines is obtained from which α-phenylpyridine (9%), β-phenylpyridine (4%), and γ-phenylpyridine (4%) can be isolated in pure form.

By this procedure a considerable number of arylpyridines have been prepared. Pyridine derivatives can be prepared also from amines containing the pyridyl group. Thus, the nitrosoacetyl derivative of m-α-pyridyl-aniline can be coupled with benzene to yield 3-α-pyridylbiphenyl (XVI).

Similarly, the β- and γ-pyridyl derivatives of biphenyl can be prepared.

Side Reactions

One of the side reactions is the formation of linear polyaryls, which may be considered to be formed by further reaction of the biaryl initially produced. From the high-boiling residue remaining after the removal of the biphenyl, formed from diazotized aniline, benzene, and alkali, p-terphenyl [3] and quaterphenyl [16] have been isolated; and in the mixture formed in the preparation of 4-methylbiphenyl a hydrocarbon was found

[19] Haworth, Heilbron, and Hey, J. Chem. Soc., 1940, 373.
[20] Haworth, Heilbron, and Hey, J. Chem. Soc., 1940, 349.

which appeared to be a di-p-tolylbenzene.[4]   It is of interest that the decomposition of benzenediazonium formate in acetic acid in the presence of copper yields quinquiphenyl (XVII) and sexiphenyl (XVIII) in addition to biphenyl, p-terphenyl, and quaterphenyl.[21]

XVII

XVIII

Another side reaction which occurs is reduction; in the reaction the —N₂Cl or —N(NO)COCH₃ group is replaced by hydrogen. m-Bromotoluene was isolated in 6% yield from the reaction between the sodium diazotate from 2-bromo-4-methylaniline and benzene, and in 10% yield in a similar reaction from 2-methyl-4-bromoaniline.[4]   Some nitrobenzene is obtained in the preparation of 3-nitrobiphenyl from nitroso-m-nitroacetanilide (p. 250).   The source of the hydrogen effecting the reduction has not been determined.

Azo compounds are formed to some extent in the biaryl reactions. From the reaction between diazotized p-toluidine and benzene, azo-p-toluene, $CH_3C_6H_4N{=}NC_6H_4CH_3$, was isolated, indicating that, in this particular instance at least, the azo compound was derived entirely from the diazonium compound.   In addition to these types of compounds, a considerable amount of high-boiling material is usually formed in the reactions.

The disadvantages of the methods are the low yields in many of the reactions, the limitations to coupling with liquid aromatic compounds, the difficulty in some instances of getting the product out of the mixture containing the high-boiling by-products, and the difficulty of separating isomers when more than one compound is formed.

Related Reactions

Employment of Dry Diazonium Salts.   Of interest is the reaction between dry diazonium salts and aromatic compounds in the presence of anhydrous aluminum chloride.[18, 22]   The reaction resembles a Friedel and Crafts reaction; nitrogen is evolved in addition to hydrogen chloride.

[21] Gerngross and Dunkel, *Ber.*, **57**, 739 (1924).

[22] Möhlau and Berger, *Ber.*, **26**, 1198 (1893).

From dry solid benzenediazonium chloride, benzene, and aluminum chloride, biphenyl is obtained in 33% yield.

Similar reactions have been carried out with naphthalene and thiophene. The method has been employed only to a limited extent [23] since its discovery, probably because it involves the isolation of the dry diazonium salts and because a number of aryldiazonium salts (from o- and p-toluidine and β-naphthylamine) gave no biaryls but only the corresponding aryl halides.

Pschorr Synthesis. In this synthesis of phenanthrene derivatives, one of the steps involves the union of two aryl nuclei through a diazotization reaction. By treatment of diazotized α-phenyl-o-aminocinnamic acid with copper, 9-phenanthroic acid is obtained.[24]

Ring closure of cis-o-aminostilbene (XIX) to phenanthrene, o-aminobibenzyl (XX) to 9,10-dihydrophenanthrene, and o-aminodiphenylmethane (XXI) to fluorene can be effected likewise through the diazonium reaction.[25] A number of substituted fluorenones have been prepared by this method.[25a]

Reaction of Diazonium Salts with Quinones and with Phenols. Aryldiazonium salts couple with quinones in the presence of sodium acetate to

[23] Knowles, *J. Am. Chem. Soc.*, **43**, 896 (1921).
[24] See Johnson, *Org. Reactions*, **I**, 246 (1942).
[25] See Kornblum, *Org. Reactions*, this volume.
[25a] Lothrop and Goodwin, *J. Am. Chem. Soc.*, **65**, 363 (1943).

give arylquinones.[26] By means of this reaction a number of arylquinones (and the corresponding dihydroxybiphenyls by reduction) have been prepared in 55–85% yields.[27] The solid diazonium salt is added to a solution of the quinone in alcohol, followed or preceded by the addition of an excess of sodium acetate. From diazotized aniline and benzoquinone, phenylquinone is obtained.

The phenylquinone can be made to react further to give 2,5-diphenylquinone. 1,4-Naphthoquinone reacts readily only with reactive diazonium compounds such as diazotized p-aminobenzoic acid; with the latter compound it yields 2-(p-carboxyphenyl)-1,4-naphthoquinone (XXII).

XXII

Hydroxy derivatives of biphenyl can be prepared from diazonium salts, such as the chloride or sulfate, and phenols if no alkali is added.[28, 29, 30, 31, 32] From a solution of diazotized aniline in a large excess of phenol, a good yield of a mixture of 2- and 4-hydroxybiphenyl is obtained in addition to diphenyl ether.

[26] I. G. Farbenind. A. G., Brit. pat., 390,029 (1933).
[27] Kvalnes, J. Am. Chem. Soc., **56**, 2478 (1934).
[28] Hirsch, Ber., **23**, 3705 (1890).
[29] Graebe and Schestakow, Ann., **284**, 306 (1895).
[30] Norris, MacIntire, and Corse, Am. Chem. J., **29**, 121 (1903).
[31] Chatterjee, J. Ind. Chem. Soc., **12**, 410, 690 (1935).
[32] Huntress and Seikel, J. Am. Chem. Soc., **61**, 1066 (1939).

From diazotized aniline and p-nitrosophenol Borsche [33] obtained 2-hydroxy-5-nitrosobiphenyl (XXIII) in 8% yield, and with 2-methyl-4-nitrosophenol he obtained 2-hydroxy-3-methyl-5-nitrosobiphenyl (XXIV).

OH

C_6H_5—

NO

XXIII

OH

C_6H_5— —CH_3

NO

XXIV

Decomposition of Aromatic Acyl Peroxides. The decomposition of aromatic acyl peroxides in liquid aromatic compounds is similar to the decomposition of nitrosoacetylarylamines and appears to involve the intermediate formation of free radicals. When dibenzoyl peroxide is heated in benzene, biphenyl, benzoic acid, and small amounts of phenyl benzoate, p-terphenyl, and quaterphenyl are produced.[34] That the second component enters into the reaction is shown by the formation of 4-chlorobiphenyl from the decomposition of di-p-chlorobenzoyl peroxide in benzene [34] and of dibenzoyl peroxide in chlorobenzene.[35]

$$ClC_6H_4CO \cdot O—O \cdot COC_6H_4Cl + C_6H_6 \longrightarrow$$

$$ClC_6H_4—C_6H_5 + CO_2 + ClC_6H_4COOH$$

$$C_6H_5CO \cdot O—O \cdot COC_6H_5 + C_6H_5Cl \longrightarrow$$

$$C_6H_5—C_6H_4Cl + CO_2 + C_6H_5COOH$$

Similar results have been obtained with other peroxides and benzene derivatives. A 29% yield of p-terphenyl can be obtained by careful decomposition of benzoyl peroxide in molten biphenyl at 95°.[36]

OTHER METHODS OF SYNTHESIS OF UNSYMMETRICAL BIARYLS

Direct Substitution in Biphenyl. Direct nitration, chlorination, and bromination of biphenyl can be used to prepare certain derivatives.[37] Direct nitration is probably the most satisfactory method of preparing large quantities of 2- and 4-nitrobiphenyl. In certain substitution reactions it is sometimes difficult to separate the mixture of

[33] Borsche, *Ann.*, **312**, 211 (1900).
[34] Gelissen and Hermans, *Ber.*, **58**, 285, 476, 984 (1925).
[35] Hey, *J. Chem. Soc.*, **1934**, 1966.
[36] Gelissen and Hermans, *Ber.*, **58**, 764 (1925).
[37] See Jenkins, McCullough, and Booth, *Ind. Eng. Chem.*, **22**, 31 (1930).

isomers formed.[38] Moreover, it is difficult or impossible to prepare many compounds by direct substitution. Certain compounds which are not available through direct substitution in biphenyl itself have been prepared by deamination of substituted aminobiphenyls and benzidines.[25]

Grignard Reaction. By addition of an arylmagnesium halide to a cyclic ketone, a carbinol is formed which can be dehydrated and dehydrogenated to a biaryl compound.[39, 40, 41, 42, 43, 43a] For example, m-tolylmagnesium bromide and cyclohexanol yield 1-m-tolylcyclohexanol, which on dehydration and dehydrogenation gives 3-methylbiphenyl.

When applicable, this method is excellent. However, only those biaryls can be prepared which contain substituents that do not enter into reaction readily with Grignard reagents and that can withstand the conditions of dehydrogenation.

Diels-Alder Reaction. By means of the Diels-Alder reaction a considerable number of hydrobiphenyls have been prepared,[43b] from which it should be possible to obtain unsymmetrical biaryls by dehydrogenation. Only a few of the adducts have been converted to the completely aromatic compounds. o-Terphenyl has been prepared from the adduct of maleic anhydride and 3,4-diphenylcyclopentadienone,[43c] and p-terphenyl has been obtained in practically quantitative yield from the adduct of the methyl ester of acetylenedicarboxylic acid and 1,4-diphenylbutadiene.[43d]

[38] Case, *J. Am. Chem. Soc.*, **58**, 1251 (1936).
[39] Weiss and Woidich, *Monatsh.*, **46**, 453 (1925).
[40] Mayer and Schiffner, *Ber.*, **65**, 1337 (1932).
[41] Sherwood, Short, and Stansfield, *J. Chem. Soc.*, **1932**, 1832.
[42] v. Braun, Irmisch, and Nelles, *Ber.*, **66**, 1471 (1933).
[43] Chatterjee, *J. Ind. Chem. Soc.*, **12**, 591 (1935).
[43a] Arnold, Collins, and Zenk, *J. Am. Chem. Soc.*, **62**, 983 (1940).
[43b] See Table 2 of the review by Norton, *Chem. Revs.*, **31**, 319 (1942).
[43c] Allen and Pingert, *J. Am., Chem. Soc.* **64**, 1365 (1942).
[43d] Lohaus, *Ann.*, **516**, 295 (1935).

Ullmann Reaction. Although the Ullmann reaction is considered usually in connection with the preparation of symmetrical biaryls, it has been employed also to prepare unsymmetrical biaryls. Thus, o-terphenyl has been synthesized by heating a mixture of iodobenzene and 2-iodobiphenyl with copper; [44] biphenyl and 2,2'-diphenylbiphenyl were by-products of the reaction.

The Ullmann reaction appeared to be the only satisfactory method for preparing certain highly substituted unsymmetrical biphenyl derivatives which were required by Adams and coworkers [45] in their study of the stereoisomerism of biphenyl compounds.

SELECTION OF EXPERIMENTAL CONDITIONS

Choice of Method. The particular method to be used depends to some extent on the compound to be prepared. On the basis of yield, the N-nitrosoacetyl method is generally to be preferred. However, the diazo reaction has been employed frequently, probably because it is less troublesome to carry out.

Gomberg and Pernert [4] recommended the use of the sodium diazotates for the preparation of biaryls from aniline and from p-toluidine and the normal diazo method for negatively substituted amines such as the bromo- and nitro-anilines. Grieve and Hey [7] found little difference in the yields of biaryls obtained by the two procedures when they coupled diazotized aniline with six different components: benzene, toluene, m-xylene, chlorobenzene, nitrobenzene, and ethyl benzoate. Where it is applicable, this modification offers the advantage that the dropwise addition of alkali is eliminated.

Some comparative studies have been made of the use of sodium acetate in place of sodium hydroxide in the diazo reaction.[5] In five out of twelve reactions, the yield of the biaryl was improved by using sodium acetate. Better yields were obtained by this variation with the following

[44] Bachmann and Clarke, J. Am. Chem. Soc., **49**, 2089 (1927).
[45] See Adams and Teeter, J. Am. Chem. Soc., **62**, 2188 (1940), and previous papers of this series.

amines: the nitroanilines, *o*-chloroaniline, and β-naphthylamine, as shown in the following table. All the reactions were with benzene.

COMPARISON OF YIELDS USING SODIUM HYDROXIDE AND SODIUM ACETATE

| | | *Yields* | |
Amine	Product	NaOH	CH₃COONa
Aniline	Biphenyl	22%	16%
o-Nitroaniline	2-Nitrobiphenyl	21	45
m-Nitroaniline	3-Nitrobiphenyl	18	45
p-Nitroaniline	4-Nitrobiphenyl	26	60
o-Chloroaniline	2-Chlorobiphenyl	25	38
m-Chloroaniline	3-Chlorobiphenyl	25	13
p-Chloroaniline	4-Chlorobiphenyl	40	35
p-Toluidine	4-Methylbiphenyl	22	11
p-Bromoaniline	4-Bromobiphenyl	44	12
p-Anisidine	4-Methoxybiphenyl	25	4
p-Phenetidine	4-Ethoxybiphenyl	29	11
β-Naphthylamine	β-Phenylnaphthalene	16	25

The effect of various other reagents on the yield of biphenyl from diazotized aniline and benzene has been studied. The following yields of biphenyl were obtained from one mole of aniline under the conditions noted.[16, 46]

REAGENTS	METHOD	YIELD OF BIPHENYL
NaOH	Diazohydroxide	22%
NaOH	Diazotate	24
Ca(OH)₂	Diazohydroxide	29
Ca(OH)₂	Diazotate	22
Mg(OH)₂	Diazohydroxide	33
MgSO₄, then NaOH	Diazohydroxide	35

Grieve and Hey [13] obtained no markedly improved yields of biphenyl when they tried various reagents under different conditions. They did observe that the yield of biphenyl is just as good in the sodium diazotate method when the reaction is run at 30° as at 5–10°. This modification allows the use of components which are solid at the lower temperature but liquid at the higher one (30°).

The use of stabilized diazonium salts is a recent modification, and the exact limits of this reaction have not yet been established. It has been found to be particularly good for nitroanilines (4-nitrobiphenyl is obtained in 70% yield from *p*-nitroaniline) and for coupling with nitrobenzene. Coupling of the stabilized salt of aniline failed with toluene, biphenyl, naphthalene, and 1-nitronaphthalene, and the stabilized salt of β-naphthylamine gave no β-phenylnaphthalene when coupling with ben-

[46] Gomberg and Bachmann, *J. Am. Chem. Soc.*, **49**, 236 (1927).

zene was attempted. Interesting data on the relative merits of various stabilizing agents and reagents for bringing about coupling with aromatic compounds may be found in the original paper.[6]

The nitrosoacetyl method usually gives good yields of biaryl compounds. It has the disadvantage that oxides of nitrogen must be generated and that unless the nitrosation is carried out carefully the yield suffers. A recent innovation employing nitrosyl chloride has eliminated the objections of the older nitrosation procedure and promises to be the best method.

Isolation of the Product. The usual method of working up the reaction mixtures is to remove the excess of benzene derivative by distillation or steam distillation and then obtain the biaryl by steam distillation by means of superheated steam or by keeping the reaction flask in a hot oil bath. This is a tedious process, for continued distillation is necessary in order to get the product out of the high-boiling tarry by-products, but the product obtained is fairly pure. A more rapid method, but one which gives a less pure product, is to distil the mixture under reduced pressure. In the preparation of 3-nitrobiphenyl good results were obtained by precipitating the tar from the benzene solution by means of petroleum ether and then recrystallizing the product.[47]

EXPERIMENTAL PROCEDURES

Diazo Reaction

The diazotization of the amines is carried out in the usual manner. The volume of water is kept at a minimum since the success of the reaction depends in part on the efficiency with which the unstable intermediate is extracted from the aqueous layer by the organic liquid. Either the previously prepared amine hydrochloride is employed or a paste of the hydrochloride is prepared by dissolving the amine in concentrated hydrochloric acid and then cooling rapidly with stirring. For diazotization a nearly saturated solution of sodium nitrite (1 g. in 2 cc. of water) is used. Little work has been done with very weakly basic amines in the diazo reaction.[48] In one instance, the base, 1-nitro-2-naphthylamine, was diazotized by means of nitrosylsulfuric acid in sulfuric acid; benzene was added and then sodium hydroxide until the mixture was slightly alkaline.[49] For the very weak bases, the nitrosoacetyl reaction is recommended, since it is carried out entirely under anhydrous conditions.

[47] Blakey and Scarborough, *J. Chem. Soc.*, **1927**, 3000.
[48] For a discussion of the diazotization of weakly basic amines see Saunders, "Aromatic Diazo Compounds," Edward Arnold and Co., London, 1936.
[49] Hey and Lawton, *J. Chem. Soc.*, **1940**, 374.

A fairly large container, such as a large wide-mouthed bottle, should be used for the diazo reaction in order to provide for the increase in volume through foaming of the mixture. The aqueous solution of sodium hydroxide (or sodium acetate) is added dropwise to the vigorously stirred mixture of the diazonium salt and aromatic liquid, which is kept at 5–10° throughout the reaction. Usually the mixture is stirred for an hour or two at this temperature after the addition has been completed; occasionally, the mixture is then allowed to warm up to room temperature and stirring is continued for a few hours longer. The layers are then separated and the product is isolated from the organic liquid.

When it is difficult to remove traces of azo compounds from the biaryl by distillation or recrystallization, chemical means may be employed. Colorless 4-bromobiphenyl was obtained by treating an alcoholic solution of the yellow product with a little zinc dust and hydrochloric acid.[50] In the preparation of 3-bromobiphenyl, the crude reaction mixture was shaken with portions of concentrated sulfuric acid until the red color of the solution was removed.[51]

Procedure Utilizing Sodium Hydroxide (A-1)

A detailed procedure for the preparation of 4-bromobiphenyl by this method is described in *Organic Syntheses*.[50]

2-Methoxy-4'-bromobiphenyl and 4-Methoxy-4'-bromobiphenyl.[52] A mixture of 215 g. of *p*-bromoaniline and 100 cc. of water is heated until the amine melts; 250 cc. of concentrated hydrochloric acid is then added, and the whole is cooled rapidly to 0° with stirring. A solution of 90 g. of sodium nitrite in 200 cc. of water is added slowly with cooling and agitation. The clear solution of the diazonium salt and 500 cc. of anisole are cooled in ice and stirred vigorously as 280 cc. of 5 N sodium hydroxide solution is added during the course of one hour. After twelve hours of continued stirring, the heavy brown oil which has separated is removed and steam-distilled, the flask being heated ultimately to 220°. Unchanged anisole comes over rapidly at first, and it is then followed by crude 2-methoxy-4'-bromobiphenyl, which solidifies in the chilled receiver. When, however, crystallization starts in the condenser, a third fraction, 4-methoxy-4'-bromobiphenyl, is collected. Prolonged steam distillation is required to obtain a good yield of the latter compound, since it is only slightly volatile with steam even at 220°.

The intermediate fraction of 2-methoxy-4'-bromobiphenyl is crystal-

[50] Gomberg and Bachmann, *Org. Syntheses*, *Coll. Vol.* I, 113, 2nd ed., 1941.

[51] Marvel, Ginsberg, and Mueller, *J. Am. Chem. Soc.*, **61**, 77 (1939).

[52] Harley-Mason and Mann, *J. Chem. Soc.*, **1940**, 1383.

lized from ethanol and then distilled under reduced pressure to remove traces of the less volatile 4-methoxy isomer. It boils at 200–201°/18 mm. and melts at 63–64°; yield, 64 g. (20%).

The 4-methoxy-4'-bromobiphenyl is recrystallized from benzene-ethanol; yield, 22 g. (7%); m.p. 144–145°. Direct distillation of the mixture lowers the yield.

Procedure Utilizing Sodium Diazotate (A-2)

4-Methylbiphenyl.[4] One hundred and seven grams (1 mole) of p-toluidine is dissolved in 185 cc. of concentrated hydrochloric acid (sp. gr. 1.2), the solution is cooled by the addition of ice and diazotized by the addition of a solution of 76 g. of sodium nitrite in 150 cc. of water. The solution is added during the course of two to three minutes to a vigorously stirred mixture of 275 cc. of 10 N sodium hydroxide, 600 cc. of benzene, and ice sufficient to keep the temperature at 5°. A small part of the benzene is kept frozen by the ice. When all the diazonium solution has been added, a vigorous reaction ensues, nitrogen is evolved, and the solution becomes yellow. Stirring is continued for five hours; no more ice is added after the first hour.

After the removal of the benzene by distillation, steam is passed into the residue (flask in oil bath at 150–175°). The 4-methylbiphenyl which comes over solidifies readily. After distillation at atmospheric pressure (b.p. 267–268°), it weighs 38 g. (22%) and melts at 47°. Vacuum distillation is recommended for working up larger quantities. The product from three runs (321 g. of p-toluidine) is distilled at 20 mm. pressure. The fraction boiling at 145–153° is nearly pure 4-methylbiphenyl; yield, 109 g. (21%).

Procedure Utilizing Sodium Acetate (A-3)

o-Chlorobiphenyl.[5] Thirty-two grams of o-chloroaniline is added to 80 cc. of hydrochloric acid (sp. gr. 1.16) and 45 cc. of water, and the mixture is cooled to 0° and diazotized in the usual manner. The filtered diazonium salt solution is stirred vigorously with 500 cc. of benzene as a solution of 80 g. of sodium acetate trihydrate in 200 cc. of water is added dropwise; throughout the addition the temperature is kept at 5–10°. Stirring is continued for forty-eight hours; after the first three hours, the reaction is allowed to proceed at room temperature. The benzene solution is separated, washed with water, and the benzene removed by distillation. The o-chlorobiphenyl is then distilled under reduced pressure, the fraction boiling at 150–155°/10 mm. being collected; yield, 18 g. (38%). After recrystallization from ethanol the product melts at 34°.

Procedure Utilizing a Stabilized Diazonium Salt (A-4)

α-Phenylnaphthalene.[6] α-Naphthylamine (14.3 g.) is diazotized at 0° in a mixture of 24 cc. of hydrochloric acid (sp. gr. 1.16) and 150 cc. of water, and the diazonium salt solution is treated with 16 g. of finely powdered naphthalene-1,5-disulfonic acid. Some stabilized diazonium salt separates immediately, but the mixture is stirred for one hour to complete the precipitation. The salt is then filtered and dried.

To 10 g. of the dry salt, well agitated with 30 g. of benzene, at room temperature, are added 3 g. of anhydrous sodium acetate and 1 g. of acetic anhydride. After forty-eight hours, the mixture is heated to 80° until nitrogen ceases to be evolved, the mixture is treated with water, the benzene layer is separated, the solvent is removed, and the α-phenylnaphthalene is isolated (no details given); yield, 1.4 g. (30%).

Procedure with Pyridine (A-5)

α-, β-, and γ-Phenylpyridine.[20] A solution of benzenediazonium chloride prepared in the normal manner from 30 g. of aniline is added dropwise in the course of two hours to 300 cc. of pyridine with stirring at 30°. The mixture is then warmed on a steam bath for one hour, cooled, and treated with concentrated sodium hydroxide. The pyridine layer is separated and poured into water, the product is extracted with ether, and the ether extract is dried over potassium hydroxide. After removal of the ether, the mixture of phenylpyridines is distilled under reduced pressure; b.p. 170–190°/10–20 mm.; weight; 20 g. The mixture is separated through the picrates and yields 12 g. of the pure picrate (m.p. 175–176°) of α-phenylpyridine, 5 g. of the picrate (m.p. 159–160°) of β-phenylpyridine, and 5 g. of the picrate (m.p. 195–196°) of γ-phenylpyridine, from which the pure bases can be generated. The α- and β-phenylpyridines are liquids; γ-phenylpyridine melts at 69–70°.

Nitrosoacetylamine Reaction

Nitrosation by Nitrous Fumes. The general procedure consists in passing nitrous fumes into a solution or suspension of the acetylamine in glacial acetic acid at about 10° until a clear green solution is obtained. Frequently some acetic anhydride is used with the acetic acid in order to lower the freezing point and thus permit a lower temperature for the reaction. The addition of a small quantity of phosphorus pentoxide often serves to speed up the reaction and give a slightly higher yield of product.

If the passage of nitrous fumes is continued after the dark green solution stage, the yield is reduced considerably and the product is tarry. Unfortunately, there is no simple way of determining exactly when nitrosation is complete. The nitrosoacetylamine is precipitated when the solution is poured into a large volume of ice water. If the product is an oil, it is dissolved in the aromatic liquid (Component B), and the solution is washed rapidly with water and then kept over a drying agent; if the nitrosoacetylamine is solid, it may be filtered and dried on a porous plate. Most of the solid nitrosoacetylarylamines can be kept at room temperature for over a day without appreciable decomposition.

A considerable number of acylarylamines, among them o-chloroacetanilide, 2,6-dichloro-4-nitroacetanilide, and 1-acetamido-2-methylanthraquinone, form abnormal nitroso compounds with nitrous fumes; others, such as 4-dimethylamino-4'-acetamidoazobenzene, benzene-p-toluidide, and diacetyl-1,3-phenylene diamine, do not yield nitroso compounds with nitrous fumes; a third group, which includes p-nitroacetanilide and α- and β-acetamidoanthraquinone, is recovered unchanged after the same treatment.[53] In general, the acetamido group submits to nitrosation, whereas the benzoyl and benzenesulfonyl and toluenesulfonyl derivatives of amines are resistant to the action of nitrous fumes.

Directions for generating nitrous fumes by means of the reaction between arsenious oxide and nitric acid are given in *Organic Syntheses*.[54] The preparation of nitrous fumes by means of solid sodium nitrite and nitric acid appears to be more rapid and convenient.[53]

Nitrous Fumes Method (B-1)

3-Nitrobiphenyl. (Procedure of France, Heilbron, and Hey [55] revised and augmented by R. A. Hoffman. In this preparation the acetyl derivative of the amine is prepared in the mixture used for nitrosation.) Through a three-hole rubber stopper in the neck of a 1-l. flask containing 125 g. of sodium nitrite is placed a 250-cc. long-stemmed dropping funnel containing 125 cc. of concentrated nitric acid. A compressed air outlet is connected to a T-tube, one side of which leads to the top of the dropping funnel (to overcome the back pressure of the gas) and the other side to a mercury trap, which serves as a bubble counter. A connection is made from the trap to a tube passing through the stopper in the generating flask. The outlet tube of the flask is connected to a drying tower packed with 4-mesh calcium chloride.

[53] Haworth and Hey, *J. Chem. Soc.*, **1940**, 361.
[54] Dox, *Org. Syntheses*, Coll. Vol. I, 266, 2nd ed., 1941.
[55] France, Heilbron, and Hey, *J. Chem. Soc.*, **1939**, 1288.

In a 1-l. three-necked flask are placed 50 g. of m-nitroaniline, 250 cc. of glacial acetic acid, and 125 cc. of acetic anhydride. The flask is warmed on a steam bath for about an hour with occasional swirling; the solid m-nitroaniline dissolves, and a light-yellow solution is obtained. The outlet tube from the drying tower is attached to a tube which passes through a stopper in one neck of the flask and extends below the surface of the solution. The center neck is fitted with a stirrer passing through a glycerol seal,[56] and the other neck holds a calcium chloride tube. The flask containing the hot solution is immersed in an ice bath, and the solution is stirred in order to precipitate the m-nitroacetanilide as a fine powder. When the mixture is at 5°, nitric acid is allowed to drip on the sodium nitrite in the generator at the rate of 1–2 drops per second. The compressed air is adjusted so that there is no nitric oxide (which turns into the brown nitrogen dioxide as it comes in contact with air) escaping from the calcium chloride outlet tube; the rate varies from one to three bubbles per second through the mercury trap. The addition of nitric acid is continued until all the white m-nitroacetanilide goes into the dark green solution (forty-five to sixty minutes); the nitrous fumes are then passed in for an additional fifteen minutes.

The solution of the nitroso compound is poured into 1.5 l. of ice water in a 5-l. separatory funnel (made by sealing a stopcock to the bottom of a round-bottomed flask). The light brown oil which separates immediately is extracted with 1.5 l. of thiophene-free benzene. The water layer is separated and extracted with an additional 500 cc. of benzene, and the benzene extracts are combined in the large funnel and washed twice with 1.5 l. of ice water and finally with 1 l. of cold 2% sodium hydroxide. The benzene layer is separated carefully and run into a 3-l. beaker containing 75 g. of anhydrous sodium sulfate and 50 g. of anhydrous sodium carbonate. The volume of the clear light-yellow solution is brought up to 2.5 l. by the addition of benzene, and the mixture is stirred to keep the salts suspended throughout the solution. In a few minutes evolution of nitrogen and carbon dioxide commences, becoming increasingly vigorous during the first hour. The solution is stirred for about six hours and then allowed to stand for about eight hours more. After this period the solution is dark brown in color.

The filtered solution is placed in a 5-l. flask, and the benzene is removed by distillation on a steam bath; reduced pressure is necessary toward the end in order to bring the volume down to about 75 cc. The residue is transferred to a 125-cc. Claisen flask, and after preliminary removal of the benzene the 3-nitrobiphenyl is distilled under reduced pressure. At 0.01–0.02 mm., after a 3–5 cc. fore-run of nitrobenzene, the product distils

[56] Kyrides, *Org. Syntheses*, **21**, 40 (1941).

ιt 136–138°, with the flask immersed in an oil bath at 170–190°. About
40–43 g. (56–60%) of product, m.p. 54–56°, is obtained. Recrystallization from 35 cc. of methanol yields 38–40 g. (53–56%) of large yellow
crystals of 3-nitrobiphenyl melting at 58–59°. France, Heilbron, and
Hey [55] obtained 7 g. of 3-nitrobiphenyl from 10 g. of m-nitroacetanilide.

Nitrosation by Nitrosyl Chloride. The use of nitrosyl chloride in the
presence of sodium acetate [8] as a nitrosating agent shows much promise.
Both the yield and the quality of the nitrosoacetylamines prepared by
this method are superior to those resulting from the action of nitrous
fumes, and the time required for the reaction is reduced from hours to
minutes. Moreover, the reaction can be put on a quantitative basis,
since a liquid (NOCl) or a solution of the liquid is employed. In this way,
the detrimental results due to an excess of the nitrosating agent can be
avoided.

Normal nitroso derivatives which cannot be prepared with nitrous
fumes from certain compounds can be formed by means of nitrosyl
chloride. In particular, the nitroso derivatives of p-nitroacetanilide and
of diacetyl-1,3-phenylenediamine can be prepared. However, 2,4,6-
trinitroacetanilide and 2,5-diethoxydiacetyl-1,4-phenylenediamine have
resisted nitrosation even by this method.

A procedure which dispenses with the isolation of the nitroso derivative has been employed in one instance.[8] Addition of a benzene solution
of nitrosyl chloride to a benzene solution of acetanilide in the presence
of fused potassium acetate at 5°, followed by warming at 30° for two
hours, gave a 40% yield of biphenyl.

A method for preparing nitrosyl chloride from sulfur dioxide, fuming
nitric acid, and hydrogen chloride is given in *Inorganic Syntheses*.[57] The
following adaptation employing sodium chloride was found to be much
simpler.

$$SO_2 + HNO_3 \rightarrow NO \cdot SO_4H$$

$$NO \cdot SO_4H + NaCl \rightarrow NOCl + NaHSO_4$$

Preparation of Nitrosyl Chloride. One hundred cubic centimeters of
fuming nitric acid (sp. gr. 1.6) is placed in a 500-cc. distilling flask under
an efficient hood. Sulfur dioxide is bubbled into the nitric acid at the
rate of four to eight bubbles per second until no more is absorbed (about
four hours); after about two and one-half hours, a yellow solid separates.
The flask is then immersed in a beaker of water and air is passed through
the mass for about three hours while the temperature of the water is
raised gradually to the boiling point; the solid melts to a light yellow

[57] Coleman, Lillis, and Goheen, *Inorg. Syntheses*, **I**, 55 (1939).

liquid. After no more nitrous fumes are evolved, the flask is cooled to 40° and 150 g. of dry sodium chloride is added. The side arm of the flask is connected to a tube running down to the bottom of a 10-inch test tube immersed in an acetone-dry ice mixture. The top of the distilling flask is closed with a rubber stopper, and the water bath is warmed slowly to about 80° and kept there until no more yellow-orange fumes of nitrosyl chloride come off from the mixture. The red liquid NOCl which is collected weighs 60 g. Pure nitrosyl chloride boils at −5.5°.

Nitrosyl Chloride Procedure (B-2)

p-Terphenyl.[8, 58]   To a stirred solution of 10 g. of diacetyl-1,4-phenylenediamine in a mixture of 150 cc. of glacial acetic acid and 75 cc. of acetic anhydride containing 12 g. of anhydrous potassium acetate and 1 g. of phosphorus pentoxide at 8° is added dropwise a solution of 8 g. of nitrosyl chloride in acetic anhydride. The mixture is poured onto ice and water, and the yellow *bis*-nitrosoacetyl-1,4-phenylenediamine is filtered and dried; yield, 11.4 g.; m.p. 124° dec.

A mixture of 11 g. of the nitroso compound and 300 cc. of benzene is stirred at 35° for twelve hours; during this time the solid passes into solution with evolution of nitrogen. The residue obtained on removal of the solvent is distilled at 110–120°/10⁻³ mm. The yield of *p*-terphenyl is 7 g. (69%). After recrystallization from acetic acid it melts at 210–212°.

COMPOUNDS PREPARED BY THE REACTIONS

The compounds which have been prepared by replacement of the amino group of aromatic amines by aryl groups are listed in the table. The biphenyl compounds are listed in the following order: (*a*) monosubstitution products (2-, 3-, and then 4-derivatives) arranged according to the elements in the groups (order: C, O, N, Cl, Br, I); (*b*) disubstitution products with both groups in one ring (2,3-; 2,4-; 2,5-; etc.); (*c*) disubstitution products with a group in each ring (2,3′-; 2,4′-; 3,4′-; etc.); (*d*) polysubstitution products. After these the terphenyls, arylnaphthalenes, arylthiophenes, and arylpyridines are given in the order mentioned.

The yields in the diazo reaction are based on the amines; in the nitrosoacetylamine reaction, on the acetylamine or on the nitrosoacetylamine, indicated by a double dagger (‡). A dagger (†) indicates that the yield refers to a mixture of isomers.

⁵⁸ France, Heilbron, and Hey, *J. Chem. Soc.*, **1938**, 1364.

TABLE OF COMPOUNDS PREPARED BY THE REACTIONS

The procedures are designated by letters and numbers.

A–1   Diazohydroxide reaction (NaOH).
A–2   Sodium diazotate procedure.
A–3   Sodium acetate modification.
A–4   Stabilized diazonium salt procedure.
A–5   Pyridine method.
B–1   Nitrosoacetylamine reaction (N_2O_3).
B–2   Nitrosoacetylamine reaction (NOCl).

Product	Component A	Component B	Method	Yield	Reference *

Monosubstitution Products of Biphenyl, $RC_6H_4 \cdot C_6H_5$

Product	Component A	Component B	Method	Yield	Reference *
2-Methyl	o-Toluidine	Benzene	A–2	8%	4
2-Carbomethoxy	Methyl anthranilate	Benzene	A–1	24%	13
2-, 3-, and 4-Carboethoxy	Aniline	Ethyl benzoate	A–1	12– 14% †	7
2-Nitro	o-Nitroaniline	Benzene	A–1	20%	5
			A–3	45%	5
			A–4	35%	6
	o-Nitroacetanilide	Benzene	B–2	60%	8
2-Chloro	o-Chloroaniline	Benzene	A–1	25%	5
			A–3	38%	5
3-Methyl	m-Toluidine	Benzene	A–2	28%	4
3-Cyano	m-Cyanoaniline	Benzene	A–1	19%	3
3-Nitro	m-Nitroaniline	Benzene	A–1	15–18%	3, 5, 47
			A–3	45%	5
			A–4	56%	6
	m-Nitroacetanilide	Benzene	B–1	63%	53
			B–2	64%	8
3-Bromo	m-Bromoaniline	Benzene	A–1	18–28%	3, 51
3-Chloro	m-Chloroaniline	Benzene	A–1	25%	3, 5
			A–3	13%	5
4-Methyl	p-Toluidine	Benzene	A–2	22%	4, 5
			A–3	11%	5
x-Methyl	Aniline	Toluene	A–2	9–16% †	4, 7
4-Carbomethoxy	Aniline	Methyl benzoate	A–1	—	3
4-Carboethoxy	Ethyl p-Aminobenzoate	Benzene	A–1	12%	3
4-Aldehydo	Acetanilide	Benzaldehyde	B–1	26% †	7

* References 59–76 appear on p. 261.
† The product was a mixture of isomers.

TABLE OF COMPOUNDS PREPARED BY THE REACTIONS—*Continued*

Product	Component A	Component B	Method	Yield	Reference *
4-Cyano	p-Cyanoaniline	Benzene	A–1	15%	3
	Aniline	Cyanobenzene	A–1	10%	3
4-Methoxy	p-Anisidine	Benzene	A–1	25%	5
			A–3	4%	5
			A–4	26%	6
	p-Methoxyacetanilide	Benzene	B–1	55%	53
4-Ethoxy	p-Phenetidine	Benzene	A–1	29%	5
			A–3	11%	5
	p-Ethoxyacetanilide	Benzene	B–1	50%	53
4-Nitro	p-Nitroaniline	Benzene	A–1	30%	3, 5
			A–3	60%	5
			A–4	70%	6
	Aniline	Nitrobenzene	A–1	—	3, 7
			A–4	33%	6
	Acetanilide	Nitrobenzene	B–1	—†	7
	p-Nitroacetanilide	Benzene	B–2	60%	8
4-Chloro	p-Chloroaniline	Benzene	A–1	40%	5
			A–3	35%	5
			A–4	34%	6
x-Chloro	Aniline	Chlorobenzene	A–1	13–15%	7
	Acetanilide	Chlorobenzene	B–1	—	7
4-Bromo	p-Bromoaniline	Benzene	A–1	34–46%	3, 5, 50
			A–3	12%	5
x-Bromo	Aniline	Bromobenzene	A–1	—	3
4-Benzamido	p-Benzamidoacetanilide	Benzene	B–1	—	53

Disubstitution Products of Biphenyl, $R,R'C_6H_3 \cdot C_6H_5$

Product	Component A	Component B	Method	Yield	Reference *
2,3-Dicarbomethoxy	Methyl 3-aminophthalate	Benzene	A–1	35%	59
2,4-Dimethyl	Aniline	m-Xylene	A–1	9%	7
	Acetanilide	m-Xylene	B–1	45%	7
2-Methyl-4-chloro	2-Methyl-4-chloroaniline	Benzene	A–1	14%	60
2-Methyl-4-bromo	2-Methyl-4-bromoaniline	Benzene	A–1	7%	4
2-Carbomethoxy-4-nitro	Methyl 5-nitroanthranilate	Benzene	A–1	7%	15

* References 59–76 appear on p. 261.
† The product was a mixture of isomers.

TABLE OF COMPOUNDS PREPARED BY THE REACTIONS—*Continued*

Product	Component A	Component B	Method	Yield	Reference *
2-Carbomethoxy-4-chloro	Methyl 5-chloroanthranilate	Benzene	A–1	29%	15
2-Carbomethoxy-4-bromo	Methyl 5-bromoanthranilate	Benzene	A–1	29%	15
2,4-Dinitro	2,4-Dinitroaniline	Benzene	B–1	10%	8
2-Bromo-4-methyl	2-Bromo-4-methylaniline	Benzene	A–1	25%	4
2,4-Dibromo	2,4-Dibromoaniline	Benzene	A–1	22%	61
2-Carbomethoxy-5-chloro	Methyl 4-chloroanthranilate	Benzene	A–1	25%	15
2-Carbomethoxy-5-bromo	Methyl 4-bromoanthranilate	Benzene	A–1	25%	15
2-Cyano-5-methyl	2-Cyano-5-methylacetanilide	Benzene	B–1	45%	14
2-Nitro-5-methyl	2-Nitro-5-methylacetanilide	Benzene	B–1	51%	55
2-Chloro-5-methyl	2-Chloro-5-methylaniline	Benzene	A–1	15%	62
2-Bromo-5-methyl	2-Bromo-5-methylaniline	Benzene	A–1	16%	62
2-Bromo-5-nitro	2-Bromo-5-nitroaniline	Benzene	A–1	30%	38
3,4-Dicarbomethoxy	Methyl 4-aminophthalate	Benzene	A–1	37%	59
3,4-Dicarboethoxy	Ethyl 4-acetamidophthalate	Benzene	B–2	—	8
	Acetanilide	Ethyl phthalate	B–1	37% †‡	59
x,x'-Dicarboethoxy	Aniline	Ethyl phthalate	A–1	12% †	59
3-Methyl-4-nitro	3-Methyl-4-nitroaniline	Benzene	A–1	—	63
	Aniline	o-Nitrotoluene	A–1	9%	7
	Acetanilide	o-Nitrotoluene	B–1	15%	7
3-Methyl-4-bromo	3-Methyl-4-bromoaniline	Benzene	A–1	19%	38
3-Nitro-4-methyl	3-Nitro-4-methylaniline	Benzene	A–1	0	64
3-Nitro-4-acetamido	2-Nitrodiacetyl-1,4-phenylene diamine	Benzene	B–1	32%	58
3-Chloro-4-nitro	3-Chloro-4-nitroaniline	Benzene	A–1	20%	65
3-Bromo-4-methyl	3-Bromo-4-methylaniline	Benzene	A–1	22–30%	38, 65
3-Bromo-4-nitro	3-Bromo-4-nitroaniline	Benzene	A–1	30%	66

* References 59–76 appear on p. 261.
† The product was a mixture of isomers.
‡ Based on the nitrosoacetylamine.

TABLE OF COMPOUNDS PREPARED BY THE REACTIONS—*Continued*

Product	Component A	Component B	Method	Yield	Reference *
Disubstitution Products of Biphenyl, $RC_6H_4 \cdot C_6H_4R'$					
2-Methyl-4'-nitro	*p*-Nitroaniline	Toluene	A–1	9%	67
2-Methyl-4'-chloro	*p*-Chloroaniline	Toluene	A–1	—	15
2-Carbomethoxy-4'-chloro	Methyl anthranilate	Chlorobenzene	A–1	17% †	15
2-Carbomethoxy-4'-bromo	Methyl anthranilate	Bromobenzene	A–1	13% †	15
2-Methoxy-4'-bromo	*p*-Bromoaniline	Anisole	A–1	20%	52
2-Methoxy-4'-iodo	*p*-Iodoaniline	Anisole	A–1	—	52
2-Nitro-4'-methyl	*p*-Toluidine	Nitrobenzene	A–2	—	64
2,4'-Dinitro	*o*-Nitroaniline	Nitrobenzene	A–4	30%	6
2-Bromo-*x'*-methyl	*o*-Bromoaniline	Toluene	A–1	— †	58
3,4'-Dinitro	*m*-Nitroaniline	Nitrobenzene	A–4	54%	6
3-Bromo-4'-nitro	*m*-Bromoaniline	Nitrobenzene	A–1	2%	68
4-Methyl-*x'*-methyl	*p*-Toluidine	Toluene	A–2	23% †	4
4-Methyl-4'-nitro	*p*-Nitroaniline	Toluene	A–1	4%	67
	p-Toluidine	Nitrobenzene	A–2	—	64
4-Methyl-4'-chloro	*p*-Chloroaniline	Toluene	A–1	—	15
4-Methyl-2'- and 4'-bromo	*p*-Toluidine	Bromobenzene	A–1	— †	58
			A–2	22% †	4
4-Methoxy-4'-benzoyl	*p*-Anisidine	Benzophenone	A–1	2%	13
4-Methoxy-4'-bromo	*p*-Bromoaniline	Anisole	A–1	7%	52
4-Methoxy-4'-iodo	*p*-Iodoaniline	Anisole	A–1	—	52
4,4'-Dinitro	*p*-Nitroaniline	Nitrobenzene	A–4	69%	6
4-Bromo-*x'*-methyl	*p*-Bromoaniline	Toluene	A–1	28%	4
Polysubstitution Products of Biphenyl					
2,4,6-Trimethyl	Aniline	Mesitylene	A–1	10–15%	69
	Acetanilide	Mesitylene	B–1	10–42%	7, 69
	2,4,6-Trimethylaniline	Benzene	A–1	—	69
	2,4,6-Trimethylacet-anilide	Benzene	B–1	—	69
3,4-Dicarbomethoxy-*x'*-methoxy	Methyl 4-amino-phthalate	Anisole	A–1	32% †	59

* References 59–76 appear on p. 261.
† The product was a mixture of isomers.

TABLE OF COMPOUNDS PREPARED BY THE REACTIONS—*Continued*

Product	Component A	Component B	Method	Yield	Reference *
3,4-Dicarbomethoxy-x'-chloro	Methyl 4-aminophthalate	Chlorobenzene	A–1	43% †	59
2-Cyano-5-methyl-2',5'-dimethoxy	2-Cyano-5-methylacetanilide	p-Dimethoxybenzene	B–1	41% ‡	14
2-Cyano-5-methyl-2',5'-diethoxy	2-Cyano-5-methylacetanilide	p-Diethoxybenzene	B–1	24%	14
2-Cyano-5-methyl-2',5'-dimethoxy-4'-n-amyl	2-Cyano-5-methylacetanilide	2,5-Dimethoxy-n-amylbenzene	B–1	27% ‡	14

Terphenyls and Derivatives

Product	Component A	Component B	Method	Yield	Reference *
m-Terphenyl	3-Acetamidobiphenyl	Benzene	B–1	24%	55
			B–2	32%	8
	Diacetyl-1,3-phenylene diamine	Benzene	B–2	21%	8
p-Terphenyl	p-Aminobiphenyl	Benzene	A–1	—	3
	Aniline	Biphenyl	A–1	—	13
	Acetanilide	Biphenyl	B–1	—	58
	4-Acetamidobiphenyl	Benzene	B–1	50% ‡	8, 58
	Diacetyl-1,4-phenylene diamine	Benzene	B–1	55–60% ‡	8
			B–2	55–60% ‡	58
2-Methyl	2-Methyl-4'-acetamidobiphenyl	Benzene	B–1	17%	67
2-Nitro	2-Nitro-4'-acetamidobiphenyl	Benzene	B–1	—	58
	4-Acetamidobiphenyl	Nitrobenzene	B–1	25% ‡	58
2-, 3-, and 4-chloro	4-Acetamidobiphenyl	Chlorobenzene	B–1	33% ‡	58
2-, 3-, and 4-bromo	4-Acetamidobiphenyl	Bromobenzene	B–1	31% ‡	58
4-Methyl	4-Methyl-4'-acetamidobiphenyl	Benzene	B–1	54%	67

* References 59–76 appear on p. 261.
† The product was a mixture of isomers.
‡ Based on the nitrosoacetylamine.

TABLE OF COMPOUNDS PREPARED BY THE REACTIONS—*Continued*

Product	Component A	Component B	Method	Yield	Reference *
4-Methoxy	4-Methoxy-4'-acetamidobiphenyl	Benzene	B–1	58%	67
4-Nitro	p-Nitroaniline	Biphenyl	A–1	—	13
	4-Acetamidobiphenyl	Nitrobenzene	B–1	22% ‡	58
	4-Nitro-4'-acetamidobiphenyl	Benzene	B–1	—	58
4-Bromo	4-Bromo-4'-acetamidobiphenyl	Benzene	B–1	—	58
4-Iodo	4-Iodo-4'-acetamidobiphenyl	Benzene	B–1	—	58
x-Methyl	4-Acetamidobiphenyl	Toluene	B–1	25% †‡	67
x-Methoxy	4-Acetamidobiphenyl	Anisole	B–1	— †	67
2,5-Dimethoxy	4-Acetamidobiphenyl	p-Dimethoxybenzene	B–1	15%	67
4,3'-Dinitro	3,4'-Dinitro-4-acetamidobiphenyl	Benzene	B–1	—	58
4,4''-Dinitro	Diacetyl-1,4-phenylene diamine	Nitrobenzene	B–1	5%	58
2,5,2'',5''-Tetramethyl	Diacetyl-1,4-phenylene diamine	p-Xylene	B–1	10%	67
2,5,2'',5''-Tetramethoxy	Diacetyl-1,4-phenylene diamine	p-Dimethoxybenzene	B–1	7%	67
2,5,2'',5''-Tetrachloro	Diacetyl-1,4-phenylene diamine	p-Dichlorobenzene	B–1	6%	58
Quaterphenyl	Diacetylbenzidine	Benzene	B–1	17%	53
Dimethoxy	Benzidine	Anisole	A–1	0%	52
	Diacetylbenzidine	Anisole	B–1	0%	52

Arylnaphthalenes

Product	Component A	Component B	Method	Yield	Reference *
1-Phenylnaphthalene	α-Naphthylamine	Benzene	A–1	Low	13
			A–4	30%	6
	α-Acetamidonaphthalene	Benzene	B–1	—	53
4'-Nitro	α-Naphthylamine	Nitrobenzene	A–4	39%	6
2-Methyl-2'-carbomethoxy	Methylanthranilate	2-Methylnaphthalene	A–1	—	71
2-Methoxy-2'-carbomethoxy	Methyl anthranilate	2-Methoxynaphthalene	A–1	—	70

* References 59–76 appear on p. 261.
† The product was a mixture of isomers.
‡ Based on the nitrosoacetylamine.

TABLE OF COMPOUNDS PREPARED BY THE REACTIONS—*Continued*

Product	Component A	Component B	Method	Yield	Reference *
2-Phenylnaphthalene	β-Naphthylamine	Benzene	A–1	16%	5, 13
			A–4	0	6
			A–3	25%	5
	β-Acetamidonaphthalene	Benzene	B–1	25–30% †	49, 53
			B–2	25–30% †	49
1-Nitro	1-Nitro-2-naphthylamine	Benzene	A–1	—	49
5-Nitro	5-Nitro-2-acetamidonaphthalene	Benzene	B–1	29%	49
6-Methoxy	6-Methoxy-2-acetamidonaphthalene	Benzene	B–1	29%	49
6-Nitro	6-Nitro-2-acetamidonaphthalene	Benzene	B–1	42% †	49
6-Bromo	6-Bromo-2-acetamidonaphthalene	Benzene	B–1	31%	49
7-Phenyl	2,7-Diacetamidonaphthalene	Benzene	B–1	18%	49
7-Methoxy	7-Methoxy-2-acetamidonaphthalene	Benzene	B–1	31%	49
8-Nitro	8-Nitro-2-acetamidonaphthalene	Benzene	B–1	46% †	49
2'-Nitro	β-Naphthylamine	Nitrobenzene	A–3	14%	5
			A–4	0	6
	β-Acetamidonaphthalene	Nitrobenzene	B–1	14%	49
4'-Nitro	β-Naphthylamine	Nitrobenzene	A–3	26%	5
5-Nitro-6-methoxy	5-Nitro-6-methoxy-2-acetamidonaphthalene	Benzene	B–1	19%°	72
8-Nitro-7-methoxy	8-Nitro-6-methoxy-2-acetamidonaphthalene	Benzene	B–1	22%	72
2-Carbomethoxy-x'-phenylnaphthalene	Methyl anthranilate	Naphthalene	A–1	—	13
x-(2'-Carboamyloxynaphthyl-1-naphthalene	α-Acetamidonaphthalene	Amyl 2-Naphthoate	B–1	—	73

* References 59–76 appear on p. 261.
† Based on the nitrosoacetylamine.

TABLE OF COMPOUNDS PREPARED BY THE REACTIONS—*Continued*

Product	Component A	Component B	Method	Yield	Reference *
x-(2'-Carboamyl-oxynaphthyl-2-naphthalene	β-Acetamidonaphtha-lene	Amyl 2-naph-thoate	B–1	—	73
x-(1'-Carboamyl-oxynaphthyl-2-naphthalene	β-Acetamidonaphtha-lene	Amyl 1-naph-thoate	B–1	—	73

Arylthiophenes

Phenylthiophene	Aniline	Thiophene	A–1	11%	3
	Acetanilide	Thiophene	B–1	—	1
3'-Cyano	m-Cyanoaniline	Thiophene	A–1	15%	3
4'-Nitro	p-Nitroaniline	Thiophene	A–1	23%	3
4'-Chloro	p-Chloroaniline	Thiophene	A–1	24%	3
4'-Bromo	p-Bromoaniline	Thiophene	A–1	20%	3

Arylpyridines

Phenylpyridines	Aniline	Pyridine	A–5	40% †	20
	Acetanilide	Pyridine	B–1	60% †‡	19
2-Methoxy	o-Anisidine	Pyridine	A–5	50% †	75
2-Nitro	o-Nitroaniline	Pyridine	A–5	35% †	20
3-Methoxy	m-Anisidine	Pyridine	A–5	30% †	75
3-Nitro	m-Nitroaniline	Pyridine	A–5	35% †	20
4-Carboxy	p-Aminobenzoic acid	Pyridine	A–5	83% †	74
4-Methoxy	p-Anisidine	Pyridine	A–5	54% †	75
4-Ethoxy	p-Phenetidine	Pyridine	A–5	36% †	74
4-Nitro	p-Nitroaniline	Pyridine	A–5	70% †	20
4-Amino	Diacetyl-1,4-phenyl-ene diamine	Pyridine	B–1	13% †	19
4-Chloro	p-Chloroaniline	Pyridine	A–5	36% †	74
4-Bromo	p-Bromoaniline	Pyridine	A–5	17% †	74
3-Nitro-4-meth-oxy	3-Nitro-4-methoxy-aniline	Pyridine	A–5	26% †	75
4-Nitro-2-meth-oxy	4-Nitro-2-methoxy-aniline	Pyridine	A–5	21% †	75

* References 59–76 appear on p. 261.
† The product was a mixture of isomers.
‡ Based on the nitrosoacetylamine.

TABLE OF COMPOUNDS PREPARED BY THE REACTIONS—*Continued*

Product	Component A	Component B	Method	Yield	Reference
5-Nitro-2-methoxy	5-Nitro-2-methoxyaniline	Pyridine	A–5	20% *	75
3-α-Pyridylbiphenyl	3-α-Pyridylacetanilide	Benzene	B–2	36%	76
3-β-Pyridylbiphenyl	3-β-Pyridylacetanilide	Benzene	B–2	33%	76
3-γ-Pyridylbiphenyl	3-γ-Pyridylacetanilide	Benzene	B–2	36%	76
3-Pyridylbiphenyls	3-Aminobiphenyl	Pyridine	A–5	39% *	76
4-α-Pyridylbiphenyl	4-α-Pyridylacetanilide	Benzene	B–2	40%	76
4-β-Pyridylbiphenyl	4-β-Pyridylacetanilide	Benzene	B–2	38%	76
4-γ-Pyridylbiphenyl	4-γ-Pyridylacetanilide	Benzene	B–2	38%	76
4-Pyridylbiphenyls	4-Aminobiphenyl	Pyridine	A–5	35% *	76

* The product was a mixture of isomers.

[59] Butterworth, Heilbron, Hey, and Wilkinson, *J. Chem. Soc.*, **1938**, 1386.
[60] Huntress and Seikel, *J. Am. Chem. Soc.*, **61**, 820 (1939).
[61] Suter and Smith, *J. Am. Chem. Soc.*, **61**, 166 (1939).
[62] Cook and Cook, *J. Am. Chem. Soc.*, **55**, 1216 (1933).
[63] Grieve and Hey, *J. Chem. Soc.*, **1932**, 2247.
[64] Grieve and Hey, *J. Chem. Soc.*, **1932**, 1888.
[65] Schoepfle and Truesdail, *J. Am. Chem. Soc.*, **59**, 375 (1937).
[66] Case and Sloviter, *J. Am. Chem. Soc.*, **59**, 2381 (1937).
[67] France, Heilbron, and Hey, *J. Chem. Soc.*, **1939**, 1283.
[68] Case, *J. Am. Chem. Soc.*, **60**, 424 (1938).
[69] Hey, *J. Chem. Soc.*, **1932**, 2636.
[70] Heilbron, Hey, and Wilkinson, *J. Chem. Soc.*, **1938**, 700.
[71] Baddar, *J. Chem. Soc.*, **1941**, 310.
[72] Hey and Lawton, *J. Chem. Soc.*, **1940**, 384.
[73] Swain and Todd, *J. Chem. Soc.*, **1941**, 677.
[74] Butterworth, Heilbron, and Hey, *J. Chem. Soc.*, **1940**, 355.
[75] Haworth, Heilbron, and Hey, *J. Chem. Soc.*, **1940**, 358.
[76] Heilbron, Hey, and Lambert, *J. Chem. Soc.*, **1940**, 1279.

CHAPTER 7

REPLACEMENT OF THE AROMATIC PRIMARY AMINO GROUP BY HYDROGEN

Nathan Kornblum

Oberlin College and Harvard University *

CONTENTS

* National Research Fellow, 1942–1943. Present address, Purdue University.

INTRODUCTION

The replacement of an aromatic primary amino group by hydrogen is usually effected by reduction of the diazonium salt derived from the amine.

$$ArNH_2 \rightarrow ArN_2^+X^- \rightarrow ArH + N_2 + HX$$

It is evident that the success of the deamination process is a function of the completeness of diazotization as well as of the reduction. Fortunately, practically any primary aromatic amine is susceptible of diazotization, usually in yields approaching the theoretical. The conditions for this reaction are comparatively standard and are fully described in monographs on the diazo compounds.[1]

Diazonium compounds have been treated with a great variety of reducing agents, some of which have become incorporated into procedures for replacing the diazo group by hydrogen. The more important of these processes involve reduction by:

1. Alcohols.[2]

2. Hypophosphorous acid.[3]

3. Alkaline formaldehyde.[4]

4. Stabilization of the diazonium salt with naphthalene-1,5-disulfonic acid followed by treatment with zinc or copper.[5]

5. Sodium stannite.[6]

6. Stannous chloride or sodium sulfite; reduction to the hydrazine from which the hydrocarbon is obtained by oxidation.[7]

[1] Saunders, "The Aromatic Diazo-Compounds and Their Technical Applications," pp. 1–27, Edward Arnold and Co., London, 1936; Gilman and Blatt, "Organic Syntheses," Collective Volume I, revised, p. 558, John Wiley & Sons, New York, 1941; Groggins, "Unit Processes in Organic Synthesis," 2d ed., pp. 115–152, McGraw-Hill Book Company, New York, 1938; Cain, "Chemistry and Technology of the Diazo-Compounds," pp. 6–12, Edward Arnold and Co., London, 1920. For some recent examples of the technique of diazotizing weakly basic amines, see de Milt and van Zandt, J. Am. Chem. Soc., **58**, 2044 (1936); Lothrop, ibid., **60**, 725 (1938); Niemann and Redemann, ibid., **63**, 1550 (1941).

[2] Griess, Phil. Trans., **154**, 683 (1864).

[3] Mai, Ber., **35**, 163 (1902).

[4] Brewster and Poje, J. Am. Chem. Soc., **61**, 2418 (1939).

[5] Hodgson and Marsden, J. Chem. Soc., **1940**, 207.

[6] Friedländer, Ber., **22**, 587 (1889).

[7] Haller, Ber., **18**, 90 (1885).

In addition, a variety of other reducing agents have been employed (see pp. 288–289).

USE OF ALCOHOLS

In 1864 Griess reported that benzenediazonium salts, upon treatment with boiling ethyl alcohol, yield benzene.[2]

$$C_6H_5N_2{}^+X^- + CH_3CH_2OH \rightarrow C_6H_6 + CH_3CHO + N_2 + HX$$

The reaction came to be regarded as a general one, in spite of the fact that evidence to the contrary soon began to accumulate.

The first irregularity appeared in 1870. It was found that two chlorotoluidines, when diazotized and boiled with ethanol, gave the corresponding ethyl ethers;[8] the reaction of a diazonium salt with ethyl alcohol had taken an alternative course.

$$ArN_2{}^+X^- + CH_3CH_2OH \rightarrow ArOCH_2CH_3 + N_2 + HX$$

Later it was found that the decomposition of benzenediazonium salts with ethanol actually yields phenyl ethyl ether contaminated with a little benzene.[9] This, coupled with the fact that a number of instances of ether formation had been recorded, led to the suggestion that the normal products of reaction between diazonium salts and ethanol are the ethers.

Actually, the reaction with alcohol may result in replacement of the —N₂X group by —H or —OC₂H₅, and very often both types of products result. The most important factor in determining the course of the reaction is the nature of the substituents in the diazonium salt. The character of the products is also affected by the acid used for diazotization, the alcohol employed in the reduction, the presence of water and catalysts, and the reaction temperature.

Influence of Substituents

Careful studies of the action of absolute ethyl alcohol on various diazonium salts obtained from aniline have proved that phenetole is the main product, along with a very small quantity of benzene.[10] The decomposition of benzenediazonium chloride, for example, results in a 61% yield of phenetole and a 5% yield of benzene.[11] The remainder of

---

[8] Wroblewsky, *Ber.*, **3**, 98 (1870).

[9] Remsen and Palmer, *Am. Chem. J.*, **8**, 247 (1886).

[10] Remsen and Orndorff, *Am. Chem. J.*, **9**, 387 (1887).

[11] Hantzsch and Jochem, *Ber.*, **34**, 3337 (1901).

the diazonium chloride is converted into tarry non-volatile substances.*

The decomposition of α-naphthalenediazonium acid sulfate in absolute ethyl alcohol yields both naphthalene (40%) and α-ethoxynaphthalene (23%). With the *beta* isomer much less naphthalene (7%) results, and β-ethoxynaphthalene is obtained in 30% yield.[12, 13]

Upon heating the tetrazonium chloride derived from benzidine with ethanol, an 80% yield of biphenyl is obtained without any evidence of ether formation. Extreme care is necessary to prevent the reaction from occurring violently.[14]

When a methyl group is introduced into the *ortho* or *meta* position of aniline, the yield of hydrocarbon falls to zero; only ethers (I and II) are isolated (in 50% and 40% yields, respectively).[10, 13]

An interesting example of the deleterious effect of an *ortho* methyl group is to be found in the tetraphenylmethane series.[15, 16] While 4-aminotetraphenylmethane (III) is converted to the hydrocarbon (IV) in 46% yield, the homolog (V) gives only the ether (VI).

A methyl group *ortho* to each of the amino groups in benzidine again exerts a definite effect in favor of ether formation, for, whereas benzidine gives only biphenyl, *o*-tolidine yields approximately equal quantities of ether and hydrocarbon.[14]

* Tar formation is observed in the reduction of most diazo compounds and is not peculiar to the use of alcohol as the reducing agent. In some instances only slight losses are thus incurred; in others, appreciable amounts of diazonium salt are resinified.

[12] Orndorff and Kortright, *Am. Chem. J.*, **13**, 153 (1891).
[13] Raiford and Oberst, *Am. J. Pharm.*, **107**, 242 (1935).
[14] Winston, *Am. Chem. J.*, **31**, 119 (1904).
[15] Ullmann and Münzhuber, *Ber.*, **36**, 408 (1903).
[16] Van Alphen, *Rec. trav. chim.*, **46**, 503 (1927).

$$Cl^-N_2^+-\underset{CH_3}{\text{[ring]}}-\underset{CH_3}{\text{[ring]}}-N_2^+Cl^- \rightarrow$$

$$\underset{CH_3}{\text{[ring]}}-\underset{CH_3}{\text{[ring]}} + C_2H_5O-\underset{CH_3}{\text{[ring]}}-\underset{CH_3}{\text{[ring]}}-OC_2H_5$$

The influence of an *ortho* methyl group does not completely determine the course of a deamination. One of the early and important examples of the utility of the deamination process in determining structures involved an amino group adjacent to a methyl, namely, the conversion of the leuco base of fuchsine to the diphenyltolylmethane.[17]

$$\left(H_2N-\text{[ring]}-\right)_2-CH-\underset{CH_3}{\text{[ring]}}-NH_2 \rightarrow \left(\text{[ring]}-\right)_2-CH-\underset{CH_3}{\text{[ring]}}$$

In contrast to the *ortho* and *meta* isomers, a substantial fraction of *p*-toluidine can be converted into toluene (45% yield); the ether is also obtained (20% yield).[10, 13] A *para* methyl group apparently facilitates replacement of the diazo group by hydrogen.

The influence of the sulfonic acid group upon the course of ethanol deaminations somewhat resembles that of the methyl group. Thus, *o*-aminobenzenesulfonic acid gives only the ether;[18] the *meta* isomer yields a mixture of *m*-ethoxybenzenesulfonic acid and benzenesulfonic acid (the ether predominates);[18, 19] and from *p*-aminobenzenesulfonic acid the only product isolated is benzenesulfonic acid.[20]

With the aminosulfonic acid (VII), in which a methyl group is *para* to the amino group, the main product is *o*-toluenesulfonic acid (59%), and not the ethyl ether (37%).[21]

$$\underset{NH_2}{\overset{CH_3}{\text{[ring]}}}SO_3H \rightarrow \overset{CH_3}{\text{[ring]}}SO_3H + \underset{OC_2H_5}{\overset{CH_3}{\text{[ring]}}}SO_3H$$

VII

[17] Fischer and Fischer, *Ber.*, **37**, 3359 (1904).
[18] Franklin, *Am. Chem. J.*, **20**, 455 (1898).
[19] Shober and Kiefer, *Am. Chem. J.*, **17**, 454 (1895).
[20] Shober, *Am. Chem. J.*, **15**, 379 (1893).
[21] Remsen and Dashiell, *Am. Chem. J.*, **15**, 105 (1893).

Aminosulfonic acids of the naphthalene and biphenyl series also have been deaminated,* but the smoothness of the reaction cannot be estimated from the available experimental data.

The influence of carboxyl and nitro groups as well as chlorine and bromine atoms has been the subject of systematic investigations. All these groups promote the replacement of the diazonium group by hydrogen. Though the data do not lend themselves to broad generalizations, it appears that, in the main, the effect is at a peak when the group is situated *ortho* to the diazo group, is diminished somewhat in the *meta* position, and is weakest in the *para* position.

This gradation is illustrated by the results obtained with the diazonium salts from the isomeric aminobenzoic acids. When the *ortho* diazonium nitrate is treated with absolute ethanol only reduction occurs; [22, 23] ethyl benzoate is obtained in 53% yield.† The diazonium acid sulfate derived from *m*-aminobenzoic acid is converted into a mixture of ethyl benzoate and ethyl *m*-ethoxybenzoate, the former preponderating.[24, 23, 22] Finally, with the *p*-diazonium salts the ether reaction is the favored one; [22, 23] from the nitrate the yields of *p*-ethoxybenzoic acid and ethyl benzoate are 50% and 12%, respectively.

It has been demonstrated that the presence of chlorine or bromine in the nucleus facilitates replacement of the diazo group by hydrogen; little or no ether formation occurs.[25] Apparently iodine also favors the reducing action of alcohols, but this point has not been investigated carefully.[26, 27] No attempts to deaminate fluorinated amines are recorded. Representative of the efficiency with which ethanol reduces diazonium salts derived from halogenated amines are the deaminations of *m*-chloroaniline [25] (87% yield), of 2-bromo-4-methylaniline [28] (57% yield), of 2,4,6-tribromoaniline [29] (*ca.* 80% yield), and of 2-carboxy-4-iodoaniline [30] (*ca.* 45% yield); in the biphenyl series the deamination of VIII in 53% yield [31] may be cited.

* See Table II, pp. 317–319.

† In this, and a few other instances, esterification takes place during the reduction; it is by no means a common occurrence.

[22] Remsen and Graham, *Am. Chem. J.*, **11**, 319 (1889).

[23] Griess, *Ber.*, **21**, 978 (1888).

[24] Weida, *Am. Chem. J.*, **19**, 547 (1897).

[25] Cameron, *Am. Chem. J.*, **20**, 229 (1898).

[26] Jackson and Behr, *Am. Chem. J.*, **26**, 58 (1901).

[27] Wheeler and Liddle, *Am. Chem. J.*, **42**, 441 (1909).

[28] Bigelow, Johnson, and Sandborn, *Org. Syntheses, Coll. Vol* **I**, 133, 2d ed., 1941.

[29] Coleman and Talbot, *Org. Syntheses*, **13**, 96 (1933).

[30] Wallingford and Kreuger, *Org. Syntheses*, **19**, 57 (1939).

[31] Case, *J. Am. Chem. Soc.*, **61**, 769 (1939).

It is significant that, on treatment with water, pentabromobenzene-diazonium acid sulfate does not yield the expected phenol. Instead, part of the salt is converted into pentabromobenzene and part is resinified.[32]

The nitro group exerts a powerful influence in facilitating the reduction of diazonium salts by alcohols.[22, 24] With ethyl alcohol little, if any, ether is formed.[33] In addition to minimizing ether formation, the presence of a nitro group tends to decrease the amount of tar produced. Consequently nitro substituted amines are frequently susceptible of deamination in excellent yields; this is especially true when several nitro groups are present. Thus, 3-nitro-4-aminotoluene is converted to m-nitrotoluene in 67% yield,[34] p-nitroaniline gives nitrobenzene in approximately 70% yield,[22] and 3,5-dinitro-4-aminotoluene is converted to 3,5-dinitrotoluene in yields approaching the theoretical.[35] Other typical examples are the deaminations of 2,4-dinitro-1-naphthylamine (50% yield),[36] of the *trans* dinitroaminostilbene (IX) in 56% yield,[37] and of the dinitrodimethylbenzidine (X) in 53% yield.[38]

One of the rare instances of failure to deaminate a nitroamine was reported in 1875;[39] despite repeated attempts, m-nitrotoluene could not

[32] Hantzsch and Smythe, *Ber.*, **33**, 505 (1900).
[33] Orndorff and Cauffman, *Am. Chem. J.*, **14**, 45 (1892).
[34] Clarke and Taylor, *Org. Syntheses, Coll. Vol. I*, 415, 1941.
[35] Cohen and McCandlish, *J. Chem. Soc.*, **87**, 1271 (1905).
[36] Hodgson and Walker, *J. Chem. Soc.*, **1933**, 1620.
[37] Ruggli and Dinger, *Helv. Chim. Acta*, **24**, 182 (1941).
[38] Case and Koft, *J. Am. Chem. Soc.*, **63**, 510 (1941).
[39] Ladenburg, *Ber.*, **8**, 1212 (1875).

be obtained from 2,4-diamino-5-nitrotoluene (XI). Tetrazotization converted most of the diamine into alcohol-insoluble, amorphous material from which no definite product could be isolated; the alcohol-soluble portion gave a small quantity of 2-ethoxy-5-nitrotoluene (XII).

The effect of hydroxyl groups upon the reactions of diazonium salts with ethyl alcohol appears not to be established.[25, 40, 41,*]

Very recently it has been shown that treatment of the double salt of zinc chloride and p-hydroxybenzenediazonium chloride with ethyl alcohol leads to phenol (38% yield) and p, p'-azophenol (ca. 50–55% yield).[41]

It appears, therefore, that in this case the primary decomposition product is phenol and that by coupling with undecomposed diazonium salt it is converted into the azophenol. Addition of zinc oxide to the reaction mixture raises the yield of phenol to 60% while that of the azo compound falls to approximately 30%.

Hydroxydiazonium salts derived from o- and p-aminophenols change

* The literature contains statements which lead to the conclusion that the presence of a phenolic hydroxyl is generally conducive to replacement of the diazonium group by hydrogen. (See references 40, 41.) The sole authority cited for this claim is a paper by Cameron published in 1898. (See reference 25.) However, careful scrutiny of this article reveals that the generalization is clearly not warranted by Cameron's results. He merely reports that the diazonium chlorides derived from o-, m-, and p-aminophenol give phenol (yield unstated) and tar when decomposed with methyl or ethyl alcohol. Ethers could not be detected. Cameron himself states that "the experiments with the diazophenols here recorded are to be regarded as indecisive."

[40] Saunders, "The Aromatic Diazo-Compounds and Their Technical Applications," p. 145, Edward Arnold and Co., London, 1936.

[41] Hodgson and Foster, J. Chem. Soc., 1940, 1150.

into compounds known as diazo oxides or diazophenols (XIII, XIV), either spontaneously or under the influence of alkali.*

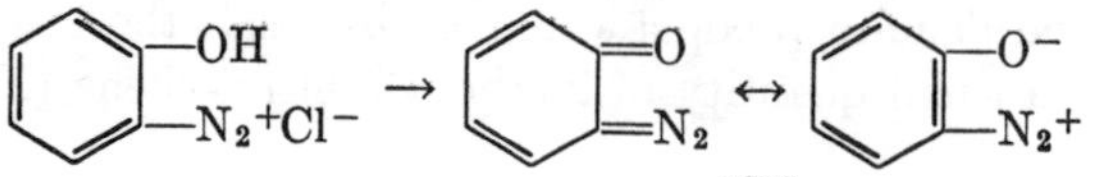

XIII

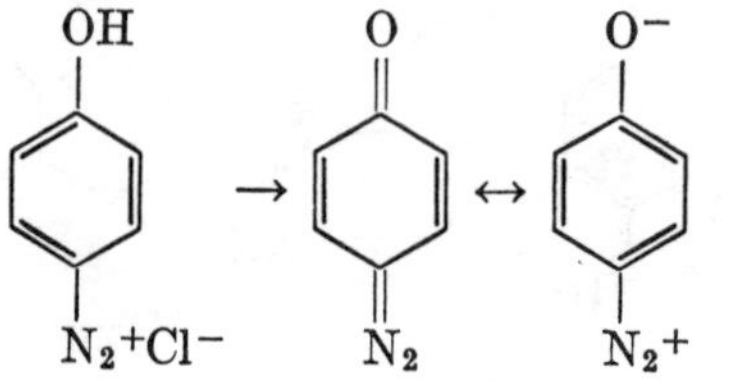

XIV

Replacement of the diazo group by hydrogen has been reported for a number of diazo oxides. For example, the diazo oxide from 2-nitro-4-aminophenol yields o-nitrophenol in 53% yield,[42, 43] and that from 1-amino-2-hydroxy-6-bromonaphthalene-4-sulfonic acid gives XV in approximately 50% yield.[44]

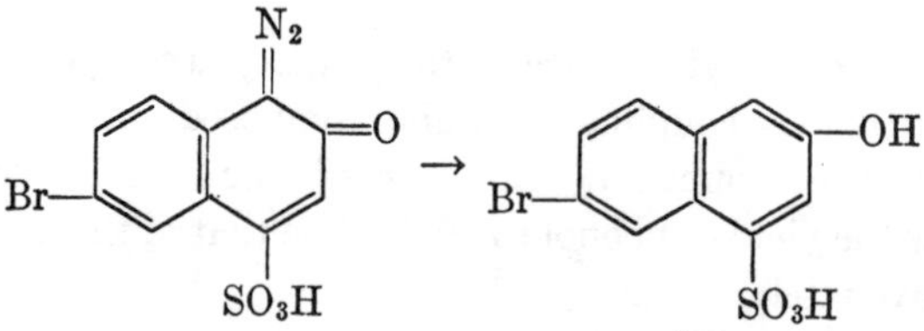

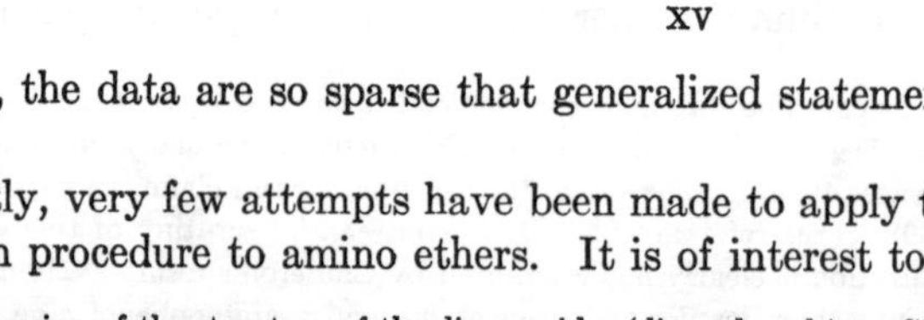

XV

Once again, the data are so sparse that generalized statements are not justified.

Apparently, very few attempts have been made to apply the ethanol deamination procedure to amino ethers. It is of interest to note that,

---

* For a discussion of the structure of the diazo oxides (diazophenols) see Sidgwick, "The Organic Chemistry of Nitrogen," revised by Taylor and Baker, pp. 422–423, Oxford University Press, 1937. For convenience, the first of the two resonance structures (XIII, XIV) will be used in this chapter.

[42] Klemenc, Ber., 47, 1413 (1914).

[43] Morgan and Porter, J. Chem. Soc., 107, 652 (1915).

[44] Ruggli and Michels, Helv Chim. Acta, 14, 781 (1941).

whereas benzidine is converted to biphenyl in 80% yield,[14] the deamination of 3,3'-dimethoxybenzidine takes place in but 24% yield.[45]

Acid Used for Diazotization

In most of the recorded deaminations with ethanol, sulfuric acid has been used rather than hydrochloric or nitric acid. As a general practice this appears to be a good choice since, in certain cases, diazotization with hydrochloric acid involves a risk that the deamination product may contain chlorine in place of a bromine atom or a nitro group originally present in the aromatic amine.*

In the deamination of polybromoamines, if the bromine atoms are *ortho* or *para* to the amino group and if the diazotization is carried out with hydrochloric acid, nuclear bromine is exchanged for chlorine. Bromine atoms *meta* to the diazo group are not affected.[32, 46]

Monobromodiazonium chlorides do not isomerize, but dibromodiazonium chlorides do so readily, even at low temperatures. Thus, in $\frac{1}{16}$ normal methanol solutions of 2,4-dibromo- and 2,6-dibromobenzenediazonium chlorides, after one hour at 0°, 6.2% and 21.4%, respectively, of the

* It must be emphasized, however, that a number of satisfactory deaminations have been effected via the diazonium chlorides.

[45] Starke, *J. prakt. Chem.*, [2] **59**, 221 (1899).

[46] Hantzsch, *Ber.*, **30**, 2334 (1897).

ionic halogen is bromide ion. In ethanol, loss of nuclear bromine is considerably faster. The diazonium chloride obtained from symmetrical tribromoaniline exchanges with great rapidity. After two hours at $+5°$, a $\frac{1}{28}$ normal ethanol solution contains only 4.2% of ionic chlorine, the remainder having displaced nuclear bromine atoms. In general, the interchange takes place more rapidly as the number of bromine atoms in the ring increases.

The presence of water cuts down the speed of the halogen exchange. Tribromobenzenediazonium chloride in 90% ethyl alcohol isomerizes at a rate less than one-twentieth that in absolute ethanol; in pure water, the reaction becomes exceedingly slow.

On the other hand, raising the temperature causes a striking increase in the rate of isomerization; and since alcohol deaminations almost invariably involve reflux conditions, or temperatures close to the boiling point of the alcohol, the diazonium chloride of a polybromoamine should not be used in this reaction.

Diazotization in the presence of sulfuric acid affords a simple means of avoiding the exchange reaction since diazonium acid sulfates do not rearrange. Thus, by treating the diazonium acid sulfate of tribromoaniline with boiling ethanol, pure tribromobenzene is obtained in about 80% yield.[29] Even pentabromoaniline suffers no loss of bromine when deaminated via the diazonium acid sulfate.[32]

No interchange occurs with 2,4,6-triiodobenzenediazonium chloride or 2,4,6-tribromobenzenediazonium fluoride. Apparently halogen exchange is restricted to the diazonium chlorides of polybrominated amines.[47]

Chlorine sometimes replaces a nitro group *ortho* to a diazonium group. When 2,3-dinitro-4-methoxyaniline is diazotized in the presence of hydrochloric acid and then treated with ethyl alcohol, 2-nitro-3-chloroanisole is obtained[48] in unspecified yield.

On the other hand, the nitro group is not eliminated when sulfuric or nitric acid is used in the diazotization.

The same interchange occurs in the naphthalene series. Diazotization of 1-nitro-2-naphthylamine in hydrochloric acid results in replacement

[47] Hantzsch, *Ber.*, **36**, 2069 (1903).
[48] Meldola and Eyre, *J. Chem. Soc.*, **81**, 988 (1902).

of the nitro group [49, 50] with the formation of 1-chloro-2-naphthalenediazonium chloride. Here again, diazotization with sulfuric acid prevents the loss of the nitro group.[51]

The use of diazo nitrates instead of the acid sulfates offers no advantage and may result in nitrated products.[25]

Deamination of large quantities of 2-nitro-3'-bromobenzidine by the sulfuric acid procedure proves tedious. A convenient method involves preparation of the dry bisdiazofluoborate and decomposition in absolute ethyl alcohol. The yield of pure product is 78%, a 26% increase over that obtained by employing the tetrazonium acid sulfate.[52]

Nature of the Alcohol

All alcohols do not produce the same result with a given diazonium salt. The use of methanol greatly increases the probability that ethers will be formed. For example, if the tetrazonium chloride derived from benzidine is treated with absolute ethyl alcohol, biphenyl is obtained in 80% yield, whereas decomposition with absolute methanol gives a 65% yield of p,p'-dimethoxybiphenyl and a trace of the hydrocarbon.[14] Although methanol has been known to bring about replacement of the diazo group by hydrogen, it is never superior to and rarely as good as ethanol for this purpose.[25, 18, 53]

The higher aliphatic alcohols have been employed in the deamination reaction with the hope that the increased yields of hydrocarbon noted in passing from methanol to ethanol would continue as the series was ascended. This expectation has not been realized.[53, 54, 55, 56] The results

[49] Morgan, J. Chem. Soc., 81, 1377 (1902).
[50] Schiemann and Ley, Ber., 69, 960 (1936).
[51] Vorozhtsov, Kozlov, and Travkin, J. Gen. Chem. (U.S.S.R.), 9, 522 (1939) [C. A. 34, 410 (1940)].
[52] Lesslie and Turner, J. Chem. Soc., 1933, 1590.
[53] Hodgson and Kershaw, J. Chem. Soc., 1930, 2785.
[54] Orndorff and Hopkins, Am. Chem. J., 15, 518 (1893).
[55] Hantzsch and Vock, Ber., 36, 2061 (1903).
[56] Morgan and Evens, J. Chem. Soc., 115, 1126 (1919).

are far from conclusive, but apparently there is little, if any, advantage in replacing ethanol by the higher aliphatic alcohols. Benzyl alcohol may be superior to ethanol in reducing diazonium salts, but this by no means has been clearly demonstrated.[53, 55]

Influence of Water, Catalysts, and Other Substances

Water. In the main, smooth replacement of a diazo group does not depend upon perfectly anhydrous conditions. Many successful deaminations take place with alcohol containing as much as 15% of water and, in some instances, a still larger proportion.[14, 28, 44, 21, 57] Although general practice does not require rigid exclusion of moisture, the amount of water should be limited to about 5–10%.[10, 58]

Certain diazonium salts, however, are unstable in the presence of water. Thus, 2-methoxy-4,5-dinitroaniline when diazotized in sulfuric acid containing an equal volume of water gives, in addition to the expected diazonium salt, a diazo oxide * (XVII).[59] Apparently the nitro group undergoes hydrolytic cleavage, a hydroxybenzenediazonium salt (XVI) being intermediate in the diazo oxide formation.

With 3,5-dinitro-4-methoxyaniline rapid and complete conversion to the diazo oxide occurs upon diazotization with sulfuric or hydrochloric acid.[59]

---

* See p. 270.
[57] Muller and Tietz, *Ber.*, **74**, 823 (1941).
[58] Beeson, *Am. Chem. J.*, **16**, 235 (1894).
[59] Meldola and Stephens, *J. Chem. Soc.*, **87**, 1202 (1905).

An extensive study of the methoxypolynitroanilines has shown that, in this series, a nitro or methoxyl group becomes sufficiently mobile to be eliminated during the course of diazotization only when *ortho* or *para* to the diazo group and, in addition, adjacent to a nitro group.[60]

Picramide is diazotized by treating a solution of the amine in glacial acetic acid with nitrosylsulfuric acid (prepared by dissolving sodium nitrite in concentrated sulfuric acid).[61] Addition of ice-cold water to the diazonium solution results in immediate decomposition of the diazonium salt.[61, 62, *]

Nitronaphthalenediazonium salts are more susceptible of hydrolytic cleavage than the corresponding benzenoid compounds. The elimination of a nitro group from 2,4-dinitrobenzene-1-diazonium acid sulfate is not effected merely by dilution with water, whereas it readily occurs with 2,4-dinitronaphthalene-1-diazonium acid sulfate.[36, 56] Because the diazonium salts are unstable in the presence of water, the deamination of

2-nitronaphthylamine-1 and 2,4-dinitronaphthylamine-1 requires diazotization with nitrosylsulfuric acid, followed by direct decomposition with ethanol.[36]

Diazonium salts derived from nitro-β-naphthylamines also undergo hydrolysis, and again it is an *ortho* nitro group that is removed. Thus,

* The nature of the degradation products has not been established. Misslin implies (reference 61) that the 2-hydroxy-4,6-dinitrobenzenediazonium ion is produced, a view that is accepted by Karrer, "Organic Chemistry," p. 432, Nordemann Publishing Co., New York, 1938. There does not appear to be any experimental basis for this deduction, and in the light of Blangey's results (reference 62) the course of the reaction must be regarded as an open question.

[60] Meldola and Hay, *J. Chem. Soc.*, **91**, 1474 (1907).
[61] Misslin, *Helv. Chim. Acta*, **3**, 626 (1920).
[62] Blangey, *Helv. Chim. Acta*, **8**, 780 (1925).

when 1,6-dinitronaphthylamine-2 is diazotized in concentrated sulfuric acid and then diluted with ice-cold water, the diazo oxide is precipitated.

The reaction occurs so rapidly that attempts to deaminate by the usual procedures give little or no 1,6-dinitronaphthalene.[63, 64]

In consequence of hydrolytic cleavage, a diazo oxide also is obtained from the isomeric 1,8-dinitronaphthylamine-2. Here, however, elimination of the nitro group is a comparatively slow reaction so that treatment with ethanol gives a satisfactory yield of 1,8-dinitronaphthalene.[63, 64]

A dearth of quantitative information about the rate of diazo oxide formation makes it impossible to generalize about the importance which is to be attached to this side reaction. However, it appears that in many instances the reaction is a comparatively slow one, so that anhydrous conditions are unnecessary. In this connection it is significant that diazotized picramide, which is reported to be very unstable in the presence of water,[61, 62] is converted to trinitrobenzene in 60–65% yield upon treatment with 50% aqueous hypophosphorous acid.*

Metals, Metallic Oxides, and Salts. In an effort to facilitate the reduction of diazonium salts by ethanol, a number of metals, oxides, and salts are added to the reaction mixture. Finely divided copper, [28, 37, 65, 66, 67] cuprous oxide,[68, 44, 69] † and cupric sulfate [30, 70] are often employed.

Zinc [14, 41, 71, 72] inhibits the formation of ethers, but this beneficial effect is frequently offset by the heightened production of tars and

---

* Detailed directions for this deamination are given on p. 296.

† It is claimed that a deamination procedure employing cuprous oxide in conjunction with ethanol appears to be of general application; Hodgson and Turner, *J. Chem. Soc.*, 1942, 748.

[63] Gaess and Ammelburg, *Ber.*, **27**, 2211 (1894).

[64] Scheid, *Ber.*, **34**, 1816 (1901).

[65] Parsons and Bailar, *J. Am. Chem. Soc.*, **58**, 269 (1936).

[66] Ruggli and Staub, *Helv. Chim. Acta*, **20**, 50 (1937).

[67] Helle, *Ann.*, **270**, 363 (1892).

[68] Sandmeyer, *Helv. Chim. Acta*, **6**, 166 (1923).

[69] Ruggli and Welge, *Helv. Chim. Acta*, **15**, 586 (1932).

[70] Witt and Uermenyl, *Ber.*, **46**, 306 (1913).

[71] Schlenk and Brauns, *Ber.*, **48**, 666 (1915).

[72] Iddles and Hussey, *J. Am. Chem. Soc.*, **63**, 2769 (1941).

biaryls.[58, 73, 74, 75]   In the ethanol decompositions of zinc chloride-diazonium chloride double salts, the addition of zinc dust is reported to overcome the influence of substituents; only reduction occurs.[76]   Zinc oxide is helpful in the deamination of hydroxybenzenediazonium salts.[41] Aluminum powder is sometimes added to advantage.[56]

The use of these substances is unquestionably beneficial in many instances, but the utility of most of them is limited; in fact, certain reductions are adversely affected by the addition of promoters.[66, 75, 56]

Acids and Bases. Concentrated sulfuric acid is sometimes added to the alcohol, especially when the diazonium salt is isolated and dried before reduction.[52, 77, 78]

In the presence of sodium ethoxide, sodium hydroxide, or sodium carbonate, little, if any, ether formation occurs. There is, however, a marked increase in the yields of biaryls and tars so that these bases are of no real value in bringing about deaminations.[14, 57, 58, 73, 74, 79]

Temperature

Very few quantitative data concerning the effect of temperature on the deamination reaction are available. In several instances, lowering of the temperature favors replacement by hydrogen at the expense of the ether reaction;[21, 58] this, however, is not always true.[73, 14]

Very often reduction of diazonium salts by ethanol requires temperatures in the neighborhood of the boiling point of the alcohol. The reaction may take place with violence so that, once it is started, moderation by external cooling may be necessary.[14, 28, 34]

REDUCTION WITH HYPOPHOSPHOROUS ACID

In 1902 Mai discovered that aniline, p-toluidine, and benzidine could be deaminated by reducing their diazonium chlorides with 10% aqueous hypophosphorous acid. Benzene, toluene, and biphenyl were obtained in 40, 67, and 60% yields, respectively. From α-naphthalenediazonium chloride, naphthalene was produced very slowly and in unstated yield.[3] The reaction was not investigated further, and the encouraging results that had been obtained did not give rise to widespread use of hypophos-

[73] Chamberlain, *Am. Chem. J.*, **19**, 531 (1897).
[74] Griffin, *Am. Chem. J.*, **19**, 163 (1897).
[75] Morgan and Jones, *J. Soc. Chem. Ind.*, **42**, 97T (1923).
[76] Hodgson and Foster, *J. Chem. Soc.*, **1942**, 581.
[77] Pfeiffer, *Ber.*, **48**, 1793 (1915).
[78] Möhlau, *Ber.*, **15**, 2494 (1882).
[79] Moale, *Am. Chem. J.*, **20**, 298 (1898).

phorous acid in deaminations. Only recently has it been demonstrated that the reduction of diazonium compounds by hypophosphorous acid is an excellent and general method for replacing the diazo group by hydrogen.[13, 80, 81, 82, 83]

The yield depends upon the molar ratio of hypophosphorous acid to diazonium salt.[81, 82] If it is assumed that hypophosphorous acid undergoes oxidation to phosphorous acid, then one molecule of hypophosphorous acid will be required for the reduction of each diazo group.

$$\mathrm{ArN_2^+X^- + H_3PO_2 + H_2O \rightarrow ArH + H_3PO_3 + HX + N_2}$$

In practice, however, it is advisable to use 5 moles of hypophosphorous acid per mole of diazonium compound, and with the more difficultly reduced diazo salts this ratio should be 15 to 1.

Treatment of o-toluenediazonium chloride with only 2.75 moles of hypophosphorous acid per mole of diazonium chloride gives some o-cresol, much tar, and no toluene.[13] With 5 moles of acid, however, a 50% yield of pure toluene is obtained. Ten moles of hypophosphorous acid give a 63% yield, and the use of 15 moles results in the production of pure toluene in 70–75% yield.[82] Similarly, m-toluenediazonium chloride cannot be converted to toluene by using 2.75 moles of hypophosphorous acid;[13] with 5 moles, pure toluene is obtained in 27% yield, and with 15 moles, the yield is 51–62%.[82]

Although 10 or 15 moles of hypophosphorous acid may be required for the successful deamination of some amines, this is by no means generally true; 5 moles of this reducing agent usually give excellent results, and, in the case of 3-nitro-4-aminotoluene, as little as 0.76 mole gives a 70% yield of m-nitrotoluene.[84] In general, when amines that are deaminated smoothly with only 5 moles of hypophosphorous acid are treated with 15 moles, the yield is increased another 5 to 15%.[81, 82, *] Since hypophosphorous acid is not an expensive reagent, the use of more than 5 moles is justified when a valuable amine is to be deaminated.

The hypophosphorous acid procedure is notable for its simplicity of operation. Ice-cold 50 or 30% aqueous hypophosphorous acid is added to the diazonium solution, and the reaction is allowed to proceed at 0° to 5°. Reduction is usually complete within twenty-four hours. Some tetrazonium salts of the benzidine series may be deaminated either at

---

* In the case of 3-nitro-4-aminotoluene the use of more than 0.76 mole of hypophosphorous acid does not increase the yield of m-nitrotoluene (reference 84).

[80] Adams and Kornblum, J. Am. Chem. Soc., **63**, 194 (1941).

[81] Kornblum, Org. Syntheses, **21**, 30 (1941).

[82] Kornblum and Dorn, unpublished work.

[83] Kornblum, unpublished work.

[84] Manske, Marion, and Leger, Can. J. Research, **20B**, 133 (1942).

refrigerator or room temperature.[81] Although deaminations have been carried out at the boiling point of the reaction mixture it does not appear that such a high temperature is to be recommended.[85]

Hydrochloric and sulfuric acids have been employed with about equal frequency in hypophosphorous acid reductions. Recent work has shown that, in general, the reaction goes more smoothly with the diazonium chlorides,[82] so that, with certain exceptions discussed below, diazotization with hydrochloric acid is advisable. The striking results obtained with the toluidines are recorded in Table I. The isomeric nitroanilines

TABLE I

DEPENDENCE OF THE YIELD OF TOLUENE ON THE ACID USED FOR DIAZOTIZATION

Toluidine	Acid Used for Diazotization	Yield
ortho	HCl	70–75%
	H_2SO_4	12–23%
meta	HCl	51–62%
	H_2SO_4	5–12%
para	HCl	77–83%
	H_2SO_4	27–29%

do not display this sensitivity to the acid used for diazotization; with either hydrochloric or sulfuric acid, the yields of nitrobenzene are essentially the same (60–80%).[82]

As has already been noted in the section on ethanol deaminations, upon diazotizing some nitroamines in hydrochloric acid, a diazonium salt is obtained in which the nitro group has been replaced by chlorine (pp. 272–273). Consequently, hypophosphorous acid reduction gives a deaminated product containing chlorine in place of the nitro group. For example, when 5-amino-8-nitroisoquinoline (XVIII) is diazotized with hydrochloric acid and then treated with hypophosphorous acid, 8-chloroisoquinoline (XIX) is obtained in 60–70% yield instead of 8-nitroisoquinoline.[86]

$$\text{XVIII} \rightarrow \text{XIX}$$

[85] Bellavita, Atti congr. nazl. chim. pura applicata, 5th Congr., Rome, 1935, Pt. I, 294 (1936) [C. A., 31, 3901 (1937)].

[86] Keilen and Cass, J. Am. Chem. Soc., 64, 2442 (1942).

Similarly, 1-nitro-2-aminonaphthalene gives 1-chloronaphthalene in 69% yield and only a trace of 1-nitronaphthalene when diazotized in hydrochloric acid solution and reduced with hypophosphorous acid.[83] Upon diazotization with sulfuric acid, however, a 61% yield of α-nitronaphthalene is obtained.[83] The same type of side reaction occurs when 2,5-diaminotriptycene (XX) is diazotized in hydrochloric acid solution and then reduced with hypophosphorous acid.[87]

Conversion of this diamine to triptycene has, however, been accomplished in 40–45% yield by diazotizing with sulfuric acid; * 1-bromo-2,5-diaminotriptycene (XXI) has also been deaminated by this procedure.[83]

The successful deamination of 1-nitro-2-aminonaphthalene, 2,5-diaminotriptycene (XX), and 1-bromo-2,5-diaminotriptycene (XXI) suggests that 5-amino-8-nitroisoquinoline (XVIII) also could be deaminated to 8-nitroisoquinoline if the diazotization were carried out in sulfuric acid.

In aqueous solution at 0° to +5°, exchange of nuclear bromine for chlorine (pp. 271–272) does not occur. Thus, the diazonium chloride of 2,4,6-tribromoaniline when treated with hypophosphorous acid gives 1,3,5-tribromobenzene in 70% yield, while the hypophosphorous acid reduction of the diazonium chloride derived from 2,4,6-tribromo-3-methylaniline is productive of the corresponding tribromotoluene in 91% yield.[88, 13]

The conversion of diazotized 2,4,6-trinitroaniline (picramide) to 1,3,5-trinitrobenzene in 60–65% yield, upon treatment with aqueous hypophosphorous acid,[83], † is of considerable interest inasmuch as this diazonium salt is immediately decomposed by ice water [61, 62] alone (p. 275).

---

* This deamination is described in detail on p. 297.

† Described in detail on p. 296.

[87] Bartlett, Ryan, and Cohen, *J. Am. Chem. Soc.*, **64**, 2649 (1942).

[88] Oberst, M. S. thesis, State University of Iowa, 1928, p. 29.

The yields obtained on deaminating the following amines further illustrate the wide utility of hypophosphorous acid: 2,4-diethyl-6-bromoaniline (70%),[89] 3-nitro-4-aminophenylarsonic acid (45%),[90] 3-amino-6-bromobenzoic acid (75%),[13] 3,3'-dimethylbenzidine (76-82%),[80, 81] 4-amino-7-chlorohydrindone-1 (85%),[91] 5-methyl-8-aminoquinoline (72%)[84] o-(β-phenylethyl)-aniline (XXII) (47%).[66] In the last case, when ethanol is used dibenzyl is not obtained; instead the products are 9,10-dihydrophenanthrene (ca. 50%) and o-(β-phenylethyl)-phenol (23%).[66]

This is not the only instance where hypophosphorous acid is more effective than ethyl alcohol. For example, whereas deamination of o-toluidine by the hypophosphorous acid procedure affords toluene in 70-75% yield,[82] treatment with ethanol gives o-ethoxytoluene in approximately 50% yield.[10, 13] And while reduction of the diazonium salt of p-aminophenylarsonic acid by hypophosphorous acid yields phenylarsonic acid (ca. 50%),[92] ethanol gives p-ethoxyphenylarsonic acid (ca. 65%). Although 3,3'-dimethoxybenzidine may be deaminated by either procedure, the yield with hypophosphorous acid is 66-78% [80, 81] as compared to approximately 20% when ethanol is used.[45] These data, in conjunction with other results, lead to the conclusion that hypophosphorous acid is at least equal to ethanol as a reagent for deaminating an aromatic amine, and that it is usually effective in deaminations which cannot be carried out with ethanol.[13, 81, 82, 83, 87, 93, 94]

Failure of the hypophosphorous acid procedure has been reported in a rather special case; cis-o-aminostilbene, when diazotized in sulfuric acid and treated with hot, aqueous sodium hypophosphite containing copper

[89] Snyder, Adams, and McIntosh, J. Am. Chem. Soc., 63, 3282 (1941).
[90] Bertheim and Benda, Ber., 44, 3298 (1911).
[91] Fieser and Berliner, private communication. Described in detail on p. 295.
[92] Bertheim, Ber., 41, 1855 (1908).
[93] Stoermer and Heymann, Ber., 45, 3103 (1912).
[94] Finzi, Gazz. chim. ital., 61, 42 (1931).

powder, gives phenanthrene in 80% yield.[66] Ethanol also yields phenanthrene instead of *cis*-stilbene.[66, *] With the *trans* isomer, the

Pschorr reaction is not possible; conversion to the stilbene takes place whether ethanol or hypophosphorous acid is employed.[66]

Deamination of 4,5-dimethyl-8-aminoquinoline by hypophosphorous acid gives only a 6% yield of 4,5-dimethylquinoline. There is some evidence, however, that the diazotization takes an abnormal course.[84]

In hypophosphorous acid reductions varying amounts of phenols and tars are obtained. In general, however, no difficulty is experienced in isolating products of excellent quality.

REDUCTION WITH ALKALINE FORMALDEHYDE

The reduction of diazonium salts by alkaline formaldehyde affords good yields of deaminated products in a number of instances.[4] The method is simple in practice, and it is particularly effective where the ethyl alcohol procedure is of little or no value. Although there are comparatively few examples of deaminations employing alkaline formaldehyde, several generalizations can be made.

Aromatic amines and their homologs are converted to the corresponding hydrocarbons in 60–80% yields; with alkoxy- and aryloxy-amines, the yields range from 50 to 75%.[4] The deaminations of 2,4-dimethyl-

[* It would be of interest to attempt this reduction under somewhat modified conditions; deamination might be achieved by treating the diazonium chloride with hypophosphorous acid at 0° to +5° in the absence of copper.

aniline (80% yield), o-ethoxyaniline (75% yield), and 4-amino-4'-methyldiphenyl ether (50% yield) are indicative of the possibilities. Alkaline formaldehyde and hypophosphorous acid are about equally valuable in deaminating such compounds; ethanol is not satisfactory here.

Alkaline formaldehyde is also useful in removing the amino group of ortho- and para-chloroanilines; 50–55% yields of chlorobenzene are obtained. With 2,5-dichloroaniline, however, the yield falls to 10%. The formaldehyde procedure cannot be applied to nitroamines inasmuch as reduction of the nitro group occurs. Only a 20% yield of nitrobenzene is obtained from o-nitroaniline, and with the meta and para isomers the yield drops to 10%.[4]

There is a substantial group of diazonium salts to which the alkaline formaldehyde method, or any other deamination process requiring alkaline conditions, should not be applied, inasmuch as they are unstable in the presence of alkali. This instability is merely an extension of the hydrolytic cleavage reaction previously noted (pp. 274–276). Comparatively few diazonium salts are converted to the diazo oxides in aqueous mineral acid. As the acidity of the solution is decreased, however, diazo oxide formation is facilitated, and finally on the alkaline side many diazo compounds that are stable in acid media undergo hydrolytic cleavage.[95, 96] Thus, while 2,4-dinitrobenzenediazonium acid sulfate is stable to dilute aqueous sulfuric acid, in neutral or slightly alkaline solution it readily yields the diazo oxide.[56] The reaction is not quantitative; a poorly defined insoluble product is also formed in 14 to 20% yields.

Symmetrical tribromo- and trichloro-benzenediazonium salts are rapidly transformed into the diazo oxides by ice-cold aqueous sodium hydroxide.[97, 98]

[95] Meldola and Streatfeild, J. Chem. Soc., 67, 908 (1895).

[96] Saunders, "The Aromatic Diazo-Compounds and Their Technical Applications," pp. 56–59, Edward Arnold and Co., London, 1936.

[97] Bamberger and Kraus, Ber., 39, 4249 (1906).

[98] Orton, J. Chem. Soc., 83, 796 (1903).

The *para* halogen atoms are less labile than those in the *ortho* positions; about 20% of the molecules that yield diazo oxides lose an atom of bromine from the *para* position, whereas approximately 80% lose an *ortho* bromine.[99] The more highly halogenated diazonium salts are more likely to undergo hydrolytic cleavage.[100]

The generality of the hydrolytic cleavage reaction in alkaline media is illustrated by the following examples.[96, 100]

Cleavage is apparently more rapid in dilute than in concentrated alkali. A great many of the diazonium salts that undergo hydrolytic cleavage in alkaline solution are probably stable to very concentrated alkali.[98] The pH at which the reaction proceeds with maximum velocity has not been established and in all likelihood will vary from compound to compound. Even if these diazo salts were usually stable in strongly alkaline solution, it is needless to run the risk of exposing them to alkali inasmuch as either hypophosphorous acid or ethanol is effective in reducing them. Consequently, although alkaline formaldehyde is an excellent

[99] Orton and Reed, *J. Chem. Soc.*, **91**, 1555 (1907).
[100] Noelting and Battegay, *Ber.*, **39**, 79 (1906).

deaminating agent for unsubstituted amines, their homologs, and ethers, its utility appears to be largely restricted to these substances.

USE OF STABILIZED DIAZONIUM SALTS

A deamination procedure for which general application is claimed has been described by Hodgson and Marsden.[5] An aqueous solution of the diazotized amine is treated with the molar quantity of naphthalene-1,5-disulfonic acid or 2-naphthol-1-sulfonic acid, whereupon the stabilized diazonium compound is precipitated. In most cases the stabilized diazo salts require slight variations in technique for their preparation in optimum yield.* The dry salt is reduced at room temperature in ethanol containing zinc or copper. Overall yields of the order of 90% are reported; however, the purity of the product is not specified.

Conversion of stabilized diazo compounds to hydrocarbons does not depend upon the reducing action of ethyl alcohol, for the reaction takes place smoothly in acetone, ether, nitrobenzene, benzene, chloroform, and carbon tetrachloride. No acetaldehyde is produced when ethanol is the solvent. In the absence of metals, however, when the stabilized salts of diazotized α-naphthylamine are treated with ethyl alcohol, acetaldehyde, naphthalene, α-ethoxynaphthalene, and tar are obtained.

The following compounds are reported to have been deaminated by decomposing their stabilized diazonium salts: aniline;[5] o-, m-, and p-toluidine;[5] o-, m-, and p-anisidine;[5] o-, m-, and p-nitroaniline;[5] 2-methoxy-4-nitro-5-aminotoluene;[101] m-phenylenediamine;[5] m-tolylenediamine;[5] p-aminophenol;[5] benzidine;[5] α- and β-naphthylamine.[5,] †

---

* Very recently Hodgson and Turner have pointed out that "preparation of the stabilized diazonium salt may be easy or difficult" (J. Chem. Soc., **1942**, 748). Arnold and McCool were unable to deaminate 5-amino-4-nitro-2-methylcoumaran by this method because it was not possible to isolate any insoluble stabilized diazonium salt. (Private communication from Professor R. T. Arnold of the University of Minnesota.)

† In an attempt to repeat certain of these experiments, Deasy was unable to obtain any toluene from o-toluidine and only a 15% yield from p-toluidine. Nor was it possible to deaminate m-chloroaniline by this method. In all three cases, insoluble intermediate products were isolated. (Private communication from Dr. Clara Deasy of Oberlin College.)

[101] Arnold and McCool, J. Am. Chem. Soc., **64**, 1315 (1942).

TREATMENT WITH SODIUM STANNITE

In this reduction aqueous stannite is added to an alkaline solution of the diazo compound, the temperature being kept in the neighborhood of 0°; the reaction proceeds rapidly.[6]

Few sodium stannite deaminations are to be found in the literature, and of these a substantial fraction concerns unsubstituted amines and their homologs. Thus, benzene is obtained from aniline in 60% yield,[102, 13] and the hydrocarbons derived from 2,3-dimethylaniline and 2,4,5-trimethylaniline are produced in "satisfactory yields" and in a high state of purity.[103]

The conversion of 1,3-dimethyl-4-amino-5-bromobenzene to 1,3-dimethyl-5-bromobenzene occurs in 73% yield,[104] but the yield is considerably lower (*ca.* 38%) in the case of the nitroaminostilbene XXIII.[105]

XXIII

In the following instances, failures have been recorded for sodium stannite: 3-nitro-4-aminotoluene,[106] *p*-aminophenylarsonic acid,[92] *trans-o*-aminocinnamic acid.[93, *]

A number of by-products may be isolated from sodium stannite reductions. In addition to benzene, aniline gives phenol, azobenzene, phenyl azide, and phenylhydrazine.[107, 102, 108, 109] The danger of hydrolytic cleavage in alkaline media, previously discussed in connection with the

---

* The first of these compounds is successfully deaminated either by ethanol or hypophosphorous acid; with the last two, hypophosphorous acid is effective in bringing about the desired reaction.

[102] Koenigs and Carl, *Ber.*, **23**, 2672 (1890).

[103] von Auwers, *Ann.*, **419**, 96 (1919).

[104] Fieser and Heymann, *J. Am. Chem. Soc.*, **64**, 380 (1942); Heymann, Ph.D. thesis, Harvard University, 1941. A detailed description of this deamination will be found on p. 298.

[105] Pfeiffer and Monath, *Ber.*, **39**, 1305 (1906).

[106] Bigelow, *J. Am. Chem. Soc.*, **41**, 1566 (1919).

[107] Eibner, *Ber.*, **36**, 813 (1903).

[108] Bamberger and Meimberg, *Ber.*, **26**, 497 (1893).

[109] Culmann and Gasiorowski, *J. prakt. Chem.*, [2] **40**, 108 (1889).

alkaline formaldehyde method (pp. 283–284), also exists with sodium stannite. It appears, therefore, stannite should be employed only after failure of the procedures already noted.

CONVERSION TO THE HYDRAZINE FOLLOWED BY OXIDATION

Reduction of diazonium salts by sodium sulfite or stannous chloride usually produces hydrazines. These compounds may be oxidized to the hydrocarbons, thus providing a deamination sequence.[7]

$$\text{ArNH}_2 \rightarrow \text{ArN}_2^+\text{X}^- \rightarrow \text{ArNHNH}_2 \rightarrow \text{ArH}$$

Although sodium sulfite and stannous chloride are used with about equal frequency in this process, a preference for sodium sulfite is sometimes expressed.[110, 111, 112] Stannous chloride occasionally brings about direct replacement of the diazonium group by hydrogen, but this is not a reliable reaction.[113, 7, 45, 114]

The hydrazines usually are converted to hydrocarbons by treatment with hot, aqueous cupric sulfate, ferric chloride, or potassium chromate.[7, 110, 114, 115, 116] Although hydrazines often are isolated from reduction mixtures as hydrochlorides, it is advisable to convert them to the free bases before carrying out the oxidation; if this is not done, a chlorine atom may replace the hydrazine group.[117, 118, 119] Phenylhydrazine hydrochloride is converted to chlorobenzene in 86% yield when treated with a solution of cupric sulfate containing hydrochloric acid.[118]

Some idea of the utility of the hydrazine procedure may be inferred from the yields obtained on deaminating the following compounds: aniline (45–75%),[110, 111, 116] p-toluidine (55–65%),[120, 116] 3-chloro-4-aminotoluene (40%),[117] 5-bromo-6-aminoquinoline ("satisfactory yield").[121, *]

---

* Table VI, pp. 339–340, contains a number of additional examples of deaminations via the hydrazine.

[110] Gattermann and Wieland, "Laboratory Methods of Organic Chemistry," 22nd ed., pp. 286–289, Macmillan Co., New York, 1932.

[111] Coleman, "Organic Syntheses," Collective Volume I, 2nd ed., p. 442, John Wiley & Sons, New York, 1941.

[112] Davies, J. Chem. Soc., **121**, 715 (1922).

[113] Effront, Ber., **17**, 2329 (1884).

[114] Zincke, Ber., **18**, 787 (1885).

[115] Chattaway and Vonderwahl, J. Chem. Soc., **107**, 1508 (1915).

[116] Chattaway, J. Chem. Soc., **93**, 270 (1908).

[117] Wynne, J Chem. Soc., **61**, 1042 (1892).

[118] Gattermann and Hölzle, Ber., **25**, 1074 (1892).

[119] Cumming, Hopper, and Wheeler, "Systematic Organic Chemistry," 2nd ed., pp. 178–180, D. Van Nostrand Co., New York, 1931.

[120] McPherson and Stratton, J. Am. Chem. Soc., **37**, 908 (1915).

[121] Meigen, J. prakt. Chem., [2] **73**, 249 (1906).

In the oxidation of hydrazines, secondary reactions take place to a varying extent. Hydrocarbons of the biphenyl series may be formed; frequently a little tarry material, traces of azo compounds, and small amounts of phenols result.[116]

MISCELLANEOUS REDUCING AGENTS

The literature contains references to deamination procedures involving a number of other reducing agents:

  a. Hydroquinone.[122]
  b. Ferrous hydroxide.[123, 124]
  c. Glucose in the presence of alkali.[125]
  d. Copper hydride.*, [126, 127, 128, 129]
  e. Sodium hydrosulfite.[130, 119, 131]
  f. Formic acid.[132, 56]
  g. Hydrazines and hydroxylamine.[107, 133]
  h. Sodium arsenite.[102, 134]
  i. Stannous chloride.[113, 7, 45, 114]
  j. Potassium cuprocyanide.[135, 136]

For some of these no merit whatsoever appears to have been demonstrated; in this category may be placed methods f, g, h, i, and j. The remaining processes either possess some small utility or might be found useful upon investigation.

Aniline, p-nitroaniline, and symmetrical tribromoaniline have been deaminated by reducing their diazo compounds with hydroquinone.

---

* The existence of copper hydride (CuH_2) as a chemical compound has been questioned. It may actually be an adsorption mixture, a solid solution or an "interstitial" compound. Ephraim, "Inorganic Chemistry," third English edition, p. 865, Nordeman Publishing Co., New York, 1939.

[122] Orton and Everatt, J. Chem. Soc., **93**, 1021 (1908).
[123] Jolles and Busoni, Gazz. chim. ital., **62**, 1150 (1932).
[124] Berger, Ger. pat., 698,318 (Cl 12 q. 23) [C. A., **35**, 6269 (1941)].
[125] Benade, Keller, and Berger, U. S. pat., 2,230,791 [C. A., **35**, 3268 (1941)].
[126] von Pechmann and Nold, Ber., **31**, 560 (1898).
[127] Vorlander and Meyer, Ann., **320**, 143 (1902).
[128] Neogi and Mitra, J. Chem. Soc., **1928**, 1332.
[129] Fredga and Anderson, Arkiv Kemi, Mineral. Geol., **14B**, No. 38, 7 pp. (1941) [C. A., **35**, 6947 (1941)].
[130] Grandmougin, Ber., **40**, 858 (1907).
[131] Modlin and Burger, J. Am. Chem. Soc., **63**, 1117 (1941).
[132] Tobias, Ber., **23**, 1631 (1890).
[133] Hantzsch and Vock, Ber., **36**, 2065 (1903).
[134] Gutmann, Ber., **45**, 822 (1912).
[135] Terres, Ber., **46**, 1646 (1913).
[136] Ullmann and Schalk, Ann., **388**, 203 (1912).

Although yields were not given, the method was recommended for the replacement of amino groups by hydrogen.[122]

It is claimed in a recent patent that ferrous hydroxide is a reagent of considerable value for the deamination of certain aminonaphtholsulfonic acids.[124] From 3-hydroxy-4-aminonaphthalenesulfonic acid, 90–96% yields of the naphtholsulfonic acid are reported; the product, however, is not isolated. Aniline gives not only benzene but also phenyl azide and biphenyl in unspecified yields.[123]

Alkaline glucose converts the diazonium salts of 1-amino-2-hydroxynaphthalene-4-sulfonic acid and its halogen, nitro, carboxyl, or sulfonic acid derivatives into the corresponding 2-hydroxynaphthalene-4-sulfonic acids.[125] According to this patent, the yields are nearly quantitative.

The treatment of diazo compounds with copper hydride affords another means of deamination.[126, 127, 128, 129] Though the hydrocarbon may be produced in some cases, the reaction is not very efficient.[128]

It is reported that alkaline sodium hydrosulfite ($Na_2S_2O_4$) is effective in converting certain diazo compounds to the hydrocarbons,[119] a statement supported solely by reference to the work of Grandmougin.[130] Actually he obtained only a small yield of benzene from benzenediazonium salts but suggested that on further study the process might prove to be useful. Upon reduction with hydrosulfite, the diazo oxide * XXIV is converted to the phenol XXV in 95% yield (crude product.)[131]

XXIV   XXV

Further than this, the utilization of sodium hydrosulfite in deaminations apparently has received little attention.

COMPARISON OF THE VARIOUS DEAMINATION PROCEDURES

Certain generalizations are possible regarding the effectiveness of the various deamination procedures with a particular type of amine. These are noted in the table below.

* See p. 270.

AMINE	DEAMINATION PROCEDURE	
1. Unsubstituted amines and their homologs	1. Hypophosphorous acid Alkaline formaldehyde Stabilized diazonium salts *	Preferred
	Oxidation of hydrazines Sodium stannite	Useful
	Ethanol	Poor
2. Aminoethers	2. Hypophosphorous acid Alkaline formaldehyde Stabilized diazonium salts *	Preferred
3. Nitroamines	3. Hypophosphorous acid Ethanol Stabilized diazonium salts *	Preferred
	Alkaline formaldehyde	Fails
4. Halogenated amines	4. Hypophosphorous acid Ethanol	Preferred
	Oxidation of hydrazine	Useful
	Alkaline formaldehyde	Unpromising
5. Aminocarboxylic acids	5. Ethanol	Sometimes useful
	Alkaline formaldehyde	Unpromising
6. Aminophenols	6. Stabilized diazonium salts *	Promising

* See, however, footnotes on p. 285.

APPLICATIONS OF THE DEAMINATION REACTION

The deamination reaction is of considerable value both in synthesis and proof of structure. Its utility is best demonstrated by a consideration of several specific examples.

An amino group may be useful in a synthesis because of its effect on the position assumed by· an incoming substituent. The free amino group and its acyl derivatives are strongly *ortho-para* orienting; conversion to the ammonium salt produces a *meta*-directing group.* Advantage is taken, therefore, of the directing influence of this group in synthesizing compounds otherwise difficult to secure. Thus, bromination of aniline gives symmetrical tribromoaniline, which may be deaminated to 1,3,5-tribromobenzene in an over-all yield of 65–72%.[29] This appears to be the only practical method of preparing 1,3,5-tribromobenzene. Similarly, 2-nitro-3'-bromobiphenyl is obtained from benzidine in good yield by utilizing the *meta*-orienting influence of the ammonium ion, the *ortho*-orienting effect of the amino group, and finally deaminating.[52]

* For an account of this subject see Sidgwick's "Organic Chemistry of Nitrogen," revised by Taylor and Baker, pp. 69–70, Oxford Press, 1937.

$$H_3\overset{+}{N}-C_6H_4-C_6H_4-\overset{+}{N}H_3 \rightarrow H_3\overset{+}{N}-C_6H_3(NO_2)-C_6H_4-\overset{+}{N}H_3 \rightarrow$$

$$C_2H_5O\overset{O}{\overset{\|}{C}}-\overset{H}{\overset{|}{N}}-C_6H_3(NO_2)-C_6H_4-\overset{H}{\overset{|}{N}}-\overset{O}{\overset{\|}{C}}OC_2H_5 \rightarrow$$

$$C_2H_5O\overset{O}{\overset{\|}{C}}-\overset{H}{\overset{|}{N}}-C_6H_3(NO_2)-C_6H_3(Br)-\overset{H}{\overset{|}{N}}-\overset{O}{\overset{\|}{C}}OC_2H_5 \rightarrow$$

$$H_2N-C_6H_3(NO_2)-C_6H_3(Br)-NH_2 \rightarrow (NO_2)C_6H_4-C_6H_4(Br)$$

Certain primary aromatic amines that are available as a consequence of their use in the manufacture of dyes serve as convenient starting points in the preparation of organic compounds. Their range of utility is increased by the deamination reaction. The syntheses of 2,2'-dinitro-5,5'-dicarboxybiphenyl from o-tolidine [38] and of 3,3'-dihydroxybiphenyl from o-dianisidine [80] are examples.

$$H_3\overset{+}{N}-C_6H_3(CH_3)-C_6H_3(CH_3)-\overset{+}{N}H_3 \rightarrow H_3\overset{+}{N}-C_6H_2(CH_3)(NO_2)-C_6H_2(CH_3)(NO_2)-\overset{+}{N}H_3 \rightarrow$$

$$(CH_3)(NO_2)C_6H_3-C_6H_3(CH_3)(NO_2) \rightarrow (COOH)(NO_2)C_6H_3-C_6H_3(COOH)(NO_2)$$

$$H_2N-C_6H_3(OCH_3)-C_6H_3(OCH_3)-NH_2 \rightarrow (OCH_3)C_6H_4-C_6H_4(OCH_3) \rightarrow (OH)C_6H_4-C_6H_4(OH)$$

Ready conversion of nitro compounds to amines further extends the applicability of the deamination process. For example, the nitro group may be introduced into an aromatic nucleus for the purpose of closing a position to other groups in subsequent steps of a synthetic sequence, and, finally, the nitro group is replaced by hydrogen. This blocking effect is utilized in the preparation of 2-chlororesorcinol, which cannot be obtained by direct chlorination of resorcinol.[137]

Any radical that may be converted to an amino group is capable of replacement by hydrogen. In certain instances such an indirect procedure may be of value. Since polynuclear phenols are transformed into amines by the Bucherer reaction,[138] it has recently been suggested that the preparation of condensed ring hydrocarbons from the hydroxyl derivatives might best be achieved through the amines, rather than by the customary zinc dust fusion.[139]

Deamination affords an excellent method of degrading an amine of indeterminate structure to a known compound or one having fewer possible isomers. A large number of illustrations might be cited; the following are typical.

1. Upon heating p-toluidine with sulfur at 140° in the presence of litharge, the so-called thio-p-toluidine is formed. It was shown to be bis-(2-amino-5-methylphenyl) sulfide by deamination and subsequent oxidation to the crystalline sulfone.[140]

[137] Milligan and Hope, J. Am. Chem. Soc., **63**, 544 (1941).

[138] Drake, Org. Reactions, I, 105 (1942).

[139] Private communication from Professor M. S. Newman of Ohio State University.

[140] Bogert and Mandelbaum, J. Am. Chem. Soc., **45**, 3052 (1923).

2. The action of nitric acid on diacetylated *p*-aminophenol yields a dinitro derivative for which four structures are possible. Hydrolysis followed by deamination gives the known 3,5-dinitrophenol, thus proving that substitution occurs *ortho* to the acylated amino group.[141]

3. By the condensation of a molecule of aniline with one of *o*-toluidine and one of *p*-toluidine, the leuco base of fuchsine is obtained. The structure was determined by conversion to the diphenyltolylmethane.[17]

4. Nitration of 2-methoxy-4-nitrobenzoic acid produces a dinitro compound. The position of the incoming nitro group was demonstrated by the following degradation.

141 Reverdin and Dresel, *Ber.*, **38**, 1593 (1905).

Inasmuch as the known 2-methoxy-5-nitrobenzoic acid is formed, the dinitro acid must be 2-methoxy-4,5-dinitrobenzoic acid.[142]

EXPERIMENTAL PROCEDURES

Ethanol Deaminations

A number of carefully worked out ethanol procedures are available in *Organic Syntheses*. Collective Volume I, 2nd ed., 1941, contains directions for the deamination of 3-bromo-4-aminotoluene (p. 133) and 3-nitro-4-aminotoluene (p. 415). The conversion of 2,4,6-tribromoaniline to 1,3,5-tribromobenzene is described in Collective Volume II, p. 592 (1943), and directions for deaminating 2-amino-5-iodobenzoic acid are given on p. 353 of the same volume.

Hypophosphorous Acid Deaminations

The deaminations of 3,3'-dimethoxybenzidine and 3,3'-dimethylbenzidine are described in *Organic Syntheses*.[81]

m-Nitrotoluene [82] from 3-Nitro-4-aminotoluene. In a 1-l. round-bottomed flask are placed 45 cc. of concentrated hydrochloric acid (sp. gr. 1.19) and 90 cc. of water. The solution is heated to boiling, 30.4 g. (0.2 mole) of 3-nitro-4-aminotoluene is added, and the mixture is stirred mechanically. When the amine is completely dissolved, the flame is removed and an additional 50 cc. of concentrated hydrochloric acid is added. The mixture is placed in an ice-salt bath, and, while a temperature of $-5°$ to $0°$ is maintained, a solution of 14.5 g. (0.204 mole) of 97% sodium nitrite in 35 cc. of water is added from a dropping funnel over a period of approximately one hour.

To the orange-yellow diazonium solution, 104 cc. (1.0 mole) of 50% aqueous hypophosphorous acid (precooled to $0°$) is added dropwise in the course of one-half hour, the temperature being held at $-5°$ to $0°$. Nitrogen is evolved, and crystals of *m*-nitrotoluene form. Stirring at a temperature of $-5°$ to $0°$ is continued for another hour, and the solution is then placed in a refrigerator (held at or close to $0°$) for approximately twenty-four hours.

The orange solid is isolated by filtration, and the filtrate is extracted with two 125-cc. portions of benzene. The combined orange crystals and benzene extracts are washed with 10–20% aqueous sodium hydroxide and then with water. After drying over calcium chloride, the benzene is removed and the residue is distilled at 10 mm. There is obtained 22.4 g. (80%) of *m*-nitrotoluene; b.p. 100–102°; $n_D^{21°}$ 1.5468.

---

[142] Goldstein and Jaquet, *Helv. Chim. Acta,* **24**, 33 (1941).

Doubling the amount of hypophosphorous acid does not increase the yield of *m*-nitrotoluene.[82] It has recently been found that, on using only 0.76 mole of hypophosphorous acid per mole of 3-nitro-4-aminotoluene, a 70% yield of *m*-nitrotoluene is obtained.[84] Another departure from the above directions consists in permitting the cold reaction mixture to come to room temperature in six hours, after which it is allowed to remain overnight before being worked up.[84]

Toluene [82] from *o*-Toluidine. In a 1-l. flask are placed 21.4 g. (0.2 mole) of *o*-toluidine, 75 cc. of concentrated hydrochloric acid (sp. gr. 1.19), and 25 cc. of water. The flask is immersed in an ice-salt mixture and is fitted with an efficient stirrer. While a temperature of −5° to 0° is maintained, a solution of 14.5 g. (0.204 mole) of 97% sodium nitrite in 35 cc. of water is slowly added from a dropping funnel. As the reaction proceeds, the mixture becomes more fluid and the nitrite may be added somewhat more rapidly; one-half to three-quarters of an hour is required for diazotization.

While a temperature of −5° to 0° is maintained, 312 cc. (3.0 moles) of 50% hypophosphorous acid (precooled to 0°) is added to the diazonium solution in the course of ten to fifteen minutes. Moderate stirring and a temperature of −5° to 0° are continued for an additional hour; the flask is then stoppered loosely and placed in a refrigerator (at or close to 0°) for approximately twenty-four hours.

The reaction product consists of an orange oil floating on the aqueous phase. After separation of the oil, the aqueous solution is extracted with three 125-cc. portions of ether. The combined oil and ether extracts are washed with 20–30% aqueous sodium hydroxide, then with water, and dried over potassium carbonate. The ether solution is then distilled through a small modified Widmer column. The yield of toluene, b.p. 109–110°, is 12.9–13.8 g. (70–75%); $n_D^{20°}$ 1.4962.

Reduction with 0.55 mole of hypophosphorous acid gives some *o*-cresol, much tar, and no toluene.[13] With 1.0 mole (104 cc.) of acid, however, a 50% yield of pure toluene is obtained.[82] If sulfuric acid is substituted for hydrochloric acid, the yield falls to 12–23%.[82]

7-Chlorohydrindone-1 [91] from 4-Amino-7-chlorohydrindone-1. A mechanically stirred suspension of 5.45 g. of 4-amino-7-chlorohydrindone-1, 12 cc. of concentrated hydrochloric acid, and 15 cc. of water is cooled to 3°, and then a solution of 2.2 g. of sodium nitrite in 10 cc. of water is added over a period of thirty minutes. If necessary, a few grams of ice is added to maintain the temperature (usually 2–4 g. suffices). Stirring is continued for an additional five minutes, and then 100 cc. of 50% hypophosphorous acid * (precooled to 0°) is run into the diazonium

---

* No attempt was made to use less hypophosphorous acid. In all likelihood a much smaller quantity of reducing agent would prove equally effective.

solution in about five minutes; copious evolution of nitrogen occurs. After being stirred at ice temperature for two hours, the mixture is kept in an ice chest for about twenty hours and the yellow precipitate is then isolated by filtration. The filtrate is extracted with ether, and, after addition of the yellow solid, the ether solution is washed twice with 50-cc. portions of a 10% sodium hydroxide solution, then dried over sodium sulfate, and the solvent is removed. The crystalline product weighs 4.5 g. (90%); m.p. 92–93°. After one recrystallization from aqueous ethanol (charcoal), there is obtained 4.25 g. (85%) of white needles; m.p. 94.8–95.8°.

1,3,5-Trinitrobenzene from 2,4,6-Trinitroaniline.[83]   With gentle stirring, 2 g. (0.028 mole) of sodium nitrite is added to 55 cc. of sulfuric acid (sp. gr. 1.84). The resulting solution is cooled to −5° to 0°; efficient stirring is instituted, and 5.2 cc. (0.05 mole) of 50% hypophosphorous acid (precooled to −5° to 0°) is added rapidly. While a temperature of −5° to 0° is being maintained, a solution of 2.3 g. (0.01 mole) of 2,4,6-trinitroaniline (picramide) in 100 cc. of glacial acetic acid is run in over a period of one-half to three-quarters of an hour, and then, with reversion to gentle stirring, the reaction mixture is kept in the ice-salt bath for another hour; the flask is then stoppered loosely and placed in a refrigerator for approximately twenty hours.

The product is poured into ice water, thoroughly extracted with benzene, and the benzene solution washed with water. Benzene is then removed by distillation until a volume of 25–50 cc. is reached and the resulting deep-red solution is passed through a 12 by 2 cm. column of aluminum oxide.* The column is developed with ordinary, undried benzene, and that portion of the eluate which runs through before the strawberry-red zone reaches the bottom of the tube is discarded. The solution that follows is collected, and a pale yellow crystalline mass is obtained upon removal of the solvent. Recrystallization from ethanol gives 1.24–1.37 g. (60–65%) of pale yellow crystals that sinter at 119° and melt at 122.7–123.2° (cor.).

Essentially the same result is obtained when hypophosphorous acid is added after the picramide has been diazotized. An eightfold increase in the amount of hypophosphorous acid did not raise the yield.†

---

* Alorco activated alumina (Aluminum Company of America) and Celite Analytical Filter-Aid (Johns-Manville Co.) in approximately equal volumes. Brockmann's aluminum oxide (Merck and Co.) is also very satisfactory.

† Excess sodium nitrite is used in this preparation. The possibility that a large excess might increase the yield was not investigated. Nor was the effect of adding small amounts of water, which might prove beneficial, studied. Finally, it should be noted that, very possibly, a decrease in the amount of acetic acid and sulfuric acid will not lower the yield

Triptycene [83, *] **from 2,5-Diaminotriptycene.** One-half gram of sodium nitrite is added to 50 cc. of sulfuric acid (sp. gr. 1.84), and the mixture is stirred to effect complete solution. After cooling to −5° to 0°, 50 cc. of 50% hypophosphorous acid † (precooled to −5° to 0°) is added in about ten minutes. This is followed by a solution of 0.57 g. of 2,5-diaminotriptycene in 30 cc. of glacial acetic acid, approximately ten minutes being required for the addition. A temperature of −5° to 0° and gentle stirring are maintained for another three hours, after which 100 g. of crushed ice is added, with vigorous stirring, over a period of ten to fifteen minutes. Stirring is continued for an additional ten minutes, and the reaction mixture (loosely stoppered) is placed in the refrigerator for twenty-four to thirty-six hours.

The product is then poured into ice water, extracted with benzene, and washed with water, aqueous sodium hydroxide, and finally with water. After removal of the solvent, the residue is sublimed at 1 mm. and a bath temperature of 160–190°. The pale yellow crystals so obtained are dissolved in benzene, and the solution is passed through a short column of aluminum oxide.‡ Removal of the solvent gives 0.2–0.23 g. (40–45%) of white crystals which begin to sinter at 245° and melt at 252–254° (cor.).

The presence of chloride ions should be avoided. Diazotization with hydrochloric acid produces 2-chlorotriptycene.[87]

A parallel experiment, differing only in the omission of the 100 g. of ice, gave but a trace of impure triptycene. This result, and similar observations,[83] indicate that either the diazotization or the reduction (or both) does not take place smoothly unless an appreciable amount of water is present.

Alkaline Formaldehyde Deamination

4-Methyldiphenyl Ether [4,] § **from 4-Methyl-4′-aminodiphenyl Ether.** A solution of 19.9 g. (0.1 mole) of 4-methyl-4′-aminodiphenyl ether in 50 cc. of concentrated hydrochloric acid, 50 cc. of glacial acetic acid, and 200 cc. of water is chilled in ice and diazotized in the usual manner with 7 g. of sodium nitrite dissolved in a little water. A solution of 100 g. of commercial sodium hydroxide in 600 cc. of water is then prepared and placed with 500 g. of ice in a 5-l. flask fitted with a mechanical stirrer.

* See p. 280 for formulas.
† The use of a smaller amount of hypophosphorous acid was not studied.
‡ See footnote on p. 296.
§ This procedure was furnished through the courtesy of Professor R. Q. Brewster of the University of Kansas.

The stirrer is started, and 75 cc. of formalin (37% formaldehyde) is added.   The diazo solution is then poured in a slow stream into the rapidly stirred alkaline solution of formaldehyde.   The escaping nitrogen causes considerable frothing.   After all the diazonium chloride solution has been added, the stirring is continued for five minutes, after which the stirrer is removed, the mouth of the flask covered with a watch glass, and the reaction mixture allowed to stand with occasional shaking for thirty to forty minutes.   The oily 4-methyldiphenyl ether is collected by the addition of a little carbon tetrachloride and separated from the aqueous solution.   After the carbon tetrachloride has been removed by distillation, the flask containing the crude product is heated to 150° in an oil bath, and the 4-methyldiphenyl ether is purified by distillation in a current of superheated steam.   After separation from the water and drying, the product is distilled; b.p. 275–278°/744 mm.: 145–150/7 mm. The yield is 10–11 g. (54–60%).

Sodium Stannite Deamination

1,3-Dimethyl-5-bromobenzene [104] **from 1,3-Dimethyl-4-amino-5-bromobenzene.**   A suspension of 23.6 g. of 1,3-dimethyl-4-amino-5-bromobenzene hydrochloride in 60 cc. of water and 15 cc. of concentrated hydrochloric acid is diazotized with 7 g. of sodium nitrite in 30 cc. of water at 5–6°.   The clear diazonium solution is then added in portions to an ice-cold solution of sodium stannite prepared from 40 g. of stannous chloride, 50 g. of sodium hydroxide, and 260 cc. of water; about five to ten minutes is required for the addition.   After standing for an hour at room temperature the reaction mixture is steam distilled. The yellow oil is separated from the aqueous phase, and the aqueous phase is extracted with ether.   The ether extract is added to the yellow oil, and the resulting solution is dried over calcium chloride; the solvent is removed and the residue distilled at 12 mm. at a bath temperature of 120°.   There is obtained 13.2 g. (73%) of a colorless product boiling at 88–89°.

The results are essentially the same when the diazonium salt solution is made alkaline before reduction, but the yield is lower when the stannite solution is run into the acidic solution of the diazotized base instead of carrying out the reduction as described above.

EXAMPLES OF THE DEAMINATION REACTION

Each of the Tables II–VI is concerned with a single reducing agent, and, within a given table, the amines are listed in the following sequence:

Amines, polyamines, and their homologs.
Aminophenols.
Aminoethers.
Aminocarboxylic acids.
Nitroamines.
Aminoazo compounds.
Halogenated amines.
Aminosulfonic acids.
Diazo oxides.
Heterocyclics.
Aminoarsonic acids.
Aminosulfides and sulfones.

"The principle of latest position" has been invoked. For example, a bromonitroaniline will be found under halogenated amines.

The tables are unquestionably incomplete, inasmuch as the deamination reaction has often been employed in a synthesis or structure proof without any indication of this fact in the title of the paper. It is believed, however, that the list is extensive enough to afford a real cross section of the results obtained for the various reducing agents.

Where the yield is not given, the product was reported in the literature without any information about the yield.

TABLE II

ETHANOL DEAMINATIONS

Amine	Product, Yield	Remarks	Reference[*]
Aniline	Phenetole (61%) + benzene (5%)	Alkaline H_2CO, Na_2SnO_2, and H_3PO_2 all give benzene in 60% yield.	11, 10
Benzidine	Biphenyl (80%)	H_3PO_2 gives a 60% yield.	14
α-Naphthylamine	Naphthalene (40%) + α-ethoxynaphthalene (23%)		12
β-Naphthylamine	β-Ethoxynaphthalene (30%) + naphthalene (7%)	H_3PO_2 gives naphthalene in 35–45% yield.	12, 13
o-Toluidine	o-Methylphenetole (ca. 50%)	H_3PO_2 gives pure toluene in 70–75% yield. Alkaline HCHO gives 80% of pure toluene.	10, 13
m-Toluidine	m-Methylphenetole (ca. 40%)	H_3PO_2 gives a 45% yield of pure toluene.	10
p-Toluidine	Toluene (ca. 45%) + p-methylphenetole (ca. 18%)	H_3PO_2 gives 80–85% of pure toluene. Alkaline HCHO gives an 80% yield of pure toluene.	10, 13

2,5-Dimethylaniline	2,5-Dimethylphenetole		143
3,3'-Dimethyl-4,4'-diaminophenyl (o-Tolidine)	3,3'-Dimethylbiphenyl + 3,3'-dimethyl-4,4'-diethoxybiphenyl "approximately equal amounts"	In the presence of Zn dust only the hydrocarbon is isolated (58% yield). H_3PO_2 gives 76–82% yield of hydrocarbon.	14, 71, 81
2,4'-Diaminobiphenyl	4-Aminobiphenyl	Used only enough HNO_2 for one amino group.	94
4,4'-Diaminotriphenylmethane	Triphenylmethane		144
4,4',4''-Triaminotriphenylmethane	Triphenylmethane (25%, crude)		145
[structure: H_2N—C₆H₃(CH₃)—CH(—C₆H₄NH₂)₂]	[structure: (C₆H₅)₂CH—C₆H₄—CH₃] (16%, pure)		17
4-Aminotetraphenylmethane	Tetraphenylmethane (46%, pure)	In the absence of Zn dust only the ether is obtained.	15
[structure: (C₆H₅)₃C—C₆H₃(CH₃)NH₂] (54%)	[structure: (C₆H₅)₃C—C₆H₄—CH₃]		16, 72

* References 143–195 appear on p. 323.

TABLE II—*Continued*

ETHANOL DEAMINATIONS

Amine	Product, Yield	Remarks	Reference*
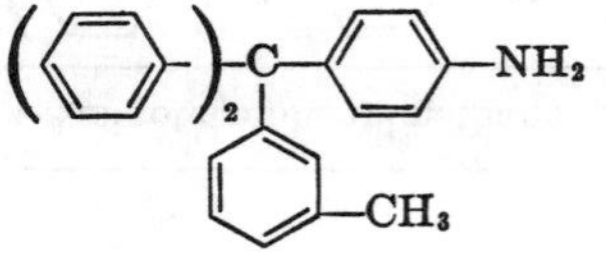	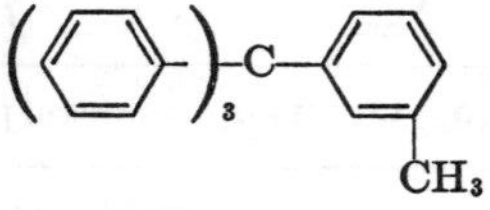 (60%)	Zn dust added.	72
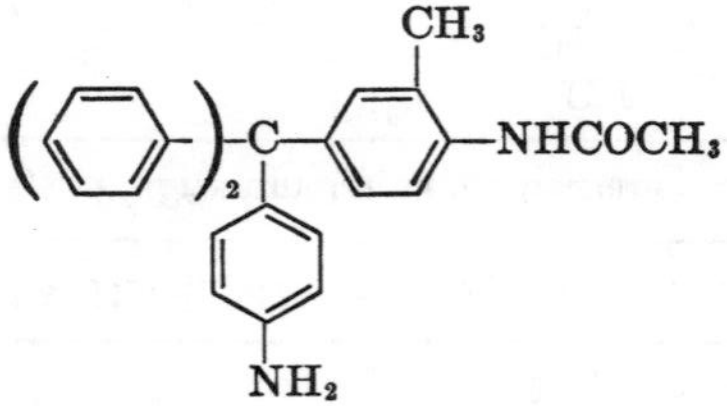	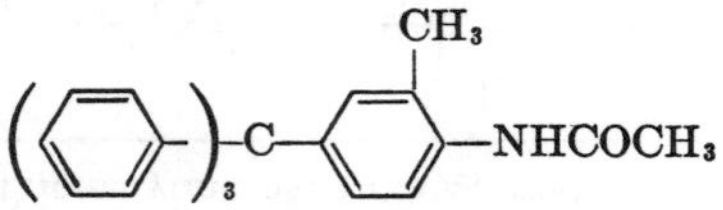 (21%)	Zn dust added.	72
trans-o-Aminostilbene (p. 282)	Stilbene (62%, incompletely purified)	Cu powder added.	66
cis-o-Aminostilbene (p. 282)	Phenanthrene (64%, pure)	Cu powder is added. NaH_2PO_2 also fails here, an 80% yield of pure phenanthrene resulting.	66

Compound	Products	Conditions	References
(structure: 2,2'-diaminostilbene, two aminophenyl rings joined by H–C=C–H, each bearing NH_2)	Phenanthrene (18%, pure)	Cu powder added.	37
o-(β-Phenylethyl)-aniline (p. 281)	9,10-Dihydrophenanthrene (ca. 50%) + o-(β-phenyl ethyl)-phenol (23%)	Cu powder added. NaH_2PO_2 gives crude $C_6H_5CH_2CH_2CH_2C_6H_5$ in 47% yield.	66
o-Aminophenol	Phenol		25
m-Aminophenol	Phenol		25
p-Aminophenol	Phenol (60%)	ZnO added.	41
p-Anisidine	Anisole	Used methanol. Diazonium salt stabilized with $ZnCl_2$. Zn dust added.	41
3,3'-Dimethoxy-4,4'-diaminobiphenyl (o-dianisidine)	3,3'-Dimethoxybiphenyl (12%, pure)	H_3PO_2 gives 66–78% yield (pure).	45
o-Aminobenzoic acid	Ethyl benzoate (53%)		22, 23
m-Aminobenzoic acid	Ethyl benzoate (main product) + ethyl-m-ethoxybenzoate		24, 23, 22

* References 143–195 appear on p. 323.

TABLE II—*Continued*

ETHANOL DEAMINATIONS

Amine	Product, Yield	Remarks	Reference*
p-Aminobenzoic acid	p-Ethoxybenzoic acid (50%) + ethyl benzoate (12%)		22, 23
3-Methyl-4-aminobenzoic acid	3-Methyl-4-ethoxybenzoic acid "quantitative conversion"		146, 10
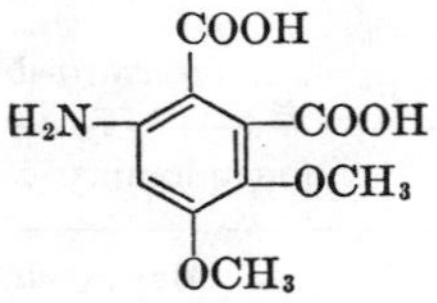 (aromatic ring: H₂N, COOH, OCH₃, OCH₃)	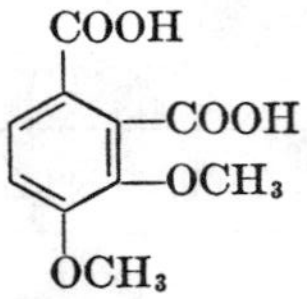 (aromatic ring: COOH, OCH₃, OCH₃) "Forms easily"		147
3,3′-Dicarboxy-4,4′-diaminobiphenyl	3,3′-Dicarboxybiphenyl		23
2-Carboxy-3-aminonaphthalene	2-Carboxynaphthalene (β-naphthoic acid)	Cu powder added.	148
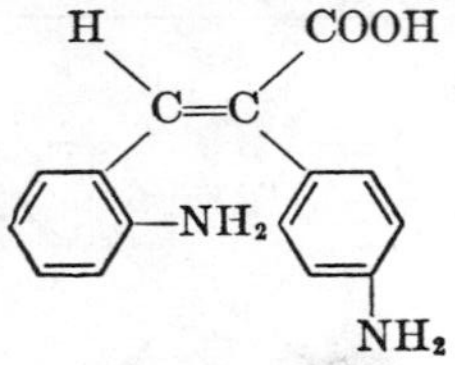 (structure: H–C=C–, NH₂, NH₂, COOH)	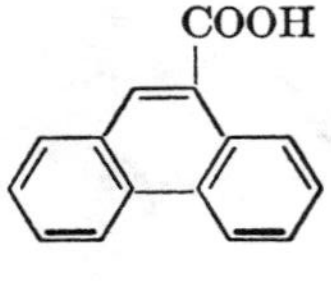 (phenanthrene COOH) (18%)	Cu powder added.	37

Compound	Product	Notes	Ref.
o-Nitroaniline	Nitrobenzene (ca. 82%)	H₃PO₂ gives 75–80% of pure nitrobenzene.	22
m-Nitroaniline	Nitrobenzene (ca. 66%)	H₃PO₂ gives 60–70% pure nitrobenzene.	22
p-Nitroaniline	Nitrobenzene (ca. 70%)	H₃PO₂ gives 55–60% yield of pure nitrobenzene.	22
1,3-Diamino-4-nitrotoluene	2-Ethoxy-4-nitrotoluene, small amount		39
3-Nitro-4-aminotoluene	m-Nitrotoluene (62–72%, pure)	H₃PO₂ gives 75–80% of pure m-nitrotoluene.	34
2-Nitro-4-aminotoluene	o-Nitrotoluene (ca. 50%)		149
2,4-Dimethyl-3-nitroaniline	1,3-Dimethyl-2-nitrobenzene "very good yield"		150
2,4-Dimethyl-5-nitroaniline	1,3-Dimethyl-4-nitrobenzene "very good yield"		150
2,4-Dimethyl-6-nitroaniline	1,3-Dimethyl-5-nitrobenzene (62%, pure)		151
[structure: CH₃–C₆H₃(NH₂)(NO₂) with O₂N; product structures with H–C≡N, N–H, O₂N, NO₂]		Only a little nitrogen was evolved.	152

*References 143–195 appear on p. 223.

TABLE II—*Continued*

ETHANOL DEAMINATIONS

Amine	Product, Yield	Remarks	Reference*
2,4-Dinitro-6-methylaniline	3,5-Dinitrotoluene (92–93%)		153
2,6-Dinitro-4-methylaniline	3,5-Dinitrotoluene (95%, pure)		35
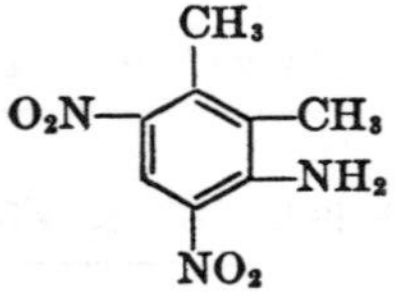 (substituted toluene with CH_3, NH_2, O_2N, NO_2)	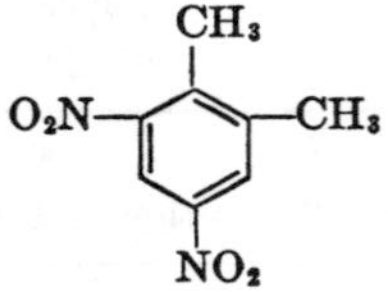 (substituted toluene with CH_3, O_2N, NO_2)		154
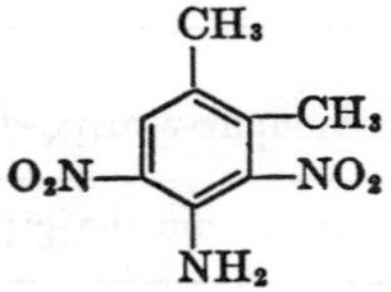 (substituted toluene with CH_3, NO_2, O_2N, NH_2)	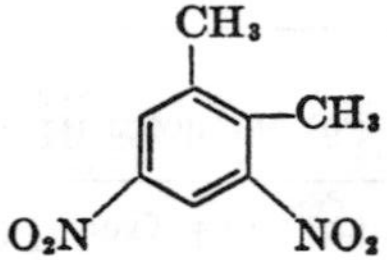 (substituted toluene with CH_3, NO_2, O_2N)		154
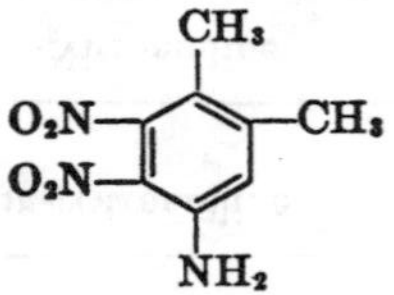 (substituted toluene with CH_3, O_2N, O_2N, NH_2)	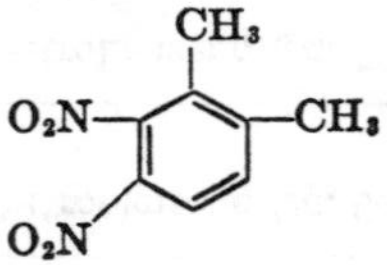 (substituted toluene with CH_3, O_2N, O_2N)		154

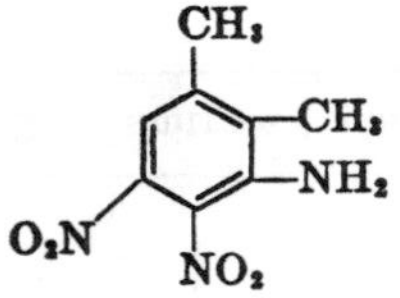	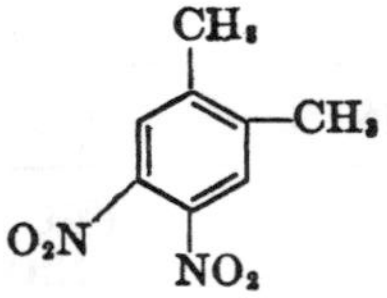		154
3-Nitro-4-hydroxyaniline	*o*-Nitrophenol		43
3-Nitro-4-methoxyaniline	*o*-Nitrophenol (33%, pure)	Diazotized at 70–80°.	42
2,6-Dinitro-4-hydroxyaniline	3,5-Dinitrophenol		141
3,5-Dinitro-4-hydroxyaniline	2,6-Dinitrophenol		141
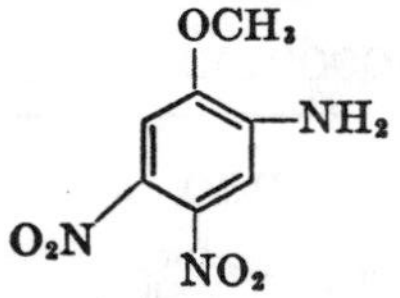	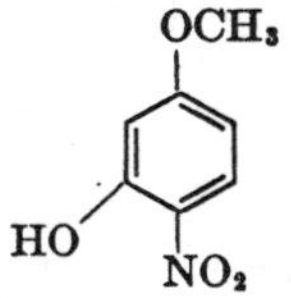		155
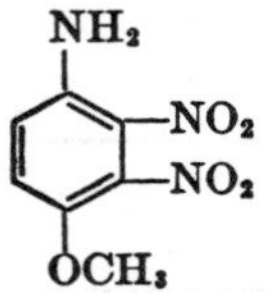	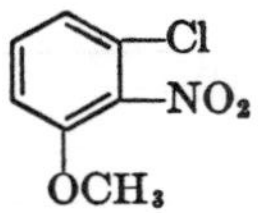	A nitro group is replaced by Cl upon diazotizing in HCl. With H_2SO_4 the nitro groups remain intact.	48

* References 143–195 appear on p. 323.

TABLE II—*Continued*

ETHANOL DEAMINATIONS

Amine	Product, Yield	Remarks	Reference*
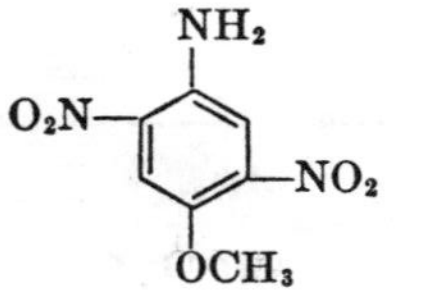	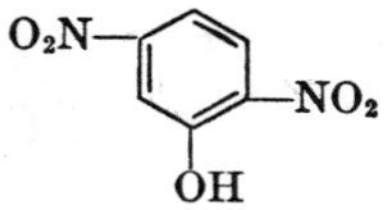		156
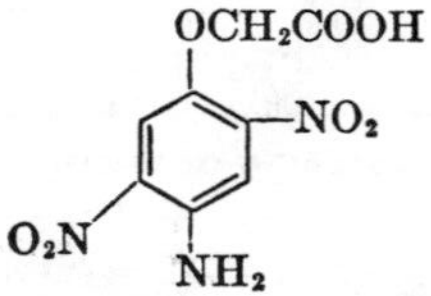	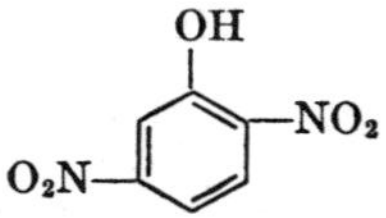		156
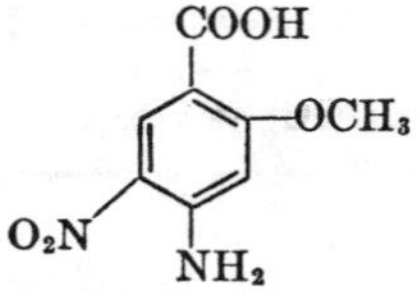	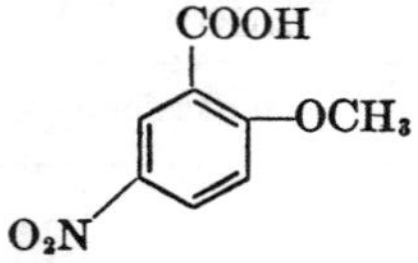 (43%)		142
3,3′-Dinitro-4,4′-diaminobiphenyl	3,3′-Dinitrobiphenyl "good yield"		157

2,2'-Dinitro-4,4'-diamino-5,5'-dimethyl-biphenyl (p. 268)	2,2'-Dinitro-5,5'-dimethylbiphenyl (53%)	38
3-Amino-4-nitrobiphenyl	4-Nitrobiphenyl	158
3-Amino-4,4'-dinitrobiphenyl	4,4'-Dinitrobiphenyl	31
2,3'-Dinitro-4,4'-diaminobiphenyl	2,3'-Dinitrobiphenyl	158
1-Nitro-2-aminonaphthalene	1-Nitronaphthalene (ca. 52%)	33
1-Nitro-4-aminonaphthalene	1-Nitronaphthalene (ca. 57%)	33
1-Amino-2-nitronaphthalene	2-Nitronaphthalene (50–80%)	36, 33
1,3-Dinitro-4-aminonaphthalene	1,3-Dinitronaphthalene (50%)	36
1,8-Dinitro-2-aminonaphthalene	1,8-Dinitronaphthalene "satisfactory yield"	64
(structure) (45%, pure)	(structure)	159, 160 Either ethanol or "amyl alcohol" may be used. Sodium stannite gives a 38% yield (pure). "Amyl alcohol", and Cu powder are the preferred reagents.

* References 143–195 appear on p. 323.

TABLE II—*Continued*

ETHANOL DEAMINATIONS

Amine	Product, Yield	Remarks	Reference*
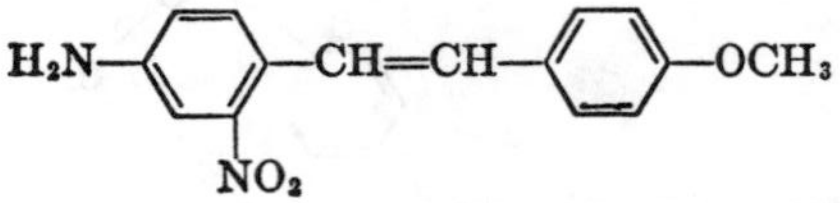	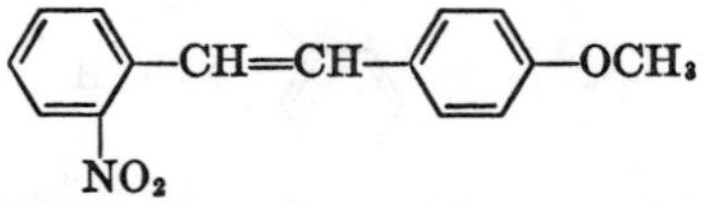 (15%, pure)		77
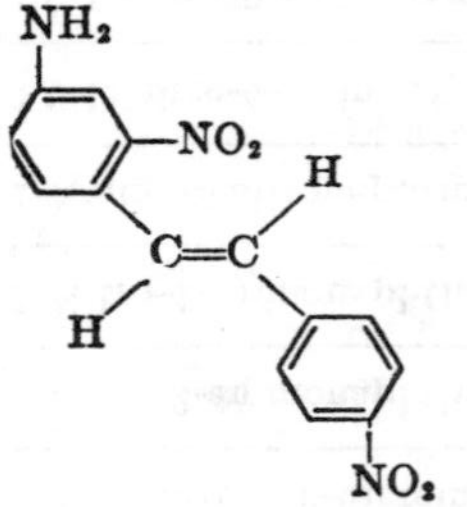	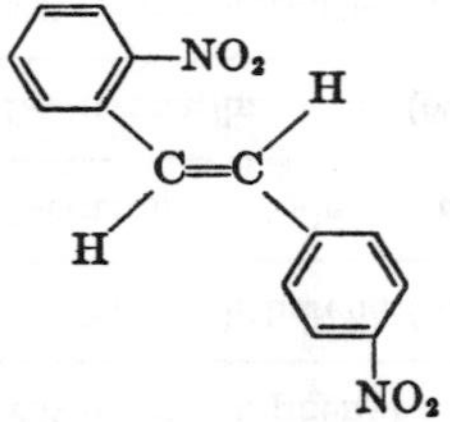 (56%, pure)	Cu powder added.	37
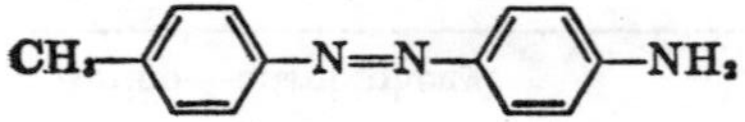	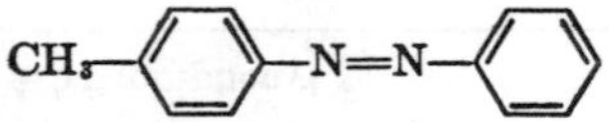 (ca. 50%)	Cu bronze added.	65

Reactant	Product	Notes	References
(azo compound with NH₂, CH₃ substituents)	(ca. 50%)	Cu bronze added.	65
(azo compound with NH₂, CH₃ substituents)	(ca. 50%)	Cu bronze added.	65
o-Chloroaniline	Chlorobenzene (86%)		25
m-Chloroaniline	Chlorobenzene (87%)		25
p-Chloroaniline	Chlorobenzene (87%)		25, 11
2,4-Dichloroaniline	1,3-Dichlorobenzene (46%)	H$_3$PO$_2$ gives a 50% yield.	13
2,4,6-Trichloroaniline	1,3,5-Trichlorobenzene (92%)		161
3,3'-Dichloro-4,4'-diaminobiphenyl	3,3'-Dichlorobiphenyl		162
2-Amino-5-chlorotoluene	m-Chlorotoluene (49%, pure)	Via hydrazine get 66% yield of crude.	163
3-Chloro-4-aminotoluene	m-Chlorotoluene (60%)	Via hydrazine get 40% yield of pure product.	164

* References 143–195 appear on p. 323.

TABLE II—*Continued*

ETHANOL DEAMINATIONS

Amine	Product, Yield	Remarks	Reference[*]
2,3,5-Trichloro-4-hydroxyaniline	2,3,6-Trichlorophenol		165
3,5-Dichloro-4-aminomethyl benzoate	3,5-Dichloro-methyl benzoate (60%, pure)	Sodium added.	57
2-Amino-4-nitro-5-chlorotoluene	3-Chloro-4-nitrotoluene (30–50%)		166
2-Nitro-6-chloroaniline	m-Chloronitrobenzene		167
o-Bromoaniline	Bromobenzene (72–80%)		25
m-Bromoaniline	Bromobenzene (65–69%)		25
p-Bromoaniline	Bromobenzene (68–80%)		25, 11
2,6-Dibromo-4-chloroaniline	1,3-Dibromo-5-chlorobenzene	HCl should not be used in the diazotization.	168
2,4,6-Tribromoaniline	1,3,5-Tribromobenzene (72–80%, pure)	H$_3$PO$_2$ gives 70% (pure). HCl should not be used in the diazotization.	13, 29
Pentabromoaniline	Pentabromobenzene	HCl should not be used in the diazotization.	32

		Cu powder added.	
3-Bromo-4-aminotoluene	m-Bromotoluene (54-59%, pure)		28
2-Amino-5-bromotoluene	m-Bromotoluene (52%)		13
3-Nitro-4-amino-5-bromotoluene	3-Nitro-5-bromotoluene		169
2-Amino-3-nitro-5-bromotoluene	3-Nitro-5-bromotoluene		169
3,5-Dibromo-4-hydroxyaniline	2,6-Dibromophenol		78
2-Amino-5-bromobenzoic acid	m-Bromobenzoic acid (32%)		13
2-Bromo-5-aminobenzoic acid	o-Bromobenzoic acid (34%)		13
2,3'-Dibromo-4'-aminobiphenyl	2,3'-Dibromobiphenyl		170
2,2'-Dibromo-5-aminobiphenyl	2,2'-Dibromobiphenyl		170
3,3'-Dibromo-6-aminobiphenyl	3,3'-Dibromobiphenyl		170
2,4'-Dibromo-5-aminobiphenyl	2,4'-Dibromobiphenyl		170
3,4',5-Tribromo-4-aminobiphenyl	3,4',5-Tribromobiphenyl		170
3,5,6'-Tribromo-4-aminobiphenyl	3,5,6'-Tribromobiphenyl (52%)		31
3,5,5'-Tribromo-6-aminobiphenyl	3,5,5'-Tribromobiphenyl		170
2,4,4',6-Tetrabromo-5-aminobiphenyl	2,4,4',6-Tetrabromobiphenyl		170

• References 143-195 appear on p. 323.

TABLE II—*Continued*

ETHANOL DEAMINATIONS

Amine	Product, Yield	Remarks	Reference*
2-Nitro-3'-bromo-4'-aminobiphenyl	2-Nitro-3'-bromobiphenyl (53%)		31
3-Bromo-4,4'-diamino-5-nitrobiphenyl	3-Bromo-5-nitrobiphenyl		170
3,5-Dibromo-3'-nitro-4-aminobiphenyl	3,5-Dibromo-3'-nitrobiphenyl (45%)		31
2-Nitro-3'-bromo-4,4'-diaminobiphenyl (p. 273)	2-Nitro-3'-bromobiphenyl (78% pure) (p. 273)	Reduction of the *bis*-diazoborofluoride gives a 78% yield of pure product. If the diazonium acid sulfate is used the yield of pure product falls to 52%.	52
1,4,6-Tribromo-2-aminonaphthalene	1,4,6-Tribromonaphthalene		171
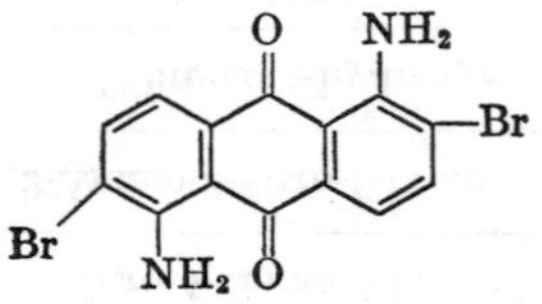 [anthraquinone structure with NH₂ and Br substituents] (ca. 70%, pure)	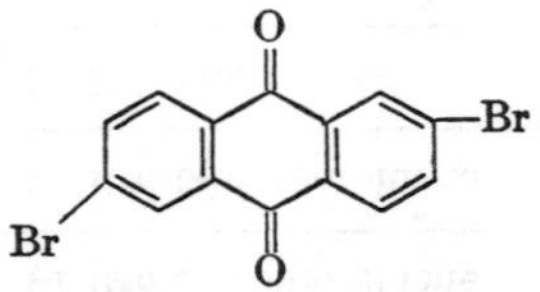 [anthraquinone structure with Br substituents] (ca. 70%, pure)		172
2,4,6-Triiodoaniline	1,3,5-Triiodobenzene (ca. 50%)		26

3,5-Diiodo-4-aminotoluene	3,5-Diiodotoluene (ca. 60%)		27
3,5-Diiodo-4-aminobenzoic acid	3,5-Diiodobenzoic acid (42%)		27
2-Amino-3,5-diiodobenzoic acid	3,5-Diiodobenzoic acid		173
2-Amino-5-iodobenzoic acid	m-Iodobenzoic acid (45–50%, pure)	CuSO₄ added.	30
2-Nitro-3-iodo-6-aminotoluene	2-Nitro-3-iodotoluene		174
o-Aminobenzenesulfonic acid	o-Ethoxybenzenesulfonic acid (only product)		18
m-Aminobenzenesulfonic acid	m-Ethoxybenzenesulfonic acid (main product) + benzenesulfonic acid		18, 19
p-Aminobenzenesulfonic acid	Benzenesulfonic acid (only product)		20
2-Aminobenzene-1,4-disulfonic acid	2-Ethoxybenzene-1,4-disulfonic acid		175
1-Aminobenzene-2,4-disulfonic acid	Benzene-1,3-disulfonic acid		175
2-Methyl-5-aminobenzenesulfonic acid	2-Methylbenzenesulfonic acid (59%) + 2-methyl-5-ethoxybenzenesulfonic acid (37%)		21
2-Amino-5-methylbenzenesulfonic acid	3-Methylbenzenesulfonic acid	CuSO₄ added. It appears to be of value in this instance.	70, 176
3-Amino-4-methylbenzenesulfonic acid	3-Ethoxy-4-methylbenzenesulfonic acid		177

* References 143–195 appear on p. 323.

TABLE II—*Continued*

ETHANOL DEAMINATIONS

Amine	Product, Yield	Remarks	Reference[*]
4-Amino-5-methylbenzene-1,3-disulfonic acid	4-Ethoxy-5-methylbenzene-1,3-disulfonic acid		178
2-Amino-3,5-dimethylbenzenesulfonic acid	2-Ethoxy-3,5-dimethylbenzenesulfonic acid (63%)		179
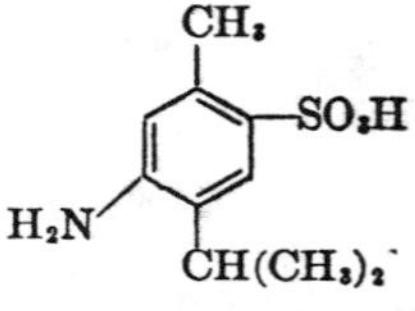	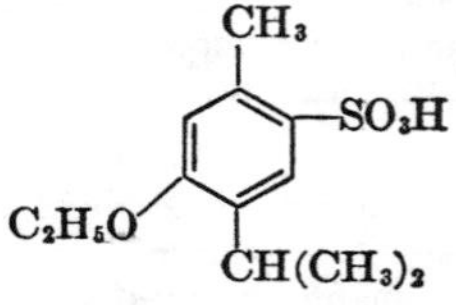		180
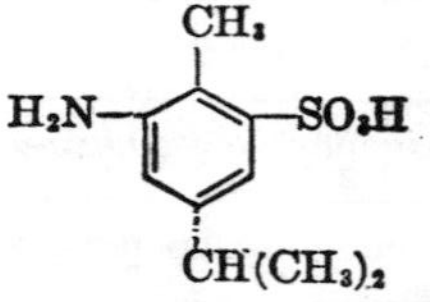	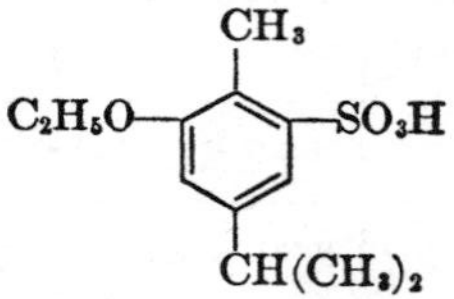		181

CH₃ / NO₂ / CH₃ / SO₃H (with H₂N)	CH₃ / NO₂ / CH₃ / SO₃H		182
3-Chloro-5-aminobenzenesulfonic acid	3-Chlorobenzenesulfonic acid		183
3-Chloro-6-aminobenzenesulfonic acid	3-Chlorobenzenesulfonic acid		184
3-Iodo-4-aminobenzenesulfonic acid	3-Iodobenzenesulfonic acid		185
2,4,6-Tribromo-3-aminobenzenesulfonic acid	2,4,6-Tribromobenzenesulfonic acid		186
H₂N—⟨⟩—N=N—⟨⟩—SO₃H	⟨⟩—N=N—⟨⟩—SO₃H		187
4,4'-Diaminobiphenyl-2,2'-disulfonic acid	Biphenyl-2,2'-disulfonic acid	Cu powder added.	188
4,4'-Diaminobiphenyl-3,3'-disulfonic acid	Biphenyl-3,3'-disulfonic acid		157
4,4'-Diamino-5,5'-dimethylbiphenyl-2,2'-disulfonic acid	5,5'-Dimethylbiphenyl-2,2'-disulfonic acid	Cu powder added.	67

* References 143–195 appear on p. 323.

TABLE II—*Continued*

ETHANOL DEAMINATIONS

Amine	Product, Yield	Remarks	Reference*
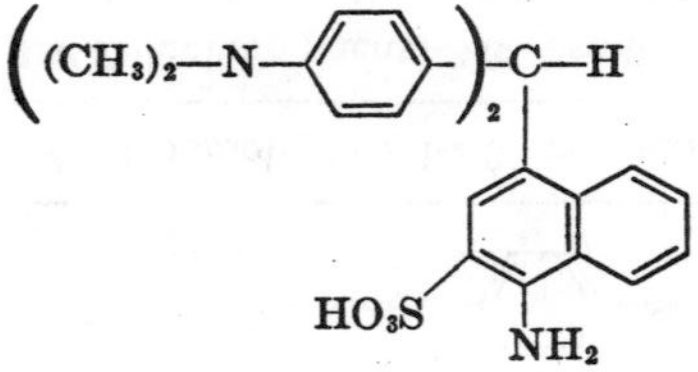	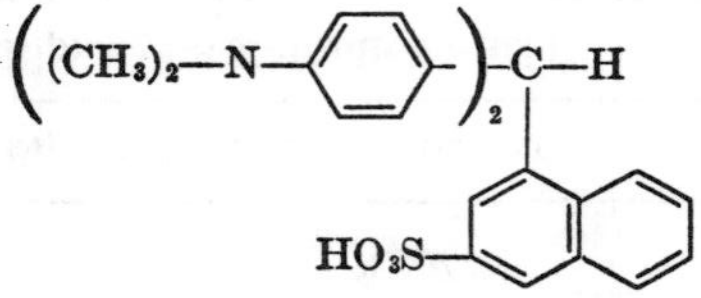		68
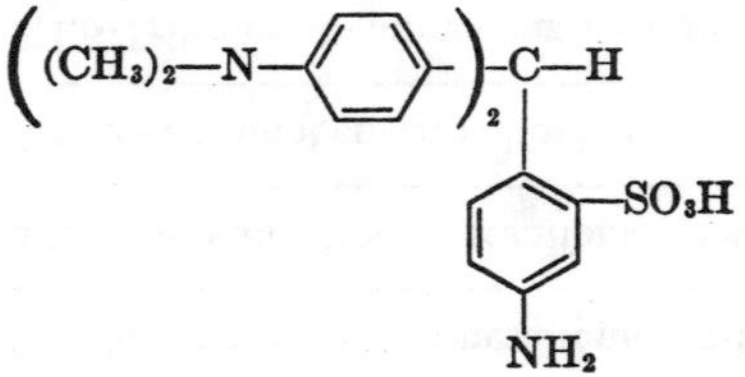	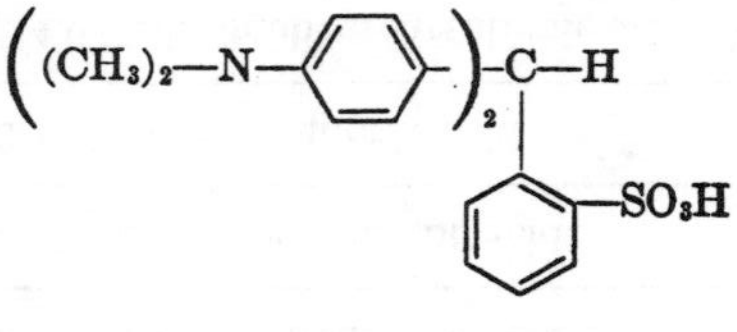	Cu$_2$O added.	68
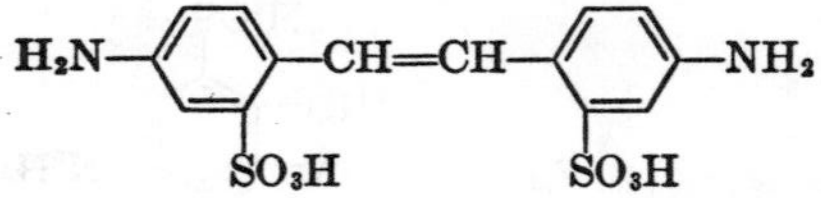	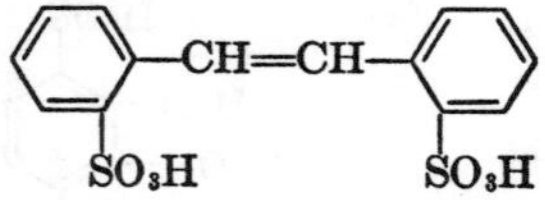	Cu$_2$O added.	69

Starting material	Product	Notes	Reference
H_2N — C≡C — NH_2 with SO_3H groups	SO_3H ... SO_3H (diphenylacetylene disulfonic acid)	Cu_2O added.	69
8-Aminonaphthalene-1,6-disulfonic acid	Naphthalene-1,6-disulfonic acid (41%)	Cu_2O added. Cu + HCOOH gave a better yield (58%).	132
N_2 benzoquinone with NO_2	NO_2 / OH (53%)		42, 43
N_2 naphthoquinone with NO_2	OH / NO_2 (58–64%)	Al powder added. Cu or Zn somewhat less effective. Replacement of ethanol by butyl alcohol lowers the yield considerably. HCOOH + Cu much inferior to Al + ethanol.	56
N_2 naphthoquinone with SO_3H	OH / SO_3H	Here ethanol alone is superior to ethanol + Al or Zn.	75

* References 143–195 appear on p. 323.

TABLE II—*Continued*

ETHANOL DEAMINATIONS

Amine	Product, Yield	Remarks	Reference[*]
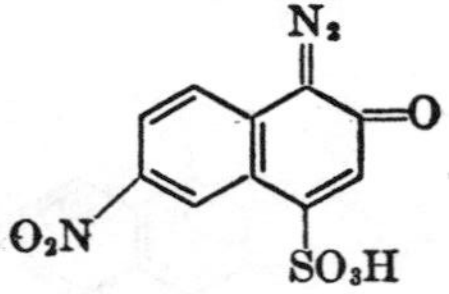	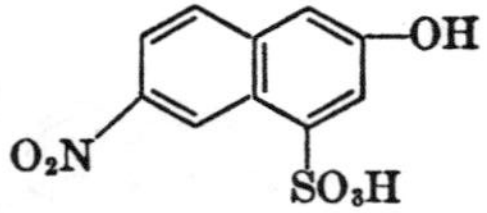 (*ca.* 90%)	Cu₂O added.	189
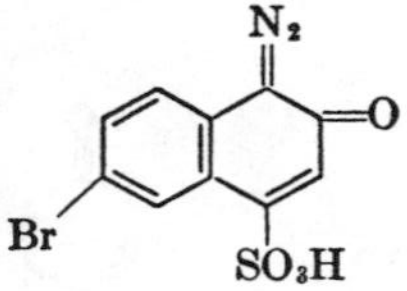	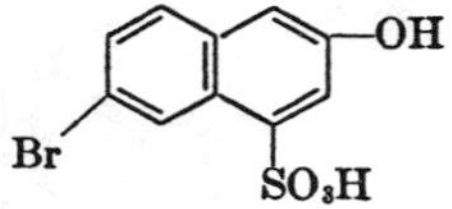 (*ca.* 50%)	Cu₂O added. 90% ethanol is used in preference to absolute alcohol.	44
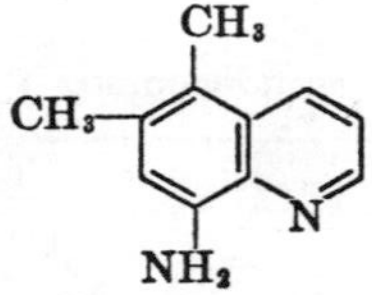	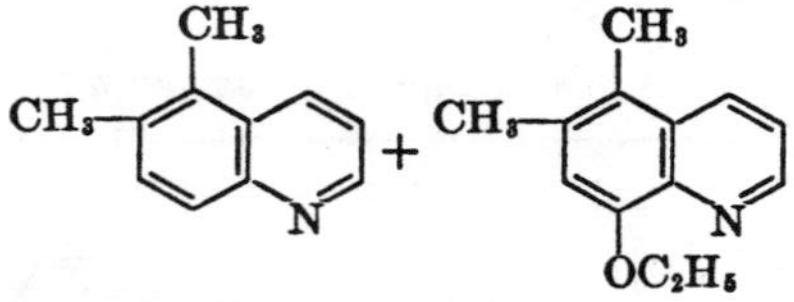		84

Reactant	Product	Notes	Ref.
(4-amino-3-bromoquinoline structure) NH_2, Br	(3-bromoquinoline structure) Br		190
(6-amino-3,5-dibromoquinoline structure) H_2N, Br	(3,5-dibromoquinoline structure) Br, Br — "Excellent yield"		191
(2-aminoacridine structure) NH_2	Acridine		192
(amino-nitro-dibenzofuran structure) O_2N, NH_2	(nitro-dibenzofuran structure) O_2N (43–64%)		193
p-Aminophenylarsonic acid	p-Ethoxyphenylarsonic acid (ca. 65%)	Na_2SnO_2 also fails. H_3PO_2 gives ca. 50% of deaminated product.	92
2-Amino-5-nitrophenylarsonic acid	m-Nitrophenylarsonic acid	Added Cu bronze.	194

* References 143–195 appear on p. 323.

TABLE II—*Continued*

ETHANOL DEAMINATIONS

Amine	Product, Yield	Remarks	Reference
2,5-Diaminophenylarsonic acid	m-Aminophenylarsonic acid	Only 1 mole of HNO_2 used. Cu added.	90
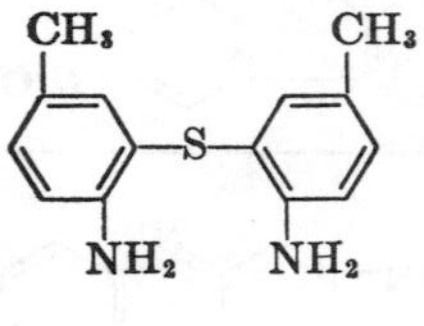 [structure: bis(methylphenyl) sulfide with two NH_2 groups, CH_3 substituents]	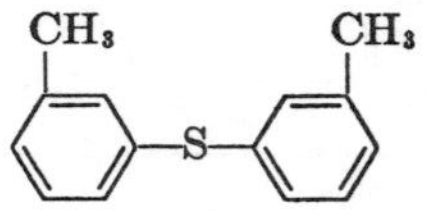 [structure: bis(methylphenyl) sulfide, CH_3 substituents] (18%)	Cu powder added.	140
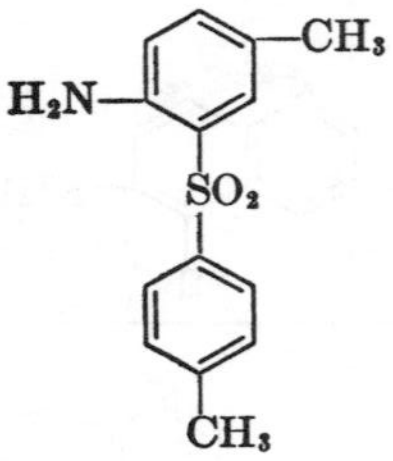 [structure: methylphenyl sulfone (SO_2) with H_2N and CH_3 groups, CH_3]	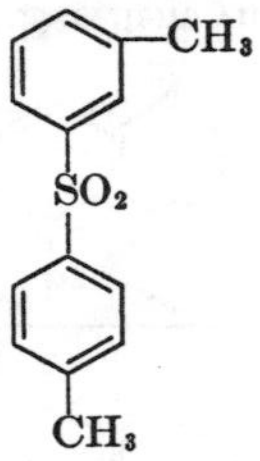 [structure: di(methylphenyl) sulfone, SO_2, CH_3 groups] "Very good yield"	$CuSO_4$ added.	70

195

CuSO₄ added.

143 Noelting, Witt, and Forel, *Ber.*, **18**, 2665 (1885).
144 O. Fischer, *Ann.*, **206**, 152 (1880).
145 E. and O. Fischer, *Ann.*, **194**, 270 (1878).
146 Remsen and Broun, *Am. Chem. J.*, **4**, 374 (1882).
147 Grüne, *Ber.*, **19**, 2303 (1886).
148 Möhlau, *Ber.*, **28**, 3099 (1895).
149 Beilstein and Kuhlberg, *Ann.*, **155**, 16 (1870).
150 Grevingk, *Ber.*, **17**, 2429 (1884).
151 Noyes, *Am. Chem. J.*, **20**, 800 (1898).
152 Brand and Eisenmenger, *J. prakt. Chem.*, [2] **87**, 498 (1913).
153 Staedel, *Ann.*, **217**, 197 (1883).
154 Crossley and Morrell, *J. Chem. Soc.*, **99**, 2349 (1911).
155 Meldola and Eyre, *Chem. News*, **83**, 285 (1901).
156 Reverdin and Bucky, *Ber.*, **39**, 2683 (1906).
157 Mascarelli and Vinsintin, *Gazz. chim. ital.*, **62**, 364 (1932).
158 Blakey and Scarborough, *J. Chem. Soc.*, **1927**, 3005.
159 Ruggli and Schmid, *Helv. Chim. Acta*, **18**, 1232 (1935).
160 Stoermer and Prigge, *Ann.*, **409**, 34 (1915).
161 Jackson and Lamar, *Am. Chem. J.*, **18**, 667 (1896).
162 Cain, *J. Chem. Soc.*, **85**, 7 (1904).
163 Feitler, *Z. physik. Chem.*, **4**, 75 (1889).
164 Wroblewsky, *Ann.*, **168**, 200 (1873).
165 Lampert, *J. prakt. Chem.*, [2] **33**, 375 (1886).
166 Wibaut, *Rec. trav. chim.*, **32**, 292 (1913).
167 Lobry de Bruyn, *Rec. trav. chim.*, **36**, 138 (1916).
168 Hurtley, *J. Chem. Soc.*, **79**, 1300 (1901).
169 Wroblewsky, *Ann.*, **192**, 203 (1878).

170 Case, *J. Am. Chem. Soc.*, **61**, 3489 (1939).
171 Claus and Jäck, *J. prakt. Chem.*, [2] **57**, 17 (1898).
172 Scholl, Eberle, and Tritsch, *Monatsh.*, **32**, 1055 (1911).
173 Wheeler and Johns, *Am. Chem. J.*, **43**, 406 (1910).
174 Wheeler, *Am. Chem. J.*, **44**, 138 (1910).
175 Zander, *Ann.*, **198**, 8 (1879).
176 Metcalf, *Am. Chem. J.*, **15**, 305 (1893).
177 Hayduck, *Ann.*, **172**, 215 (1874).
178 Hasse, *Ann.*, **230**, 293 (1885).
179 Junghahn, *Ber.*, **35**, 3762 (1902).
180 Widman, *Ber.*, **19**, 247 (1886).
181 Errera, *Gazz. chim. ital.*, **21**, 69, Part 1 (1891).
182 Zincke and Maue, *Ann.*, **339**, 215 (1905).
183 Claus and Bopp, *Ann.*, **265**, 98 (1891).
184 Paal, *Ber.*, **34**, 2754 (1901).
185 Boyle, *J. Chem. Soc.*, **95**, 1694 (1909).
186 Langfurth, *Ann.*, **191**, 193 (1878).
187 Griess, *Ber.*, **15**, 2186 (1882).
188 Limpricht, *Ann.*, **261**, 327 (1891).
189 Ruggli, Knapp, Merz, and Zimmermann, *Helv. Chim. Acta*, **12**, 1042 (1929).
190 Claus and Howitz, *J. prakt. Chem.*, [2] **50**, 238 (1894).
191 Claus and Schnell, *J. prakt. Chem.*, [2] **53**, 117 (1896).
192 Grandmougin and Smirous, *Ber.*, **46**, 3433 (1913).
193 Cullinane, *J. Chem. Soc.*, **1932**, 2367.
194 Bertheim and Benda, *Ber.*, **44**, 3299 (1911).
195 Witt and Truttwin, *Ber.*, **47**, 2794 (1914).

TABLE III

Hypophosphorous Acid Deaminations

Amine	Product, Yield	Remarks	Reference
Aniline	Benzene (60%) + biphenyl (small amount)	Na_2SnO_2 or alkaline HCHO also give 60% yield of benzene.	3, 13
Benzidine	Biphenyl (60%)	Ethanol gives an 80% yield of biphenyl.	3
β-Naphthylamine	Naphthalene (35-45%)	Ethanol gives a 7% yield of naphthalene.	82, 13
o-Toluidine	Toluene (70-75%, pure)	Must diazotize with HCl. If H_2SO_4 is used yield falls to 12-23%. Alkaline H_2CO gives pure toluene in 80% yield.	82, see p. 295
m-Toluidine	Toluene (51-62%, pure)	Diazotize with HCl. If H_2SO_4 is used yield is 5-12%.	82
p-Toluidine	Toluene (77-83%, pure)	Diazotize with HCl. If H_2SO_4 is used yield is 27-29%. Alkaline H_2CO gives an 80% yield of pure toluene.	82, 13, 3

3,3'-Dimethyl-4,4'-diaminobiphenyl (o-Tolidine) (biphenyl structure with NH_2 substituents)	3,3'-Dimethylbiphenyl (76–82%, pure)	Ethanol gives a 58% yield.	81, 80
(biphenyl structure with —NHCOCH₃)	(biphenyl structure with —NHCOCH₃)		94
2,5-Diaminotriptycene (p. 280)	Triptycene (40–45%, pure)	Must diazotize with sulfuric acid. Ethanol and sodium stannite fail here.	83, see p. 297
trans-o-Aminostilbene (p. 282)	trans-Stilbene (40–50%)	NaH_2PO_2 used.	66
cis-o-Aminostilbene (p. 282)	Phenanthrene (80%, pure)	NaH_2PO_2 used. Ethanol also fails here, a 64% yield of pure phenanthrene resulting.	66
o-(β-Phenylethyl)-aniline (p. 281)	Dibenzyl (47%)	NaH_2PO_2 used. Ethanol fails here, 9,10-dihydrophenanthrene being obtained in ca. 50% yield.	66
2-Hydroxy-4'-aminobiphenyl	2-Hydroxybiphenyl	"H_3PO_2 was the best of the various reducing agents tried."	94
3,3'-Dimethoxy-4,4'-diaminobiphenyl	3,3'-Dimethoxybiphenyl (66–78%, pure)	Ethanol gives a 12% yield of pure product.	80, 81

TABLE III—*Continued*

HYPOPHOSPHOROUS ACID DEAMINATIONS

Amine	Product, Yield	Remarks	Reference
(biphenyl with OCH₃, OCH₃ substituents and CH₃, CH₃ and H₂N—, —NH₂)	(biphenyl with OCH₃, OCH₃ and CH₃, CH₃) (80%, pure)		80
(phenyl—C-H=C-H with HOOC—C-H and —NH₂)	(phenyl—C-H=C-H with HOOC—C-H)	H_3PO_2 was the only reducing agent which succeeded.	93
(phenyl—C-H with H—C—COOH and —NH₂)	(phenyl—C-H with H—C—COOH)	H_3PO_2 was the only reducing agent which succeeded.	93
o-Nitroaniline	Nitrobenzene (75–80%, pure)	Ethanol gives nitrobenzene in *ca.* 82% yield.	82
m-Nitroaniline	Nitrobenzene (60–70%, pure)	Ethanol gives *ca.* 66% yield.	82
p-Nitroaniline	Nitrobenzene (55–60%, pure)	Ethanol gives a yield of *ca.* 70%.	82

Starting material	Product	Diazotize with H₂SO₄.	Reference
2,4,6-Trinitroaniline (picramide)	1,3,5-Trinitrobenzene (60–65%, pure)		83, see p. 296
1-Nitro-2-aminonaphthalene	1-Nitronaphthalene (61%, pure)	Must diazotize with H₂SO₄. When HCl is used get a 69% yield of 1-chloronaphthalene and but a trace of 1-nitronaphthalene.	83
[structure: toluene ring with CH₃, NH₂, NO₂]	[structure: CH₃ — ring — NO₂] (55–60%, pure)		82
[structure: CH₃ — ring with NH₂, O₂N]	[structure: CH₃ — ring — O₂N] (70–75%, pure)		82
[structure: CH₃ — ring with NO₂, NH₂]	[structure: CH₃ — ring — NO₂] (75–80%, pure)	Ethanol gives a 62–72% yield of pure product.	82, 84

TABLE III—*Continued*

HYPOPHOSPHOROUS ACID DEAMINATIONS

Amine	Product, Yield	Remarks	Reference*
OCH₃, NH₂, NO₂ (structure)	OCH₃ ... NO₂ (structure) (65-70%, pure)		82
3-Nitro-4'-aminobiphenyl	3-Nitrobiphenyl		196
2,4'-Diamino-4-nitrobiphenyl	4-Nitrobiphenyl		196
2',4-Diamino-3-nitrobiphenyl	3-Nitro-4-aminobiphenyl	Used only one mole HNO₂.	197
2,4'-Diamino-3',4-dinitrobiphenyl	3',4-Dinitrobiphenyl		196
2,2'-Dinitro-4-aminobiphenyl	2,2'-Dinitrobiphenyl		198
2,4-Dinitro-4'-aminobiphenyl	2,4-Dinitrobiphenyl		198
2-Amino-4,4'-dinitrobiphenyl	4,4'-Dinitrobiphenyl		198
2-Hydroxy-4-nitro-4'-aminobiphenyl	2-Hydroxy-4-nitrobiphenyl		196

Starting material	Product	Notes	Ref.
2,4-Dichloroaniline	m-Dichlorobenzene (50%)	Ethanol gives a 46% yield.	13
2-Nitro-4-chloroaniline	m-Nitrochlorobenzene (65–70%, pure)		82
2-Chloro-4-nitroaniline	m-Nitrochlorobenzene (65–70%, pure)		82
[structure: Cl, C=O, H₂N]	[structure: Cl, C=O] (85%, pure)		91, p. 295
2,4-Dibromoaniline	m-Dibromobenzene (73%)		13
2,5-Dibromoaniline	p-Dibromobenzene (69%)		13
2,6-Dibromoaniline	m-Dibromobenzene (49%)		13
2,4,6-Tribromoaniline	1,3,5-Tribromobenzene (70%, pure)	Ethanol gives 72–80% (pure).	13
3-Amino-6-bromotoluene	o-Bromotoluene (79%)		13
[structure: CH₃, Br, Br, H₂N]	[structure: CH₃, Br, Br] (65%)		13

* References 196–201 appear on p. 333.

TABLE III—*Continued*

HYPOPHOSPHOROUS ACID DEAMINATIONS

Amine	Product, Yield	Remarks	Reference*
[structure: toluene ring with Br, NH$_2$, Br substituents]	[structure: toluene ring with CH$_3$, Br, Br] (91%)		13
[structure: benzene ring with two C$_2$H$_5$ groups, NH$_2$, Br]	[structure: benzene ring with two C$_2$H$_5$ groups, Br] (70%, pure)		89
3-Amino-6-bromobenzoic acid	o-Bromobenzoic acid (75%)		13
1-Bromo-2,5-diamino triptycene (p. 280)	1-Bromotriptycene	Must diazotize with sulfuric acid.	83
3,4-Dibromo-4'-aminobiphenyl	3,4-Dibromobiphenyl		85
3,4-Dibromo-4',6-diaminobiphenyl	3,4-Dibromobiphenyl		85

3,4-Dibromo-2,4'-diaminobiphenyl	3,4-Dibromobiphenyl	85
3,3'5,5'-Tetrabromo-2,4'-diaminobiphenyl	3,3',5,5'-Tetrabromobiphenyl	85
3,4,4'-Tribromo-6-aminobiphenyl	3,4,4'-Tribromobiphenyl	85
2,3,4-Tribromo-4'-aminobiphenyl	2,3,4-Tribromobiphenyl	85
2-Amino-3,4-dibromo-4'-nitrobiphenyl	3,4-Dibromo-4'-nitrobiphenyl	85
2-Nitro-4,5-dibromo-4'-aminobiphenyl	2-Nitro-4,5-dibromobiphenyl	85
2,4'-Diiodo-5,5'-diaminobiphenyl	2,4'-Diiodobiphenyl	199
(8-amino-5-methylquinoline structure)	(5-methylquinoline structure) (72%, pure)	84
(8-amino-2,5-dimethylquinoline structure)	(2,5-dimethylquinoline structure) (60%, pure)	84

* References 196–201 appear on p. 333.

TABLE III—*Continued*

HYPOPHOSPHOROUS ACID DEAMINATIONS

Amine	Product, Yield	Remarks	Reference
			84
	(6%)	There is some evidence that the diazotization takes an abnormal course.	84
5-Amino-8-nitroisoquinoline (p. 279)	8-Chloroisoquinoline (60–70%)	Diazotized with HCl.	86

Amine	Product	Remarks	Ref.
(oxazole ring: N—CH, CH, O, C; C attached to phenyl bearing NH$_2$) 2-(o-Aminophenyl)-oxazole	(oxazole ring: N—CH, CH, O, C; C attached to phenyl) "Satisfactory yield" 2-phenyloxazole		200
2-(p-Aminophenyl)-oxazole	2-Phenyloxazole (34%, pure)		201
(benzene ring bearing NO$_2$ and NH$_2$; H$_3$C, H$_2$C—C—O)	(benzene ring bearing NO$_2$; H$_3$C, H$_2$C—C—O)	Stabilized diazonium salt procedure fails here.	101
p-Aminophenylarsonic acid	Phenylarsonic acid (ca. 50%)	Both Na$_2$SnO$_2$ and ethanol failed here.	92
3-Nitro-4-aminophenylarsonic acid	3-Nitrophenylarsonic acid (45%)		90

196 Finzi and Mangini, Gazz. chim. ital., 62, 671 (1932).
197 Finzi and Mangini, Gazz. chim. ital., 62, 1189 (1932).
198 Finzi and Bellavita, Gazz. chim. ital., 68, 85 (1938).
199 Finzi and Bellavita, Gazz. chim. ital., 64, 345 (1934).
200 Cass, J. Am. Chem. Soc., 64, 785 (1942).
201 Rosenbaum and Cass, J. Am. Chem. Soc., 64, 2444 (1942).

TABLE IV

ALKALINE FORMALDEHYDE DEAMINATIONS

Amine	Product, Yield	Remarks	Reference
Aniline	Benzene (60%)	Na_2SnO_2 or H_3PO_2 also give a 60% yield.	4
o-Toluidine	Toluene (80%)	H_3PO_2 gives 70–75%.	4
p-Toluidine	Toluene (80%)	H_3PO_2 gives 77–83%.	4
2,4-Dimethylaniline	m-Xylene (80%)		4
o-Anisidine	Anisole (75%)		4
p-Anisidine	Anisole (72%)		4
o-Ethoxyaniline	Phenetole (75%)		4
p-Ethoxyaniline	Phenetole (65%)		4
	Diphenyl ether (60%)		4
	Diphenyl ether (60%)		4

Starting material	Product	Notes	Ref.
[structure: o-aminodiphenyl ether with CH₃]	CH₃ [structure] (50%)		4
[structure: p-aminodiphenyl ether with CH₃, –NH₂]	CH₃ [structure] (54–60%)	Detailed directions on p. 297.	4
o-Aminobenzoic acid	Benzoic acid (25%)		4
o-Nitroaniline	Nitrobenzene (20%)	Ethanol gives ca. 82% nitrobenzene, H_3PO_2 75–80%.	4
m-Nitroaniline	Nitrobenzene (10%)	Ethanol gives ca. 66% nitrobenzene, H_3PO_2 60–70%.	4
p-Nitroaniline	Nitrobenzene (10%)	Ethanol gives ca. 70% nitrobenzene, H_3PO_2 55–60%.	4
o-Chloroaniline	Chlorobenzene (55%)		4
p-Chloroaniline	Chlorobenzene (50%)		4
2,5-Dichloroaniline	p-Dichlorobenzene (10%)		4

TABLE V

SODIUM STANNITE DEAMINATIONS

Amine	Product, Yield	Remarks	Reference[*]
Aniline	Benzene (60%), + azobenzene (*ca.* 10%) + phenol + phenyl azide + phenyl hydrazine	Alkaline H_2CO and H_3PO_2 also give a 60% yield of benzene.	13, 102, 107, 108, 109
α-Naphthylamine	Naphthalene		6
2,3-Dimethylaniline	o-Xylene "pure and in satisfactory yields"		103
2,4-Dimethylaniline	m-Xylene "pure and in satisfactory yields"		103
2,4,5-Trimethylaniline	1,2,4-Trimethylbenzene "pure and in satisfactory yields"		103
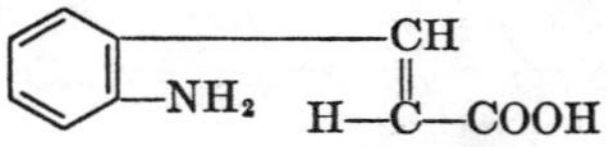	"Could not be deaminated"	Only H_3PO_2 succeeded.	93
3-Nitro-4-aminotoluene	"Unsuccessful"	H_3PO_2 gives 75–80% of m-nitrotoluene. With ethanol the yield is 62–72%.	106

Reactant	Product	Notes	Reference
(benzophenone with NO_2 and NH_2 groups)	(benzophenone with NO_2) (38%, pure)	"Amyl alcohol" and Cu powder give a 45% yield of pure product.	105
COOH, OH, Cl, OH, H_2N (substituted benzene)	COOH, OH, Cl, OH (substituted benzene)	K_2SnO_2 is actually used.	137
COOH, OH, Br, OH, H_2N (substituted benzene)	COOH, OH, Br, OH (substituted benzene)	K_2SnO_2 is actually used.	202
1,3-Dimethyl-4-amino-5-bromobenzene	1,3-Dimethyl-5-bromobenzene (73%, pure)	Detailed directions on p. 298.	104
Sulfanilic acid	Benzene sulfonic acid		6

* References 202 and 203 appear on p. 338.

TABLE V—*Continued*

SODIUM STANNITE DEAMINATIONS

Amine	Product, Yield	Remarks	Reference
(4-methylquinoline with H_2N)	CH_3 (*ca.* 35%)		203
p-Aminophenylarsonic acid	"Could not be deaminated"	H_3PO_2 is successful, *ca.* 50% yield.	92

[202] von Hemmelmayer, *Monatsh.*, **35**, 3 (1914).

[203] Koenigs, *Ber.*, **23**, 2672 (1890).

TABLE VI

DEAMINATIONS VIA THE HYDRAZINE

Amine	Product, Yield	Remarks	Reference[*]
Aniline	Benzene (45–75%) + biphenyl (very small amount)		110, 111, 116
p-Toluidine	Toluene (55–65%)		120, 116
2,4,5-Trimethylaniline	1,2,4-Trimethylbenzene	Na_2SnO_2 gives a pure product in "satisfactory yields."	7
2-Amino-5-chlorotoluene	m-Chlorotoluene (66%)	Ethanol gives a 49% yield of pure product.	117
4-Amino-3-chlorotoluene	m-Chlorotoluene (40%, pure)	Ethanol gives a 60% yield.	117
3,5-Dibromoaniline	m-Dibromobenzene		204
2-Amino-5-bromotoluene	m-Bromotoluene		205
4,4'-Diaminobiphenyl-2,2'-disulfonic acid	Biphenyl-2,2'-disulfonic acid		188
1-Aminonaphthalene-4,7-disulfonic acid	Naphthalene-2,5-disulfonic acid		206

* References 204–206 appear on p. 340.

TABLE VI—*Continued*

DEAMINATIONS VIA THE HYDRAZINE

Amine	Product, Yield	Remarks	Reference
![4-methyl-3-ethyl-7-aminoquinoline]	![4-methyl-3-ethylquinoline]		207
![2-chloro-4-methyl-7-aminoquinoline]	![2-chloro-4-methylquinoline]		208
![5-bromo-6-aminoquinoline]	![5-bromoquinoline] "Satisfactory yield"	Ethanol is not satisfactory here.	121

[204] Chattaway and Ellington, *J. Chem. Soc.*, **109**, 588 (1916).
[205] Chattaway and Hodgson, *J. Chem. Soc.*, **109**, 582 (1916).
[206] Armstrong and Wynne, *Proc. Chem. Soc.*, **6**, 17 (1890).

[207] Byvanck, *Ber.*, **31**, 2150 (1898).
[208] Besthorn and Byvanck, *Ber.*, **31**, 799 (1898).

CHAPTER 8

PERIODIC ACID OXIDATION

Ernest L. Jackson

National Institute of Health, U. S. Public Health Service

CONTENTS

THE NATURE OF THE REACTION

Periodic acid oxidation [1] is applicable to compounds having two hydroxyl groups or a hydroxyl and an amino group attached to adjacent carbon atoms and is characterized by the cleavage of the carbon-carbon bond, as illustrated by the following equations.

$$RCHOHCHOHR' + HIO_4 \rightarrow RCHO + R'CHO + H_2O + HIO_3$$

$$RCHOHCHNH_2R' + HIO_4 \rightarrow RCHO + R'CHO + NH_3 + HIO_3$$

[1] Periodic acid, as a reagent for glycols, was introduced in 1928; Malaprade (a) *Bull soc. chim.*, [4] **43**, 683 (1928); (b) *Compt. rend.*, **186**, 382 (1928).

If the hydroxyl groups or a hydroxyl and an amino group are not attached to contiguous carbon atoms no oxidation takes place.[2] This selectivity, which is the outstanding characteristic of periodic acid oxidation, adapts the reaction to testing for the presence of contiguous hydroxyl groups [3] and hydroxyl and amino groups.

Carbonyl compounds in which the carbonyl group is adjacent to a second carbonyl or hydroxyl group are oxidized also. Thus, α-ketols,[2b, 4, 5] α-diketones,[4] and α-ketonic aldehydes [4] react as illustrated by the following equations.

$$CH_2OHCOCH_2OH + HIO_4 \rightarrow HCHO + CH_2OHCOOH + HIO_3$$

$$CH_3COCHOHCH_3 + HIO_4 \rightarrow CH_3CHO + CH_3COOH + HIO_3$$

$$C_6H_5COCHOHC_6H_5 + HIO_4 \rightarrow C_6H_5CHO + C_6H_5COOH + HIO_3$$

$$CH_3COCOCH_3 + HIO_4 + H_2O \rightarrow 2CH_3COOH + HIO_3$$

$$CH_3COCHO + HIO_4 + H_2O \rightarrow CH_3COOH + HCOOH + HIO_3$$

Oxidation of carbonyl compounds was interpreted by Malaprade [6] as conforming to the α-glycol type by the assumption that the reaction proceeds through the hydrated form of the carbonyl group, $>C(OH)_2$. This hypothesis is useful in interpreting the results of the oxidation of some complex compounds, intermediates of the type $RCHOHCHO$ being oxidized like the α-glycols.

Concerning the mechanism of the periodic acid oxidation of α-glycols, the suggestion has been made,[7, 8] through analogy with lead tetraacetate oxidation, that the splitting of the carbon chain results from a series of three reactions, the first being the esterification of a hydroxyl group by paraperiodic acid (H_5IO_6 or $HIO_4 \cdot 2H_2O$).

[2] The discovery that the reaction of glycols is limited to 1,2-diols was made by Fleury; (a) Fleury and Courtois, Compt. rend., 209, 219 (1939); (b) Fleury and Lange, ibid., 195, 1395 (1932); (c) Fleury and Paris, ibid., 196, 1416 (1933); (d) Fleury and Paris, J. pharm. chim., [8] 18, 470 (1933); see also (e) Bailly, Compt. rend., 206, 1902 (1938); (f) Bailly and Gaumé, Bull. soc. chim., [5] 2, 354 (1935); (g) Yokoyama, J. Agr. Chem. Soc. Japan, 15, 499 (1939) [C. A., 33, 8570 (1939)].

[3] For an example of the use of the reaction as a test see Marvel and Denoon, J. Am Chem. Soc., 60, 1045 (1938).

[4] Clutterbuck and Reuter, J. Chem. Soc., 1935, 1467.

[5] Fleury and Lange, J. pharm. chim., [8] 17, 409 (1933).

[6] Malaprade, Bull. soc. chim., [5] 1, 833 (1934).

[7] Criegee, Sitzber. Ges. Beförder. ges. Naturw. Marburg, 69, 25 (1934) [C A., 29, 6820 (1935)].

[8] Criegee, Kraft, and Rank, Ann., 507, 159 (1933).

$$(a) \quad \begin{array}{c} | \\ -COH \\ | \\ -COH \\ | \end{array} + H_5IO_6 \rightarrow \begin{array}{c} | \\ -COIO_5H_4 \\ | \\ -COH \\ | \end{array} + H_2O$$

$$(b) \quad \begin{array}{c} | \\ -COIO_5H_4 \\ | \\ -COH \\ | \end{array} \rightarrow \begin{array}{c} | \\ -CO \\ \diagdown \\ -CO \diagup \\ | \end{array}\!\!\!IO_4H_3 + H_2O$$

$$(c) \quad \begin{array}{c} | \\ -CO \\ \diagdown \\ -CC \diagup \\ | \end{array}\!\!\!IO_4H_3 \rightarrow 2 \diagup\!\!C{=}O + H_2O + HIO_3$$

This mechanism has been considered [9, 10] in relation to the rates of the periodate oxidation of *cis*- and *trans*-glycols, and in connection with the effect of the pH of the reaction solution on the rates of oxidation of ethylene glycol, pinacol, and *cis*- and *trans*-cyclohexene glycols.

In reactive compounds containing the amino-alcohol structure, the amino group may be primary or secondary.[11, 12, 13] The reaction has not yet been tested extensively on compounds possessing a secondary or tertiary amino group. Oxidation would be expected to occur generally in the case of secondary amino derivatives, $-CH(OH)-CH(NHR)-$, but tertiary amino compounds, $-CH(OH)-CH(NR_2)-$, should not react. In agreement with this view, diethanolamine, $HN(CH_2CH_2OH)_2$, has been oxidized to produce four moles of formic acid, whereas di-ethylaminoethanol, $(C_2H_5)_2NCH_2CH_2OH$, showed virtually no reaction. Acyl derivatives [11, 14, 15] of serine have been reported to react extremely slowly, a result which suggests that acylated derivatives, $-CH(OH)-CH(NHCOR)-$, generally are substantially stable in the presence of periodic acid.

Oxidation has been reported to occur with a number of compounds which contain nitrogen but possess no α-amino-alcohol structure.[11, 13, 16] Thus, cystine, methionine, and tryptophan are oxidized, though without

[9] Price and Knell, *J. Am. Chem. Soc.*, **64**, 552 (1942).
[10] Price and Kroll, *J. Am. Chem. Soc.*, **60**, 2726 (1938).
[11] Nicolet and Shinn, *J. Am. Chem. Soc.*, **61**, 1615 (1939).
[12] Shinn and Nicolet, *J. Biol. Chem.*, **138**, 91 (1941).
[13] Van Slyke, Hiller, MacFadyen, Hastings, and Klemperer, *J. Biol Chem.*, **133**, 287 (1940).
[14] Nicolet and Shinn, *J. Biol. Chem.*, **142**, 139 (1942).
[15] Posternak and Pollaczek, *Helv. Chim. Acta*, **24**, 1190 (1941).
[16] Van Slyke, Hiller, and MacFadyen, *J. Biol. Chem.*, **141**, 681 (1941).

the production of ammonia. The reaction with cystine and methionine apparently is due to oxidation of the sulfur. Glycine, alanine, tyrosine, histidine, aspartic acid, asparagine, and glutamic acid also react,[11, 17] but at a markedly slower rate than compounds having the α-amino-alcohol structure. The data now available are insufficient to establish the nature of these reactions.

Periodic acid oxidation of α-glycols or α-amino alcohols containing the structure $CH_2OHCHOH-$, $CH_2OHCHNH_2-$, or $CH_2OHCHNHR-$ converts the terminal primary alcohol group into formaldehyde. Similarly, acetaldehyde results from the oxidation of compounds having the groupings $CH_3CHOHCHOH-$, $CH_3CHOHCHNHR-$, or $CH_3CHNHRCHOH-$, where R is H or a substituent other than acyl.[18] Since the oxidation reactions are quantitative, certain analytical procedures [12, 18, 19, 20, 21] have been based on the determination of the aldehyde produced in the reaction. Such analytical data also have afforded useful evidence on the structure of the reacting compound. The estimation of the formic acid derived from the oxidation of secondary alcohol groups in certain types of compounds also has provided procedures for analysis as well as evidence on constitution.

Oxidation of compounds of the types thus far discussed proceeds readily at room temperature. Certain compounds which show no substantial reaction with periodic acid at room temperature can be oxidized at elevated temperature.[22, 23, 24, 25] Thus, at 100° in aqueous solution the acetone molecule is split to produce acetic acid and formaldehyde; diethyl ketone yields propionic acid and probably ethanol; lactic acid gives acetaldehyde and carbon dioxide; acetaldehyde is oxidized to formic acid and methanol, which is converted into formaldehyde; and pyruvic acid yields acetic acid and carbon dioxide.

<h3 style="text-align:center">THE SCOPE OF THE REACTION</h3>

Although the widely applicable reaction has gained recognition chiefly through its use in analysis and determination of constitution, many compounds have been prepared for the first time by this method; some of them are available at the present time only through this type of oxidation. The reaction also has provided an improved method for

[17] Martin and Synge, *Biochem. J.*, **35**, 294 (1941).
[18] Nicolet and Shinn, *J. Am. Chem. Soc.*, **63**, 1456 (1941).
[19] Nicolet and Shinn, *J. Am. Chem. Soc.*, **63**, 1486 (1941).
[20] Nicolet and Shinn, *J. Biol. Chem.*, **139**, 687 (1941).
[21] Reeves, *J. Am. Chem. Soc.*, **63**, 1476 (1941).
[22] Fleury and Boisson, *Compt. rend.*, **208**, 1509 (1939).
[23] Fleury and Boisson, *J. pharm. chim.*, [8] **30**, 145 (1939).
[24] Fleury and Boisson, *J. pharm. chim.*, [8] **30**, 307 (1939).
[25] Fleury and Boisson, *Compt. rend.*, **204**, 1264 (1937).

the preparation of some compounds that usually have been obtained in other ways. An advantage in most periodic acid oxidations is the absence of side reactions and the consequent high yield. A disadvantage for large-scale operation is the relative expense of the reagent.

The more common oxidizing agents, such as permanganate and nitric acid, usually cannot be substituted for periodic acid, since they are not selective in their action. Also these reagents oxidize many of the compounds obtained as products of periodic acid oxidation. Only Criegee's reagent, lead tetraacetate,[7, 26, 27, 28, 29, 30, 31, 32] has thus far had sufficiently extensive and successful application to merit consideration as a substitute for periodic acid. Other reagents, such as manganic acetate, cobaltic acetate, thallic acetate, and ceric sulfate, have been reported [8] to oxidize α-glycols in the same manner as lead tetraacetate, but they are inferior to that oxidizing agent. The same cleavage of the carbon chain as produced by periodic acid resulted from the reaction of barium hypobromite [33, 34, 35] with α-methyl-D-mannopyranoside

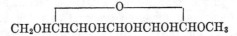

$$\overset{\displaystyle \lceil \text{———O———} \rceil}{\text{CH}_2\text{OHCHCHCHOHCHOHCHOHCHOCH}_3}$$

but the product that was isolated was a carboxyl derivative

$$\overset{\displaystyle \lceil \text{———O———} \rceil}{\text{CH}_2\text{OHCHCHCOOH   HOOCCHOCH}_3}$$

instead of the corresponding dialdehyde which was obtained by periodic acid oxidation. Also the yield was markedly lower with barium hypobromite than with periodic acid, since the reaction of the former was not limited to the α-glycol group in the mannoside molecule.

Periodic acid and lead tetraacetate react similarly with simple α-glycols, and the rate of oxidation by each reagent is more rapid for *cis*-than for *trans*-glycols. The two oxidants, however, manifest a marked difference in their action upon α-hydroxy acids and upon oxalic acid. Lead tetraacetate readily oxidizes α-hydroxy acids, as well as oxalic acid, at room temperature. Periodic acid, on the other hand, does not react with oxalic acid and oxidizes α-hydroxy acids only slowly even at

[26] Baer, *J. Am. Chem. Soc.*, **62**, 1597 (1940).
[27] Criegee, *Angew. Chem.*, **50**, 153 (1937).
[28] Criegee, *Angew. Chem.*, **53**, 321 (1940).
[29] Criegee, *Ann.*, **495**, 211 (1932).
[30] Criegee, *Ber.*, **64**, 260 (1931).
[31] Criegee, *Ber.*, **65**, 1770 (1932).
[32] Karrer and Hirohata, *Helv. Chim. Acta*, **16**, 959 (1933).
[33] Jackson and Hudson, *J. Am. Chem. Soc.*, **58**, 378 (1936).
[34] Jackson and Hudson, *J. Am. Chem. Soc.*, **59**, 994 (1937).
[35] Bergmann and Wolff, *Ber.*, **56**, 1060 (1923).

elevated temperature. The molecule of tartaric acid,[2b, 36, 37] for example, is split as an α-glycol rapidly and quantitatively at room temperature by periodic acid, to form glyoxylic acid, while lead tetraacetate cleaves the carbon-carbon bonds in two ways: (a) as an α-glycol and (b) as an α-hydroxy acid. The two reagents differ also with respect to the kind of solvent in which they function best. Water is the most suitable solvent for periodic acid oxidation. Lead tetraacetate, since it is hydrolyzed by water, is best adapted to organic solvents, such as glacial acetic acid, benzene, chloroform, nitrobenzene, and di- and tetra-chloroethane. Oxidation with lead tetraacetate, however, can be carried out in the presence of water;[38, 39, 40] a mixture of water and acetic acid is suitable, provided that the rate of oxidative cleavage of the glycol exceeds the velocity of hydrolysis of lead tetraacetate. The use of organic solvents in periodic acid oxidation will be discussed later. Further comparison of the two reagents may be found in the literature.[7, 28, 32]

Since the oxidation of simple polyhydroxy alcohols, $CH_2OH(CHOH)_n$-CH_2OH, results in the complete degradation of the molecule, the reaction with these compounds has no preparative value, although it has analytical uses, as for the determination of ethylene glycol,[41] glycerol,[41, 42, 43, 44, 45] erythritol,[44] mannitol,[46, 47, 48, 49] and sorbitol.[47, 48, 49] Inositol,[37, 50] a cyclic polyhydroxy compound, is oxidized quantitatively to formic acid. The complete degradation of the molecule in these polyhydroxy alcohols is prevented by appropriate substitution of the hydrogen atom of one or more hydroxyl groups. The α-monoethers or α-monoesters of glycerol, for example, are oxidized to ethers or esters of glycolaldehyde.[51, 52]

$$ROCH_2CHOHCH_2OH \rightarrow ROCH_2CHO + HCHO$$

[36] Fleury and Bon-Bernatets, J. pharm. chim., [8] 23, 85 (1936).

[37] Fleury and Lange, J. pharm. chim., [8] 17, 313 (1933).

[38] Baer, Grosheintz, and Fischer, J. Am. Chem. Soc., 61, 2607 (1939).

[39] Grosheintz, J. Am. Chem. Soc., 61, 3379 (1939).

[40] Criegee and Büchner, Ber., 73, 563 (1940).

[41] Allen, Charbonnier, and Coleman, Ind. Eng. Chem., Anal. Ed., 12, 384 (1940).

[42] Fleury and Fatome, Ann. Fermentations, 1, 285 (1935).

[43] Fleury and Fatome, J. pharm. chim., [8] 21, 247 (1935).

[44] Malaprade, Bull. soc. chim., [5] 4, 906 (1937).

[45] Voris, Ellis, and Maynard, J. Biol. Chem., 133, 491 (1940).

[46] Fleury and Courtois, Ann. chim. anal. chim. appl., 23, 117 (1941) [C. A., 35, 6214 (1941)].

[47] Joly, J. pharm. chim., [8] 25, 457 (1937).

[48] Rappaport and Reifer, Mikrochim. Acta, 2, 273 (1937).

[49] Rappaport, Reifer, and Weinmann, Mikrochim. Acta, 1, 290 (1937).

[50] Fleury and Joly, J. pharm. chim., [8] 26, 341, 397 (1937).

[51] Palfray, Halasz, and Rovira, Compt. rend., 210, 765 (1940).

[52] Palfray and Sabetay, Bull. soc. chim., [5] 4, 950 (1937).

A convenient method for the determination of α-glycerophosphoric acid [2c-e, 53, 54] alone or mixed with β-glycerophosphoric acid is based upon oxidation by periodic acid. In some cases it is possible to protect selected portions of the molecule by substituents which can be removed subsequent to cleavage of the carbon chain at the desired point. This is illustrated by the periodic acid oxidation of 4,5-monoacetone-D-galactose dimethylacetal [55] (I) to produce 2,3-monoacetone-D-threose (II) and glyoxal dimethylacetal (III), one of the α-glycol groups being masked by the easily hydrolyzed isopropylidene group. Similar protection of an α-glycol group was necessary in the oxidative cleavage of the ring of the shikimic acid derivative (IV). [56, 57]

$$
\begin{array}{ccc}
\text{HC}\begin{array}{l}\diagup\text{OCH}_3\\\diagdown\text{OCH}_3\end{array} & & \\
| & & \\
\text{HCOH} & & \\
| & & \\
\text{HOCH} & \text{CHO} & \\
| & | & \\
\text{OCH} & \text{OCH} & \text{HC}\begin{array}{l}\diagup\text{OCH}_3\\\diagdown\text{OCH}_3\end{array} \\
\overset{\llcorner|}{}\text{---}\text{C(CH}_3)_2 & \overset{\llcorner|}{}\text{---}\text{C(CH}_3)_2 & | \\
\text{HCO}\diagup & \text{HCO}\diagup & \text{CHO} \\
| & | & \\
\text{CH}_2\text{OH} & \text{CH}_2\text{OH} & \\
\text{I} & \text{II} & \text{III}
\end{array}
$$

$$
\begin{array}{ccc}
& \text{COOH} & \text{COOH} \\
& | & | \\
& \text{C}{=}\text{O} & \text{C}{=}\text{O} \\
& | & | \\
\text{COOH} & \text{HCH} & \text{HCH} \\
| & | & | \\
\text{HO---C} & \text{HOCH} & \text{---OCH} \\
\diagup\ \diagdown & | & | \\
\text{HOCH}\quad\text{HCH} & \text{HCO}\diagdown & \text{HCO}\diagdown \\
| \qquad | & |\quad\text{C(CH}_3)_2 & |\quad\text{C(CH}_3)_2 \\
\text{O---CH}\quad\text{HCOH} & \text{HCO}\diagup & \text{HCO}\diagup \\
\text{(CH}_3)_2\text{C}\diagdown\qquad\diagup & | & | \\
\text{O---------CH} & \text{HC}{=}\text{O} & \text{---COH} \\
& & \text{H} \\
\text{IV} & \text{V} &
\end{array}
$$

IV $\rightarrow$ V $\rightleftarrows$

[53] Gulland and Hobday, *J. Chem. Soc.*, **1940**, 752.
[54] Pyman and Stevenson, *J. Chem. Soc.*, **1934**, 448.
[55] Pacsu, Trister, and Green, *J. Am. Chem. Soc.*, **61**, 2444 (1939).
[56] Fischer and Dangschat, *Helv. Chim. Acta*, **17**, 1200 (1934).
[57] Fischer and Dangschat, *Helv. Chim. Acta*, **20**, 705 (1937).

If the α-glycol or other reactive group forms the side chain of a non-reactive ring, the type of product resulting from periodic acid oxidation varies with the structure of the side chain. The diversity of cyclic derivatives accessible in this way is apparent from the following examples of oxidations that have actually been accomplished. The oxidation of 3,5-dihydroxy-2-carboxybenzoyl methyl ketone[4] (VI) produced 3,5-dihydroxyphthalic acid (VII). In the periodic acid oxidation of the pregnene derivative VIII, which has a reactive hydroxyl group attached to carbon atom 17 of the ring, the side chain was degraded completely to

yield the cyclic ketone IX.[58] Oxidation of X, the side chain of which is an α-ketol instead of an α-glycol as in VIII, yielded the α-hydroxy acid XI.[59] In the case of XII the product was the α-ketol XIII,[60, 61] which was formed through reaction with the hydroxyl groups at carbon atoms 20 and 21. The course of the reaction is thus preferential to the production of a cyclic ketone by way of the pair of hydroxyl groups attached to carbon atoms 17 and 20. By the reaction of one molecular equivalent

[58] Reichstein, *Helv. Chim. Acta*, **20**, 978 (1937).

[59] Reichstein, Meystre, and v. Euw, *Helv. Chim. Acta*, **22**, 1107 (1939).

[60] v. Euw and Reichstein, *Helv. Chim. Acta*, **24**, 418 (1941).

[61] Fuchs and Reichstein, *Helv. Chim. Acta*, **24**, 804 (1941).

of periodic acid with XIV the α-hydroxyaldehyde XV has been prepared [62, 63] in 65% yield. The preparation of this unusual type of product, only a few examples of which have been reported, must be carried out under selected conditions, since α-hydroxy-aldehydes are oxidized by periodic acid; XV yields the cyclic ketone XVI.[63] With increasing aromatic substitution the α-glycol molecule is reported [7, 28] to become less reactive toward periodic acid; diphenylacenaphthenediol (XVII), for example, does not react.[7]

Polyhydroxy acids are split in the characteristic way by periodic acid. Gluconic and saccharic acids, like tartaric acid, yield glyoxylic acid.[2b, 37]

$$CH_2OH(CHOH)_4COOH + 4HIO_4 \rightarrow$$

$$OCHCOOH + HCHO + 3HCOOH + H_2O + 4HIO_3$$

$$HOOC(CHOH)_4COOH + 3HIO_4 \rightarrow$$

$$2OCHCOOH + 2HCOOH + H_2O + 3HIO_3$$

[62] Prins and Reichstein, *Helv. Chim. Acta*, **24**, 396 (1941).
[63] Prins and Reichstein, *Helv. Chim. Acta*, **24**, 945 (1941).

Since etherification of one or more of the alcohol groups arrests the degradation process, the oxidation of 2,3-dimethylmannosaccharic acid (XVIII)[64, 65] yields besides glyoxylic acid the dimethoxyaldehydo acid (XIX). Lactones react like substituted hydroxy acids, provided that the lactone ring is sufficiently stable to resist hydrolysis during the oxidation reaction. Thus, the carbon chain of the 3,6-monolactone (XX) of D-saccharic acid [66, 67] is cleaved between carbon atoms 4 and 5 to yield XXI, which is an ester of glyoxylic acid with L-threuronic acid (XXII). The hydrolysis of XXI and subsequent oxidation of the products with calcium hypobromite produced in high yield D-tartaric acid (XXIII) and oxalic acid.

$$
\begin{array}{ccc}
\text{COOH} & & \text{COOH} \\
| & & | \\
\text{H}_3\text{COCH} & & \text{HCOH} \\
| & & | \\
\text{H}_3\text{COCH} & \text{COOH} & \text{—CH} \\
| & | & | \\
\text{HCOH} & \text{H}_3\text{COCH} & \text{HCOH} \\
| & | & | \\
\text{HCOH} & \text{H}_3\text{COCH} & \text{HCOH} \\
| & | & | \\
\text{COOH} & \text{H—C}=\text{O} & \text{—C}=\text{O} \\
\text{XVIII} & \text{XIX} & \text{XX}
\end{array}
$$

$$
\begin{array}{ccc}
\text{COOH} & & \\
| & & \\
\text{HCOH} & & \\
| & & \\
\text{—CH} & \text{COOH} & \text{COOH} \\
| & | & | \\
\text{H—C}=\text{O} & \text{HCOH} & \text{HCOH} \\
| & | & | \\
\text{H—C}=\text{O} & \text{HOCH} & \text{HOCH} \\
| & | & | \\
\text{—C}=\text{O} & \text{H—C}=\text{O} & \text{COOH} \\
\text{XXI} & \text{XXII} & \text{XXIII}
\end{array}
$$

Periodic acid has proved to be a useful reagent for the analysis of certain *vic.*-hydroxyamino acids. Since the oxidation produces one mole of ammonia the determination of the ammonia generated provides a

[64] Hirst, Jones, and Jones, *J. Chem. Soc.*, **1939**, 1880.
[65] Hirst, Jones, and Jones, *Nature*, **143**, 857 (1939).
[66] Reeves, *J. Am. Chem. Soc.*, **61**, 664 (1939).
[67] Schmidt and Günthert, *Ber.*, **71**, 493 (1938).

simple method for the quantitative estimation [15-17, 68-73] of these acids in the presence of other types of amino acids. Methods for the determination of serine [17, 20] and threonine [12, 17, 74, 75] are based on the estimation of the formaldehyde or acetaldehyde resulting from periodate oxidation.

$$CH_2OHCHNH_2COOH + NaIO_4 \rightarrow$$

$$HCHO + OCHCOOH + NH_3 + NaIO_3$$

$$CH_3CHOHCHNH_2COOH + NaIO_4 \rightarrow$$

$$CH_3CHO + OCHCOOH + NH_3 + NaIO_3$$

Procedures have thus been provided for the determination of serine and threonine in protein hydrolysates [14-17, 74-81] and of the hydroxyamino acids of insulin.[19]

Among the sugars and their glycosidic derivatives, periodic acid oxidation has had many important applications. Glucose,[2b, 5, 6, 46, 49, 82-84] galactose,[49, 82, 85] and mannose [82] produce one mole of formaldehyde and five moles of formic acid per mole of aldohexose. The methylpentoses yield acetaldehyde and formic acid. Since the degradation of the molecule is complete, the reaction is limited to analytical applications. The estimation of the acetaldehyde or formaldehyde generated by periodate oxidation has provided methods for the determination of methylpentoses [18] in the presence of pentoses and hexoses, and of primary alcohol groups [21, 84, 86] in carbohydrates. The reaction with the ketose fructose follows two courses: [2b, 5, 6, 48, 85, 87, 88] one (a) (like that of

[68] Christensen, Edwards, and Piersma, *J. Biol. Chem.*, **141**, 187 (1941).
[69] Folch and Schneider, *J. Biol. Chem.*, **137**, 51 (1941).
[70] Hotchkiss, *J. Biol. Chem.*, **141**, 171 (1941).
[71] Lowndes, Macara, and Plimmer, *Biochem. J.*, **35**, 315 (1941).
[72] Macara and Plimmer, *Biochem. J.*, **34**, 1431 (1940).
[73] Stein, Moore, and Bergmann, *J. Biol. Chem.*, **139**, 481 (1941).
[74] Martin and Synge, *Nature*, **146**, 491 (1940).
[75] Winnick, *J. Biol. Chem.*, **142**, 461 (1942).
[76] Borchers, Totter, and Berg, *J. Biol. Chem.*, **142**, 697 (1942).
[77] Brown, *J. Biol. Chem.*, **142**, 299 (1942).
[78] Nicolet and Saidel, *J. Biol. Chem.*, **139**, 477 (1941).
[79] Nicolet and Shinn, *J. Biol. Chem.*, **140**, 685 (1941).
[80] Nicolet and Shinn, *Proc. Am. Soc. Biol. Chem., J. Biol. Chem.*, **140**, xcviii (1941).
[81] Nicolet, Shinn, and Saidel, *J. Biol. Chem.*, **142**, 609 (1942).
[82] Hérissey, Fleury, and Joly, *J. pharm. chim.*, [8] **20**, 149 (1934).
[83] Karrer and Pfaehler, *Helv. Chim. Acta*, **17**, 363 (1934).
[84] Karrer and Pfaehler, *Helv. Chim. Acta*, **17**, 766 (1934).
[85] Khouvine and Arragon, *Compt. rend.*, **212**, 167 (1941) [*C. A.*, **36**, 1018 (1942)].
[86] Ariyama and Kitasato, *J. Biochem. Japan*, **25**, 357 (1937) [*C. A.*, **31**, 5396 (1937)].
[87] Fleury, *Mikrochemie*, **25**, 263 (1938).
[88] Rappaport, *Mikrochemie*, **25**, 265 (1938).

dihydroxyacetone) to yield glycolic acid, and the other (b) (like that of tartaric acid) to yield glyoxylic acid; reaction (a) predominates.

(a) $CH_2OH(CHOH)_3COCH_2OH + 4HIO_4 \rightarrow$

$$HCHO + 3HCOOH + CH_2OHCOOH + 4HIO_3$$

(b) $CH_2OH(CHOH)_3COCH_2OH + 4HIO_4 \rightarrow$

$$2HCHO + 2HCOOH + OCHCOOH + H_2O + 4HIO_3$$

Periodic acid oxidation of non-glycosidic derivatives of the aldoses yields various products, the identity of which depends upon the nature of the substituent and its position in the molecule. 5,6-Dimethyl-glucose,[89] for example, gives dimethylglyceraldehyde. Glucose phenyl-osazone (XXIV)[84] yields an unusual type of product, 1-phenyl-4-benzeneazo-5-pyrazolone (XXVI), which apparently is derived by further oxidation of the expected three-carbon atom cleavage product (XXV).

$$
\begin{array}{ccc}
\begin{array}{l}
HC{=}N{-}NHC_6H_5 \\
\;\;| \\
C{=}N{-}NHC_6H_5 \\
\;\;| \\
HOCH \\
\;\;| \\
HCOH \\
\;\;| \\
HCOH \\
\;\;| \\
CH_2OH \\
\;\;\;\text{XXIV}
\end{array}
&
\rightarrow
\begin{bmatrix}
HC{=}N{-}NHC_6H_5 \\
\;\;| \\
C{=}N{-}NHC_6H_5 \\
\;\;| \\
HC{=}O
\end{bmatrix}
\rightarrow
&
\begin{array}{l}
\;\;\;\;\;\;\;\;\;\;C_6H_5 \\
\;\;\;\;\;\;\;\;\;\;N \\
O{=}C\;\;\;\;\;\;N \\
\;\;\;|\;\;\;\;\;\;\;\| \\
C_6H_5HN{-}N{=}C{-}{-}CH \\
\;\;\;\text{XXVI}
\end{array} \\
\text{XXIV} & \text{XXV} &
\end{array}
$$

Many compounds of types not otherwise available are accessible through application of the cleavage type of oxidation to the glycosidic derivatives of the sugars. Periodic acid oxidation is applicable to glycosides [34, 82, 84, 90, 91] of various groups of sugars, as shown by the following equations.

$$
\overset{\boxed{\quad\quad O \quad\quad}}{CH_2OHCH(CHOH)_3CHOCH_3} + 2HIO_4 \rightarrow
$$

Methylaldohexopyranoside

$$
\overset{\boxed{\quad\quad O \quad\quad}}{CH_2OHCHCHCHO \;\; OHCCHOCH_3} + HCOOH + H_2O + 2HIO_3
$$

Dialdehyde

[89] Salmon and Powell, *J. Am. Chem. Soc.*, **61**, 3507 (1939).
[90] Jackson and Hudson, *J. Am. Chem. Soc.*, **61**, 1530 (1939).
[91] Pacsu, *J. Am. Chem. Soc.*, **61**, 2669 (1939).

$$\overset{\lceil\quad\quad O\quad\quad\rceil}{CH_2(CHOH)_3CHOCH_3} + 2HIO_4 \rightarrow$$
Methylaldopentopyranoside

$$\overset{\lceil\quad\quad\quad O\quad\quad\quad\rceil}{CH_2CHO\ \ OHCCHOCH_3} + HCOOH + H_2O + 2HIO_3$$
Dialdehyde

$$\overset{\lceil\quad\quad O\quad\quad\rceil}{CH_2OHCH(CHOH)_2CHOCH_3} + HIO_4 \rightarrow$$
Methylaldopentofuranoside

$$\overset{\lceil\quad\quad\quad O\quad\quad\quad\rceil}{CH_2OHCHCHO\ \ OHCCHOCH_3} + H_2O + HIO_3$$
Dialdehyde

$$\overset{\lceil\quad\quad O\quad\quad\rceil}{CH_2(CHOH)_3C(OCH_3)CH_2OH} + 2HIO_4 \rightarrow$$
Methylketohexopyranoside

$$\overset{\lceil\quad\quad O\quad\quad\rceil}{CH_2CHO\ \ OHCC(OCH_3)CH_2OH} + HCOOH + H_2O + 2HIO_3$$
Dialdehyde

It will be noted that the oxidation of a methylaldohexopyranoside removes all the asymmetric carbon atoms from the molecule except carbon atoms 1 and 5, and oxidation of a pentopyranoside eliminates all except carbon atom 1. Consequently, only two products can be obtained from the periodic acid oxidation of the sixteen possible methyl-D-aldohexopyranosides. One of these (XXVIII) is the product from the eight α-methyl-D-aldohexopyranosides, and the other (XXXI) is derived from the eight β-methyl-D-aldohexopyranosides, as illustrated by the oxidation of α-methyl-D-glucopyranoside (XXVII) and β-methyl-D-glucopyranoside (XXX). The methylpentopyranosides (see table) can yield only two products, XXXIII from the α-methyl-D-pentopyranosides, and its optical antipode (XXXV) from the β-methyl-D-pentopyranosides.[34, 39] The same dialdehydes should result from oxidation of the methyl-D-aldopentofuranosides as from the methyl-D-aldohexopyranosides; the preparation of XXVIII from α-methyl-D-arabinofuranoside actually has been accomplished.[34] Although the product of the oxidation of a methylketohexopyranoside has not been isolated, indirect evidence has been obtained for the formation of the dialdehyde shown in the above equation from α-methyl-L-sorbopyranoside.[91]

```
   H     OCH₃        H     OCH₃         H     OCH₃
    \   /             \   /              \   /
     C                 C                  C
     |                 |               ┌──│──────┐
   HCOH              O=C─H             │ O─C=O   │
     |                 |               │ │  │    │
   HOCH   O    →       │   O   → Sr   │  │  │   O
     |   │           O=C─H   │        │ └─O─C=O │
   HCOH  │             │     │        │          │
     |   │            HC─────┘        HC─────────┘
    HC───┘             |                |
     |                CH₂OH            CH₂OH
    CH₂OH              XXVIII           XXIX
    XXVII
```

```
  H₃CO      H        H₃CO      H        H₃CO      H
     \     /            \     /            \     /
      C                  C                  C
      |                  |              ┌───│──────┐
    HCOH               O=C─H            │  O─C=O   │
      |                  |              │  │  │     │
    HOCH   O   →         │   O  → Ba   │  │  │    O
      |   │            O=C─H  │         │  └─O─C=O │
    HCOH  │              |    │         │           │
      |   │            HC─────┘         HC──────────┘
     HC───┘             |                 |
      |                CH₂OH             CH₂OH
     CH₂OH              XXXI              XXXII
     XXX
```

```
  H     OCH₃        H     OCH₃       H₃CO      H        H₃CO      H
   \   /             \   /              \     /            \     /
    C                 C                  C                  C
    |              ┌──│──────┐           |              ┌───│──────┐
  O=C─H           │  O─C=O   │         O=C─H            │  O─C=O   │
    |             │  │  │     │           |             │  │  │     │
    │   O    Sr   │  │  │    O            │   O   Sr   │  │  │    O
  O=C─H  │        │  └─O─C=O │          O=C─H  │        │  └─O─C=O │
    |    │        │           │           |    │        │           │
   CH₂───┘       CH₂──────────┘          CH₂───┘       CH₂──────────┘
  XXXIII         XXXIV                  XXXV           XXXVI
```

The methylaldohexomethylopyranosides [34, 92] (see table), which have a hydrogen atom in place of the hydroxyl group at carbon atom 6 of the corresponding methylaldohexopyranoside molecule, have yielded four dialdehydes: XXXVII, XXXVIII, XXXIX, and XL.

[92] Maclay, Hann, and Hudson, *J. Am. Chem. Soc.*, **61**, 1660 (1939).

$$
\begin{array}{cccc}
\text{H}_3\text{CO} \quad \text{H} & \text{H} \quad \text{OCH}_3 & \text{H}_3\text{CO} \quad \text{H} & \text{H} \quad \text{OCH}_3 \\
\text{C} & \text{C} & \text{C} & \text{C} \\
\text{H—C}=\text{O} & \text{O}=\text{C—H} & \text{O}=\text{C—H} & \text{H—C}=\text{O} \\
\text{O} & & & \text{O} \\
\text{H—C}=\text{O} & \text{O}=\text{C—H} & \text{O}=\text{C—H} & \text{H—C}=\text{O} \\
\text{CH} & \text{HC} & \text{HC} & \text{CH} \\
\text{CH}_3 & \text{CH}_3 & \text{CH}_3 & \text{CH}_3 \\
\text{XXXVII} & \text{XXXVIII} & \text{XXXIX} & \text{XL}
\end{array}
$$

Although the methylglycosides predominate among the examples, the possibility of applying the reaction to other glycosides with various alkyl or cyclic groups in place of the methyl group should be noted. Also a variety of products is possible from the oxidation of glycosides appropriately substituted at the alcohol groups.

Periodic acid oxidation of the glycosides proceeds quantitatively, and the dialdehydes produced can be isolated in high yields. With the exception of the four crystalline dialdehydes from the methylaldohexomethylopyranosides the products have been obtained as syrups. By virtue of their aldehydic structure they are capable of yielding a variety of derivatives. A number of crystalline strontium and barium salts,[34] illustrated by formulas XXIX, XXXII, XXXIV, and XXXVI, have been prepared in good yields by oxidation of the dialdehydes with bromine water kept neutral with the appropriate metallic carbonate. The dibasic acids derived from these salts, it will be noted, are acetals and consequently are readily hydrolyzed. From the products of hydrolysis have been prepared glycolic,[34] D-glyceric,[34] and D- and L-lactic acids,[92] the identity of the product depending upon the glycoside subjected to oxidation. The reaction thus provides the best way at the present time for the preparation in pure condition of the stereoisomeric glyceric and lactic acids.

The principles outlined for the periodic acid oxidation of the methylglycosides apply also to the oxidation of other classes of carbohydrates having the glycosidic type of structure. N-Acetyl-D-glucosylamine (XLI) is oxidized to XLII;[93] levoglucosan (XLIII), an example of the sugar anhydrides, yields XLIV;[94] α,α-trehalose (XLV), a non-reducing disaccharide, gives XLVI;[90] the galacturonide unit of polygalacturonide methyl ester (XLVII or XLVIII) from citrus pectin produces XLIX or L;[95] alginic acid, which is composed of the β-D-mannuronic acid units,

[93] Niemann and Hays, J. Am. Chem. Soc., 62, 2960 (1940).
[94] Jackson and Hudson, J. Am. Chem. Soc., 62, 958 (1940).
[95] Levene and Kreider, J. Biol. Chem., 120, 591 (1937).

LI or LII, yields the polymeric dialdehyde (LIII or LIV); [96] and starch, the molecule of which is built principally of the unit LV, produces oxidized starch, the chief unit of which is LVI.[97, 98] With the exception of

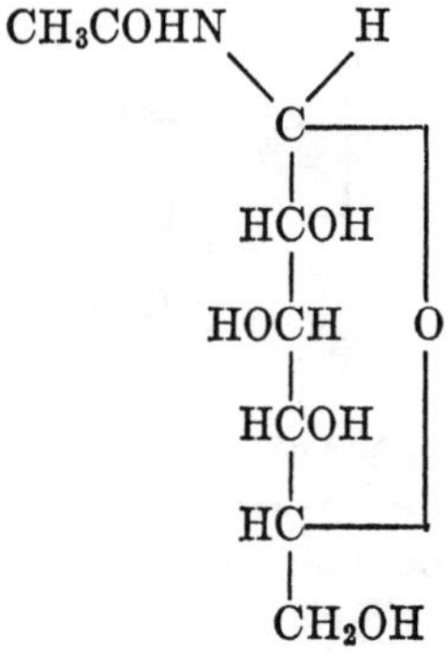

XLI 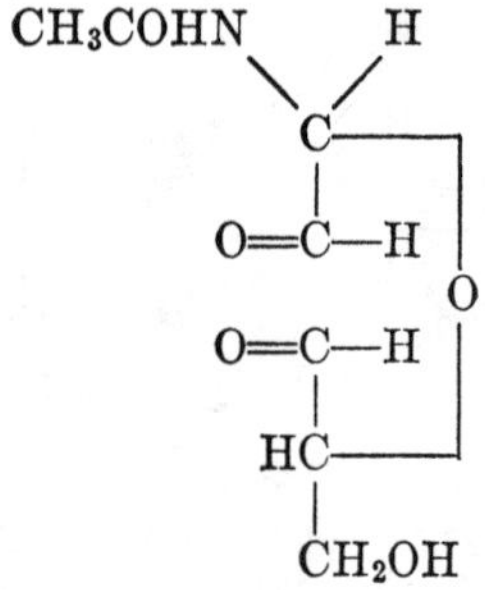 XLII 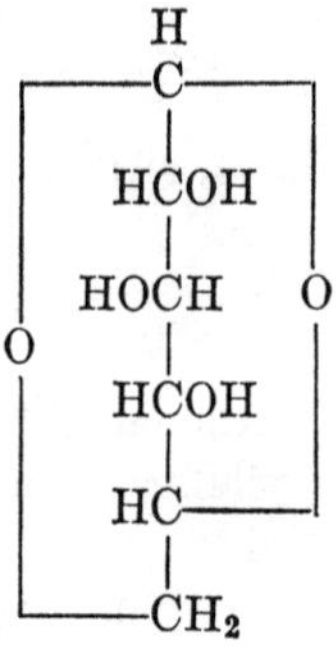 XLIII

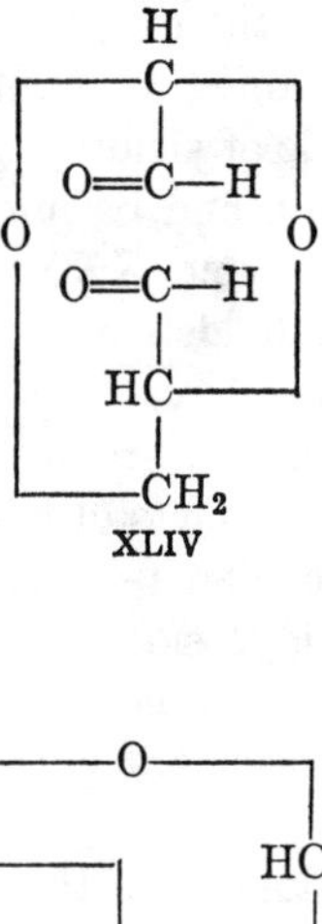

XLIV 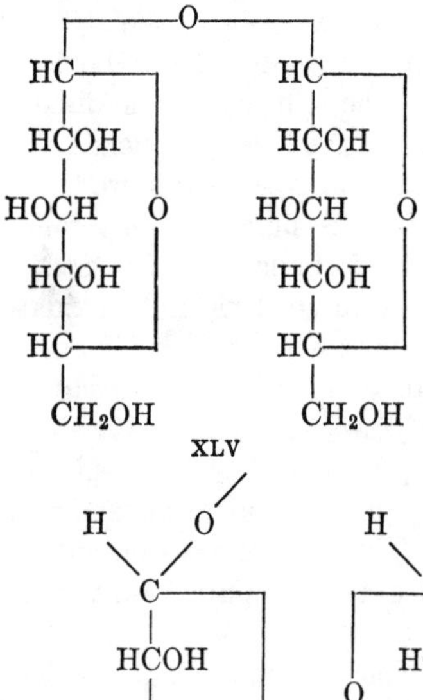 XLV

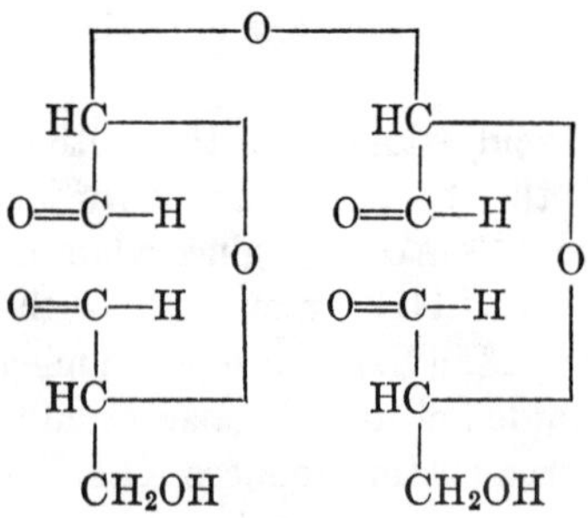

XLVI 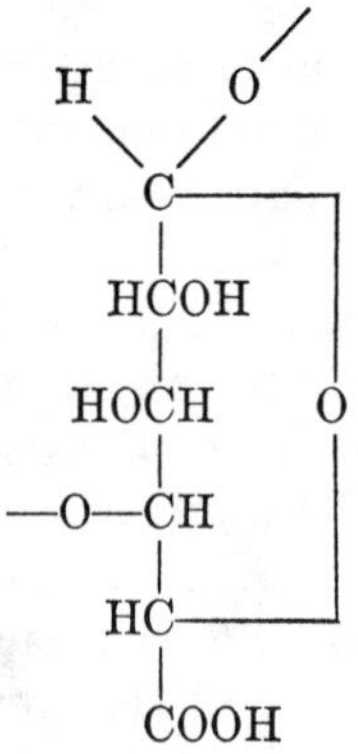 XLVII 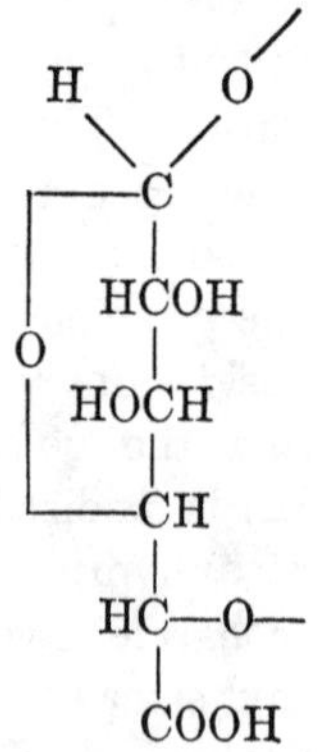 XLVIII

[96] Lucas and Stewart, *J. Am. Chem. Soc.*, **62**, 1792 (1940).
[97] Jackson and Hudson, *J. Am. Chem. Soc.*, **59**, 2049 (1937).
[98] Jackson and Hudson, *J. Am. Chem. Soc.*, **60**, 989 (1938).

```
   H   O /        H   O /      O \   H        O \   H
     \ /            \ /          \ /            \ /
      C────          C────        C────          C────
      |             |            |              |
  O=C—H        H—C=O           HOCH            HOCH
      |         O   |            |              |        O
  O=C—H   O       H—C=O           HOCH    O       HOCH
      |             |            |              |
 —O—CH           ——CH           HC—O—          HC────
      |             |            |              |
  HC────          HC—O—          HC────          HC—O—
      |             |            |              |
  COOH            COOH          COOH           COOH
  XLIX              L             LI             LII
```

```
  O \   H        O \   H        H   O /        H   O /
    \ /            \ /            \ /            \ /
     C────          C────          C────          C────
     |             |              |              |
 O=C—H         O=C—H           HCOH          O=C—H
     |             |        O     |              |
 O=C—H   O       O=C—H           HOCH    O       O=C—H   O
     |             |              |              |
 HC—O—           HC────          HC—O—          HC—O—
     |             |              |              |
 HC────          HC—O—           HC────          HC────
     |             |              |              |
 COOH            COOH           CH2OH          CH2OH
 LIII             LIV             LV             LVI
```

the product from N-acetyl-D-glucosylamine, for which no data are available, and the dialdehyde and corresponding dibasic acid from levoglucosan, which are exceptionally resistant to acid hydrolysis, these oxidation derivatives are known to yield simpler scission products through hydrolysis, preferably after oxidation by hypobromite. Thus, the oxidation product from α,α-trehalose yielded D-glyceric acid; the derivative of polygalacturonide methyl ester produced L-tartaric acid; the polymeric dialdehyde from alginic acid gave mesotartaric acid; and oxidized starch yielded D-erythronic acid.

EXPERIMENTAL CONDITIONS

Important considerations in carrying out periodate oxidations are the choice between periodic acid and a suitable salt of the acid as the oxidant, and the selection of the solvent and the temperature.

Crystalline paraperiodic acid, H_5IO_6, which is hygroscopic and readily soluble in water, is commercially available. Most of the salts of periodic acid are characterized by their slight solubility in water. For oxidation experiments sodium metaperiodate, $NaIO_4$, is the most suitable salt because of its solubility in water (9.3% at 20° and 12.6% at 25°).[99] Sodium metaperiodate is commercially available and also can be obtained readily from the slightly soluble trisodium paraperiodate, $Na_3H_2IO_6$, by crystallization from nitric acid in the ratio of 150 cc. of water and 45 cc. of concentrated nitric acid to 100 g. of salt.[99] Trisodium paraperiodate is formed in 90% yield by the reaction of bromine and sodium iodide in aqueous sodium hydroxide solution at 80°.[100] It is also produced in 80% yield by the oxidation of sodium iodate with chlorine in aqueous sodium hydroxide solution.[99] In connection with this preparation of trisodium paraperiodate from sodium iodate, it should be noted that in the usual periodate oxidation reactions the periodate is converted quantitatively into iodate. Paraperiodic acid has been prepared in about 93% yield from trisodium paraperiodate; [99, 100] it has been prepared also by the electrolytic oxidation [101, 102] of iodic acid.

An aqueous solution of periodic acid free from metals can be prepared from commercial potassium metaperiodate; this salt can be converted in high yield to the slightly soluble barium dimesoperiodate, $Ba_2I_2O_9$, which through reaction with an equivalent amount of sulfuric acid yields a solution of pure periodic acid.[34]

Solutions of periodic acid and of sodium metaperiodate in water are quite stable at room temperature. The periodate content is readily determined by titrating, with standard sodium arsenite solution, the iodine liberated from iodide in neutral solution.[49, 103–107] Periodate also may be determined accurately in the presence of iodate, since in neutral solution periodate is reduced by iodide to iodate. The reaction in the presence of a boric acid-borax buffer is shown by the following equation.

$$NaIO_4 + 2NaI + 4H_3BO_3 \rightarrow NaIO_3 + I_2 + Na_2B_4O_7 + 6H_2O$$

Oxidation by sodium metaperiodate resembles that by periodic acid except with regard to the rate.[6] The salt, a dilute aqueous solution of

[99] Hill, J. Am. Chem. Soc., 50, 2678 (1928).
[100] Lange and Paris, J. pharm. chim., [8] 21, 403 (1935).
[101] Hickling and Richards, J. Chem. Soc., 1940, 256.
[102] Willard and Ralston, Trans. Electrochem. Soc., 62, 239 (1932).
[103] Fleury and Lange, J. pharm. chim., [8] 17, 107 (1933).
[104] Fleury and Lange, J. pharm. chim., [8] 17, 196 (1933).
[105] Willard and Greathouse, J. Am. Chem. Soc., 60, 2869 (1938).
[106] Müller and Friedberger, Ber., 35, 2655 (1902).
[107] Müller and Weglin, Z. anal. Chem., 52, 758 (1913).

which has a pH near 4.0, is used instead of periodic acid in applications to α-glycol derivatives that show extreme ease of hydrolysis by acids.[55, 108] Oxidation by sodium metaperiodate is preferable when the formic acid [44, 90] generated in the oxidation reaction is to be determined as the increase in the acidity of the reaction solution. Oxidations also have been carried out with an aqueous solution of trisodium paraperiodate buffered to pH 4.2 with acetic acid.[109-113] In analytical applications involving the determination of the acetaldehyde generated in the periodate oxidation of threonine [12, 17, 74, 75] and the methylpentoses,[18, 21] the reaction is carried out in the presence of excess sodium bicarbonate. For the estimation of the ammonia produced in the periodate oxidation of α-amino alcohols the oxidation solution is kept alkaline with sodium hydroxide of selected concentration.[13, 16] With an excess of free periodic acid the reaction with hydroxylysine and serine was slow and incomplete but proceeded rapidly to completion in the presence of excess sodium bicarbonate.[16]

An aqueous solution of sulfuric acid and a salt of periodic acid, trisodium paraperiodate, or one of the potassium periodates, has been used frequently as a substitute for pure periodic acid. When the product of the oxidation reaction is to be isolated, the effect of the presence of metal ions on the yield should be considered. If the product is volatile or slightly soluble, or is isolated either as a slightly soluble derivative or by extraction with organic solvents, the presence of metal ions should not reduce the yield. In the case of certain methylhexosides [34] which were oxidized by periodic acid formed from potassium metaperiodate and an equivalent of sulfuric acid in aqueous solution, the presence of potassium ions was found to cause a low yield of the crystalline strontium salt prepared by the strontium hypobromite oxidation of the dialdehyde resulting from the periodic acid reaction. Oxidation by pure periodic acid, a solution of which is prepared either from crystalline paraperiodic acid or by the previously mentioned method from potassium metaperiodate, is desirable when the presence of difficultly removed metal ions affects the yield adversely.

Periodate oxidations usually are carried out in aqueous solution at or below room temperature. Although water is the solvent commonly employed, it is emphasized that periodate oxidation is not limited to water-soluble compounds. Starch, starch formate, and cellulose, sus-

[108] Hann, Maclay, and Hudson, *J. Am. Chem. Soc.*, **61**, 2432 (1939).
[109] Grangaard, Michell, and Purves, *J. Am. Chem. Soc.*, **61**, 1290 (1939).
[110] Mahoney and Purves, *J. Am. Chem. Soc.*, **64**, 9 (1942).
[111] Mahoney and Purves, *J. Am. Chem. Soc.*, **64**, 15 (1942).
[112] Michell and Purves, *J. Am. Chem. Soc.*, **64**, 585 (1942).
[113] Michell and Purves, *J. Am. Chem. Soc.*, **64**, 589 (1942).

pended in aqueous periodic acid solution, have been oxidized [97, 98, 114] at room temperature, the heterogeneous reaction in the case of starch being substantially complete within a few hours. An emulsifying agent [52] was employed in the oxidation of the α-benzyl ether of glycerol. A mixture of water and ethanol was a successful solvent in the oxidation of 9,10-dihydroxystearic acid,[115] glucose phenylosazone,[84] and other compounds.[4, 116, 117] Mixtures of water with acetic acid,[7, 32] dioxane,[61, 118-120] and methanol [58] also have been used, the proportion of organic solvent in some instances exceeding 90% of the mixture. t-Butyl alcohol and a mixture of ethanol and ethyl acetate (ethanol being more resistant to oxidation by periodic acid when mixed with ethyl acetate) have been suggested as possible solvents.[121]

The consumption of the oxidant in periodate reactions is determined readily by means of the arsenite method. This analytical procedure also provides a convenient method for establishing the completion of the reaction. In the oxidation of optically active compounds the end of the reaction usually can be determined by observing the time when the rotation of the reaction solution becomes constant.

Usually the oxidation products are substantially stable in the presence of periodate and iodate, the excess of the periodate preferably being small. An example of a somewhat reactive product is glyoxylic acid, which results from the periodic acid oxidation of certain polyhydroxy acids. Glyoxylic acid is oxidized [36] by periodic acid to formic acid and carbon dioxide, but the rate of the reaction at room temperature is exceedingly slow compared with the rate of its formation from the polyhydroxy acids. Formic acid and formaldehyde, though oxidized by periodic acid only slowly at room temperature, show appreciable reaction in the course of a number of hours.[122] The reaction solution normally shows no color change due to liberation of iodine, the formation of which indicates the presence of a substance capable of reducing the iodine compounds beyond the iodate stage. The development of iodine color in some cases, however, may not affect materially the preparation of the normal oxidation product.[89]

The procedure for the isolation of the various kinds of oxidation products must be adapted to the properties of the particular substances.

[114] Gottlieb, Caldwell, and Hixon, J. Am. Chem. Soc., 62, 3342 (1940).
[115] King, J. Chem. Soc., 1938, 1826.
[116] King, J. Chem. Soc., 1936, 1788.
[117] Mason, Myers, and Kendall, J. Biol. Chem., 116, 267 (1936).
[118] v. Euw and Reichstein, Helv. Chim. Acta, 23, 1114 (1940).
[119] v. Euw and Reichstein, Helv. Chim. Acta, 24, 401 (1941).
[120] v. Euw and Reichstein, Helv. Chim. Acta, 24, 1140 (1941).
[121] Willard and Boyle, Ind. Eng. Chem., Anal. Ed., 13, 137 (1941).
[122] Davidson, J. Textile Inst., 29, T195 (1938); 31, T81 (1940); 32, T25, T109 (1941)

As already pointed out, some of the products of periodate oxidation, especially the mixed acetals from the glycosidic derivatives of the sugars, are readily hydrolyzed by acids. Although the known compounds of this type are stable in dilute aqueous solution of iodic acid at room temperature, heating the acid solution would be expected to cause hydrolysis. Before isolation of these oxidation products, the reaction solution customarily is neutralized to a pH of 8-9. Barium hydroxide and strontium hydroxide have proved to be advantageous bases for neutralization of the reaction solution, since iodate and excess periodate are largely removed at the same time as the slightly soluble barium or strontium salts. Silver acetate and hydriodic acid also have been used to remove iodic acid.[123]

EXPERIMENTAL PROCEDURES

Preparation of an Aqueous Solution of Periodic Acid. Aqueous solutions of periodic acid prepared from commercial paraperiodic acid frequently deposit a small precipitate upon standing at room temperature. If this occurs, the solution should be kept for twenty-four hours and filtered before analysis and use in oxidation experiments. When this procedure is followed, a concentration near 0.54 M is usually found by analysis for a solution prepared with 124.5 g. of crystalline paraperiodic acid per liter of solution at 20°.

Analysis for Periodic Acid.[103-105] Standard 0.1 N sodium arsenite solution containing 20 g. of sodium bicarbonate per liter and 0.1 N iodine solution are required.

The sample of periodic acid solution, 5 cc. for approximately 0.2 M or 2 cc. for 0.5 M solution, is diluted with water to about 10 cc. The solution is neutralized with sodium bicarbonate, 1.5 g. of the solid or its equivalent as a saturated aqueous solution being required. An excess (25 cc.) of 0.1 N sodium arsenite solution is added, then 1 cc. of 20% aqueous solution of potassium iodide. After being kept at room temperature for ten to fifteen minutes, the excess of sodium arsenite is titrated in the usual way with 0.1 N iodine solution. The concentration of the periodic acid solution is calculated from the amount of sodium arsenite consumed: 1 cc. of 0.1 N sodium arsenite solution is equivalent to 0.0095965 g. of HIO_4 or 0.010696 g. of $NaIO_4$.

The same procedure is used for the analysis of oxidation solutions where excess periodate is to be determined in the presence of iodate.

Oxidation of Methylglycosides.[34] The following directions for the oxidation of α-methyl-D-glucopyranoside apply generally to the methylpyranosides of the aldohexoses and aldopentoses.

[123] Fischer and Dangschat, *Helv. Chim. Acta*, **17**, 1196 (1934).

A solution of 12.5 g. of pure α-methyl-D-glucopyranoside (XXVII) in distilled water is added to 250 cc. of 0.54 M aqueous periodic acid solution (2.1 molecular equivalents). The solution, after being diluted with water to 500 cc., is kept at 20–25° for about twenty-four hours. If desired, the excess periodic acid can be determined by the arsenite method. The rotation of the reaction solution should correspond to $[\alpha]_D^{20} = +121°$ calculated for the dialdehyde XXVIII. The solution is neutralized to phenolphthalein with hot strontium hydroxide solution with care to avoid any excess. The precipitate of strontium iodate and strontium periodate is filtered and washed with cold water. After the addition of 1 g. of strontium carbonate, the solution is concentrated in vacuum with the water bath at 50° to a volume of about 50 cc., filtered to remove strontium carbonate, and the concentration (bath, 40°) continued to dryness. The residue is extracted six times with 25-cc. portions of cold absolute ethanol, which separates the dialdehyde completely from slightly soluble strontium salts, as shown by the lack of optical activity of an aqueous solution of these salts. The dialdehyde XXVIII is recovered from the ethanol solution as a colorless syrup in quantitative yield by distillation of the solvent in vacuum with the bath at 40–45°.

Oxidation of N-Acetyl-D-glucosylamine.[93] Six grams (0.027 mole) of N-acetyl-D-glucosylamine (XLI) in 100 cc. of water is added to 18.5 g. (0.081 mole) of paraperiodic acid in 100 cc. of water, and the reaction mixture is maintained at 25° for four and one-half hours, which is known from analytical data obtained in small-scale experiments to be sufficient time for completion of the reaction with the consumption of two moles of the oxidant. The solution is exactly neutralized with barium hydroxide, the precipitate removed, and the filtrate evaporated to dryness in vacuum. The solid is extracted with 100 cc. of absolute ethanol, the ethanol extract evaporated to dryness, the residue taken up in ethanol, and the solution is centrifuged and again evaporated to dryness. The product, the dialdehyde XLII, can be converted into the corresponding barium salt (see reference 93).

Oxidation of Alginic Acid.[96] Fifteen grams (0.085 equivalent) of dried alginic acid (LI or LII) is stirred vigorously with 425 cc. of 0.380 M periodic acid solution until peptized, which requires about one and one-half hours. The mixture is kept at room temperature for twenty to twenty-four hours, during which time periodic acid is reduced (1.1 mole per equivalent of alginic acid). The oxidation proceeds comparatively rapidly during the first two hours. Addition of 1600 cc. of t-butyl alcohol throws down an amorphous precipitate. This is centrifuged down and washed four times with 50-cc. portions of aqueous t-butyl alcohol

(1 part of the alcohol to 3 of water). After being dried at 30 mm. over sulfuric acid, the resulting fluffy white residue, which corresponds to reaction product LIII or LIV, weighs 13 g. This material is easily peptized when added to water, and the aqueous solution reduces Fehling's solution; $[\alpha]_D^{25} = +36.7°$ $(c, 0.3\%)$.

Oxidation of 9,10-Dihydroxystearic Acid.[115] The Use of Aqueous Ethanol as the Solvent. A solution of 6 g. of potassium periodate in 300 cc. of N sulfuric acid at 20° is added rapidly to a solution of 8 g. of 9,10-dihydroxystearic acid (m.p. 132°) in 400 cc. of alcohol at 40°. After ten minutes the clear solution is cooled to 15° and diluted with sufficient water to dissolve the precipitated potassium sulfate. Extraction with ether gives an oily product, which is submitted to steam distillation. Extraction of the distillate with ether yields 3.2 g., or 89%, of pure pelargonaldehyde as a colorless oil boiling at 76–77° (11 mm.).

The aqueous solution (about 180 cc.) of non-volatile products from the steam distillation is cooled to room temperature, filtered to remove a little insoluble material, and then cooled in ice water. The somewhat impure azelaic half aldehyde (3.33 g., or 76%) which separates is collected, dried, and extracted with 400 cc. of boiling light petroleum (b.p. 40–60°) in which all but 0.5 g., identified as the trimer of the aldehyde acid, dissolves. When the petroleum solution is cooled in ice-salt mixture, the semialdehyde separates as plates which, after several recrystallizations from 50 parts of warm water, yields 1.5 g. of pure azelaic aldehyde acid as colorless rhombic plates melting at 38°.

Oxidation of Starch.[97, 98, 114] Oxidation in Aqueous Suspension. Ten grams of cornstarch or potato starch, previously dried at 100° for about twenty hours, is suspended in 290 cc. of 0.533 M aqueous periodic acid solution. After being shaken thoroughly, the mixture is kept at 20–25° for twenty-four hours. About one mole of periodic acid per $C_6H_{10}O_5$ unit of starch reacts to yield oxidized starch (LVI). The product is filtered, washed free from iodic acid and excess periodic acid with cold water, and dried at 40–50°. The yield is quantitative. Over 99% of the substance dissolves in forty parts of water at 100° during two hours; $[\alpha]_D^{20} = +9°$.

Sodium metaperiodate can be substituted for periodic acid as the oxidant.

Oxidation of the α-Benzyl Ether of Glycerol.[52] The Use of an Emulsifying Agent. A mixture of 10 g. of the α-benzyl ether of glycerol, 15 g. of potassium metaperiodate, 6.6 g. of sulfuric acid, 2 g. of Gardinol, $CH_3(CH_2)_{11}OSO_3Na$, and 200 cc. of water is shaken mechanically at room temperature for thirty minutes and then extracted with ether.

The ether extract is washed thoroughly with sodium bicarbonate solution, the solvent evaporated, and the residue distilled in vacuum. The benzyloxyacetaldehyde thus obtained boils at 115°/15 mm.

Degradation of the Side Chain of Δ^4-Pregnene-11,17,20,21-tetrol-3-one (VIII) by Periodic Acid Oxidation.[58] **Small-Scale Oxidation.** To a solution of 25 mg. of Δ^4-pregnene-11,17,20,21-tetrol-3-one in 1.5 cc. of methanol is added a solution of 40 mg. of periodic acid in 0.3 cc. of water. After twenty hours the solution is diluted with water and freed from methanol in vacuum. The residue is extracted with ethyl acetate and ether. The extract is washed with water and sodium carbonate solution, and then dried over anhydrous sodium sulfate. The crystalline neutral product, obtained by evaporation of the solvent, is recrystallized from ether, then sublimed at 160° and 0.01 mm., and finally recrystallized from a mixture of ether and pentane. The yield of hygroscopic, fine needles of Δ^4-androstene-11-ol-3,17-dione (IX) melting at 189–191° (cor.) is 12 mg., or 60%.

SURVEY OF PERIODIC ACID OXIDATIONS REPORTED IN THE LITERATURE

Most of the compounds that had been reported (before March, 1942) to show cleavage oxidation by periodic acid are recorded in the table; the substances are listed alphabetically in the following groups of related compounds: (1) carbocyclic compounds; (2) carbohydrates; (3) α-diketones and α-ketols; (4) hydroxyamino compounds; (5) polyhydroxy and hydroxyketo acids; (6) polyhydroxy alcohols; (7) steroids; (8) miscellaneous compounds. French journals after May, 1940, and the majority of other foreign publications after June, 1941, were unavailable for the survey.

Analytical data, such as the consumption of the oxidant or production of formic acid, have been reported for a number of compounds without isolation of the products. In these cases the substances oxidized are listed but the products are omitted, although their identity in many instances is apparent from the analytical data. The yields recorded for the products of the oxidation of some of the glycosidic derivatives of the sugars are based on analytical and rotatory data. In such cases the products were isolated in unspecified amounts as intermediates in the preparation with high yields of the corresponding crystalline strontium or barium-salts.

The Roman numerals appended to the names of some of the compounds refer to the structural formulas given in the text.

PRODUCTS AND YIELDS OBTAINED IN PERIODIC ACID OXIDATIONS

Substance	Product	Yield	Reference*
1. Carbocyclic Polyhydroxy Compounds			
Cyclohexanediol, cis	Not isolated	—	7, 9
Cyclohexanediol, trans	Not isolated	—	7, 9
Dihydroshikimic acid	Not isolated	—	124
Dihydroshikimic acid methyl ester	Tricarballylic acid 1,5-dialdehyde methyl ester	—	56
1,6-Dihydroxy-4,5-isopropylidene-shikimic acid (IV)	Aldehydo keto acid (V)	—	57
Dimethylacenaphthenediol, cis	Not isolated	—	7
Inositol	Formic acid	—	37
Quinic acid methyl ester	Citric acid dialdehyde methyl ester	—	123
Quinic amide-acetone	Citric acid dialdehyde amide-acetone	80%	123
Shikimic acid methyl ester	Aconitic acid dialdehyde methyl ester	75%	125
Tetrahydroterrein	Aldehydocarboxyl deriv.	—	4
2. Carbohydrates			
Acetone-D-mannosan	L'-Oxy-D-methylenediglycolic aldehyde	85%	126
N-Acetyl-D-glucosylamine (XLI)	Acetamino-D-hydroxymethyl diglycolic aldehyde (XLII)	—	93
Alginic acid (LI or LII)	Polymeric dialdehyde (LIII or LIV)	88%	96
D-Altrosan	L'-Oxy-D-methylenediglycolic aldehyde	85%	127
α-Amylose	Not isolated	—	128
β-Amylose	Not isolated	—	128
Cellulose methyl and ethyl ethers	Not isolated	—	111
Cotton cellulose	Oxycelluloses	—	97, 98, 113, 122, 129
Dextrins	Not isolated	—	130
2,3-Dimethylgalactose	Not isolated	—	131

* References 124–171 appear on pp. 374–375.

PRODUCTS AND YIELDS OBTAINED IN PERIODIC
ACID OXIDATIONS—*Continued*

Substance	Product	Yield	Reference*
2,3-Dimethylglucose	Formaldehyde	100%	21, 86
5,6-Dimethylglucose	Dimethylglyceraldehyde	—	89
Dipotassium D-glucopyranose-1-phosphate (Cori ester)	Not isolated	—	132
Ethylated ethylglucosides from ethylcellulose	Not isolated	—	110
α-Ethyl-D-galactopyranoside	Not isolated	—	82
α-Ethyl-D-glucopyranoside	Not isolated	—	82
β-Ethyl-L-sorbopyranoside	Not isolated	—	91
Fructose	Formaldehyde	86%	2b, 5, 21
	Formic acid	—	
	Glycolic acid	—	
	Glyoxylic acid	—	
Fucose in seaweed	Acetaldehyde	100%	18
D-Galactosan <1,5>β<1,6>	Not isolated	—	133
Galactose	Formaldehyde	100%	49, 82,
	Formic acid	100%	21
Glucoheptose	Formaldehyde	—	85
	Formic acid	—	
Glucosamine	*See* Hydroxyamino Compounds		
Glucose	Formaldehyde	100%	2b, 5, 86,
	Formic acid	100%	6, 21, 84
Glucose phenylosazone (XXIV)	Formaldehyde	93%	84
	1-Phenyl-4-benzeneazo-5-pyrazolone (XXVI)	15–20%	
Glucose-6-phosphoric acid	Not isolated	—	134
Glycogen	Not isolated	—	48
Levoglucosan (XLIII)	L'-Oxy-D-methylenediglycolic aldehyde (XLIV)	85%	94
D-Mannosan	L'-Oxy-D-methylenediglycolic aldehyde	85%	126
Mannose	Formaldehyde	100%	82
	Formic acid	—	
Mannose phenylhydrazone	Formaldehyde	35%	84
Methyl alginate	Methyl ester of polymeric dialdehyde (LIII or LIV)	—	96
α-Methyl-D-altropyranoside	D'-Methoxy-D-hydroxymethyldiglycolic aldehyde	100%	135
α-Methyl-D-arabinofuranoside	D'-Methoxy-D-hydroxymethyldiglycolic aldehyde	*ca.* 90%	34

* References 124–171 appear on pp. 374–375.

PRODUCTS AND YIELDS OBTAINED IN PERIODIC
ACID OXIDATIONS—*Continued*

Substance	Product	Yield	Reference*
α-Methyl-D-arabinopyranoside	D'-Methoxydiglycolic aldehyde (XXXIII)	100%	34
β-Methyl-D-arabinopyranoside	L'-Methoxydiglycolic aldehyde (XXXV)	100%	34
α-Methyl-L-galactomethylo-pyranoside	L'-Methoxy-L-methyldiglycolic aldehyde (XXXVII)	95%	92
β-Methyl-L-galactomethylo-pyranoside	D'-Methoxy-L-methyldiglycolic aldehyde (XL)	95%	92
α-Methyl-D-galactopyranoside	D'-Methoxy-D-hydroxymethyl-diglycolic aldehyde	100%	34
β-Methyl-D-galactopyranoside	L'-Methoxy-D-hydroxymethyl-diglycolic aldehyde	100%	34, 136
6-Methylgalactose	Not isolated	—	131
α-Methyl-D-glucomethylo-pyranoside	D'-Methoxy-D-methyldiglycolic aldehyde (XXXVIII)	95%	92
β-Methyl-D-glucomethylo-pyranoside	L'-Methoxy-D-methyldiglycolic aldehyde (XXXIX)	95%	92
α-Methyl-D-glucopyranoside (XXVII)	D'-Methoxy-D-hydroxymethyl-diglycolic aldehyde (XXVIII)	100%	33, 34
β-Methyl-D-glucopyranoside (XXX)	L'-Methoxy-D-hydroxymethyl-diglycolic aldehyde (XXXI)	100%	34
2-Methylglucose	Formaldehyde	81%	86
3-Methylglucose	Formaldehyde	51%	86
6-Methylglucose	Not isolated	—	86
α-Methyl-D-gulopyranoside	D'-Methoxy-D-hydroxymethyl-diglycolic aldehyde	100%	34
α-Methyl-D-lyxopyranoside	D'-Methoxydiglycolic aldehyde	100%	137
β-Methyl-D-lyxopyranoside	L'-Methoxydiglycolic aldehyde	—	138
α-Methyl-L-mannomethylo-pyranoside	L'-Methoxy-L-methyldiglycolic aldehyde	95%	34, 92
α-Methyl-D-mannopyranoside	D'-Methoxy-D-hydroxymethyl-diglycolic aldehyde	100%	33, 34
β-Methyl-D-mannopyranoside	L'-Methoxy-D-hydroxymethyl-diglycolic aldehyde	100%	136
β-Methyl-D-ribopyranoside	L'-Methoxydiglycolic aldehyde	100%	139
α-Methyl-L-sorbopyranoside	Not isolated	—	91
α-Methyl-D-xylopyranoside	D'-Methoxydiglycolic aldehyde	100%	34
β-Methyl-D-xylopyranoside	L'-Methoxydiglycolic aldehyde	100%	34
5,6-Monoacetone-β-ethylgalacto-furanoside	Not isolated	—	131

* References 124–171 appear on pp. 374–375.

PRODUCTS AND YIELDS OBTAINED IN PERIODIC
ACID OXIDATIONS—*Continued*

Substance	Product	Yield	Reference*
4,5-Monoacetone-D-galactose dimethylacetal (I)	2,3-Monoacetone-D-threose (II)	97%	55
	Glyoxal dimethylacetal (III)	70%	
Monoacetoneglucose	Not isolated	—	21
Pentose-phosphoric acid from cozymase	Not isolated	—	134
Polygalacturonide methyl ester (XLVII or XLVIII)	Methyl ester of polymeric dial-dehyde (XLIX or L)	—	95
Raffinose	Not isolated	—	48
Rhamnose	Acetaldehyde	100%	18
	Formic acid	100%	
Ribose-3-phosphoric acid	Formaldehyde	61%	134
Ribose-5-phosphoric acid	Not isolated	—	134
Sorbose	Formaldehyde	90%	85
	Formic acid	—	
	Glycolic acid	—	
	Glyoxylic acid	—	
Starch	Polymeric dialdehyde (LVI)	100%	97, 98, 109, 112, 113, 130
Starch monoformate	Monoformyl oxidized starch	100%	114
α,α-Trehalose (XLV)	D′,D′-Oxy-bis-(D-hydroxymethyl-diglycolic aldehyde) (XLVI)	100%	90
2,3,4-Trimethylglucose	Formaldehyde	5%	86
Xylose	Formaldehyde	100%	18, 21
	Formic acid	—	

3. α-Diketones and α-Ketols

Acetoin	Acetaldehyde	—	4
	Acetic acid	100%	
Benzil	Benzoic acid	—	4
Benzofuroin	Benzaldehyde	—	4
	Pyromucic acid	96%	
Benzoin	Benzaldehyde	90%	4
	Benzoic acid	95%	
Diacetyl	Acetic acid	90–100%	4

* References 124–171 appear on pp. 374–375.

PRODUCTS AND YIELDS OBTAINED IN PERIODIC
ACID OXIDATIONS—*Continued*

Substance	Product	Yield	Reference*
Dihydroxyacetone	Formaldehyde	90%	2*b*, 5
	Glycolic acid	84%	
3,5-Dihydroxy-2-carboxybenzoyl methyl ketone (VI)	Acetic acid	—	4
	3,5-Dihydroxyphthalic acid (VII)		
3,5-Dihydroxy-2-carboxyphenyl-acetylcarbinol	Acetic acid	—	4
	6-Aldehydo-2,4-dihydroxyben-zoic acid	—	
p-Toluoylphenylcarbinol	Benzaldehyde	100%	4
	p-Toluic acid	98%	

4. Hydroxyamino Compounds

N-Acetyl-D-glucosylamine	*See* Carbohydrates		
N-Acetyl-α-methylglucosaminide	Not isolated	—	140
D,L-Allothreonine	Acetaldehyde	70%	17
N-Benzoyl-α-methylglucos-aminide	Not isolated	—	140
Diethanolamine	Formic acid	100%	11
Ethanolamine	Not isolated	—	16
Ethyl N-benzoylglucosamate	Not isolated	—	140
Glucosamic acid	Not isolated	—	140
Glucosamine	Not isolated	—	16
D,L-β-Hydroxyglutamic acid	Not isolated	—	13, 14
Hydroxylysine	Formaldehyde	100%	13, 16, 17
3-Methylglucosamic acid	Formaldehyde	100%	141
	Formic acid	100%	
Serine	Formaldehyde	98%	11, 17, 12, 20
	Glyoxylic acid	—	
Threonine	Acetaldehyde	100%	17, 74,
	Glyoxylic acid	—	11, 12, 20

5. Polyhydroxy and Hydroxyketo Acids

9,10-Dihydroxystearic acid (m.p. 132°)	Nonaldehyde	89%	115
	Azelaic aldehyde-acid	76%	

* References 124–171 appear on pp. 374–375.

PRODUCTS AND YIELDS OBTAINED IN PERIODIC
ACID OXIDATIONS—*Continued*

Substance	Product	Yield	Reference*
9,10-Dihydroxystearic acid (m.p. 95°)	Nonaldehyde	89%	115
	Azelaic aldehyde-acid	76%	
2,3-Dimethyl-D-mannosaccharic acid (XVIII)	Glyoxylic acid	—	64, 65
	meso-Dimethoxysuccinic acid semialdehyde (XIX)	—	
2,3-Dimethylmucic acid	Glyoxylic acid	—	142
	D-Dimethoxysuccinic acid semialdehyde	—	
Gluconic acid	Formaldehyde	89%	37
	Formic acid	—	
	Glyoxylic acid	—	
9-Hydroxy-10-ketostearic acid	Nonanoic acid	75%	116
	Azelaic aldehyde-acid	62%	
10-Hydroxy-9-ketostearic acid	Nonaldehyde	63%	116
	Azelaic acid	91%	
Saccharic acid	Formic acid	—	37
	Glyoxylic acid	—	
D-Saccharic acid 3,6-monolactone (m.p. 135°) (XX)	Glyoxylic acid ester of L-threuronic acid (XXI)	—	67
Saccharolactone methyl ester	Methyl ester of XXI	—	66
Tartaric acid	Glyoxylic acid	100%	6, 36, 37
D-Tartaric acid ester	Not isolated	—	7
meso-Tartaric acid ester	Not isolated	—	7
2,3,6-Trimethyl-D-galactonic acid	Not isolated	—	55

6. Polyhydroxy Alcohols

Adonitol	Formaldehyde	—	1
	Formic acid	100%	
2,3-Butanediol	Acetaldehyde	100%	143
1,6-Diacetyldulcitol	Not isolated	—	108
1,4-Dibenzoyl-D,L-galactitol	Not isolated	—	108
2,5-Dibenzyldulcitol	Not isolated	—	144
Dulcitol	Not isolated	—	5, 37, 108
Erythritol	Formaldehyde	100%	1a, 6
	Formic acid	100%	1b
Ethylene glycol	Formaldehyde	100%	1a, 1b, 6
L-Fucitol	Acetaldehyde	98%	18
Glycerol	Formaldehyde	100%	1a, 6,
	Formic acid	100%	1b
α-Glycerol benzoate	Glycolaldehyde benzoate	—	51

* References 124–171 appear on pp. 374–375.

PRODUCTS AND YIELDS OBTAINED IN PERIODIC
ACID OXIDATIONS—*Continued*

Substance	Product	Yield	Reference*
Glycerol α-benzyl ether	Benzyloxyacetaldehyde	—	52
α-Glycerol butyrate	Glycolaldehyde butyrate	—	51
α-Glycerol nonanoate	Glycolaldehyde nonanoate	—	51
α-Glycerol phenylacetate	Glycolaldehyde phenylacetate	—	51
α-Glycerophosphoric acid	Formaldehyde	84%	2a, c, d
	Phosphoglycol aldehyde	—	
Hydrobenzoin	Not isolated	—	7
1-Isobutyl-2,2-dimethylethyleneglycol	Isovaleraldehyde	34%	32
	Isovaleric acid	3%	
Mannitol	Formaldehyde	100%	1a, 84,
	Formic acid	100%	1b, 6, 21
1-Methyl-2-p-methoxyphenylethyleneglycol	Not isolated	—	7
1-Phenyl-2,2-dimethylethyleneglycol	Benzaldehyde	83%	32
	Benzoic acid	2%	
Pinacol	Not isolated	—	7, 9, 10
Sorbitol	Formaldehyde	100%	47, 48,
	Formic acid	100%	49
Volemitol	Not isolated	—	5, 37

7. Steroids

Substance	Product	Yield	Reference*
Allohomo-(ω)-pregnane-3β,20β-diacetoxy-17β,21α,22-triol	Allopregnane-3β,20β-diacetoxy-17β-ol-21-al	45%	119
Allohomo-(ω)-pregnane-3β,20β-diacetoxy-17β,21β,22-triol	Allopregnane-3β,20β-diacetoxy-17β-ol-21-al	53%	119
Allohomo-(ω)-pregnanepentol	Not isolated	—	119
Allohomo-(ω)-pregnane-3β,17β,-20β,21β,22-pentol	t-Androsterone	—	119
Allopregnane-3β,17β-diacetoxy-21-ol-20-one	3β,17β-Diacetoxyetioallocholanic acid	73%	145
Allopregnane-3,11,17,20,21-pentol (Reichstein's compound A)	11-Hydroxyandrosterone	64%	146, 147
Allopregnane-3,11,20,21-tetrol	17-Formyletioallocholane-3,11-diol	—	148
Allopregnane-3,17,20,21-tetrol	Formaldehyde	—	149
	t-Androsterone	60%	
Allopregnane-3β,17β,20β,21-tetrol	17-Formylandrostane-3β,17β-diol	35%	62, 63

* References 124–171 appear on pp. 374–375.

PRODUCTS AND YIELDS OBTAINED IN PERIODIC ACID OXIDATIONS—*Continued*

Substance	Product	Yield	Reference*
Allopregnane-3,11,17,21-tetrol-20-one	Formaldehyde	100%	150
	Etioallocholane-17-carboxy-3,-11,17-triol	84%	
Allopregnane-3,17,20-triol	Acetaldehyde	—	149
	t-Androsterone	—	
Allopregnane-3β,17α,20α-triol	t-Androsterone	—	151
Allopregnane-3β,17α,20β-triol	Acetaldehyde	19%	152
	t-Androsterone	35%	
Allopregnane-3,20,21-triol	17-Formyletioallocholane-3-ol	90%	148
Allopregnane-3,17,21-triol-11,-20-dione	Formaldehyde	84%	150
	Etioallocholane-17-carboxy-3,-17-diol-11-one	99%	
Allopregnane-3,17,21-triol-20-one	3β,17β-Dihydroxyetioallocholanic acid	85%	153
Corticosterone	Formaldehyde	—	154, 155, 156
	3-Keto-11-hydroxy-4-etiocholenic acid	70%	
Dehydrocorticosterone (Kendall's compound A)	Formaldehyde	100%	154, 155, 156, 157
	3,11-Diketo-4-etiocholenic acid	83%	
4,5-Dihydrocorticosterone	Formaldehyde	60%	156
	Etiocholane-17-carboxy-11-ol-3-one	82%	
4,5-Dihydrodehydrocorticosterone	Etiocholane-17-carboxy-3,11-dione	80%	156
Dihydroxyprogesterone	Hydroxy-3-ketoetiocholenic acid	—	158
17-Formyl-4-androstene-17α-ol-3-one (XV)	Δ⁴-Androstene-3,17-dione (XVI)	72%	63
17-Formyl-4-androstene-17β-ol-3-one	Δ⁴-Androstene-3,17-dione	66%	63
Homo-(ω)-Δ⁵,¹⁷-pregnadiene-3β,-21α,22-triol	Δ⁵,¹⁷-Pregnadiene-3β-ol-21-al	80%	61
Homo-(ω)-Δ⁵,¹⁷-pregnadiene-3β,-21β,22-triol	Δ⁵,¹⁷-Pregnadiene-3β-ol-21-al	81%	61
Homo-(ω)-Δ⁵-pregnene-3β,20β-diacetoxy-17β,21α,22-triol	Δ⁵-Pregnene-3β,20β-diacetoxy-17β-ol-21-al	34%	61
Homo-(ω)-Δ⁵-pregnene-3β,20β-diacetoxy-17β,21β,22-triol	Δ⁵-Pregnene-3β,20β-diacetoxy-17β-ol-21-al	53%	61
Homo-(ω)-Δ⁴-pregnene-17β,20β,-21β,22-tetrol-3-one	Δ⁴-Pregnene-17β,20β-diol-21-al-3-one	—	120

* References 124–171 appear on pp. 374–375.

PRODUCTS AND YIELDS OBTAINED IN PERIODIC
ACID OXIDATIONS—*Continued*

Substance	Product	Yield	Reference*
20-Hydroxymethylallopregnane-3β,20,21-triol	3-Hydroxy-etioallocholanic acid	—	159
20-Hydroxymethyl-Δ^5-pregnene-3β,20,21-triol	3-Hydroxy-5-etiocholenic acid	—	159
17-Isodesoxycorticosterone	17-Iso-3-keto-4-etiocholenic acid	79%	160
20-Methylallopregnane-3β,16,-17,21-tetrol (postulated)	Not isolated	—	161
20-Methylallopregnane-3β,17β,-20,21-tetrol (XII)	Allopregnane-3β,17β-diol-20-one (XIII)	—	60, 159
21-Methylol-Δ^4-pregnene-17,21-diol-3-one	Δ^4-Pregnene-17-ol-3-one-21-al	—	162
21-Methylol-Δ^5-pregnene-3t,17,-21-triol	Δ^5-Pregnene-3t,17-diol-21-al	—	162
20-Methyl-Δ^5-pregnene-3β,17β,-20,21-tetrol	Δ^5-Pregnene-3β,17β-diol-20-one	—	61, 159
20-Methyl-Δ^5-pregnene-3β,20α,-21-triol	Δ^5-Pregnene-3β-ol-20-one	93%	159
20-Methyl-Δ^5-pregnene-3β,20β,-21-triol	Δ^5-Pregnene-3β-ol-20-one	100%	159
Pregnane-3,12-diacetoxy-21-al-20-one	3,12-Diacetoxyetiocholanic acid	—	163, 164
Pregnane-3,21-diol-11,20-dione (Kendall's compound H)	Formaldehyde	—	156
	Etiocholane-17-carboxy-3-ol-11-one	82%	
Pregnane-3α,17,20-triol	Etiocholane-3α-ol-17-one	71%	165
Δ^4-Pregnene-17,21-diol-3,20-dione (X)	3-Keto-17β-hydroxy-4-etiocholenic acid (XI)	58%	59, 166, 167
Δ^4-Pregnene-17,21-diol-3,11,20-trione (Kendall's compound E)	Formaldehyde	83%	117, 168
	4-Etiocholene-17-carboxy-17-ol-3,11-dione	70%	
Δ^4-Pregnene-11,17,20,21-tetrol-3-one (VIII)	Δ^4-Androstene-11-ol-3,17-dione (IX)	60%	58
Δ^4-Pregnene-17,21,22-triol-20-acetoxy-3-one	Δ^4-Pregnene-17-ol-20-acetoxy-21-al-3-one	76%	118
Δ^4-Pregnene-11,17,21-triol-3,20-dione	Formaldehyde	80%	150
	4-Etiocholene-17-carboxy-11,17-diol-3-one	68%	
Δ^4-Pregnene-17α,20β,21-triol-3-one (XIV)	17-Formyl-4-androstene-17α-ol-3-one (XV)	66%	63
Δ^4-Pregnene-17β,20β,21-triol-3-one	17-Formyl-4-androstene-17β-ol-3-one	52%	62, 63

* References 124–171 appear on pp. 374–375.

PRODUCTS AND YIELDS OBTAINED IN PERIODIC
ACID OXIDATIONS—*Continued*

Substance	Product	Yield	Reference
	8. Miscellaneous Compounds		
Dihydroxydihydrobetulin	Formaldehyde	57%	169
	Dihydroxynorlupanone	—	
Glyoxylic acid	Formic acid	—	36
Heparin (inactivated)	Not isolated	—	170
Lactoflavin (riboflavin)	Formaldehyde	60%	134
Leucodrin methyl ether	Formaldehyde	—	171
	Anisylsuccinic acid	—	
Methylglyoxal	Formic acid	76%	4
	Acetic acid	—	

[124] Fischer and Dangschat, *Helv. Chim. Acta*, **18**, 1206 (1935).
[125] Fischer and Dangschat, *Helv. Chim. Acta*, **18**, 1204 (1935).
[126] Knauf, Hann, and Hudson, *J. Am. Chem. Soc.*, **63**, 1447 (1941).
[127] Richtmyer and Hudson, *J. Am. Chem. Soc.*, **62**, 961 (1940).
[128] Pacsu and Mullen, *J. Am. Chem. Soc.*, **63**, 1168 (1941).
[129] Davidson, *J. Soc. Dyers Colourists*, **56**, 58 (1940).
[130] Caldwell and Hixon, *J. Biol. Chem.*, **123**, 595 (1938).
[131] Pacsu and Trister, *J. Am. Chem. Soc.*, **62**, 2301 (1940).
[132] Wolfrom and Pletcher, *J. Am. Chem. Soc.*, **63**, 1050 (1941).
[133] Hann and Hudson, *J. Am. Chem. Soc.*, **63**, 1484 (1941).
[134] v. Euler, Karrer, and Becker, *Helv. Chim. Acta*, **19**, 1060 (1936).
[135] Richtmyer and Hudson, *J. Am. Chem. Soc.*, **63**, 1727 (1941).
[136] Jackson and Hudson, *J. Am. Chem. Soc.*, **61**, 959 (1939).
[137] Maclay and Hudson, *J. Am. Chem. Soc.*, **60**, 2059 (1938).
[138] Isbell and Frush, *J. Research Natl. Bur. Standards*, **24**, 125 (1940).
[139] Jackson and Hudson, *J. Am. Chem. Soc.*, **63**, 1229 (1941).
[140] Neuberger, *J. Chem. Soc.*, **1941**, 47.
[141] Neuberger, *J. Chem. Soc.*, **1941**, 50.
[142] Beaven and Jones, *Chemistry & Industry*, **58**, 363 (1939).
[143] Birkinshaw, Charles, and Clutterbuck, *Biochem. J.*, **25**, 1527 (1931).
[144] Haskins, Hann, and Hudson, *J. Am. Chem. Soc.*, **64**, 132 (1942).
[145] Reichstein and Montigel, *Helv. Chim. Acta*, **22**, 1212 (1939).
[146] Reichstein, *Helv. Chim. Acta*, **19**, 402 (1936).
[147] Reichstein, *Helv. Chim. Acta*, **19**, 979 (1936).
[148] Steiger and Reichstein, *Helv. Chim. Acta*, **21**, 161 (1938).
[149] Steiger and Reichstein, *Helv. Chim. Acta*, **21**, 546 (1938).
[150] Mason, Hoehn, and Kendall, *J. Biol. Chem.*, **124**, 459 (1938).
[151] Reich, Sutter, and Reichstein, *Helv. Chim. Acta*, **23**, 170 (1940).
[152] Prins and Reichstein, *Helv. Chim. Acta*, **23**, 1490 (1940).
[153] Reichstein and Gätzi, *Helv. Chim. Acta*, **21**, 1185 (1938).
[154] Kendall, Mason, Hoehn, and McKenzie, *Proc. Staff Meetings Mayo Clinic*, **12**, 136 (1937).

[155] Kendall, Mason, Hoehn, and McKenzie, *Proc. Staff Meetings Mayo Clinic*, **12**, 270 (1937).
[156] Mason, Hoehn, McKenzie, and Kendall, *J. Biol. Chem.*, **120**, 719 (1937).
[157] Reichstein and Fuchs, *Helv. Chim. Acta*, **23**, 676 (1940).
[158] Ehrhart, Ruschig, and Aumüller, *Ber.*, **72**, 2035 (1939).
[159] Hegner and Reichstein, *Helv. Chim. Acta*, **24**, 828 (1941).
[160] Shoppee, *Helv. Chim. Acta*, **23**, 925 (1940).
[161] Lardon and Reichstein, *Helv. Chim. Acta*, **24**, 1127 (1941).
[162] Miescher, Wettstein, and Scholz, *Helv. Chim. Acta*, **22**, 894 (1939).
[163] Hoehn and Mason, *J. Am. Chem. Soc.*, **60**, 1493 (1938).
[164] Reichstein and v. Arx, *Helv. Chim. Acta*, **23**, 747 (1940).
[165] Hirschmann, *J. Biol. Chem.*, **140**, 797 (1941).
[166] Kendall, Mason, and Myers, *Proc. Staff Meetings Mayo Clinic*, **11**, 351 (1936).
[167] Reichstein, *Helv. Chim. Acta*, **19**, 1107 (1936).
[168] Mason, *J. Biol. Chem.*, **124**, 475 (1938).
[169] Ruzicka and Brenner, *Helv. Chim. Acta*, **23**, 1325 (1940).
[170] Charles and Todd, *Biochem J.*, **34**, 112 (1940).
[171] Rapson, *J. Chem. Soc.*, **1940**, 1271.

CHAPTER 9

THE RESOLUTION OF ALCOHOLS

A. W. INGERSOLL

Vanderbilt University

CONTENTS

INTRODUCTION

The resolution of nearly one hundred and fifty alcohols and phenols is recorded in the literature. Practically every known method of resolution has been applied to these classes of substances, and several methods of considerable utility have been developed. It is the purpose of this chapter to describe and evaluate the results thus far obtained.

Methods of resolution seldom possess the scope and generality of application associated with purely synthetic processes. The worker in this field therefore is obliged to place more than the usual reliance upon knowledge of underlying principles and upon patient and resourceful experimentation guided by extensive acquaintance with the literature. For this reason, a brief statement of the underlying principles and the main steps in the experimental procedure for all the important methods of resolution are included.*

RESOLUTION BY SEGREGATION OF ANTIPODES BY CRYSTALLIZATION

(Pasteur's First Method) [1]

A solution of a solid racemic substance under suitable conditions may deposit individual crystals each of which is composed chiefly or exclusively of one or the other of the two active components. The crystalline deposit as a whole contains equal weights of the two active components and is commonly known as a racemic mixture or conglomerate. The

* The reader is assumed to be familiar with the elements of stereochemical theory and terminology and with at least the main features of the more common general methods of resolution. An excellent treatment of these subjects is contained in the chapter on stereoisomerism by Shriner, Adams, and Marvel in "Organic Chemistry—An Advanced Treatise," edited by Gilman, John Wiley & Sons, New York, 1938, 1943.

[1] Pasteur, *Compt. rend.*, **26**, 535 (1848); *Ann. chim. phys.*, [3] **24**, 442 (1848).

individual crystals often exhibit enantiomorphism in external form or show dissymmetrical optical or electrical properties by which the *dextro* and *levo* forms may be distinguished. When such distinction is possible a resolution may be effected by sorting out mechanically the crystals of each antipode.

Alternatively, it may be possible to induce the partial crystallization of one component alone by inoculating the supersaturated solution with a crystal of that component [2, 3] or with some other suitable material.[4] In this case the second component remains in solution, at least temporarily, for lack of a suitable nucleus for crystallization. The initial deposit is removed before crystallization of the other antipode is permitted to occur. Usually the mother liquor then may be made to deposit the second antipode by suitable concentration and seeding. The two antipodes thus may be crystallized more or less alternately until the solution is exhausted.

Both modifications of the method depend upon a natural segregation of the molecules of each active component into their individual crystal lattices. Experience has shown that such segregation, though common for dissimilar solutes, seldom occurs in the solution of a racemic substance and then usually in a narrow range of conditions that cannot be predicted or attained readily. In the great majority of instances the molecules of both active components combine in equal numbers to form one species of crystals known as a racemic compound or combine in variable proportions to form a series of solid solutions. Also, when segregation does occur, the experimental procedure necessary to produce distinguishable crystals or a uniform deposit of one variety is usually troublesome and slow. Hence the method has assumed practical value only in a few instances in which all the circumstances are especially favorable.

There have been few attempts to apply this method to the resolution of alcohols. Le Bel,[5] following earlier experiments of Pasteur,[6] failed to resolve racemic s-butyl carbinol by crystallization of the barium salt of the racemic hydrogen sulfate. *dl*-Erythritol [7] was found to be a racemic mixture, but the active crystals were too poorly formed to permit separation. It has been stated [8] that *dl-cis-β*-decalol shows indications of being a resolvable racemic mixture, but no resolution has been described.

The only recorded clear-cut resolution by this method is that of the

[2] Gernez, *Compt. rend.*, **63**, 843 (1866); *Ann.*, **143**, 387 (1867).
[3] Ruff, *Ber.*, **34**, 1362 (1901).
[4] Ostromisslenski, *Ber.*, **41**, 3035 (1908).
[5] Le Bel, *Compt. rend.*, **87**, 213 (1878); *Bull. soc. chim.*, [2] **31**, 104 (1878).
[6] Pasteur, *Compt. rend.*, **42**, 1259 (1856).
[7] Maquenne and Bertrand, *Compt. rend.*, **132**, 1565 (1901).
[8] Hückel and Kuhn, *Ber.*, **70**, 2479 (1937).

glycol, *dl*-isohydrobenzoin. Erlenmeyer,[9] following earlier observations of Bodewig,[10] found that crystallization of this substance from ether gave optically active hemimorphic crystals with rotations of the order of ±8°. Read and co-workers [11, 12] have shown that the resolution in ether [9, 13] is sometimes incomplete, since the rotations of the pure active forms are ±92°. Crystallization from ethyl acetate or chloroform,[12, 14] however, readily gave both of the pure active forms.

Perhaps the most that can be said for this method is that it has been neglected in favor of more reliable methods and that it might at least be tried when other methods have failed. Many phenols and alcohols are crystalline or form a variety of crystalline derivatives that could be tested without great difficulty.

RESOLUTION BY FRACTIONATION OF DIASTEREOISOMERIC DERIVATIVES

(Pasteur's Second Method) [15]

The most useful and general of all methods of resolution is that which involves combination of a racemic substance with an optically active reagent (a so-called resolving agent) to give two diastereoisomeric derivatives, one derived from each of the two active components. These diastereoisomers often may be separated by conventional fractional crystallization. Each isomer then is treated to regenerate the pure active component.

No satisfactory method has yet been devised for separation of such diastereoisomers if they are liquids, since the vapor pressures are so nearly alike. Bailey and Hass [16] effected for the first time partial separations of certain diastereoisomeric esters, including the lactates of 2-butanol and 2-pentanol and related esters by fractional distillation through an efficient column.

In the customary use of the method, the first step is the formation of a semi-permanent linkage between the resolving agent and the two components of the substance to be resolved. This step obviously should be as convenient and as nearly quantitative as possible. The linkage must be stable enough to remain intact during the subsequent operations in-

[9] Erlenmeyer, *Ber.*, **30**, 1531 (1897).
[10] Bodewig, *Ann.*, **182**, 279 (1876).
[11] Read and Steele, *J. Chem. Soc.*, **1927**, 910.
[12] Read, Campbell, and Barker, *J. Chem. Soc.*, **1929**, 2305.
[13] Ott, *Z. anorg. Chem. (Schenck-Festschrift)*, **188**, 47 (1930).
[14] Reis and Schneider, *Z. Krist.*, **69**, 62 (1928).
[15] Pasteur, *Compt. rend.*, **35**, 176 (1852); **37**, 162 (1853).
[16] Bailey and Hass, *J. Am. Chem. Soc.*, **63**, 1969 (1941).

volved in the fractional crystallization process, yet it must also be capable of being broken readily in the final step without causing racemization or other damage to the desired active component or to the resolving agent, and without requiring conditions that interfere with the ready recovery of both products.

For the resolution of an alcohol or phenol, the most common type of linkage that meets these requirements is that formed by esterification with an acid or acid derivative. In practice, the method takes two principal forms:

(a) The racemic alcohol is esterified with an optically active acid. The acid is chosen, if possible, so that the two resulting diastereoisomeric esters are solids capable of separation. After the separation, the active alcohol and resolving agent are recovered from either (or both) of the pure active esters, usually by alkaline hydrolysis.

(b) The racemic alcohol is esterified with a diacid (such as phthalic acid) so that the corresponding acid ester is produced. The ester is then resolved *as an acid*, the resolving agent usually being an optically active base, such as an alkaloid. When either or both of the salts derived from the two active forms of the acid ester have been purified, the resolving agent is removed and the corresponding active acid ester is saponified to regenerate the active alcohol.

Although the two procedures just outlined, especially (b), actually have been used for more than 90% of all recorded resolutions of alcohols, neither is invariably successful or convenient. The scope and some of the limitations of the various methods are indicated in the following sections.

Resolution through Simple Esters

Frankland and Price [17] were the first to attempt the resolution of alcohols (and acids) by fractional crystallization of their solid esters. The isomeric solid esters formed from *l-s*-butylcarbinol and *dl*-dibenzoylglyceric acid failed to separate on crystallization; the corresponding *dl*-alcohol-*l*-acid ester was liquid. Marckwald and McKenzie [18, 19] effected partial resolutions of *dl*-mandelic acid and related acids with *l*-menthol and *d*-borneol, and of *dl*-2-octanol with *d*-tartaric acid, but did not develop a satisfactory method for resolving alcohols. Later investigators, however, have employed the following resolving agents in several more or less successful resolutions of certain alcohols: (a) *l*-menthyl isocyanate, (b) *d*-camphoric acid, (c) *d*- or *l*-mandelic acid, (d) *d*- or

[17] Frankland and Price, *J. Chem. Soc.*, **71**, 253, 696 (1897).

[18] Marckwald and McKenzie, *Ber.*, **32**, 2130 (1899); **34**, 485, 1419 (1901).

[19] Marckwald and McKenzie, *Ber.*, **34**, 469 (1901).

l-camphor-10-sulfonyl chloride, (*e*) *l*-menthoxy- and *d*-bornoxyacetic acids, (*f*) *l*-menthylglycine, and (*g*) *d*-tartranilic acid.

l-**Menthyl Isocyanate.** Pickard and Littlebury [20, 21] found that *l*-menthyl isocyanate forms crystalline esters (urethanes) with many alcohols and phenols. The two diastereoisomeric urethanes from *dl*-1-phenyl-1-*p*-hydroxyphenylethane and from *dl*-*ac*-tetrahydro-β-naphthol were separated readily.[20] The method has not been applied widely. *l*-Menthyl isocyanate is the most readily available resolving agent of this type but is difficult to prepare. The urethanes are not easily hydrolyzed, and the isocyanate is not recovered in the hydrolysis but is converted to the amine.

d-**Camphoric Acid.** Mascarelli and Deliperi [22] obtained only partial resolutions of several alcohols by the use of *d*-camphoric acid or its anhydride. Most of the pairs of hydrogen camphorate esters formed from this acid could not be separated by crystallization.

d- and *l*-**Mandelic Acid.** Active mandelic acids have been used successfully in the resolution of *dl*-menthol.[23, 24] This method suffers the disadvantage of almost complete racemization of the rather costly resolving agent during the final hydrolysis of the diastereoisomeric esters.

d- and *l*-**Camphorsulfonyl Chloride.** *dl*-Menthol was resolved readily by fractionation of the crystalline esters formed from *d*- and *l*-camphor-10-sulfonyl chloride.[25] The yield of active menthols was unsatisfactory, however, because the drastic conditions necessary for the hydrolysis of the sulfonates caused extensive dehydration of the alcohol.

l-**Menthoxyacetic Acid.** In order to overcome most of the disadvantages of the reagents mentioned above, Read and his associates [26] introduced a new class of resolving agents, typified by *l*-menthoxyacetic acid, $C_{10}H_{19}OCH_2CO_2H$. Acids of this type meet many of the requirements of satisfactory resolving agents. Thus they are prepared easily from chloroacetic acid and the sodium derivatives of various readily available active alcohols, such as *l*-menthol and *d*-borneol. The alcohol to be resolved is esterified readily by means of the corresponding acid chloride and pyridine. The esters have convenient rotation values and often crystallize well enough to permit satisfactory resolutions. The resulting

[20] Pickard and Littlebury, *J. Chem. Soc.*, **89**, 467, 1254 (1906).

[21] Pickard, Littlebury, and Neville, *J. Chem. Soc.*, **89**, 93 (1906).

[22] Mascarelli and Deliperi, *Atti acad. Lincei*, **25**, (i) 43 (1916); *Gazz. chim. ital.*, **46**, (i) 416 (1916).

[23] McKenzie and Luis, *J. Chem. Soc.*, **1934**, 715.

[24] Findlay and Hickman, *J. Chem. Soc.*, **91**, 905 (1907).

[25] Read and Grubb, *J. Chem. Soc.*, **1931**, 188.

[26] Read and Grubb, *J. Soc. Chem. Ind.*, **51**, 329T (1932); Brit. pat., 397,212; Ger. pat., 600,983.

active esters may be hydrolyzed easily so that both the pure active alcohol and the resolving agent are recovered.

Although not yet widely used, resolving agents of this type have proved to be remarkably versatile. Both active antipodes of the menthoxy- and bornoxy-acetic acids have been used, thus facilitating the purification of both active forms of alcohols. Thus *dl*-menthol [26] and *dl*-neomenthol [27] were completely resolved by the successive use of *l*- and *d*-menthoxyacetic acids, and crude *d*- and *l*-borneol were purified through use of *d*- and *l*-bornoxyacetic acids,[28] respectively. Also, *l*-menthoxyacetic acid has been used successfully for resolving *dl-trans*-cyclohexane-1,2-diol [29] into both active forms. The resolution of glycols is usually difficult by other methods.

The success of Knauf, Shildneck, and Adams [30] in adapting *l*-menthoxyacetic acid to the resolution of phenols is especially useful since only one member of this class had been resolved previously by other methods.[20] Fujise and Nagasaki [31] extended the method to the resolution of 7-hydroxyflavanone and demethoxymateucinol, but perhaps the most interesting example is the complete resolution of *dl*-equilenin by Bachmann, Cole, and Wilds.[32] The attempted resolution of *dl*-isoequilenin [32] was unsuccessful.

The method thus appears to be particularly promising for the resolution of phenols, glycols, and alcohols of high molecular weight. Esters of menthoxy- and bornoxy-acetic acids with lower alcohols tend to be liquids, and in some instances [33] diastereoisomeric esters cannot be separated even when crystalline. It appears probable that active alkoxyacetic acids derived from other highly crystalline terpenoid or steroid alcohols might prove useful in overcoming these difficulties and in extending the scope of the method. The preparation of *l*-menthoxyacetic acid and its use for the resolution of *dl*-menthol are described in a later section (p. 398).

l-**Menthylglycine.** Clark and Read [34] also have introduced still another type of agent for resolving alcohols. The method of application is essentially similar to that just described but has additional features making for greater range and flexibility. The racemic alcohol is first esterified with chloroacetic acid and the product is then caused to react with an optically active amine, such as *l*-menthylamine. The resulting

[27] Read and Grubb, *J. Chem. Soc.*, **1933**, 167.
[28] Clark and Read, *J. Chem. Soc.*, **1934**, 1773.
[29] Wilson and Read, *J. Chem. Soc.*, **1935**, 1269.
[30] Knauf, Shildneck, and Adams, *J. Am. Chem. Soc.*, **56**, 2109 (1934).
[31] Fujise and Nagasaki, *Ber.*, **69**, 1893 (1936); *J. Chem. Soc. Japan*, **57**, 1245 (1936).
[32] Bachmann, Cole, and Wilds, *J. Am. Chem. Soc.*, **62**, 824 (1940).
[33] Read, Grubb, and Malcolm, *J. Chem. Soc.*, **1933**, 170.
[34] Clark and Read, *J. Chem. Soc.*, **1934**, 1775.

diastereoisomeric *l*-menthylglycine esters are separated by crystallization, and the active alcohol is recovered from each form by hydrolysis.

$$(dl)\text{RO—CO—CH}_2\text{Cl} + \text{H}_2\text{NR*} \rightarrow$$

$$(dl)\text{RO—CO—CH}_2\text{—NHR*—}\left[\begin{array}{l} (d)\text{RO—CO—CH}_2\text{—NHR*} \rightarrow (d)\text{ROH} \\ \text{and/or} \\ (l)\text{RO—CO—CH}_2\text{—NHR*} \rightarrow (l)\text{ROH} \end{array}\right. +$$

$$\text{HOOC—CH}_2\text{—NHR*}$$

It was found that the majority of *l*-menthylglycine esters, even those of the lower aliphatic alcohols, are highly crystalline and stable enough for satisfactory fractionation.   Moreover, should the fractionation of the esters themselves be unsatisfactory, they may be converted to their crystalline N-acyl derivatives or to the salts of ordinary acids, which are then fractionated instead.   Thus *l*-menthyl-*l*-menthylglycine was purified as the sulfate and *d*-menthyl-*l*-menthylglycine as the *p*-nitrobenzoyl derivative.[34] Recovered *l*-menthylglycine or its N-acyl derivatives may be used again, being employed directly for esterification of the alcohol to be resolved.

The method so far has been applied only to the resolution of *dl*-menthol.[34] Its range doubtless can be extended still further by replacing *l*-menthylamine with other readily available terpenoid amines such as the active carvomenthyl-,[35] thujyl-,[36] and fenchyl-amines[36] as well as simpler amines like α-phenylethylamine[37] and its analogs.[38, 39]

d-Tartranilic Acid. Barrow and Atkinson[40] have investigated the use of the esters of *d*-tartranilic acid for resolving certain lower alcohols. They succeeded in obtaining pure active 2-octanol, 2-hexanol, 2-pentanol, and menthol from the racemic modifications but were unsuccessful in resolving 2-butanol and 2-methyl-1-butanol because of the formation of mixed crystals.   The procedure was also unsuccessful in resolving methylphenylcarbinol and α-terpineol because of the ease of dehydration of these alcohols.

The esters are formed by heating the alcohol with *d*-tartranil in the presence of an acid

$$
\begin{array}{ll}
\text{HOCH—CO} & \text{HOCH—CONHC}_6\text{H}_5 \\
\quad\quad\Big\backslash & \quad\quad\big| \\
\quad\quad\quad\text{NC}_6\text{H}_5 + \text{ROH} \xrightarrow{\text{H}_2\text{SO}_4} \\
\quad\quad\Big/ & \quad\quad\big| \\
\text{HOCH—CO} & \text{HOCH—COOR}
\end{array}
$$

[35] Read and Johnston, *J. Chem. Soc.*, **1934**, 226; **1935**, 1138.
[36] Dickison and Ingersoll, *J. Am. Chem. Soc.*, **61**, 2477 (1939).
[37] Ingersoll, *Org. Syntheses*, **17**, 76, 80 (1937).
[38] Ingersoll and White, *J. Am. Chem. Soc.*, **54**, 274 (1932).
[39] Ingersoll and Burns, *J. Am. Chem. Soc.*, **54**, 4712 (1932).
[40] Barrow and Atkinson, *J. Chem. Soc.*, **1939**, 638.

and are separated by crystallization. The resolving agent is not recoverable after the final hydrolysis, but its preparation is easy and cheap.[40] p-Bromotartranilates also were used with moderate success; presumably still other common amines could be substituted for aniline in forming the original tartranil.

Resolution through Salts of Acid Esters

In this method the alcohol is converted to an acid ester, usually the sulfate, phthalate, or succinate. The acid ester is then resolved by crystallization of its salts with active bases, and the active esters are recovered from the salts and saponified to yield the corresponding active alcohols. The method has been by far the most generally applicable. It was developed because of the relative ease and certainty with which racemic acids may be resolved by means of their salts with active bases. Basic resolving agents are sufficiently numerous and accessible so that it usually is possible to find some combination of active base and solvent that will yield separable crystalline salts with nearly any type of acid. A list of basic resolving agents is given later (p. 394).

Acid Sulfates. Pasteur[5] and also Le Bel[4] fractionated the cinchonine salts of the mixture of amyl hydrogen sulfates derived from fusel oil and effected a partial separation of the structurally isomeric alcohols. Krüger[41] failed to resolve the alkaloid salts of the hydrogen sulfate of ethyl-n-propylcarbinol but Meth,[42] after failures in other instances, finally effected a partial resolution of s-butyl hydrogen sulfate as the brucine salt. The method has proved to be impracticable for most alcohols[43] because the majority of alkyl hydrogen sulfates are unstable and inconvenient to handle.

It has been shown, however, that the method is particularly useful for resolving certain glycols such as propylene glycol[44] and various cycloalkanediols.[45, 46, 47] The glycol is converted to the dihydrogen sulfate by reaction at −15° with excess concentrated sulfuric acid, and the product is obtained as a solution of the barium salt. This is treated with two equivalents of the sulfate of some active base, such as strychnine.

[41] Krüger, *Ber.*, **26**, 1203 (1893).
[42] Meth, *Ber.*, **40**, 695 (1907).
[43] Hano, *Folia pharm. Japon.*, **27**, 315 (1939).
[44] Grün, *Ber.*, **52**, 260 (1919).
[45] Derx, *Rec. trav. chim.*, **41**, 312 (1922).
[46] Godchot and Mousseron, *Compt. rend.*, **198**, 837 (1934).
[47] Godchot, Mousseron, and Richaud, *Compt. rend.*, **199**, 1233 (1934).

After removal of barium sulfate and fractionation of the alkaloid salts, the glycol sulfate ester is recovered as alkali salt and saponified with alkali.[45, 46] The method is tedious and not yet well developed, but it may be noted that the glycols cannot be resolved by the phthalic ester procedure described below because they tend to form polymeric esters instead of simple hydrogen phthalates when treated with phthalic anhydride.

Acid Phthalates and Succinates. The resolution of alcohols through acid esters was given especially useful form when Pickard and Littlebury introduced the use of hydrogen phthalates and hydrogen succinates.[48] These are easily prepared from nearly all types of primary or secondary (but not tertiary) alcohols by reaction with the corresponding acid anhydride. The resulting acid esters are stable, moderately strong acids that usually can be resolved with active bases. After the resolution the recovery of the active acid esters from the salts, and of the active alcohols from the acid esters, may be accomplished easily and in excellent yield. The procedure for the use of phthalates is outlined in the following scheme.

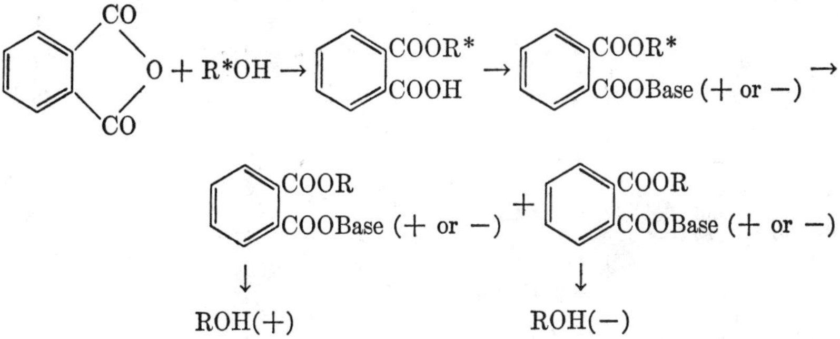

The method was used first for the purification of crude d- and l-borneol and for the resolution of dl-isoborneol by crystallization of the l-menthylamine salts of the hydrogen phthalates.[48] The method was then extended, particularly by Pickard and Kenyon [49-55] and by Levene

[48] Pickard and Littlebury, *J. Chem. Soc.*, **91**, 1973 (1907).
[49] Pickard and Kenyon, *J. Chem. Soc.*, **91**, 2058 (1907).
[50] Pickard and Kenyon, *J. Chem. Soc.*, **99**, 45 (1911).
[51] Pickard and Kenyon, *J. Chem. Soc.*, **101**, 620 (1912).
[52] Pickard and Kenyon, *J. Chem. Soc.*, **101**, 1427 (1912); **105**, 2677 (1914).
[53] Pickard and Kenyon, *J. Chem. Soc.*, **103**, 1923 (1913).
[54] Pickard and Kenyon, *J. Chem. Soc.*, **105**, 830 (1914).
[55] Pickard and Kenyon, *J. Chem. Soc.*, **105**, 1115 (1914).

and others,[56-78] to many series of simple secondary alcohols and eventually to alcohols of nearly all types. Among the series that have been most completely studied are CH_3CHOHR,[50, 54, 55, 72] C_2H_5CHOHR,[50, 53] $(CH_3)_2CHCHOHR$,[51] $(CH_3)_2CHCH_2CHOHR$,[67] C_6H_5CHOHR,[50, 73] $C_6H_{11}CHOHR$,[74, 69] CH_2=$CHCHOHR$,[64, 65] and CH_2=$CHCH_2$-$CHOHR$,[56] in which R represents normal or variously branched alkyl radicals ranging from methyl to pentadecyl. In the great majority of these resolutions the alkaloids brucine, strychnine, quinine, and/or cinchonidine were used instead of the l-menthylamine originally employed.

The procedure usually is unsuitable for tertiary alcohols since the reaction with phthalic anhydride or succinic anhydride either fails or results in dehydration of the alcohol. A few tertiary alkyl phthalates, however, have been prepared and resolved by first converting the alcohols to sodium or potassium salts and allowing these to react [79, 80] with phthalic anhydride. This modification has been applied successfully to dl-α- and β-santalols [81] and dl-linalool.[81] As already mentioned, glycols cannot be resolved by this procedure because they form polymeric esters when heated with phthalic or succinic anhydride. Phenols also usually form phthaleins or other condensation products instead of simple acid esters.

For these resolutions, phthalic anhydride has been much the most widely used reagent. The 3-nitrophthalates, however, have been pre-

[56] Levene and Haller, J. Biol. Chem., 76, 415 (1928).
[57] Levene and Haller, J. Biol. Chem., 77, 555 (1928).
[58] Levene and Haller, J. Biol. Chem., 79, 475 (1928).
[59] Levene and Haller, J. Biol. Chem., 81, 425 (1929).
[60] Levene and Haller, Science, 69, 47 (1929).
[61] Levene and Haller, J. Biol. Chem., 81, 703 (1929).
[62] Levene and Haller, J. Biol. Chem., 83, 177 (1929).
[63] Levene and Haller, J. Biol. Chem., 83, 185 (1929).
[64] Levene and Haller, J. Biol. Chem., 83, 579 (1929).
[65] Levene and Haller, J. Biol. Chem., 83, 591 (1929).
[66] Levene and Harris, J. Biol. Chem., 113, 55 (1936).
[67] Levene and Marker, J. Biol. Chem., 90, 669 (1931).
[68] Levene and Marker, J. Biol. Chem., 91, 405 (1931).
[69] Levene and Marker, J. Biol. Chem., 97, 379 (1932).
[70] Levene and Marker, J. Biol. Chem., 106, 173 (1934).
[71] Levene, Marker, and Rothen, J. Biol. Chem., 100, 589 (1933).
[72] Levene and Mikeska, J. Biol. Chem., 65, 507 (1925).
[73] Levene and Mikeska, J. Biol. Chem., 70, 355 (1926).
[74] Levene and Mikeska, J. Biol. Chem., 75, 587 (1927).
[75] Levene, Rothen, and Kuna, J. Biol. Chem., 120, 759 (1937).
[76] Levene, Rothen, and Kuna, J. Biol. Chem., 120, 777 (1937).
[77] Levene and Stevens, J. Biol. Chem., 87, 375 (1930).
[78] Levene and Stevens, J. Biol. Chem., 89, 471 (1930).
[79] Fuller and Kenyon, J. Chem. Soc., 125, 2304 (1924).
[80] Paolini, Gazz. chim. ital., 55, 804, 812, 818 (1925).
[81] Paolini and Divizia, Atti acad. Lincei, [5] 23, (ii) 226 (1914).

pared in a few cases [82, 71] and proved more suitable for resolving s-butyl-carbinol, β-phenylpropyl alcohol, and γ-phenylbutyl alcohol than the corresponding phthalates. The tetrachlorophthalates were unsatisfactory.[50, 42] The hydrogen succinates also have been employed in the resolution of menthol,[83] phenylmethylcarbinol,[50] phenylethylcarbinol [50] and various members of the series CH_3CHOHR,[50, 51] $(CH_3)_2CHCHOHR$,[51] and C_2H_5CHOHR.[53] The succinates are superior to the corresponding phthalates when more soluble or more stable salts are required,[50] or for completing resolutions only partly effected by means of the phthalates.[51, 53, 83]

Resolution through Ethers and Coordination Complexes

Walker and Read [84] attempted to resolve alcohols through ether formation with d-hydroxymethylenecamphor, but the products were not suitably crystalline. Helferich and Hiltmann [85] recently have been more successful with a method employing glycoside formation. Thus dl-trans-cyclopentane-1,2-diol was converted to the acetylated monoglucoside (or, preferably, the diglucoside) by reaction with d-β-acetobromoglucose and silver carbonate. The less soluble fractions, after deacetylation and subsequent hydrolysis with the aid of emulsin, gave the pure dextro-glycol in moderate yield. The method would appear to have considerable promise for resolving glycols, and possibly phenols, but has been insufficiently studied as yet.

Sobotka and Goldberg [86] have resolved dl-4-phenyl-2-butanol by fractional crystallization of the solid coordination complex formed with desoxycholic acid. Similar resolutions of dl-camphor, dl-limonene, and dl-methylethylacetic acid indicate that no specific functional group is necessary for the coordination process. The method deserves further study as a possible means of resolving various types of compounds, including alcohols that are not readily esterified.

A method employing a similar effect is that of Windaus, Weinhold, and Klänhardt,[87] who found that digitonin precipitates the digitonide of one (partially) active form of α-terpineol and ac-tetrahydro-β-naphthol when added to a solution of the racemic form. The method failed with dl-carvomenthol and dl-methylphenylcarbinol and with the majority of

[82] Cohen, Marshall, and Woodman, J. Chem. Soc., **107**, 887 (1915).

[83] Pickard and Littlebury, J. Chem. Soc., **101**, 109 (1912).

[84] Walker and Read, J. Soc. Chem. Ind., **53**, 53T (1934).

[85] Helferich and Hiltmann, Ber., **70**, 308, 588 (1937).

[86] Sobotka and Goldberg, Biochem. J., **26**, 905 (1932).

[87] Windaus, Weinhold, and Klänhardt, Z. physiol. Chem:, **126**, 299, 308 (1923).

other alcohols and phenols studied.   Eisenlohr and Meyer [88] likewise were
unsuccessful in the attempt to use numerous other molecular compounds.

RESOLUTION BY DIFFERENTIAL INTERACTION WITH AN ACTIVE AGENT

When the two active components of a racemic substance are brought
into contact with an *optically active* agent with which some form of slow or
reversible combination may occur, it usually is found that the two
antipodes do not combine at the same rate.   Also, after combination has
taken place, the rates of the reversal usually are different for the two
products.   The two effects may operate simultaneously when the process
is reversible.

Presumably the difference in rates in either direction is the result of
steric factors that influence the chemical or thermal stabilities of the
two combinations concerned.   In any event, after the interaction has
continued for a time but has not gone to completion, then more of one
active component and less of the other will be found in combination.   A
partial resolution of the antipodes therefore can be effected by separating
the combined and the uncombined portions of the system.   Several
methods of stepwise resolution have been based upon the effects just
described.

Fractional Reaction with an Optically Active Agent

The principles outlined above were applied by Marckwald and McKenzie [18] for the partial resolution of a racemic acid with an active alcohol.
Thus when *dl*-mandelic acid was heated with less than one equivalent of
l-menthol, the resulting ester contained somewhat more *l*-menthyl-*d*-
mandelate than *l*-menthyl-*l*-mandelate and the unesterified acid contained a corresponding excess of *l*-mandelic acid.   Also, when a mixture
of equal amounts of the two diastereoisomeric esters was partially
hydrolyzed, the regenerated acid and that still combined in the residual
ester contained unequal amounts of the two antipodes.   The process has
been extended to the resolution of acids and amines through the formation and hydrolysis of amides.[89]

In general, the degree of separation obtainable in processes of this
kind will depend on the differential rate coefficient of the two competing
reactions.   At one extreme, one antipode alone will enter into combination or one diastereoisomeric combination only will undergo decomposition; at the other extreme the antipodes will show no significant dif-

[88] Eisenlohr and Meyer, *Ber.*, **71**, 1005 (1938).
[89] Marckwald and Meth, *Ber.*, **38**, 801 (1905).

ference in rates. Usually the difference in rates is comparatively small. The disparity in proportions of the two antipodes can be increased by repeating the procedure upon either or both portions of the system obtained in the first treatment. Theoretically, the substantially pure antipodes might result from enough repetitions. Unfortunately each repetition at the same time increases the number and decreases the size of fractions beyond practical limits. Hence, unless means can be found to operate the process continuously, according to the countercurrent principle, it would appear to have little practical value.

No very useful resolutions of alcohols have been based upon this method, but a few instances are recorded in which partial resolutions were effected. Thus Marckwald and McKenzie [18] partially esterified dl-2-octanol with d-tartaric acid. The unesterified portion of the alcohol was slightly levorotatory; that recovered from the ester was slightly dextrorotatory. Pozzi-Escot [90] obtained similar results with the d-tartrates of dl-2-butanol.

Fractional Decomposition on an Optically Active Catalyst

A method apparently fundamentally related to the above is illustrated by the fractional catalytic dehydration of dl-2-butanol observed by Schwab and Rudolph.[91] The alcohol recovered after partial thermal dehydration upon a film of copper supported on powdered d- or l-quartz was faintly active in the same sense as the quartz. Similar results were noted after partial catalytic oxidation on the same surfaces. These results have not been explained fully; it is possible that each of the two active forms of the alcohol is adsorbed momentarily on the quartz-copper interface; the two "diastereoisomeric" combinations thus formed then react at different rates. The method is not practical in its present form.

Fractional Adsorption on an Optically Active Surface

Henderson and Rule [92] separated dl-p-phenylenebisiminocamphor into its active forms by passing its dilute petroleum ether solution through a column containing powdered d-lactose. The procedure was similar to that commonly used in chromatographic analysis. The d-form was more strongly adsorbed and hence collected near the top of the column; the l-form was carried toward the bottom. Several repetitions of the

[90] Pozzi-Escot, J. pharm. chim., VI, 29, 57 (1909).
[91] Schwab and Rudolph, Naturwissenschaften, 20, 363 (1932).
[92] Henderson and Rule, Nature, 141, 917 (1939); J. Chem. Soc., 1939, 1568.

process on the partially separated fractions finally gave both pure antipodes. Less complete separations of various racemic substances appear to have been made with certain other sugars and with *d*- or *l*-quartz [93, 94] powder as adsorbents. Numerous earlier attempts to effect differential adsorption of optical antipodes on amorphous active adsorbents, such as wool, silk, and cotton, gave negative or doubtful results,[92] apparently because both antipodes were strongly adsorbed. The success of crystalline adsorbents may be attributed [92] to the presence of active crystal surfaces having limited, but sterically specific, adsorptive power.

The method has not been studied sufficiently to assess its generality and usefulness. The principal defect, even when the differential adsorption coefficient is fairly large, is the necessity for handling large volumes of solvent and adsorbent in order to separate a small amount of material. On the other hand it may be noted that the method is based upon the continuous countercurrent principle and is therefore capable of effecting substantially quantitative separation of both antipodes. Hydroxylic compounds are usually readily adsorbed, and the method would appear to have interesting possibilities for resolving alcohols and phenols if a suitable variety of adsorbents and solvents can be found. Since chemical reactions are not involved, the method might be particularly useful for demonstrating the resolvability of certain unstable or tertiary alcohols for which other methods are unsuitable.

Asymmetric Biochemical Reaction

Biosynthesis appears to be controlled by asymmetric influences of a highly specific nature. Since the fundamental constituents of living matter are almost always optically active, it is probable that metabolic products are formed in the active condition through mechanisms essentially similar to those described in the preceding paragraphs. The controlling agents are probably optically active enzymes or other asymmetric cell constituents which are able to exert a selective influence upon metabolites through differential reaction, adsorption, or catalysis.

Two interesting methods of preparing optically active substances (including alcohols) are based on these phenomena.

Biochemical Resolution (Pasteur's Third Method).[95] Pasteur observed that, when salts of *dl*-tartaric acid were introduced into cultures of yeast or of certain molds, the *dextro* component was decomposed com-

[93] Tsuchida, Kobayashi, and Nakamura, *J. Chem. Soc. Japan*, **56**, 1339 (1935) [*C. A.*, **30**, 926 (1936)].

[94] Karagunis and Coumoulos, *Nature*, **142**, 162 (1938) [*C. A.*, **32**, 7411 (1938); **33**, 7165 (1939)].

[95] Pasteur, *Compt. rend.*, **45**, 1032 (1857); **46**, 615 (1858); **51**, 298 (1860).

pletely while the *levo* form largely remained and could be isolated. Le Bel and others extended this procedure to various racemic substances and demonstrated its generality. Thus the partially pure active forms of *s*-butyl carbinol,[5] propylene glycol,[96, 97] and various other lower secondary alcohols [98, 99, 100] were obtained, the organisms usually employed being *Penicillium glaucum* or various species of mildew. These results, incidentally, are the earliest recorded examples of the resolution of alcohols by any method.

It also was found by various workers that the active components of certain racemic substances were unequally affected when fed to or injected into animals; [101-104] the more resistant component or one of its derivatives could then be isolated in partially pure form from the urine. Thus *dl*-borneol when fed to rabbits or dogs was excreted as the glycuronate; hydrolysis of this gave slightly levorotatory borneol.[101, 102] Similarly, when *dl*-menthol was fed to rabbits, the excreted glycuronate contained an excess of the *d*-form; refeeding this product gave a small yield of the pure *d*-form.[105] The feeding of *dl*-camphor to dogs gave a glycuronate from which impure *l*-campherol was obtained.[106]

Though a considerable number of active alcohols have been prepared by these methods, there are many serious limitations and disadvantages. In order to obtain one antipode, the other usually must be sacrificed. Sometimes both forms are largely destroyed or the more resistant form is still optically impure. The form that is obtained is not always the one desired. Only one instance is recorded in which both forms were obtained by using two different agents; [96, 97] the natural antipode is usually the less resistant to all agents. Many alcohols, and especially phenols, cannot be used at all because they are toxic to the organism or are not affected by it, or because they are physically unsuitable.

Aside from these inherent defects the fermentation method of resolution in particular is experimentally difficult since it requires large volumes of dilute solutions (1 to 5%) and periods of time ranging from 2 to 60 days. The facilities and technique for isolating pure cultures of micro-

[96] Le Bel, *Compt. rend.*, **92**, 532 (1881); *Bull. soc. chim.*, [2] **34**, 129 (1882).

[97] Kling, *Compt. rend.*, **129**, 1252 (1899).

[98] Le Bel, *Compt. rend.*, **89**, 312 (1879); *Bull. soc. chim.*, [2] **33**, 106, 147 (1879).

[99] Le Bel, *Bull. soc. chim.*, [3] **9**, 676 (1893).

[100] Combes and Le Bel, *Bull. soc. chim.*, [3] **7**, 552 (1892).

[101] Neuberg and Wohlgemuth, *Z. physiol. Chem.*, **35**, 41 (1902).

[102] McKenzie, *J. Chem. Soc.*, **81**, 1409 (1902).

[103] Magnus-Levy, *Biochem. Z.*, **2**, 319 (1907).

[104] Hamalainen, *Skand. Arch. Physiol.*, **23**, 86, 297 (1910); *Abs. Chem. Soc.*, **98**, (i) 326 (1910)

[105] Williams, *Biochem. J.*, **32**, 1849 (1938); **33**, 1519 (1939).

[106] Mayer, *Biochem. Z.*, **9**, 439 (1908).

organisms and providing for their highly specialized nutritional and environmental requirements are usually not available to the chemist. The method based upon animal feeding and subsequent isolation of products from the urine is perhaps less inconvenient and deserves further study. At present it appears that all the biochemical resolution methods for alcohols can be used profitably only in a few specially favorable instances or when other methods fail.

Controlled Asymmetric Biosynthesis. Various optically active alcohols have been prepared by processes employing purified enzyme preparations or well-defined enzyme systems developed by living tissues under controlled conditions. Thus when dl-bornyl dihydrogen phosphate was gradually hydrolyzed in the presence of yeast phosphatase [107] the first half of the process gave nearly pure l-borneol, the latter half nearly pure d-borneol. The introduction of benzaldehyde into a solution of sugar undergoing fermentation by yeast gave l-phenylacetylcarbinol; [108] similarly the perfusion of acetaldehyde through the liver or muscles of pigeons gave d-acetoin.[109] These results are presumably due to asymmetric acyloin syntheses controlled by enzymes. The introduction of methyl ethyl ketone into fermenting sugar gave a moderate yield of dextrorotatory methylethylcarbinol.[110] The effective agent in this instance was the sterically specific yeast reductase system. All these processes doubtless are fundamentally the same as natural asymmetric biosynthesis. The laboratory application, however, has the advantage that, within limits, the nature of the starting material and the type of reaction are under experimental control.

The yeast reduction method has been applied with considerable success, notably by Neuberg and Levene and their associates, to several simple ketones,[110] as well as to a few diketones [111, 108] and many hydroxy ketones [112, 56, 57, 58, 113, 114, 115] and hydroxy aldehydes,[112, 116, 114] the products being active alcohols or glycols. Among the more interesting examples are the series of active glycols derived from ketones of the type $RCOCH_2OH(R = $ methyl to n-amyl) [112, 57, 58, 113, 115] and from 3-keto-2-butanol [56] and 3-keto-1-butanol.[114] Active glycols have been prepared

[107] Neuberg, Jacobsohn, and Wagner, *Biochem. Z.*, **188**, 227 (1927); *Fermentforschung,* **10**, 491 (1929).

[108] Neuberg and Ohle, *Biochem. Z.*, **127**, 327 (1922); **128**, 610 (1922).

[109] Tanko, Munk, and Abonyi, *Z. physiol. Chem.*, **264**, 91 (1940).

[110] Neuberg and Nord, *Ber.*, **52**, 2237 (1919).

[111] Neuberg and Nord, *Ber.*, **52**, 2248 (1919).

[112] Farber, Nord, and Neuberg, *Biochem. Z.*, **112**, 313 (1920).

[113] Levene and Walti, *Org. Syntheses*, **10**, 84 (1930).

[114] Levene and Walti, *J. Biol. Chem.*, **94**, 361 (1931).

[115] Levene and Walti, *J. Biol. Chem.*, **98**, 735 (1932).

[116] Neuberg and Kerb, *Biochem. Z.*, **92**, 96 (1918).

also from 3-hydroxybutanal,[116] 2-hydroxypentanal,[114] and 2-hydroxyhexanal.[114] The method appears to be particularly suitable for the preparation of glycols and certain alcohols that are not readily obtained by other methods. The yields usually do not exceed 50%, and the method is subject to most of the disadvantages referred to above (p. 391).

EXPERIMENTAL CONDITIONS IN RESOLUTIONS THROUGH SALTS OF ACID ESTERS

Preparation of Acid Esters

The hydrogen phthalates may be prepared from nearly all stable secondary alcohols by heating equimolar quantities of pure phthalic anhydride and the *dl*-alcohol for twelve to fifteen hours in a flask in an oil bath at 110–115°. Primary alcohols usually require a shorter period of heating. A milder and much more rapid procedure consists in heating the alcohol and phthalic anhydride in the presence of about two molecular equivalents of dry pyridine,[74] with or without a diluent such as benzene or xylene. Heating for two to three hours in a steam bath is then usually sufficient. When the alcohol or the phthalate is unstable the esterification may be completed simply by refluxing the reagents in a low-boiling solvent [55] such as chloroform or petroleum ether or by allowing the mixture to remain overnight or longer at the ordinary temperature.[117] The solution finally is poured onto a mixture of ice and excess hydrochloric acid, and the crude ester is extracted with chloroform or benzene. It is then taken up in cold sodium carbonate solution, reprecipitated by acidification, and purified as usual.

It is important to use rather pure acid esters for the resolution step. The hydrogen phthalates are usually solids that may be crystallized from petroleum ether, benzene, or acetic acid. Phthalic acid is the usual major impurity and may interfere with the crystallization of the ester. If it does, or if the ester is liquid, it is convenient to extract the crude product with chloroform or benzene, in which phthalic acid is nearly insoluble. Distillation of the solvent from the dried extract usually leaves the ester pure enough to crystallize or to use directly.

The hydrogen succinates are prepared by procedures closely similar to those followed for the phthalates, except that succinic anhydride is used.[50] The crude ester is best taken up at once in ether or benzene, and the solution is washed with water to remove succinic acid. The hydrogen succinates are more soluble in the usual solvents than the corresponding phthalates and often do not crystallize readily. Their alkaloid salts also

[117] Duveen, *Compt. rend.*, **206**, 1185 (1938).

are usually more soluble than those of the phthalates. This may be an advantage when the alcohol is of high molecular weight or whenever the alkaloid salts of the phthalate are too sparingly soluble or too unstable [51, 53] for convenient recrystallization.

Formation and Separation of Salts

Since specific conditions for obtaining appropriate diastereoisomeric salts of any particular acid ester are difficult to define, the comments which follow refer to a general procedure and some of the more common variations for preparing and separating such compounds.

Solvents. The salts of the acid esters with the alkaloid or other active base are usually formed by adding one equivalent of the base in powdered form or in a solvent to the acid ester dissolved in acetone, pure or aqueous methanol or ethanol, or ethyl acetate. Warming usually results in the formation of a complete solution which on cooling, or on concentration and cooling, deposits the greater part of the less soluble salt. This is then recrystallized from the same or another solvent. Sometimes it is advantageous to form the salts in a small amount of an effective solvent, such as acetone or methanol, and induce crystallization by adding chloroform or some other less powerful solvent.[51] Occasionally the desired salt is too sparingly soluble to be recrystallized conveniently; it may then be purified by repeated extraction of the more soluble salt with hot solvent.[74] Water is almost never suitable as a solvent since the salts are usually partially hydrolyzed.

Resolving Agents. The active bases most frequently used are brucine, strychnine, cinchonine, cinchonidine, quinine, and quinidine, in about the order given. A few other alkaloids, such as ephedrine, pseudoephedrine, yohimbine, cocaine, morphine, and apomorphine have found some general use for resolving acids but rarely or never have been used for resolving acid esters. Synthetic amines, such as *l*-menthylamine [48] and *d*- or *l*-α-phenylethylamine,[118] have found only occasional use. It is suggested that these amines, as well as numerous other synthetic amines that have been introduced as potential resolving agents,[36, 38, 39] might well be investigated further when alkaloids are unsuitable or unobtainable.

Fractional Crystallization. Experimental difficulties are encountered principally in the problem of separating the two diastereoisomeric derivatives by fractional crystallization. This, of course, is a special case of

[118] Gough, Hunter, and Kenyon, *J. Chem. Soc.*, **1926**, 2052.

the general problem involved in dealing with a heterogeneous system of three components.[119, 120] In practice three fairly distinct situations may be encountered:

(a) The two diastereoisomers may have adequate crystallizing power and at the same time may differ considerably in crystalline character and/or in solubility in the available solvents. Such isomers are readily separated by simple fractional crystallization, and not infrequently the more soluble as well as the less soluble can be obtained pure.

(b) The two diastereoisomers do not differ greatly in solubility. A prolonged *systematic* fractionation is then required, and usually only the less soluble salt is obtained pure. The course of the separation is followed generally by determining the rotatory power of the various fractions and by observing the changes in solubility and crystalline appearance of the successive fractions.

(c) Much more frequently than is commonly realized the two isomers cannot be separated satisfactorily by crystallization. This situation results when the substances are so low in crystallizing power or so similar in solubilities or so unstable chemically that separation is impracticable. Moreover, in the most unfavorable instances (which are far from uncommon) the two diastereoisomers may crystallize together as a stable double compound or as a series of solid solutions. The resolution then necessarily fails.

When a favorable result is not obtained with a given resolving agent and solvent, a change must be made to another system. In general, it is most convenient first to remove the original solvent and substitute another; mixed solvents are sometimes useful. Should no satisfactory solvent be found, the original resolving agent may be replaced by another, and so on, if necessary, until a successful resolution is effected or until all available combinations of resolving agents and solvents have been tried. No method for predicting the combination of resolving agent and solvent for any particular substance has been discovered. Even minor structural differences such as exist between neighboring homologs may lead to the necessity of using different resolving agents and solvents.

Pickard and Kenyon used brucine and acetone successfully for the initial resolution of the hydrogen phthalates of a series of alcohols of the type $CH_3-CHOH-R$,[50] in which R represents normal alkyl groups from ethyl to undecyl. The d-form of the phthalate formed the less

[119] Rooseboom, *Z. physik. Chem.*, **28**, 494 (1899).

[120] Findlay, "The Phase Rule," Chapters XXV and XXVI, 7th ed., Longmans, Green & Co., New York, 1931.

soluble salt in most instances. Partially resolved fractions rich in the
d-form also were purified readily through the strychnine salts, but this
agent was not useful for initial resolution of the dl-form. The l-forms of
most of this series were purified, with some difficulty, through the rather
soluble cinchonidine salts prepared from the residual levorotatory
phthalates.

The phthalates of a similar series of the type $(CH_3)_2CH$—CHOH—R [51]
were resolved with strychnine, which gave the d-forms; the l-forms usually were purified from the residual material through the brucine salts.
The phthalates of a series of the type C_2H_5—CHOH—R [53] were resolved
with strychnine. Up to R = hexyl the less soluble salt was that of the
d-form; for the remainder of the series it was that of the l-form. Except
when R was methyl or n-propyl, brucine formed only stable double salts
in this series.

Purification of Both Active Forms. In many otherwise satisfactory
resolutions only the less soluble of the two diastereoisomers can be purified; this yields only one of the desired active forms. When the second
form also is required, the usual procedure is to seek another combination
of solvent and resolving agent such that the second active form now produces the less soluble of the two derivatives. This procedure may be
applied to the original racemic substance; more commonly it is applied to
the partially resolved material recovered from the more soluble fractions
of the original resolution, since this already contains an excess of the
desired form.

Marckwald [121] has introduced a generally reliable method of obtaining
the second form pure by the use of the enantiomorph of the original resolving agent; the enantiomorph of the less soluble salt in the initial
resolution is then formed. The difficulty is that alkaloids, which almost
invariably have been used for resolving acid esters, are rarely available
in both forms. Purely synthetic amines, such as d- and l-α-phenyl-
ethylamine, are not subject to this limitation [118] and might well find increasing use for this reason. The fact that the dl-amine itself must be
resolved before the active forms are available has prevented extensive
use of Marckwald's method, but it may be noted that a procedure has
been described [122, 38, 39, 123, 124] by which the dl-form of an amine sometimes may be used directly for completing a resolution. Other procedures
for obtaining both active forms of alcohols are included in the examples
and text, pp. 397–398, 400, 402.

[121] Marckwald, *Ber.*, **29**, 43 (1896).

[122] Ingersoll, *J. Am. Chem. Soc.*, **47**, 1168 (1925); **50**, 2264 (1928).

[123] Ingersoll, Babcock, and Burns, *J. Am. Chem. Soc.*, **55**, 411 (1933).

[124] Ingersoll and Little, *J. Am. Chem. Soc.*, **56**, 2123 (1934).

Isolation of Active Acid Esters

In general, the active acid esters are set free from the salts merely by adding the salts, alone or dissolved in acetone or ethanol, to warm water containing a moderate excess of hydrochloric acid. The crude active hydrogen phthalates separate sometimes as oils which solidify on cooling and standing. They are filtered, ground in a mortar with water, refiltered, and washed with dilute hydrochloric acid and water to remove any entrapped base.

Purification of Active Acid Esters

It is usually advisable, after removing the resolving agent, to test the purity of the crude active ester. The fractionation of the alkaloid salts may not have given optically pure products, and, in any event, the crude ester may contain traces of the resolving agent and other impurities. When the active acid ester crystallizes well it may be examined by recrystallization and observation of the melting points and rotatory powers of the various fractions. Usually this procedure will show whether some of the racemic form is still present since this form probably will tend to accumulate at either the head or the foot of the series, depending on whether it is less soluble or more soluble than the active form. When the active form is pure or becomes so on recrystallization it is ready for hydrolysis. Otherwise the impure product (or any incompletely resolved fractions) may be recombined with the original or another resolving agent and the fractionation continued.

Hydrolysis of Active Acid Esters

The hydrolysis of the active alkyl phthalates is usually carried out by dissolving them in a 20–25% aqueous solution of sodium hydroxide containing 2.5 moles of alkali and distilling the mixture with steam. Filtration or extraction [77] of the alcohol may be necessary when it is not volatile with steam. No evidence of racemization has been observed with various types of saturated alcohols even on prolonged boiling with concentrated aqueous alkali. Certain alcohols of the allylic type [125, 126] or alcohols otherwise sensitive to alkali or to heating may require more cautious treatment, both in the hydrolysis [82] and in the subsequent final purification.[127] Should the alcohol be found to be optically impure at this stage it sometimes may be purified by recrystallization. Either the

[125] Kenyon, Partridge, and Phillips, *J. Chem. Soc.*, **1936,** 85.
[126] Kenyon, Partridge, and Phillips, *J. Chem. Soc.*, **1937,** 207.
[127] Bartlett, Kuna, and Levene, *J. Biol. Chem.*, **118,** 513 (1937).

alcohol itself or a suitable solid derivative, such as the benzoate or *p*-nitrobenzoate, may be used for this purpose. The purification in this way, of course, is practicable only when the active and racemic forms are separable by crystallization.

EXPERIMENTAL PROCEDURES

Procedures are given for (1) resolution by the use of a simple ester; (2) resolution by crystallization of brucine salts of acid phthalates which are readily separated; and (3) a similar resolution in which the separation of the diastereoisomeric salts is difficult. In addition to the preparations described in this chapter other instructive examples, showing various further modifications and helpful devices, may be found in references 53, 74, 76, 128, 69, and 125.

Preparation of *l*-Menthoxyacetic Acid [129, 130, 131, 131a]

To a solution of 312 g. (2.0 moles) of *l*-menthol in 750 cc. of sodium-dried toluene in a 5-l. flask there is added 55 g. (2.4 atoms) of sodium in thin slices or wire form. The flask is attached to an upright condenser provided with a soda-lime tube, and the mixture is heated in a steam bath with frequent shaking for five to eight hours. Higher temperatures or excessively prolonged heating are inadvisable since isomerization of the menthol may occur.[132, 133, 134] The mixture is allowed to cool somewhat, and the excess sodium is removed mechanically. A solution of 80 g. (0.85 mole) of anhydrous chloroacetic acid in 1 l. of dry toluene is then gradually added while the solution is stirred rapidly so that the precipitate of sodium chloride and sodium chloroacetate remains finely divided. The mixture finally is heated in a steam bath for twenty-four hours or longer; during this period it is protected by a soda-lime tube and is maintained in a fluid condition by the addition of more toluene and by frequent shaking.

About 500 cc. of water is then added, and the mixture is shaken and separated in the usual way, each layer being carefully washed with the other solvent. (Emulsions usually may be broken by passing the mix-

[128] Houssa and Kenyon, *J. Chem. Soc.*, **1930**, 2260.
[129] Frankland and O'Sullivan, *J. Chem. Soc.*, **99**, 2375 (1911).
[130] Rule and Tod, *J. Chem. Soc.*, **1931**, 1932.
[131] Holmes and Adams, *J. Am. Chem. Soc.*, **56**, 2093 (1934).
[131a] Leffler and Calkins, *Org. Syntheses*, **23**, 52, 55 (1943).
[132] Wagner and Brykner, *J. Russ. Phys. Chem. Soc.*, **35**, 537 (1903).
[133] Hückel and Naab, *Ber.*, **64**, 2137 (1931).
[134] Windaus, *Ber.*, **49**, 1733 (1916).

ture slowly through a suction filter.) The toluene layer contains more than half of the menthol originally taken. This may be recovered by distillation, or, when several runs are to be made, the solution is dried by distilling a portion of the toluene and is used in the next run.

The aqueous layer is acidified, the crude *l*-menthoxyacetic acid is extracted with a liberal amount of toluene, the extract is distilled to remove toluene and water, and the *l*-menthoxyacetic acid is distilled under reduced pressure. The principal fraction, b.p. 160–170°/10 mm., is satisfactory for conversion to the chloride. The yield is 70–78%, based on the chloroacetic acid. The pure acid has b.p. 163–164°/10 mm., m.p. 52–54°, and $[\alpha]_D^{25} - 91.5°$ ($c = 2$, 95% ethanol).

l-Menthoxyacetyl chloride is conveniently prepared immediately before use; the yield in the following procedure is assumed to be quantitative. One part of the acid is mixed with 2.7 parts by weight of thionyl chloride in a flask connected by a ground-glass joint to an upright condenser (hood). The mixture is warmed in a water bath at 50° for three hours. Most of the excess thionyl chloride is then distilled through the condenser at atmospheric pressure and the remainder is removed by warming the mixture for a short time under slightly reduced pressure (water pump). The residue is satisfactory for most purposes; if desired, the chloride may be distilled, b.p. 132°/10 mm.

d-Menthoxyacetic acid and its chloride may be prepared similarly by starting with *d*-menthol. The active menthoxyacetyl chlorides have been employed in a useful method for resolving amino acids [131] as well as for the resolution of alcohols and phenols.

Resolution of *dl*-Menthol [26]

l-Menthoxyacetyl chloride (233 g., 1 mole) is added slowly to 157 g. (1 mole) of *dl*-menthol dissolved in 750 cc. of anhydrous pyridine, and the mixture is left overnight. The major part of the pyridine is then recovered by distillation, and the residue is poured into 2 l. of water. The crystalline precipitate is filtered, and the filtrate is extracted with several portions of ether or benzene. The solid is then dissolved in the same solvent (including the extract), and the solution is washed with dilute hydrochloric acid, dilute sodium hydroxide, and water. The solvent is then distilled, and the residue is distilled with steam to remove unchanged menthol. This may be slightly levorotatory. A little menthoxyacetic acid may be recovered by acidifying the sodium hydroxide washings. The crude *dl*-menthyl-*l*-menthoxyacetate after filtering and drying amounts to 310–320 g. and is used directly in the next step; $[\alpha]_D - 50°$ to $-55°$ ($c = 2$, chloroform).

The crude ester is resolved by semi-systematic crystallization from methanol. In this process the successive crops obtained from the original solution are examined polarimetrically and are then rearranged for recrystallization in the order of increasing negative rotation; closely similar fractions may be combined. The fraction of lowest negative rotation is recrystallized from fresh solvent, and the remaining fractions are crystallized in order from the mother liquors of the preceding fraction. Fractions initially having specific rotations substantially lower than that of the dl-alcohol-l-acid ester usually yield pure d-menthyl-l-methoxyacetate after five or six crystallizations. This has m.p. 91.5° and $[\alpha]_D - 6.6°(c = 2$, chloroform). About 40% of the calculated amount of this ester can be obtained fairly readily. Fractions having high negative rotations are best combined, without attempting complete purification, for the later recovery of crude l-menthol. Pure l-menthyl-l-menthoxyacetate has $[\alpha]_D - 109.7°$.

Pure d-menthyl-l-menthoxyacetate is hydrolyzed by refluxing for an hour with 1.2 mole equivalents of 5–10% ethanolic potassium hydroxide. (More vigorous hydrolysis is inadvisable since l-menthol may thus be formed from the resolving agent by rupture of the ether linkage.) The mixture is almost neutralized to phenolphthalein with hydrochloric acid and is distilled with steam to remove first the ethanol and then the menthol. The menthol is conveniently extracted with benzene and purified by distillation under reduced pressure. It has b.p. 97–99°/10 mm., 215–216°/760 mm.; m.p. 42°; and $[\alpha]_D^{20} + 49.5°(c = 2, 95\%$ ethanol). The yield in this step is 80–85%.

Crude l-menthol is obtained similarly from the strongly levorotatory fractions of the ester. It may be purified by esterification with d-menthoxyacetyl chloride and crystallization of the resulting mixture of esters. The l-alcohol-d-acid ester is then readily purified since it is the less soluble and also the more abundant component. Various other methods for purifying the partially active l-menthol also may be used if desired. See references in Table III, p. 408).

Resolution of dl-2-Octanol [49, 135, 136]

Preparation of dl-Octyl Hydrogen Phthalate. A mixture of 130 g. (1 mole) of dl-2-octanol and 148 g. (1 mole) of resublimed phthalic anhydride is heated for twelve to fifteen hours in a flask in an oil bath at 110–115°; higher temperatures produce a lower yield of dark product. The

[135] Kenyon, *J. Chem. Soc.*, **121**, 2540 (1922).
[136] Kenyon, *Org. Syntheses, Coll. Vol.* **I**, 418, 2nd ed., 1941.

mixture is stirred occasionally during the heating to give a homogeneous liquid. The cooled mixture is poured into a solution of 150 g. (1.4 moles) of sodium carbonate in about 8 l. of water, and the mixture is stirred without warming until the solid dissolves. Unless the solution is completely clear it is best extracted with a little benzene (to remove unreacted alcohol and neutral phthalate ester) and passed through a wet filter to remove suspended benzene. A slight excess of hydrochloric acid is then added, and the initially oily precipitate of *dl*-octyl hydrogen phthalate is allowed to harden, crushed to a powder, filtered, and dried. The yield is substantially quantitative when pure alcohol is used. The product may be used directly for the next step if colorless and dry. Otherwise it may be recrystallized from about its own weight of 90% acetic acid or from petroleum ether (b.p. 60–90°). The pure product melts at 55°.

A somewhat lower yield may be obtained by a shorter method. A mixture of 130 g. (1 mole) of *dl*-2-octanol and 155 g. (1.05 moles) of resublimed phthalic anhydride in 150 cc. of *dry* pyridine is refluxed in a steam bath for three hours. (If the mixture first is allowed to stand overnight, the heating may be shortened to one hour.) The mixture, while still somewhat warm, is poured upon 500 g. of clean ice to which 175 cc. of hydrochloric acid (sp. gr. 1.18) has been added. When the ice has melted, the aqueous portion is decanted from the oily or semi-solid hydrogen phthalate and extracted with three 50-cc. portions of chloroform. The extracts, with a little additional chloroform, are used to dissolve the crude hydrogen phthalate, and the solution is freed from adhering water and phthalic acid by gentle suction filtration through a layer of powdered anhydrous sodium sulfate. The crude product is recovered by distillation of the chloroform and recrystallized, preferably from 90% acetic acid. The yield by this method is 82–88%.

Resolution with Brucine in Acetone. A warm solution of 278 g. (1 mole) of *dl*-octyl hydrogen phthalate in 600 cc. of acetone is treated with 394 g. (1 mole) of powdered anhydrous brucine, and the solution is warmed until clear. A wide-mouthed Erlenmeyer flask covered by a "cold finger" or Friedrichs condenser is convenient for this step. On cooling, preferably overnight in a cold room, the nearly pure brucine salt of *d*-octyl hydrogen phthalate crystallizes and is filtered. The salt is removed from the funnel, stirred with 250 cc. of warm acetone, and again filtered. The filtrates and washings, which contain principally the brucine salt of *l*-octyl hydrogen phthalate, are united and used in the next step.

Decomposition of the Brucine Salts. The acetone filtrate is concentrated by distillation to about half its original volume and is stirred slowly while still warm into 1.5 l. of water to which 100 cc. of concentrated hydrochloric acid (sp. gr. 1.18) has been added. Crude *l*-octyl hydrogen phthalate precipitates as an oil. When this has solidified it is filtered, transferred to a mortar, and ground to a powder in the presence of a little water. It is then filtered, washed, and dried. Thorough washing in this way is necessary to remove entrapped brucine hydrochloride. A small additional amount of the phthalate may be obtained from the mother liquors and washings by extraction with benzene.

Crude *d*-octyl hydrogen phthalate is obtained similarly from the crystalline brucine salt. This is first dissolved in the minimum amount of hot ethanol, and the solution is poured into the dilute acid. The aqueous solutions containing brucine hydrochloride are retained for the recovery of brucine.

Purification of the Crude Active Hydrogen Phthalates. The purpose of this step is to remove the small proportion of *dl*-octyl hydrogen phthalate that still is present in the crude active forms. The active forms are crystallized separately from about 2 parts by weight of 90% acetic acid, in which the racemic form is much more soluble than the active forms. Two crystallizations are usually required to give products melting at 75° and having $[\alpha]_D \pm 48.4°$ ($c = 5$, 95% ethanol). The yield of the active forms at this point is about 70%. The crude *dl*-form may be recovered from the acetic acid mother liquors and used in another run.

Recovery of the Active Alcohols. Each of the pure hydrogen phthalates is hydrolyzed by dissolving it in 2.5 moles of sodium hydroxide (in 20–25% solution) and distilling the mixture with steam. The alcohol layer of the distillate is separated, dried with potassium carbonate, and distilled. Alternatively the alcohols may be taken up in about 5 volumes of pure benzene and dried by distilling the moist benzene. The active alcohols boil at 86°/20 mm. and have $[\alpha]_D^{17} \pm 9.8°$ ($c = 5$, 95% ethanol). The yield in this step is practically quantitative.

It may be noted that the purification of the crude active hydrogen phthalates by recrystallization [135] permits a considerable simplification of the original procedure. [49] In the original procedure the crystalline brucine salt of *d*-octyl hydrogen phthalate had to be recrystallized two or more times from acetone, in which it is sparingly soluble, before it became pure; also the crude *l*-octyl hydrogen phthalate, after recovery from the mother liquors, had to be converted to the cinchonidine salt, and this required six or more recrystallizations from acetone, in which it is rather soluble, before it became pure. The crude active hydrogen phthalates obtained by removing the resolving agents were then hydrolyzed without further purification.

Resolution of s-Butyl Alcohol [50, 53, 137, 138, 139]

A solution of 447 g. (2 moles) of pure s-butyl hydrogen phthalate [50] in 2 l. of warm acetone is treated with 790 g. (2.01 moles) of anhydrous brucine and the mixture is kept under reflux at about 40° for an hour. The solution is then heated to boiling and filtered hot. The solution is kept for several hours in a cold room or icebox, after which the first crop (A_1) of crude brucine d-s-butyl phthalate is filtered and washed with about 300 cc. of cold acetone. The combined filtrate and washings are concentrated to about 1 l., and a second crop (A_2) is taken. Further concentration to about 400 cc. may yield a small third crop (A_3). The final mother liquor is set aside.

The crystalline crops amount to 60–75% of the total salt. Crop A_1 is recrystallized from about 1.5 l. of acetone, and crops A_2 and A_3 are united and crystallized from the mother liquor. The filtrate on concentration may give additional small crops. The final mother liquor is united with that from the original solution.

The crystalline fractions are now systematically recrystallized from methanol. The head crop is recrystallized from about 600 cc. of this solvent, and the remaining crops are crystallized in order from the successive mother liquors. At each stage the volume of the solution is adjusted by addition or distillation of solvent so that from one-third to one-half of the salt crystallizes. A series of large Erlenmeyer flasks, fitted with a reflux condenser or distilling head as required, is convenient for the purpose. The recrystallization is continued, using fresh or recovered solvent, until the head fraction has $[\alpha]_D^{20} - 2.8°$ or less ($c = 4$, methanol). It is unnecessary to take rotation values until the crystalline appearance and solubility behavior of the head fraction become approximately constant. Usually five to seven recrystallizations are necessary for purification. When pure, the head fraction is removed from the series and the recrystallization of the remaining crops is continued as long as it appears profitable. The final mother liquor from each series is reserved.

Working in this way it is possible to obtain fairly readily about 50–55% of the calculated amount of pure brucine d-s-butyl phthalate; the yield depends on how long the fractionation is continued and how the mother liquors are handled (see below). When large quantities of alcohol are to be resolved it is convenient to unite the material from several runs at this stage.

[137] Viditz, Biochem. Z., **259**, 294 (1933).
[138] Sprung and Wallis, J. Am. Chem. Soc., **56**, 1717 (1934).
[139] Butler and Dickison, J. Pharmacol., **69**, 225 (1940).

The d-s-butyl hydrogen phthalate and the corresponding pure alcohol may be obtained from the brucine salt by the general procedure previously described for the octyl hydrogen phthalates (p. 402). Pure d-s-butyl hydrogen phthalate has $[\alpha]_D + 38.5°$ ($c = 4$, 95% ethanol). Alternatively, the process may be shortened considerably by treating the brucine salt directly with a small excess of dilute sodium hydroxide and distilling the alcohol with steam.[138] The alcohol is extracted or is salted out with potassium carbonate, dried, and distilled; b.p. 98°/750 mm.; $[\alpha]_D^{27} + 10.83°$ (without solvent).

The l-form of the alcohol can be obtained in 85–90% purity from the combined acetone and final methanol mother liquors by a rather laborious process of fractional crystallization aided by mechanical separation.[137, 140] Thus on long standing the acetone solution may deposit characteristic nodular aggregates of leaflets of nearly pure brucine l-s-butyl phthalate, $[\alpha]_D - 18.0°$; these are separated by filtration or decantation. The solution, upon concentration, may then yield more of the crude d-salt and then again the l-salt. The method is tedious but gives rather good yields, especially when large quantities of material may be worked up in a leisurely fashion.

The l-alcohol also can be purified by fractionation of the cinchonidine salts of the hydrogen succinate.[53] For this purpose the alcohol is recovered from the mother liquors of the brucine salt and converted to the hydrogen succinate by the general procedures previously outlined (p. 393). The oily succinate is combined with one molecular proportion of cinchonidine in acetone. The very soluble cinchonidine l-s-butyl succinate is purified by five or six crystallizations and then has m.p. 54–55°; $[\alpha]_D - 85°$ ($c = 5$, 95% ethanol). The alcohol is recovered from the pure salt in the usual way.

TABLES OF OPTICALLY ACTIVE ALCOHOLS AND PHENOLS

In the tables which follow are listed the various alcohols and phenols which have been resolved or which have been obtained in optically active forms from natural sources by equivalent procedures. They are arranged in the order of increasing molecular weight and are classified as follows: acyclic saturated monoalcohols, Table I; alkylcycloalkylcarbinols, Table II; alicyclic and terpenoid alcohols, Table III; saturated alcohols containing aryl groups, Table IV; unsaturated alcohols containing aryl groups, Table V; acyclic unsaturated alcohols, Table VI; miscellaneous monoalcohols; Table VII; glycols and polyalcohols, Table VIII; phenols, Table IX.

[140] Dickison, private communication.

TABLE I

ACYCLIC SATURATED MONOALCOHOLS

Alcohol	Derivative Employed or Method of Resolution	Reference
C$_4$ Methylethylcarbinol	Brucine sulfate	42
	Brucine tetrachlorophthalate *	42
	Brucine phthalate	50, 137, 138, 139, 141
	Strychnine succinate	50, 139
	Tartranilate	40
	Biochemical resolution †	99, 142
	Asymmetric biosynthesis	110
	Decomposition on active catalyst †	91
	Distillation of esters †	16
	Partial esterification with tartaric acid *	90
C$_5$ Methyl-n-propylcarbinol	Brucine phthalate	50, 143
	Strychnine succinate	50, 143
	Strychnine phthalate	74
	Asymmetric biosynthesis	110
	Biochemical resolution †	98
	Tartranilate	40
Methylisopropylcarbinol	Strychnine and brucine phthalates	51
	Brucine succinate	51
s-Butylcarbinol	Brucine 3-nitrophthalate	82
	Cinchonidine 3-nitrophthalate	82
	Brucine, strychnine, cinchonidine and l-menthylamine phthalates *	82
	Tartranilate, p-bromotartranilate †	40
C$_6$ Methyl-n-butylcarbinol	Brucine and strychnine phthalates	50, 53, 75
	Cinchonidine succinate	50, 53
	Tartranilate	40
	Biochemical resolution †	96, 100
	Distillation of esters †	16
	Brucine sulfate *	42
Methylisobutylcarbinol	Brucine phthalate	50, 72, 67
	Cinchonidine succinate	50
Methyl-t-butylcarbinol	Brucine and strychnine phthalates	55
	Cinchonidine phthalate †	55
Ethyl-n-propylcarbinol	Brucine and strychnine phthalates	53, 144
	Quinidine phthalate †	144
	Biochemical resolution †	96, 99
	Strychnine and morphine sulfates *	41

* Methods resulting in failure or unsatisfactory results.
† Partial resolution only.

TABLE I—*Continued*

ACYCLIC SATURATED MONOALCOHOLS

Alcohol	Derivative Employed or Method of Resolution	Reference
Ethylisopropylcarbinol	Strychnine phthalate	51
	Brucine phthalate †	51
C₇ Methyl-*n*-amylcarbinol	Brucine and cinchonidine phthalates	50, 54
	Biochemical resolution †	99
Ethyl-*n*-butylcarbinol	Strychnine phthalate	53, 144, 75
	Brucine and quinidine phthalates †	53, 144
Ethylisobutylcarbinol	Strychnine phthalate	67
	Brucine phthalate †	49, 145
α-Ethyl-*s*-butylcarbinol	Brucine phthalate	146
β-Ethyl-*s*-butylcarbinol	Brucine phthalate *	146
n-Propylisopropylcarbinol	Strychnine and brucine phthalates	51
C₈ Methyl-*n*-hexylcarbinol	Brucine phthalate	49, 50, 54, 135, 136, 147
	Cinchonidine phthalate	49, 50
	Tartranilate	40
Ethyl-*n*-amylcarbinol	Strychnine phthalate	53
	Brucine phthalate †	53
n-Propyl-*n*-butylcarbinol	Strychnine and brucine phthalates	68, 75
n-Propylisobutylcarbinol	Brucine phthalate	145, 67
n-Propyl-*s*-butylcarbinol	Brucine phthalate	145
n-Propyl-*t*-butylcarbinol	Strychnine phthalate	148
Isopropyl-*n*-butylcarbinol	Strychnine and brucine phthalates	50
2-Ethyl-1-hexanol	Brucine phthalate †	149
	Distillation of ester †	16
C₉ Methyl-*n*-heptylcarbinol	Brucine phthalate	50
Ethyl-*n*-hexylcarbinol	Brucine and cinchonidine phthalates	50, 144
	Strychnine and cinchonidine phthalates	53, 75
Isopropyl-*n*-amylcarbinol	Strychnine phthalate	51
	Cinchonidine succinate †	51
n-Butylisobutylcarbinol	Strychnine phthalate	67
C₁₀ Methyl-*n*-octylcarbinol	Brucine phthalate	50
Ethyl-*n*-heptylcarbinol	Strychnine phthalate	53
Isopropyl-*n*-hexylcarbinol	Strychnine phthalate	51
	Cinchonidine succinate †	51
Isobutyl-*n*-amylcarbinol	Strychnine phthalate	67
C₁₁ Methyl-*n*-nonylcarbinol	Brucine phthalate	50, 54
	Asymmetric biosynthesis †	110
Ethyl-*n*-octylcarbinol	Strychnine phthalate	53

* Methods resulting in failure or unsatisfactory results.
† Partial resolution only.

TABLE I—*Continued*

ACYCLIC SATURATED MONOALCOHOLS

Alcohol	Derivative Employed or Method of Resolution	Reference
C_{12} Methyl-*n*-decylcarbinol	Brucine phthalate	50
Ethyl-*n*-nonylcarbinol	Strychnine phthalate	53
Isopropyl-*n*-octylcarbinol	Strychnine phthalate	51
C_{13} Methyl-*n*-undecylcarbinol	Brucine phthalate	50
Ethyl-*n*-decylcarbinol	Strychnine phthalate	53
C_{14} Ethyl-*n*-undecylcarbinol	Strychnine phthalate	53
Isopropyl-*n*-decylcarbinol	Strychnine phthalate	51
C_{15} Ethyl-*n*-dodecylcarbinol	Strychnine phthalate	53
C_{16} Ethyl-*n*-tridecylcarbinol	Strychnine phthalate	53
C_{18} Ethyl-*n*-pentadecylcarbinol	Strychnine phthalate	53

[141] Kuhn and Albrecht, *Ber.*, **60**, 1297 (1927).
[142] Norris and Green, *Am. Chem. J.*, **26**, 293 (1901).
[143] Levene, Walti, and Haller, *J. Biol. Chem.*, **72**, 591 (1927).
[144] Kenyon, *J. Chem. Soc.*, **105**, 2226 (1914).
[145] Lowry, Pickard, and Kenyon, *J. Chem. Soc.*, **105**, 94 (1914).
[146] Duveen and Kenyon, *Bull. soc. chim.*, [5] **5**, 1120 (1938).
[147] Shriner and Young, *J. Am. Chem. Soc.*, **52**, 3332 (1930).
[148] Stevens, Higbee, and Armstrong, *J. Am. Chem. Soc.*, **60**, 2558 (1938).
[149] Kenyon and Platt, *J. Chem. Soc.*, **1939**, 633.

TABLE II

ALKYLCYCLOALKYLCARBINOLS

Alcohol	Derivative Employed or Method of Resolution	Reference
Methylcyclohexylcarbinol	Brucine and cinchonine phthalates	150, 74, 66
	Strychnine phthalate	69
Ethylcyclohexylcarbinol	Strychnine phthalate	74, 69
n-Propylcyclohexylcarbinol	Strychnine phthalate	69
n-Butylcyclohexylcarbinol	Strychnine phthalate	69

[150] Domleo and Kenyon, *J. Chem. Soc.*, **1926**, 1841.

TABLE III

ALICYCLIC AND TERPENOID ALCOHOLS

Alcohol	Derivative Employed or Method of Resolution	Reference
α-2-Methylcyclohexanol	Strychnine phthalate	118
β-2-Methylcyclohexanol	l-α-Phenylethylamine phthalate	118
	Strychnine phthalate	118
ac-Tetrahydro-β-naphthol	l-Menthylurethane †	20
	Cinchonine and brucine phthalates	52
	Digitonide †	87
cis-β-Decalol	Hydrogen d-camphorate *	22
	Various alkaloid phthalates *	8
Borneol	l-Menthylamine phthalate	48
	d- and l-Bornoxyacetates	28
	Enzymic hydrolysis of acid phosphate †	107
	Animal feeding †	104
Isoborneol	l-Menthylamine and cinchonine phthalates	48
	Cinchonidine succinate †	151
Carvomenthol	Strychnine phthalate †	152, 80
	Digitonide *	87
α-(?)-Fenchol	Enzymic hydrolysis of pyrophosphate †	153
Linaloöl	Strychnine phthalate	81
Menthol	Cinchonine and brucine phthalates	83, 154
	Cinchonidine succinate †	83
	Strychnine phthalate	155
	d-Camphor-10-sulfonate	25
	d- and l-Menthoxyacetates	26
	Tartranilate	40
	Enzymic hydrolysis of acid phosphate †	107
	Animal feeding †	105
Neomenthol	Brucine phthalate	83
	Quinine succinate	83
	Cinchonidine and quinine phthalates †	83
	Cinchonidine succinate †	83
	d-Camphor-10-sulfonate *	27
	l-Menthoxyacetate *	27
Isomenthol	Animal feeding †	105
	d-Camphor-10-sulfonate *	33
	l-Menthoxyacetate *	33
Neoisomenthol	Fractionation of crystalline esters	156
Pulegol	Strychnine phthalate	155
Isopulegol	Strychnine phthalate	157

* Methods resulting in failure or unsatisfactory results.
† Partial resolution only.

TABLE III—*Continued*

ALICYCLIC AND TERPENOID ALCOHOLS

Alcohol	Derivative Employed or Method of Resolution	Reference
α-Santalol	Strychnine phthalate	81, 158
β-Santalol	Strychnine phthalate	81, 158
α-Terpineol	Brucine and strychnine phthalates	79, 80
	Digitonide †	87
	Tartranilate *	40
Thujol (Tanacetol)	Cinchonine and strychnine phthalates	159, 160
Isothujol	Cinchonine and strychnine phthalates	160
Neothujol	Cinchonine and strychnine phthalates	160

[151] Beckmann, *Ber.*, **42**, 487 (1909).
[152] Paolini, *Atti acad. Lincei*, [5] **28**, (i) 82, (ii) 134 (1919) [*C. A.*, **14**, 1672 (1920)].
[153] Ochiai, *Biochem. Z.*, **253**, 185 (1932).
[154] Kenyon and Pickard, *J. Chem. Soc.*, **107**, 45 (1915).
[155] Paolini, *Atti acad. Lincei*, [5] **28**, (ii) 190 (1919) [*C. A.*, **14**, 2173 (1920)].
[156] Hückel and Niggemeyer, *Ber.*, **72**, 1354 (1939).
[157] Pickard, Hunter, Lewcock, and Pennington, *J. Chem. Soc.*, **117**, 1248 (1920).
[158] Bradfield, Penfold, and Simonsen, *J. Chem. Soc.*, **1935**, 309.
[159] Tschugaeff and Fomin, *Ber.*, **45**, 1293 (1912).
[160] Short and Read, *J. Chem. Soc.*, **1939**, 1040.

TABLE IV

SATURATED ALCOHOLS CONTAINING ARYL GROUPS

Alcohol	Derivative Employed or Method of Resolution	Reference
C₈ Methylphenylcarbinol	Brucine succinate	50, 161, 163, 128
	Brucine phthalate	73, 76, 162, 163, 128
	Asymmetric biosynthesis †	110
	Asymmetric acylation †	164
	Hydrogen *d*-camphorate *	22
	Digitonide *	87
	Tartranilate *	40
C₉ Methylbenzylcarbinol	Brucine and strychnine phthalates	55, 165, 78, 166

* Methods resulting in failure or unsatisfactory results.
† Partial resolution only.

TABLE IV—*Continued*

SATURATED ALCOHOLS CONTAINING ARYL GROUPS

Alcohol	Derivative Employed or Method of Resolution	Reference
Ethylphenylcarbinol	Brucine and cinchonidine succinates	50
	Strychnine phthalate	73, 76
	Hydrogen *d*-camphorate *	20
Dideuteroethylphenylcarbinol	Fractionation of crystalline esters *	167
2-Phenyl-1-propanol	Brucine and cinchonidine 3-nitro-phthalates	82, 71
	Cinchonine and strychnine 3-nitro-phthalates †	82
	Brucine phthalate *	82
C$_{10}$ Methyl-β-phenethylcarbinol	Brucine and cinchonidine phthalates	55
	Desoxycholic acid †	86
Ethylbenzylcarbinol	Strychnine phthalate	77
n-Propylphenylcarbinol	Strychnine phthalate	73, 69, 76
	Quinidine and strychnine phthalates	168
Isopropylphenylcarbinol	Strychnine and brucine phthalates	73
3-Phenyl-1-butanol	Strychnine 3-nitrophthalate	82, 71
C$_{11}$ Ethyl-β-phenethylcarbinol	Strychnine and cinchonidine phthalates	169
n-Butylphenylcarbinol	Cinchonidine phthalate	73, 69
C$_{12}$ Methyl-α-naphthylcarbinol	Brucine and strychnine phthalates	55, 74
Methyl-β-naphthylcarbinol	Cinchonidine and strychnine phthalates	170
n-Propyl-β-phenethylcarbinol	Brucine phthalate	169
C$_{13}$ Cyclohexylphenylcarbinol	Cinchonidine phthalate	74
C$_{14}$ Phenylbenzylcarbinol	Quinine phthalate	72
	Quinine and cinchonine phthalates	171
Phenyl-*p*-tolylcarbinol	Brucine phthalate *	14
C$_{15}$ Phenyl-β-phenethylcarbinol	Brucine and strychnine phthalates	169
C$_{17}$ *n*-Hexyl-α-naphthylcarbinol	Brucine phthalate	172

* Methods resulting in failure or unsatisfactory results.

† Partial resolution only.

[161] McKenzie and Clough, *J. Chem. Soc.*, **103**, 687 (1913).

[162] Downer and Kenyon, *J. Chem. Soc.*, **1939**, 1156.

[163] Ott, *Ber.*, **61**, 2139 (1928).

[164] Wegler, *Ann.*, **498**, 62 (1932); **506**, 72 (1933).

[165] Kenyon and Pickard, *J. Chem. Soc.*, **105**, 2262 (1914).

[166] Kenyon, Phillips, and Pittman, *J. Chem. Soc.*, **1935**, 1072.

[167] Coppock, Kenyon, and Partridge, *J. Chem. Soc.*, **1938**, 1069.

[168] Kenyon and Partridge, *J. Chem. Soc.*, **1936**, 128.

[169] Hewitt and Kenyon, *J. Chem. Soc.*, **127**, 1094 (1925).

[170] Collyer and Kenyon, *J. Chem. Soc.*, **1940**, 676.

[171] Gerrard and Kenyon, *J. Chem. Soc.*, **1928**, 2564.

[172] Kenyon and Pickard, *J. Chem. Soc.*, **105**, 2644 (1914).

TABLE V

Unsaturated Alcohols Containing Aryl Groups

Alcohol	Derivative Employed or Method of Resolution	Reference
Vinylphenylcarbinol	Quinidine phthalate	117
α-Propenylphenylcarbinol	Quinidine phthalate	125, 126, 117
Methyl-α-styrylcarbinol	Quinidine phthalate	125, 126
Ethyl-α-styrylcarbinol	Cinchonidine phthalate †	77
	Brucine and strychnine phthalates *	77

TABLE VI

Acyclic Unsaturated Alcohols

	Alcohol	Derivative Employed or Method of Resolution	Reference
C$_4$	Methylvinylcarbinol	Brucine phthalate	169
C$_5$	Methylallylcarbinol	Brucine phthalate	59, 60
	Methyl-α-propenylcarbinol	Brucine phthalate	61, 173
	Ethylvinylcarbinol	Strychnine phthalate	169
		Brucine phthalate	174
	Ethylethynylcarbinol	Brucine phthalate	175
C$_6$	1-Hexene-5-ol	Brucine phthalate	58
	2-Methyl-2-pentene-4-ol	Brucine and strychnine phthalates	176, 177
	Ethylallylcarbinol	Strychnine phthalate	56
	n-Propylvinylcarbinol	Strychnine and brucine phthalates	169, 65
	Vinylallylcarbinol	Brucine phthalate	63
C$_7$	2-Methyl-2-hexene-5-ol	Brucine phthalate	62
	3-Heptene-5-ol	Strychnine phthalate	178
	n-Propylallylcarbinol	Brucine phthalate	179
	n-Propyl-α-propenylcarbinol	Brucine phthalate	70
		Strychnine phthalate	180
	Isopropyl-α-propenylcarbinol	Strychnine phthalate	181
	n-Butylvinylcarbinol	Strychnine and morphine phthalates	169, 64, 76
	Isobutylvinyl carbinol	Brucine and strychnine phthalates *	127
	Allyl-α-propenylcarbinol	Brucine phthalate	182
		Ephedrine phthalate *	182
		Cinchonidine and quinidine phthalates *	182

* Methods resulting in failure or unsatisfactory results.
† Partial resolution only.

TABLE VI—*Continued*

ACYCLIC UNSATURATED ALCOHOLS

Alcohol	Derivative Employed or Method of Resolution	Reference
C$_8$ *n*-Butyl-α-propenylcarbinol	Cinchonidine phthalate †	64
Isobutyl-α-propenylcarbinol	Strychnine phthalate †	127
C$_9$ *n*-Amylallylcarbinol	Strychnine phthalate	183
C$_{10}$ Cyclohexyl-α-propenylcarbinol	Brucine phthalate	184

[173] Hills, Kenyon, and Phillips, *Chemistry & Industry*, **52,** 660 (1933); *J. Chem. Soc.*, **1936,** 576.

[174] Kamai, *J. Gen. Chem. U.S.R.R.*, **1,** 460 (1931).

[175] McGrew and Adams, *J. Am. Chem. Soc.*, **59,** 1497 (1937).

[176] Duveen and Kenyon, *J. Chem. Soc.*, **1936,** 1451.

[177] Kenyon and Young, *J. Chem. Soc.*, **1938,** 1452.

[178] Platt, *J. Chem. Soc.*, **1941,** 316.

[179] Consden, Duveen, and Kenyon, *J. Chem. Soc.*, **1938,** 2104.

[180] Arcus and Kenyon, *J. Chem. Soc.*, **1938,** 312, 1912.

[181] Bartlett, Kuna, and Levene, *J. Biol. Chem.*, **118,** 503 (1937).

[182] Duveen and Kenyon, *Bull. soc. chim.*, [5] **5,** 704 (1938).

[183] Levene and Walti, *J. Biol. Chem.*, **94,** 593 (1931).

[184] Kuna and Levene, *J. Biol. Chem.*, **118,** 315 (1937).

TABLE VII

MISCELLANEOUS MONOALCOHOLS

Alcohol	Derivative Employed or Method of Resolution	Reference
Tetrahydrofurylcarbinol	Brucine phthalate	185
Methyl-α-furylcarbinol	Quinidine and brucine phthalates	186, 187
Methyl-α-tetrahydrofurylcarbinol (α-form)	Brucine phthalate	187
Phenylacetylcarbinol	Asymmetric biosynthesis	108
Benzoin	Asymmetric biosynthesis †	111
	d- and *l*-δ-(α-phenylethylamine) semi-carbazide	188
Methylethylphenylcarbinol	*d*-Camphorsulfonate ester *	189
	Hydrolysis of active thioglycollic acid derivative *	189

* Methods resulting in failure or unsatisfactory results.

† Partial resolution only.

TABLE VII—*Continued*

MISCELLANEOUS MONOALCOHOLS

Alcohol	Derivative Employed or Method of Resolution	Reference
Phenyldiphenylyl-α-naphthylcarbinol	Hydrolysis of active thioglycollic acid derivative *	189
p-Azo-α-naphthol-diphenylmethylcarbinol	Differential adsorption *	190

[185] Balfe, Irwin, and Kenyon, *J. Chem. Soc.*, **1941**, 312.
[186] Duveen and Kenyon, *J. Chem. Soc.*, **1936**, 621.
[187] Duveen and Kenyon, *Bull. soc. chim.*, [5] **7**, 165 (1940).
[188] Hopper and Wilson, *J. Chem. Soc.*, **1928**, 2483.
[189] Wallis and Adams, *J. Am. Chem. Soc.*, **53**, 2253 (1931); **55** 3838 (1933).
[190] Porter and Hirst, *J. Am. Chem. Soc.*, **41**, 1264 (1919).

TABLE VIII

GLYCOLS AND POLYALCOHOLS

Alcohol	Derivative Employed or Method of Resolution	Reference
Propane-1,2-diol (propylene glycol)	Biochemical resolution †	96, 97, 99
	Strychnine disulfate †	104
	Asymmetric biosynthesis	112, 113
Butane-1,3-diol	Asymmetric biosynthesis	116
trans-Butane-2,3-diol	Asymmetric biosynthesis	111, 56
	Asymmetric induction	191
erythro-3-Bromo-2-butanol	Asymmetric induction	191
threo-3-Bromo-2-butanol	Asymmetric induction	191
Erythritol	Spontaneous segregation †	7
Pentane-1,2-diol	Asymmetric biosynthesis	57, 114
Pentane-1,3-diol	Asymmetric biosynthesis	114
Hexane-1,2-diol	Asymmetric biosynthesis	58, 114
Heptane-1,2-diol	Asymmetric biosynthesis	115
trans-Cyclopentane-1,2-diol	Strychnine disulfate	47
	Enzymic hydrolysis of d-glucoside	85
trans-Cyclohexane-1,2-diol	l-Menthylurethane	186
	Strychnine disulfate	45
	l-Menthoxyacetate	29

* Methods resulting in failure or unsatisfactory results.
† Partial resolution only.

TABLE VIII—*Continued*

GLYCOLS AND POLYALCOHOLS

Alcohol	Derivative Employed or Method of Resolution	Reference
trans-Cycloheptane-1,2-diol	Strychnine disulfate	46, 47
trans-1-Methylcyclohexane-3,4-diol	Strychnine disulfate	47
cis-1-Methylcyclohexane-3,4-diol	Strychnine disulfate	47
Isohydrobenzoin	Spontaneous segregation from ether †	10, 9, 11, 14, 12
	Spontaneous segregation from ethyl acetate	11, 14, 12, 13
trans-Hydrindene-1,2-diol	*l*-Menthylurethane	192

[191] Winstein and Lucas, *J. Am. Chem. Soc.*, **62**, 1576, 2845 (1940).
[192] Van Loon, Thesis, Delft, 1919 [*C. A.*, **17**, 1956 (1923)].

TABLE IX

PHENOLS

Alcohol	Derivative Employed or Method of Resolution	Reference
α-Phenyl-α-*p*-hydroxyphenyl-ethane	*l*-Menthylurethane	20
3,6-Di(2,4-dimethylphenyl)-2,5-dibromohydroquinone	*l*-Menthoxyacetate	30
cis-3,6-Di(3-bromo-2,4,6-trimethylphenyl)-2,5-dibromohydroquinone	*l*-Menthoxyacetate	30
7-Hydroxyflavanone	*l*-Menthoxyacetate	31
Demethoxymateucinol	*l*-Menthoxyacetate	31
Equilenin	*d*- and *l*-Menthoxyacetates	32
Isoequilenin	*l*-Menthoxyacetate *	32
α-Tocopherol	*d*-Camphor-10-sulfonate ester †	193

* Methods resulting in failure or unsatisfactory results.
† Partial resolution only.

[193] Karrer, Fritzsche, Ringier, and Salomon, *Helv. Chim. Acta*, **21**, 520, 820 (1938); **22**, 1139 (1939).

CHAPTER 10

THE PREPARATION OF AROMATIC ARSONIC AND ARSINIC ACIDS BY THE BART, BECHAMP, AND ROSENMUND REACTIONS

CLIFF S. HAMILTON AND JACK F. MORGAN

University of Nebraska

CONTENTS

INTRODUCTION

Arsonic acids may be regarded as derived from orthoarsenic acid, $(HO)_3As \rightarrow O$, by replacement of one of the hydroxyl groups with an organic residue; the arsinic acids are similarly derived by replacement of two hydroxyl groups. The general formulas for the two types are $RAs(OH)_2$ for arsonic acids and R_2As—OH for arsinic acids. The neutral arsine oxides, $R_3As{\rightarrow}O$, may be considered as derivatives in which all the hydroxyl groups have been replaced by organic residues.

Three methods for the preparation of aromatic arsonic acids are described in this review. By far the most widely applicable of these is the Bart reaction, which involves the interaction of a diazonium salt with an inorganic arsenic compound. In the original Bart process [1] and most of its modifications an alkali arsenite is used, as shown in the following equation.

$$C_6H_5N_2{}^+Cl^- + As(ONa)_3 \rightarrow C_6H_5AsO_3Na_2 + NaCl + N_2$$

In the Scheller modification (p. 418) arsenic trichloride, rather than the alkali arsenite, is employed.

The next most useful process is that of Bechamp,[2] which involves the direct arsonation of phenols, aromatic amines, and certain of their derivatives by heating with arsenic acid.

$$HO\text{—}\langle\text{ }\rangle + H_3AsO_4 \rightarrow HO\text{—}\langle\text{ }\rangle\text{—}AsO_3H_2 + H_2O$$

In the Rosenmund synthesis salts of arsonic acids are obtained by treatment of aryl halides with sodium or potassium arsenite.[3]

$$\langle\text{ }\rangle\genfrac{}{}{0pt}{}{Br}{CO_2K} + As(OK)_3 \rightarrow \langle\text{ }\rangle\genfrac{}{}{0pt}{}{AsO_3K_2}{CO_2K} + KBr$$

This method is of only limited application.

Arsinic acids and arsine oxides may be prepared by extensions of the Bart synthesis. Thus, diphenylarsinic acid is obtained from benzenediazonium chloride and disodium phenylarsenite.

$$C_6H_5N_2{}^+Cl^- + C_6H_5As(ONa)_2 \rightarrow (C_6H_5)_2AsO_2Na + NaCl + N_2$$

Similarly, the reaction of benzenediazonium chloride with sodium diphenylarsenite, $(C_6H_5)_2AsONa$, leads to triphenylarsine oxide, $(C_6H_5)_3AsO$.[4]

Arsinic acids are obtained also as by-products in the Bechamp synthesis. For example, 4,4'-diaminodiphenylarsinic acid, along with a

[1] Bart, Ger. pat., 250,264 (1910) [*Chem. Zentr.*, II, 882 (1912)].

[2] Bechamp, *Compt. rend.*, **56**, 1172 (1863).

[3] Rosenmund, *Ber.*, **54**, 438 (1921).

[4] Bart, Ger. pat., 254,345 (1910) [*Chem. Zentr.*, I, 196 (1913)].

lesser amount of 2,4'-diaminodiphenylarsinic acid, is formed when aniline is heated with arsenic acid.

$$C_6H_5NH_2 + H_3AsO_4 \longrightarrow p\text{-}NH_2C_6H_4AsO_3H_2 + H_2O$$

$$p\text{-}NH_2C_6H_4AsO_3H_2 + C_6H_5NH_2 \longrightarrow (p\text{-}NH_2C_6H_4)_2AsO_2H + H_2O$$

BART REACTION

Since 1910 the method of Bart [1] has been modified by a number of investigators, Bart, himself, being the first to improve the reaction. He found that coupling of aryldiazonium compounds with alkali arsenites is catalyzed by copper salts and by silver or copper powder.[5] In a later patent [6] the use of metallic catalysts, copper, nickel, or cobalt, as well as their salts is said to facilitate the removal of diazo nitrogen at low temperatures and to obviate the formation of by-products. Though many have since observed that the coupling reaction is speeded by the use of the above catalysts, no systematic study has been made to determine the effect of such catalysts on the final yield.

Sodium carbonate is often employed as a buffering agent in the ordinary Bart reaction. In this way phenylarsonic acid has been prepared in yields ranging from 50–60% [7] to as high as 86% [8] as compared with yields of 40–50% by the original process. The yield from benzenediazonium chloride and sodium arsenite is greatly influenced by the concentration of the arsenite, the speed of reaction, and especially by the pH of the solution (which should remain constant). All compounds, like sodium carbonate, which play the role of buffer, tend to increase the yield.[9]

Mouneyrat [10] modified Bart's procedure by the simultaneous use of two catalysts, one a salt of copper and the other a reducing agent. The nature of the reducing agent is varied according to the hydrogen-ion concentration of the reaction mixture. For example, hypophosphorous acid may be employed in acid solution; sodium hydrosulfite or sodium formaldehyde sulfoxylate can be used in neutral or alkaline solution; and in alkaline solution, sodium formaldehyde sulfoxylate, sodium hydrosulfite, or excess alkali arsenites are substances available as reducing agents. The reaction medium is either water or a water-alcohol solution. This modification has been utilized in very few instances, and in these

[5] Bart, Ger. pat., 254,092 (1910) [*Chem. Zentr.*, I, 196 (1913)]; Ger. pat., 264,924 (1910) [*C.A.*, **8**, 213 (1914)].

[6] Bart, Ger. pat., 268,172 (1912) [*Chem. Zentr.*, I, 308 (1914)].

[7] Palmer and Adams, *J. Am. Chem. Soc.*, **44**, 1356 (1922).

[8] Blas, *Anales soc. españ. fis. quím.*, **36**, 107 (1940) [*C.A.*, **34**, 7286 (1940)].

[9] Blas, *Génie civil*, **115**, 448 (1939) [*C.A.*, **34**, 2342 (1940)].

[10] Mouneyrat, Brit. pat., 142,947 (1919) [*J. Chem. Soc.*, **118**, 579i (1920)].

cases no yields are available.   Whether the modification has certain advantages over the original method of Bart is uncertain.

Schmidt [11] suggested that the coupling reaction be carried out in neutral solution and without a catalyst.   The best yields were obtained when the aryldiazonium chloride reacted with dipotassium arsenite in aqueous solution.

By means of this method, o-nitrophenylarsonic acid was prepared in a yield of 86% as compared with a yield of only 60% by the original Bart process.   According to Schmidt, the proportion of by-products, especially the parent hydrocarbon (benzene in the illustration), increases with higher alkalinity.   In acid solution the yields are low unless the aromatic diazo compounds contain strongly negative substituents, such as nitro groups, in the *ortho* and *para* positions (as in 2,4-dinitrobenzenediazonium chloride, for example).

Sakellarios [12] improved the synthesis of o-nitrodiphenylarsinic acid by coupling o-nitrobenzenediazonium chloride with phenylarsenous oxide in a buffered acid solution (acetic acid-sodium acetate) without the aid of a catalyst; this technique increased the yield from 54%,[13] by the original method of Bart, to 87%.   Special conditions are required to effect the reaction in the case of 2,4-dinitroaniline.   The reaction may be carried out in strong mineral acid solution or preferably by the procedure of Sakellarios.[14, 15, 16]   Though the modification of Sakellarios may be of relatively general application to weakly basic amines, the method has been so little used that no statement as to its applicability can be made.

Scheller [17] modified the Bart reaction to such an extent that his method is often referred to as the "Scheller reaction."   Primary aromatic amines, dissolved in methanol or glacial acetic acid, are diazotized in the presence of arsenic trichloride and a trace of cuprous chloride.   Removal of the solvent followed by treatment with water and sodium hydrosulfite gives the expected arsonic acids.

[11] Schmidt, *Ann.*, **421**, 159 (1920).

[12] Sakellarios, *Ber.*, **57**, 1514 (1924).

[13] Kalb, *Ann.*, **423**, 39 (1921).

[14] Bart, *Ann.*, **429**, 55, 103 (1922).

[15] Sievers, Ger. pat., 547,724 (1929) [*C.A.*, **26**, 3519 (1932)].

[16] Benda, U. S. pats., 1,075,537; 1,075,538 [*C.A.*, **7**, 4046 (1913)]; Ger. pat., 266,944 (1911) [*Chem. Zentr.*, II, 1905 (1913)]; Brit. pat., 24,667 (1912) [*C.A.*, **8**, 401 (1914)].

[17] Scheller, Brit. pat., 261,026 (1925) [*C.A.*, **21**, 3371 (1927)].

$$RN_2^+HSO_4^- + AsCl_3 \rightarrow N_2 + R-As \underset{\underset{OSO_3H}{\diagup Cl}}{\overset{\overset{Cl}{\diagup Cl}}{\diagdown}} \xrightarrow{H_2O} R-AsO_3H_2$$

In this manner Scheller has been able to convert p-nitroaniline and p-aminoacetophenone to the corresponding arsonic acids.

The method of Scheller has been extended by Doak,[18] Oneto and Way,[19, 20] and Foldi.[21] Scheller's reaction gives better yields than the original Bart synthesis in several instances, particularly if a negative substituent is present in the *meta* position. Although m-aminobenzenesulfonamide cannot be converted to an arsonic acid by the usual methods, nevertheless, a 58% yield is obtained in a modified Scheller reaction using ethanol as the solvent and cuprous bromide as catalyst. The same procedure improves the synthesis of m-nitrophenylarsonic acid, 3-nitro-4-methylphenylarsonic acid, m-carboxyphenylarsonic acid, and p-sulfamidophenylarsonic acid.[18] However, the method has failed to convert metanilic acid, 3,5-xylidine, and 2,6-xylidine into the corresponding arsonic acids. Apparently the difficulty with 2,6-xylidine is not due to steric hindrance, since a 30% yield of 2,6-dimethylphenylarsonic acid is realized by the original Bart process.

The most recent modification of Bart's reaction involves the use of aryldiazonium borofluorides in place of the customary diazonium chlorides. Because of their increased stability the diazonium borofluorides were observed to have less tendency to decompose or to form by-products when allowed to react with sodium arsenite; furthermore, the reactions could be carried out at room temperature. The modification appears to be particularly useful in the preparation of p-nitrophenylarsonic acid, the yield being 79% as compared with 45% by the original method of Bart. When other diazonium borofluorides were used as starting materials the yields were sometimes lower than those reported by the usual Bart procedure, but more often they were as good or slightly better.[22]

Effect of Substituent Groups on Yields

In general, primary aromatic amines can be converted into the corresponding arsonic acids by the Bart reaction or by one of its modifications. This method has been used to prepare arsonic acids of the benzene, naphthalene, fluorene, and anthraquinone series as well as of a number

---

[18] Doak, *J. Am. Chem. Soc.*, **62**, 167 (1940).

[19] Oneto and Way, *J. Am. Chem. Soc.*, **62**, 2157 (1940).

[20] Oneto and Way, *J. Am. Chem. Soc.*, **63**, 3068 (1941).

[21] Foldi, *Ber.*, **56**, 2489 (1923).

[22] Ruddy, Starkey, and Hartung, *J. Am. Chem. Soc.*, **64**, 828 (1942).

of heterocyclic types. For a study of the effect of substituents on yields, examples from the benzene series only will be considered.

The preparation of phenylarsonic acid, which proceeds in an average yield of 45–55%, must of necessity serve as the basis for comparison of yields from substituted amines. The following discussion deals primarily with reactions taking place in neutral or alkaline solution; practically all the yields reported in this discussion are by either the original Bart process or by Schmidt's modification, the few exceptions being noted.

Alkyl Groups. As expected, all three toluidines give toluenearsonic acids in good yields (45–55%). From the o-, m-, and p-aminobenzyl alcohols the corresponding arsonic acids result in yields of 12–20%.[23] When the reaction is applied to 2-hydroxy-4-nitro-5-alkylanilines,[24] the yield of arsonic acid decreases as the length of the side chain is increased. o-Butylphenylarsonic acid is obtained by the Bart method in only a 12% yield.[25]

Nitro Groups. Nitroanilines are converted to the corresponding arsonic acids in the following yields:

	YIELD, %
m-Nitrophenylarsonic acid	0–35
p-Nitrophenylarsonic acid	36–45
o-Nitrophenylarsonic acid	80–90
2,4-Dinitrophenylarsonic acid	68–70

A comparison of the yields of the *meta* and *ortho* isomers is significant. A survey of Bart reactions on variously substituted m- and o-nitroanilines further illustrates the hampering effect of m-nitro groups and the strong beneficial influence of o-nitro groups. Two examples are given below:

	YIELD, %
p-Hydroxyphenylarsonic acid [14]	92
3-Nitro-4-hydroxyphenylarsonic acid [14]	38
m-Hydroxyphenylarsonic acid [26]	0
2-Nitro-5-hydroxyphenylarsonic acid [27]	37

An apparent exception to the favorable influence of an o-nitro group is found in 2-bromo-6-nitroaniline.[28] The failure of the Bart reaction on this compound may be due to steric hindrance.

[23] Fourneau and Lestrange, *Bull. soc. chim.*, [4] **53**, 330 (1933).

[24] Baranger, *Bull. soc. chim.*, [4] **49**, 1213 (1931).

[25] John, M. S. Thesis, University of Nebraska, 1930.

[26] McGrew, M. S. Thesis, University of Nebraska, 1935.

[27] Phillips, *J. Chem. Soc.*, **1930**, 1910.

[28] Gibson and Johnson, *J. Chem. Soc.*, **1931**, 3270.

Halogen. In general, the presence of halogen in the nucleus does not interfere with Bart's method. *o*-Chloroaniline and *m*-chloroaniline are converted to the corresponding arsonic acids in yields of 40–70%,[29, 30, 31] and *p*-chloroaniline gives somewhat better yields (60–80%).[30, 32] Similarly, the three monobromoanilines are converted into bromophenylarsonic acids in slightly lower yields. With *m*-iodoaniline as a starting material a 24% yield of the corresponding arsonic acid is obtained.[29] When *o*-iodoaniline is subjected to the Bart reaction two products result, *o*-phenylenediarsonic acid in 20% yield, together with a lesser amount of *o*-iodophenylarsonic acid.[29] The *o*-iodophenylarsonic acid first formed reacts with another molecule of sodium arsenite (Rosenmund reaction) to produce the diarsonic acid. The conversion of 2,4-, 2,5-, and 3,4-dichloroaniline to the corresponding arsonic acids takes place in yields of 60–70%.[33]

Hydroxyl Groups. Although *o*- and *p*-aminophenols have been converted into *o*- and *p*-hydroxyphenylarsonic acids in satisfactory yields (35–90%),[14, 34] the reaction fails with the *meta* isomer.[26] Several substituted hydroxyphenylarsonic acids have been prepared by the Bart reaction. Following are a number of examples:

	YIELD, %
2-Hydroxy-4-nitrophenylarsonic acid [35, 36]	55–78
2-Hydroxy-3-nitrophenylarsonic acid [37]	29
3-Hydroxy-5-nitrophenylarsonic acid [37]	8
4-Hydroxy-3-carboxyphenylarsonic acid [38]	46

Alkoxyl Groups. Simple alkoxyl substituted phenylarsonic acids may be synthesized from the corresponding amines without difficulty. *o*-Methoxyphenylarsonic acid may be prepared in 58% yield, and a nearly quantitative yield of *p*-ethoxyphenylarsonic acid is obtained from *p*-phenetidine.[14] The favorable influence of a *p*-alkoxyl group is further illustrated by the preparation of 3-hydroxy-4-methoxyphenylarsonic acid in a 26% yield.[39] As previously mentioned, *m*-hydroxyphenylarsonic acid could not be prepared from *m*-aminophenol; *o*- and *m*-β-hy-

[29] Barber, *J. Chem. Soc.*, **1929**, 2333.
[30] Doak, Steinman, and Eagle, *J. Am. Chem. Soc.*, **63**, 99 (1941).
[31] Etzelmiller and Hamilton, *J. Am. Chem. Soc.*, **53**, 3085 (1931).
[32] Izmailskii and Simonov, *Khim. Farm. Prom.*, **1933**, 317 [*C.A.*, **28**, 3721 (1934)].
[33] Braz and Tuturin, *J. Gen. Chem. U.S.S.R.*, **9**, 992 (1939) [*C.A.*, **33** 8583 (1939)]
[34] Harrington, M. S. Thesis, University of Nebraska, 1935.
[35] Bauer, *Ber.*, **48**, 1579 (1915).
[36] Hewitt and King, *J. Chem. Soc.*, **1926**, 817.
[37] Fourneau, Trefouel, and Benoit, *Bull. soc. chim.*, [4] **41**, 499 (1927).
[38] Gough and King, *J. Chem. Soc.*, **1930**, 669.
[39] Fargher, *J. Chem. Soc.*, **1920**, 865.

droxyethylphenylarsonic acids result in yields of 10% and 53% respectively when the corresponding amines are used in the Bart reaction.[40, 36] The presence of a basic group in the alkoxyl side chain (e.g., in p-β-diethylaminoethoxyaniline) decreases the yield and may even prevent the formation of an arsonic acid.[41]

Carboxyl Groups. Yields of 50–60% of o- and p-carboxyphenylarsonic acids have been reported,[42, 43] and the *meta* isomer has been prepared but no yield was given.[14] With negative substituents in the *ortho* and *para* positions the reaction is usually improved. 2-Carboxy-4-nitrophenylarsonic acid has been prepared in a 76% yield.[44]

Ketone and Aldehyde Groups. The o-, m-, and p-aminoacetophenones may be converted to the corresponding arsonic acids in yields of 75%, 45%, and 66% respectively.[45] Strangely enough, α-chloro- and α-bromoacetophenone-p-arsonic acids could not be prepared by the Bart-Schmidt reaction on the corresponding amino compounds.[45] From m- and p-aminobenzaldehydes the arsonic acids are obtained in yields of 4% and 22% respectively.[45, 46] That a nitro group in the *ortho* position to the amino group aids the reaction is shown by a 47% yield of 3-nitro-4-arsonobenzaldehyde.[46]

Arsono Groups. The three isomeric aminophenylarsonic acids can be converted into the corresponding phenylenediarsonic acids by means of the Bart reaction. The o-isomer gives a 44% yield of the diarsonic acid,[13] and a 14% yield of p-phenylenediarsonic acid is recorded.[47] It is to be noted that the presence of the o-nitro group in 2-nitro-4-arsonoaniline increases the yield from 14% to 70–85%.[34, 48]

Sulfo and Sulfamido Groups. It has been shown that sulfanilic acid can be converted into p-sulfophenylarsonic acid (25–45%).[49, 50] By the ordinary Bart reaction p-sulfamidophenylarsonic acid (25%) may be prepared,[50] although a better yield (57%) is obtained by a modified Scheller reaction.[18] Apparently, metanilic acid and naphthionic acid will not yield the corresponding arsonic acids.[18, 51] Although m-sulfamidophenylarsonic acid is not available by the usual procedure it can be prepared in a 58% yield by the method of Scheller.[18]

[40] Binkley and Hamilton, *J. Am. Chem. Soc.*, **59**, 1716 (1937).
[41] Morgan, M. S. Thesis, University of Nebraska, 1940.
[42] Lewis and Cheetham, *J. Am. Chem. Soc.*, **43**, 2117 (1921)
[43] Lewis and Cheetham, *J. Am. Chem. Soc.*, **45**, 510 (1923).
[44] Karrer, *Ber.*, **48**, 1058 (1915).
[45] Gibson and Levin, *J. Chem. Soc.*, **1931**, 2388.
[46] Scott and Hamilton, *J. Am. Chem. Soc.*, **52**, 4122 (1930).
[47] Lieb, *Ber.*, **54**, 1511 (1921).
[48] Lieb and Wintersteiner, *Ber.*, **56**, 425 (1923).
[49] Oneto, *J. Am. Chem. Soc.*, **60**, 2058 (1938).
[50] Oneto and Way, *J. Am. Chem. Soc.*, **61**, 2105 (1939).
[51] Weitkamp, M. S. Thesis, University of Nebraska, 1935.

Procedures

PHENYLARSONIC ACID [7]

For the production of phenylarsonic acid on a large laboratory scale, a 25-l. cylindrical copper tank, provided with mechanical stirrer, is employed. In the tank are placed 4 l. of water, 2 kg. of anhydrous sodium carbonate, 1 kg. of technical arsenious oxide (about 20% excess), and 45 g. of crystallized copper sulfate. The solid material does not entirely dissolve unless the solution is heated. The stirrer is started, and the walls of the tank are cooled by several streams of water. As soon as the temperature of the arsenite solution falls to 15° (part of the sodium arsenite precipitates at this temperature), the addition of diazo solution is begun. It is convenient to prepare the diazo solution in four portions. A mixture of 186 g. (2 moles) of aniline, 400 cc. of concentrated hydrochloric acid, 1 l. of water, and sufficient ice to bring the total volume to 3 l. is made and placed in a 4-l. Florence flask. This mixture is diazotized in the usual manner with a concentrated aqueous solution of 140 g. of sodium nitrite. Three hours or more is required for running four of these ice-cold diazo solutions into the arsenite, the temperature of the arsenite being maintained at 15°. During this addition, foaming can be controlled by regulating the speed of stirring and also by adding about 10 cc. of benzene whenever excessive foaming threatens to occur.

Stirring is continued for one hour after all the diazo solution has been added. The mixture is now filtered and the filtrate concentrated to a volume of approximately 5 l.; this is deep brown in color. Concentrated hydrochloric acid is added in small portions, and the tarry material which separates is filtered off. The acid is added until after filtering a clear, pale yellow solution results. The phenylarsonic acid is now precipitated by the addition of more hydrochloric acid. An excess must be avoided since it causes a certain amount of the phenylarsonic acid to go into solution. When this neutralized mixture has cooled, the product is filtered off and washed with a little distilled water. Small quantities of phenylarsonic acid remaining in the filtrate may be precipitated as the ferric salt by adding ferric chloride. The yield of white or cream-colored product averages more than 800 g. (50%) and in many cases runs well over 1000 g. (62%). After recrystallization from water the product is practically white and softens at 158°, passing into the infusible anhydride, $C_6H_5AsO_2$.

o-NITROPHENYLARSONIC ACID [52]

One hundred grams (0.725 mole) of o-nitroaniline is ground under 500 cc. of 1 : 1 hydrochloric acid; the mixture is chilled to 10° and

[52] Jacobs, Heidelberger, and Rolf, *J. Am. Chem. Soc.*, **40**, 1580 (1918).

diazotized with a solution of 55 g. of sodium nitrite. After ten to fifteen minutes' stirring the solution is filtered from traces of undissolved nitroaniline and poured slowly, with shaking, into 550 cc. of 25% sodium hydroxide solution, the temperature being kept below 0°. The alkaline solution is then added to 135 g. of sodium arsenite dissolved in 1250 cc. of water and the mixture heated to 60–70° for an hour and a half to two hours, during which time a slow but steady nitrogen evolution occurs. Overheating is particularly to be avoided. After acidification with a slight excess of acetic acid the dark-colored solution is clarified with charcoal, and hydrochloric acid is added to the deep yellow filtrate until it is strongly acid to Congo red. On thorough chilling the nitrophenylarsonic acid crystallizes as a heavy, pale yellow powder. The yield is 110 grams (61%).

o-NITRODIPHENYLARSINIC ACID [12]

o-Nitroaniline (138 g., 1 mole) is suspended in 800 cc. of concentrated hydrochloric acid; the mixture is heated a few minutes to form the hydrochloride, and then heated with 500 cc. of boiling water to dissolve the hydrochloride. This hot solution is poured in a thin stream onto 16 kg. of well-stirred crushed ice, precipitating the hydrochloride as a fine suspension. Diazotization is accomplished by adding a solution of sodium nitrite (76 g.) to the stirred suspension. The solution may be filtered to remove any unchanged o-nitroaniline.

To the above solution is added (during forty-five minutes) a buffered phenylarsenous oxide solution containing 185 g. of phenylarsenous oxide * in 440 cc. of 5 N sodium hydroxide and 800 g. of technical sodium acetate in 5000 cc. of water. During the addition more ice (5 kg.) is added to maintain a low temperature. After about half of the phenyl-

* The phenylarsenous oxide solution is most conveniently prepared from phenyldichloroarsine, which is readily available from phenylarsonic acid. Crude phenylarsonic acid (404 g., 2 moles) is dissolved in concentrated hydrochloric acid (700 cc.) and treated with a stream of sulfur dioxide. From time to time a trace of potassium iodide solution is added (0.2–0.5 g. of potassium iodide is usually sufficient to complete the reduction). When the hydrochloric acid solution becomes clear and the addition of more potassium iodide does not form a permanent cloudiness the reaction is complete. Two to three hours is usually required for this reaction. The crude phenyldichloroarsine separates as a heavy oil. The oil is removed, dried with calcium chloride, and fractionally distilled at reduced pressure in a stream of carbon dioxide or nitrogen. The nearly colorless product boiling at 140–143°/40 mm. is collected; it weighs 334–400 g. (75–90%), depending on the purity of the original phenylarsonic acid.

Phenyldichloroarsine (245.5 g., 1.1 moles) is placed in a dropping funnel and very cautiously added dropwise to a warm stirred solution of sodium hydroxide (176 g., 4.4 moles) in water (410 cc.). The solution should be stirred for thirty minutes after the addition. It will not matter if this solution remains slightly turbid. The solution described here represents 185 g. of phenylarsenous oxide in 440 cc. of 5 N sodium hydroxide as used in the above preparation.

arsenous oxide solution is added, *o*-nitrodiphenylarsinic acid begins to precipitate. At the end of the addition, the mixture is neutralized with 5 *N* sodium hydroxide (about 920 cc.), heated for a time with charcoal, and filtered. On acidifying the light yellow solution with concentrated hydrochloric acid, *o*-nitrodiphenylarsinic acid separates as a crystalline powder. The yield is 265.5 g. (87%).

MODIFIED SCHELLER-BART REACTION [18]

General Experimental Procedure. A mixture of the amine, 0.1 mole in 250 cc. of absolute alcohol, with 10 g. of sulfuric acid and 28 g. of arsenious chloride, cooled to 0°, is diazotized with a saturated aqueous solution of the calculated amount of sodium nitrite (starch-iodide end point). Then, and not before, 1 g. of cuprous bromide is added; the mixture is thoroughly stirred, warmed to 60° until no more nitrogen is evolved, and then distilled with steam. The separated arsonic acid is recrystallized.

m-**Nitrophenylarsonic Acid.** One mole of *m*-nitroaniline (138 g.) gives 133.5 g. (54%) of *m*-nitrophenylarsonic acid, after one recrystallization from water.

The advantage of the modified Bart procedure in certain cases may be shown by the following percentage yield figures, the first figure of each pair corresponding to the ordinary procedure, and the second figure to the modified one: *p*-sulfamido, 25, 57; *m*-sulfamido, 0, 58; *m*-nitro, 28, 54; 3-nitro-4-methyl, 15.5, 40; *m*-carboxy, 36.6, 76.

α-NAPHTHYLARSONIC ACID [53]

One mole of α-naphthylamine is dissolved in a mixture of 3000 cc. of hot water and 100 cc. of concentrated hydrochloric acid. After cooling to 0°, 200 cc. of hydrochloric acid (sp. gr. 1.18) is added and the α-naphthylamine is diazotized, in the usual manner, with one mole of sodium nitrite. The diazo solution thus obtained is poured into a solution of 600 g. of anhydrous sodium arsenite in 2000 cc. of water.

The best yield is obtained by allowing the diazonium compound to decompose slowly at room temperature. The evolution of nitrogen occurs for several days, and when it is complete the liquid is filtered from the brown by-product and then acidified with hydrochloric acid. The precipitate of crude α-naphthylarsonic acid is filtered off and purified by dissolving in a cold concentrated solution of sodium bicarbonate; the insoluble residue is filtered out; and naphthylarsonic acid is reprecipitated with hydrochloric acid. The yield is 50 g. (20%). On recrystallization from water the product separates as white needles melting at 197°.

[53] Hill and Balls, *J. Am. Chem. Soc.*, **44**, 2051 (1922).

ANTHRAQUINONE-1-ARSONIC ACID [54]

α-Aminoanthraquinone (22.3 g., 0.1 mole) is dissolved in 80 cc. of sulfuric acid (66° Bé.) and diazotized at room temperature with a mixture of 70 g. of sulfuric acid containing 47% nitrosylsulfuric acid and 60 cc. of sulfuric acid (66° Bé.). The acid solution is stirred with 600 g. of ice and then allowed to stand for one-half hour, and the reddish crystals are filtered off. After washing with 250 cc. of water, the diazonium compound is dissolved in an arsenite solution containing 25 g. of sodium arsenite in 250 cc. of water and 250 cc. of 2 N sodium carbonate. A vigorous evolution of nitrogen takes place. Without heating, the reaction mixture is stirred for three to four hours, during which time the sodium salt of the desired arsonic acid usually separates in silver-gray flakes. On the next day the precipitate is dissolved in 500 cc. of hot water, treated with charcoal, filtered, and the solution acidified with hydrochloric acid. The colorless to light yellow crystalline precipitate is washed with water and dried to obtain 8 g. of pure product. From the mother liquor of the sodium salt an additional 7 g. of the free arsonic acid is precipitated on acidification. The total yield is 15 g. (46%). On recrystallization from 75% acetic acid, anthraquinone-α-arsonic acid separates as colorless needles, slightly soluble in hot water, almost insoluble in methyl or ethyl alcohol.

2-ARSONOFLUORENE [55]

Fifteen grams (0.083 mole) of 2-aminofluorene is mixed with 550 cc. of water, treated with 20 cc. of concentrated hydrochloric acid, and heated to boiling. The resulting clear solution is cooled (40°) rapidly, thereby causing the precipitation of the hydrochloride of 2-aminofluorene. While this mass is stirred, a saturated aqueous solution of 6 g. of sodium nitrite is added dropwise. The resulting brownish yellow solution is gradually heated to 60°, filtered hot, and the filtrate cooled to 20°, causing the precipitation of golden yellow needles of 2-fluorenediazonium chloride.

Thirteen grams of sodium metaarsenite and 1 g. of copper sulfate are dissolved in 300 cc. of water. This solution is stirred during the entire course of the arsonation. In small portions, the mixture of solid fluorenediazonium chloride and its saturated solution is added to the arsenite at room temperature. At once a vigorous evolution of nitrogen occurs. Sufficient 6 N sodium hydroxide solution is added from time to time to make this arsenite solution just alkaline. When all the diazo compound

[54] Benda, J. prakt. chem., [2] 95, 74 (1917).
[55] Cislak and Hamilton, J. Am. Chem. Soc., 53, 746 (1931).

has been added, the solution is stirred for fifteen hours. After heating to 90° the solution is stirred for three-quarters of an hour, filtered hot, and the filtrate acidified with 10 cc. of concentrated hydrochloric acid, thereby precipitating 2-arsonofluorene. This precipitate is washed with water, dissolved in a dilute solution of sodium carbonate, reprecipitated with hydrochloric acid, separated by filtration, washed, and dried. The yield is 4.5 g. (18.7%).

p-NITROPHENYLARSONIC ACID [22]

The preparation of p-nitrobenzenediazonium borofluoride is described in *Organic Syntheses* [56] and is carried out as follows. Thirty-four grams (0.25 mole) of p-nitroaniline is dissolved in 110 cc. of fluoboric acid solution in a 400-cc. beaker. (Fluoboric acid is made by adding 184 g. of boric acid slowly, with constant stirring, to 450 g. of hydrofluoric acid (48–52%) in a copper, lead, or silver-plated container placed in an ice bath.) The beaker is placed in an ice bath, and the solution is stirred with an efficient stirrer. A cold solution of 17 g. (0.25 mole) of sodium nitrite in 34 cc. of water is added dropwise. When the addition is complete, the mixture is stirred for a few minutes and filtered by suction on a sintered glass filter. The solid diazonium fluoborate is washed once with 25–30 cc. of cold fluoboric acid, twice with 95 per cent alcohol, and several times with ether. (A sintered glass filter should be used for filtering, and the fluoborate should be stirred well on the filter with each washing, before suction is applied. The diazonium fluoborate is stable and may be dried in a vacuum desiccator over phosphorus pentoxide.) The product weighs 56–59 g. (95–99% of the theoretical amount).

To 600 cc. of water at room temperature are added 52 g. (0.4 mole) of sodium metaarsenite ($NaAsO_2$) and 6 g. of cuprous chloride. To this mixture is added, with vigorous stirring, over a period of an hour, the diazonium borofluoride (from a quarter-mole of p-nitroaniline) suspended in 300 cc. of cold water. The foaming which accompanies the evolution of free nitrogen is controlled by the addition of small amounts of ether as needed. As the reaction proceeds, 100 cc. of a sodium hydroxide solution (0.25 mole) is gradually added to maintain the proper alkalinity. Stirring is continued for another hour, and then the mixture is allowed to stand overnight. The next morning it is warmed at 65° for about thirty minutes and then filtered with suction through a Büchner funnel. Hydrochloric acid is added to the filtrate until it is acid to litmus; any tar separating at this point is removed by filtration. Activated charcoal is added, and the solution is concentrated over a flame to approximately

[56] Starkey, *Org. Syntheses*, **19**, 40 (1939).

200 cc. The charcoal is removed by filtration, and the filtrate is made acid to Congo red with hydrochloric acid. On cooling the p-nitrophenylarsonic acid separates and a further small amount of product may be obtained by further concentration of the mother liquor. The compound is purified either by dissolving in ammonium hydroxide solution and reprecipitating with hydrochloric acid or by recrystallization from water. The total yield is 79% of the theoretical.

BECHAMP REACTION

In 1863, Bechamp [2] heated aniline arsenite with an excess of aniline at 190–200° and obtained a colorless solid which he thought was an acidic anilide. However, in 1907, Ehrlich and Bertheim [57] clearly demonstrated that the reaction, now known as the Bechamp reaction, involves the replacement of a nuclear hydrogen by the arsono group and that the compound produced is 4-aminophenylarsonic acid. Since its discovery the Bechamp reaction has been extended to include many phenols, substituted phenyl ethers, amines, and their various derivatives. In all, the literature contains more than sixty articles dealing with this method.

Scope and Limitations of the Reaction

Arsonation of aromatic compounds by treatment with arsenic acid is, in general, applicable only to the amines, phenols, and their derivatives. The reaction is somewhat analogous to sulfonation, but it is less general in application because arsonation requires a more labile hydrogen atom than sulfonation. Even though the Bechamp reaction has been applied to numerous derivatives of benzene, there is no evidence that it has been applied extensively to other aromatic nuclei. Only one naphthalene derivative, 1-amino-2-naphthalenearsonic acid, is reported as having been prepared by the Bechamp reaction.[58] β-Naphthylamine, which might be expected to undergo arsonation in the alpha position, does not react with arsenic acid.[59] Dibenzofuran reacts with arsenic acid to give an 11% yield of 2-dibenzofurylarsonic acid.[60]

The presence of methyl groups in the *ortho* position causes a marked decrease in yield, apparently due to conflicting orientation. For example, *o*-toluidine gives only a 14% yield of 3-methyl-4-aminophenylarsonic acid [61] and from *o*-cresol there results an 8% yield of 3-methyl-4-

[57] Ehrlich and Bertheim, *Ber.*, **40**, 3292 (1907).
[58] Brown and Hamilton, *J. Am. Chem. Soc.*, **56**, 151 (1934).
[59] Benda and Kahn, *Ber.*, **41**, 1672 (1908).
[60] Skiles and Hamilton, *J. Am. Chem. Soc.*, **59**, 1006 (1937).
[61] Hamilton and Major, *J. Am. Chem. Soc.*, **47**, 1128 (1925).

hydroxyphenylarsonic acid, as well as 2% of the *ortho* isomer.[62] Methyl groups in the *meta* position appear to exert little or no influence on the yield. As a result *m*-toluidine apparently can be arsonated readily,[59] and, from *m*-cresol, 2-methyl-4-hydroxyphenylarsonic acid is obtained in a 20% yield with only 0.4% of its isomers.[62]

The effect of nuclear chloro and nitro groups, alone, on the yields in the Bechamp reaction has not been studied. However, the reaction proceeds in the expected manner with *o*-[63, 64] and *p*-nitroaniline[65, 66] and *o*-[59] and *p*-chloroaniline,[67] but fails completely with *o*-nitrophenol.[68]

Aminophenols[35] and polyhydroxyphenols,[69] except for resorcinol, cannot be arsonated by arsenic acid because of their susceptibility to oxidation. If acetylated aminophenols are employed as starting materials, hydrolysis and subsequent oxidation of the aminophenol prevent arsonation.[35] The urethanes derived from aminophenols can be arsonated without difficulty,[35] and 4-carbethoxyamino-2-hydroxyphenylarsonic acid is produced from *m*-carbethoxyaminophenol in a 74% yield.[70] 2,4-Dihydroxyphenylarsonic acid is obtained from resorcinol in a 62% yield.[71] These two examples illustrate the highly favorable influence of the *m*-hydroxyl group. Strangely enough, 2,4-dimethoxyacetophenone yields 2,4-dimethoxy-5-acetoxyphenylarsonic acid in only a 7% yield.[72]

Although the arsonation of ethers of phenol has not been investigated, the mono- and di-methylethers of resorcinol can be arsonated to yield 2-methoxy-4-hydroxyphenylarsonic acid (31%) and 2,4-dimethoxyphenyl-arsonic acid (44%), respectively.[71] From *o*-aminoanisole there was formed 3-methoxy-4-aminophenylarsonic acid in a low yield.[73]

No N-alkyl or N-dialkyl anilines have been arsonated by the Bechamp method. With diphenylamine as starting material, 4-arsonodiphenyl-amine, 4,4'-diarsonodiphenylamine, and some arsinic acids were obtained in a combined yield of 18–20%.[74]

[62] Christiansen, *J. Am. Chem. Soc.*, **45**, 800 (1923).

[63] Gardner, Fr. pat., 768,921 (1934) [*C.A.*, **29**, 480 (1935)]; Brit. pat., 413,417 (1934) [*C.A.*, **29**, 180 (1935)].

[64] Mameli, *Bull. chim. farm.*, **48**, 682 (1909) [*Chem. Zentr.*, II, 1856 (1909)].

[65] Benda, *Ber.*, **44**, 3293 (1911).

[66] Lucius and Bruning, Brit. pat., 29,196 (1911) [*J. Soc. Chem. Ind. (London)*, **31**, 256 (1912)]; Ger. pat., 243,693 (1910) [*Chem. Zentr.*, I, 762 (1912)].

[67] Benda, *Ber.*, **42**, 3619 (1909).

[68] Pepe, *Rev. facultad cienc. quím Univ. nac. La Plata*, **5**, Pt. I, 105 (1928) [*C.A.*, **23**, 3216 (1929)].

[69] Sonn, *Ber.*, **52**, 1704 (1919).

[70] Beguin and Hamilton, *J. Am. Chem. Soc.*, **61**, 355 (1939).

[71] Bauer, *Ber.*, **48**, 509 (1915).

[72] Omer and Hamilton, *J. Am. Chem. Soc.*, **59**, 642 (1937).

[73] Benda, *Ber.*, **47**, 996 (1914).

[74] Lieb and Wintersteiner, *Ber.*, **61**, 107 (1928).

Side Reactions

In the Bechamp reaction, *para* orientation predominates, although small amounts of *ortho* isomers are formed, together with some arsinic acids (e.g., 4,4′-diaminodiphenylarsinic acid from aniline); none of the *meta* isomer results. If the *para* position is blocked, the reaction usually yields the *ortho* isomer in a low yield; however, in the case of *p*-hydroxybenzenesulfonic acid no reaction occurs.[75] As might be expected, *ortho* substitution prevails when α-naphthylamine is employed as the starting material.[58]

In addition to *ortho* isomers, as by-products in the Bechamp reactions, small amounts of arsinic acids are produced. As the reaction temperature rises the proportion of arsinic acids increases until at 220–230° they are the principal products. At higher temperatures oxidation brings about a decrease in yield. 4,4′-Diaminodiphenylarsinic acid has been prepared in a 20–30% yield by the interaction of aniline with arsenic acid at 230°.[76]

Procedures

A survey of procedures used in the Bechamp reaction reveals a few general rules of value in improving yields. The phenol or amine and the arsenic acid are heated in the absence of a solvent. As would be expected, the most desirable reaction temperature varies with the relative reactivity of the substance being arsonated. With the more reactive types such as resorcinol or *m*-carbethoxyaminophenol a temperature of 100° for two days is sufficient. Experience has shown that aniline, phenol, and many of their derivatives are best arsonated at temperatures of 150–160° for six to twelve hours. The best yields of 1-amino-2-naphthalene arsonic acid are obtained by heating α-naphthylamine with solid arsenic acid at 165–175° for fifteen minutes.[58] Since the reaction mixture ordinarily consists of two phases, it should be stirred efficiently, the yields are often low with larger runs because of inefficient stirring. When aniline is used, a large excess of the base is advisable to keep the mixture fluid.[77]

The reaction between phenol and arsenic acid is reversible. *p*-Hydroxyphenylarsonic acid is hydrolyzed in water to a marked degree even at 130°; when 200 g. of boiled arsenic acid, 100 g. of phenol, and 20 cc. of water are heated and stirred under sufficient pressure to maintain the mixture at 140–150°, no reaction takes place. By continuous removal of

[75] Barber, *J. Chem. Soc.*, **1930**, 2047.
[76] Kober and Davis, *J. Am. Chem. Soc.*, **41**, 451 (1919).
[77] Cheetham and Schmidt, *J. Am. Chem. Soc.*, **42**, 828 (1920).

the water formed during the arsonation of phenol the yield of p-hydroxy-phenylarsonic acid is considerably increased.[78]

Detailed procedures for the preparation of arsanilic acid and sodium p-hydroxyphenylarsonate, by arsonation of aniline and phenol, respectively, are published in *Organic Syntheses*.[79, 80]

Arsonation of α-Naphthylamine [58]

Ten grams of solid arsenic acid, dried for three hours at 110°, is slowly stirred into 50 g. of molten α-naphthylamine (previously heated to 150° for ten minutes and then allowed to cool to 75–90°), contained in a 250-cc. casserole suspended in an oil bath. The mixture is heated rapidly to 170° and then for fifteen minutes at 165–175° with constant stirring, allowed to cool to about 100°, poured into 250 cc. of 0.5 N sodium hydroxide, and heated to boiling. The extract is allowed to cool with occasional stirring until the tar has solidified; it is then filtered through a thin layer of charcoal, and the filtrate is acidified to Congo red paper with 6 N hydrochloric acid. The white precipitate of the arsonic acid is purified by dissolving in 0.5 N sodium carbonate, filtering through charcoal, and reprecipitating with hydrochloric acid. When dried in the oven at 110° the 1-amino-2-naphthalenearsonic acid turns slightly pink on the surface; maximum yield, 5.6 g., or 30% based on arsenic acid used; average yield, 20%; m.p., 175–176° (dec.).

ROSENMUND REACTION

Discussion

Meyer,[81] in 1883, developed a very interesting and useful method of preparing aliphatic arsonic acids from alkyl halides and trisodium arsenite.

$$RX + As(ONa)_3 \rightarrow RAsO(ONa)_2 + NaX$$

It was not until thirty-eight years later that this method of synthesis was applied to the aromatic series. Rosenmund,[3] in 1921, prepared phenylarsonic acid (in low yield) and o-carboxyphenylarsonic acid (44% yield) from tripotassium arsenite and bromobenzene and o-bromobenzoic acid, respectively. Since that time only one other arsonic acid, o-phenylene-diarsonic acid,[29, 82] has been obtained in good yields by Rosenmund's method. From two other aromatic bromides, p-bromobenzoic acid and

[78] Christiansen and Norton, *J. Am. Chem. Soc.*, **45**, 2188 (1923).
[79] Lewis and Cheetham, *Org. Syntheses, Coll. Vol.* I, 70, 2nd ed., 1941.
[80] Christiansen and Norton, *Org. Syntheses, Coll. Vol.* I, 490, 2nd ed., 1941.
[81] Meyer, *Ber.*, **16**, 1439 (1883).
[82] Hamilton and Ludeman, *J. Am. Chem. Soc.*, **52**, 3284 (1930).

p-bromoacetophenone, the corresponding arsonic acids have been produced in low yields.[83, 29, 82]

Apparently a rather active halogen atom is required, but this alone does not insure a successful reaction. It is somewhat surprising that o-chloronitrobenzene, o- and p-bromonitrobenzene, and even 2,4-dinitrochlorobenzene either fail to undergo the Rosenmund reaction or yield only traces of arsonic acids.[84, 29, 82] No reaction takes place when o-chloronitrobenzene is used as the starting material.[82] Refluxing o-bromonitrobenzene with an excess of 50% trisodium arsenite gives a small amount of arsonic acid; p-bromonitrobenzene yields traces of the arsonic acid together with a 45% yield of 4,4'-dibromoazoxybenzene.[82] From 2,4-dinitrochlorobenzene the corresponding phenol [84, 82] or phenetole [85] is formed, but no 2,4-dinitrophenylarsonic acid results.

Procedures

In general, the Rosenmund reaction is carried out by heating one mole of trisodium or tripotassium arsenite with one mole of aromatic halide in boiling aqueous ethanol solution. Certain minor modifications of this procedure have been employed. If the aromatic halide contains an acidic group (e.g., o-bromophenylarsonic acid), no ethanol is necessary.[82] Copper powder, as well as cuprous chloride, is sometimes employed as catalyst, but the value of either is uncertain.[82, 86] Reactions of bromobenzene and p-bromoacetophenone must be run in sealed tubes at temperatures of 150–200°.[83, 87, 82]

o-CARBOXYPHENYLARSONIC ACID [82]

A mixture of 20 g. (0.1 mole) of o-bromobenzoic acid, 63 cc. of 10% potassium hydroxide solution, 20 cc. of ethyl alcohol, 40 cc. of 50% tripotassium arsenite solution, and a little freshly reduced copper is refluxed at 90–95° for twelve hours with constant stirring. The reaction mixture is filtered hot to remove copper, made acid to Congo red paper with 20 cc. of concentrated hydrochloric acid, and evaporated to dryness on a steam cone. The resulting residue is extracted with absolute methanol; the methanol extract is evaporated to dryness, and the residue is washed with ether to remove salicylic acid and unchanged o-bromo-

[83] Albert and Schulenberg, Ger. pat., 468,403 (1923) [Chem. Zentr., I, 1148R (1929)].
[84] Balaban, J. Chem. Soc., 1926, 569.
[85] Nijk, Rec. trav. chim., 41, 461 (1922).
[86] Tanaka, Jap. pat., 129,595 (1939) [C.A., 35, 1805 (1941)].
[87] Austrian pat., 100,211 (1922) [Chem. Zentr., I, 357 (1927)].

benzoic acid. The ether-washed residue is twice recrystallized from hot water after decolorization with bone black; yield, 10.1 g. (41%) of o-carboxyphenylarsonic acid.

TABLES OF COMPOUNDS PREPARED BY THE BART AND BECHAMP REACTIONS

In the following tables are listed the compounds which have been prepared by the Bart and Bechamp reactions. No table for the Rosenmund reaction is presented because the few known examples of this reaction already have been briefly outlined.

The compounds in the table are grouped according to the number of carbon and hydrogen atoms present. This method of arrangement is the same as that used by *Chemical Abstracts*. The starting material is listed in parentheses under the product if its nature is not obvious. Nearly all the compounds were prepared by the method of Bart or Schmidt. When Scheller's modification was used, this fact is noted.

All known examples of the Bart and Bechamp reactions in which the product contains an arsonic or arsinic acid group attached directly to an aromatic carbocyclic ring structure have been included. For example, quinoline arsonic acids are included if the arsono group is linked to the 5-, 6-, 7-, or 8-position but are not included if the attachment occurs in the 2-, 3-, or 4-position.

COMPOUNDS PREPARED BY THE BART REACTION

C_6

Formula	Compound	Yield	Reference
$C_6H_5AsBrNO_5$	2-Bromo-4-nitrophenylarsonic acid	42% *	17 *
$C_6H_5AsBrNO_5$	2-Bromo-5-nitrophenylarsonic acid	25%	29
$C_6H_5AsBrNO_5$	2-Bromo-4-nitrophenylarsonic acid	42%	28
$C_6H_5AsBrNO_5$	3-Nitro-4-bromophenylarsonic acid	—	10
$C_6H_5AsClNO_5$	2-Chloro-4-nitrophenylarsonic acid	—	88
$C_6H_5AsClNO_5$	2-Chloro-5-nitrophenylarsonic acid	50%	89
		33%	90
$C_6H_5AsClNO_5$	3-Chloro-4-nitrophenylarsonic acid	45%	91
$C_6H_5AsClNO_5$	3-Nitro-4-chlorophenylarsonic acid	32%	90
		—	10
$C_6H_5AsClNO_5$	2-Nitro-5-chlorophenylarsonic acid	64%	91
$C_6H_5AsCl_2O_3$	2,4-Dichlorophenylarsonic acid	62% *	33 *
$C_6H_5AsCl_2O_3$	3,4-Dichlorophenylarsonic acid	60% *	33 *
$C_6H_5AsCl_2O_3$	2,5-Dichlorophenylarsonic acid	70% *	33 *
$C_6H_5AsN_2O_7$	2,4-Dinitrophenylarsonic acid	70%	15
		68%	14
		—	16
$C_6H_5AsN_2O_8$	3,5-Dinitro-2-hydroxyphenylarsonic acid	56%	92
		—	93
$C_6H_5AsO_2$	p-Phenylenearsinic acid	70%	94
$C_6H_6AsBrO_3$	o-Bromophenylarsonic acid	42%	29
		37%	13
$C_6H_6AsBrO_3$	m-Bromophenylarsonic acid	35%	29
$C_6H_6AsBrO_3$	p-Bromophenylarsonic acid	55%	95
		69%	96
		55%	29
		—	10
		—	1
		97%	96
$C_6H_6AsClO_3$	o-Chlorophenylarsonic acid	60–75%	7
		40%	31
		—	14
		52%	22
$C_6H_6AsClO_3$	m-Chlorophenylarsonic acid	45%	35
		—	14
$C_6H_6AsClO_3$	p-Chlorophenylarsonic acid	60–85%	7
		80%	32
		55%	95

References 88–231 appear on pp. 451–454.
* Scheller's modification was used (see p. 418).

COMPOUNDS PREPARED BY THE BART REACTION—*Continued*

Formula	Compound	Yield	Reference
		46%	14
		—	10
		63%	22
$C_6H_6AsFO_5S$	3-Sulfonylfluoridiphenylarsonic acid	— *	97 *
$C_6H_6AsIO_3$	p-Iodophenylarsonic acid	10%	98
$C_6H_6AsIO_3$	m-Iodophenylarsonic acid	24%	29
$C_6H_6AsNO_5$	o-Nitrophenylarsonic acid	86%	11
		84%	13
		60%	14
		—	100
		61%	52
		—	15
		67%	22
$C_6H_6AsNO_5$	m-Nitrophenylarsonic acid	54% *	18 *
		36%	26
		35%	101
		—	61
		28%	14
		—	52, 11
		47%	22
$C_6H_6AsNO_5$	p-Nitrophenylarsonic acid	79%	22
		45%	14
		36%	52
		—	100
		— *	102 *
		— *	17 *
		—	1
$C_6H_6AsNO_6$	2-Hydroxy-4-nitrophenylarsonic acid (2,4-Dinitroaniline)	—	103
$C_6H_6AsNO_6$	2-Hydroxy-4-nitrophenylarsonic acid	78%	36
		55%	35
		—	37
		62%	104
$C_6H_6AsNO_6$	2-Nitro-4-hydroxyphenylarsonic acid	53%	14
		—	37
		50–60%	105
		50%	104
$C_6H_6AsNO_6$	2-Hydroxy-5-nitrophenylarsonic acid	46%	14
		—	106
		—	104

References 88–231 appear on pp. 451–454.

* Scheller's modification was used (see p. 418).

COMPOUNDS PREPARED BY THE BART REACTION—*Continued*

Formula	Compound	Yield	Reference
$C_6H_6AsNO_6$	2-Nitro-5-hydroxyphenylarsonic acid	37%	27
$C_6H_6AsNO_6$	3-Nitro-4-hydroxyphenylarsonic acid	38%	14
		—	10
$C_6H_6AsNO_6$	2-Hydroxy-3-nitrophenylarsonic acid	29%	37
		50%	107
$C_6H_6AsNO_6$	3-Hydroxy-5-nitrophenylarsonic acid	8%	37
$C_6H_6AsNO_6$	2-Hydroxy-6-nitrophenylarsonic acid	15%	37
$C_6H_7AsN_2O_5$	2-Nitro-4-aminophenylarsonic acid (2-Nitro-4-acetyl-*p*-phenylenediamine)	—	108
$C_6H_7AsO_3$	Phenylarsonic acid	58%	22
		72–86%	8
		50–62%	7
		54%	14
		—	61
		40–50%	109
		45%	111
		39–45%	112
		—	11
		—	10
		—	113
$C_6H_7AsO_3S$	*p*-Thiolphenylarsonic acid	—	114
$C_6H_7AsO_4$	*o*-Hydroxyphenylarsonic acid	>90%	14
		35%	34
		—	99
$C_6H_7AsO_4$	*m*-Hydroxyphenylarsonic acid	0%	26
$C_6H_7AsO_4$	*p*-Hydroxyphenylarsonic acid	92%	14
		—	10
		—	115
		70%	116
$C_6H_7AsO_5$	3,4-Dihydroxyphenylarsonic acid	—	117
$C_6H_7AsO_6S$	*m*-Sulfophenylarsonic acid	0% *	18 *
$C_6H_7AsO_6S$	*p*-Sulfophenylarsonic acid	28%	49
$C_6H_7As_2ClO_6$	Chloro-*p*-phenylenediarsonic acid (3-Chloro-4-aminophenylarsonic acid)	—	118
$C_6H_7As_2NO_8$	4-Nitro-*m*-phenylenediarsonic acid (2-Amino-5-nitrophenylarsonic acid)	55%	118
$C_6H_7As_2NO_8$	2-Nitro-*p*-phenylenediarsonic acid	85%	119
		70%	48
$C_6H_8AsNO_5S$	*m*-Arsonobenzenesulfonamide	58% *	18 *

References 88–231 appear on pp. 451–454.
* Scheller's modification was used (see p. 418).

COMPOUNDS PREPARED BY THE BART REACTION—*Continued*

Formula	Compound	Yield	Reference
$C_6H_8AsNO_5S$	p-Arsonobenzenesulfonamide	57% *	18 *
		25%	50
$C_6H_8As_2O_6$	o-Phenylenediarsonic acid	20%	29
$C_6H_8As_2O_5$	o-Phenylenediarsonic acid	44%	13
	(o-Arsanilic acid)		
$C_6H_8As_2O_6$	m-Phenylenediarsonic acid	—	47
	(m-Arsanilic acid)		
$C_6H_8As_2O_6$	p-Phenylenediarsonic acid	28%	14
	(p-Arsanilic acid)	20%	47
		—	1
$C_6H_8As_2O_7$	4-Hydroxy-m-phenylenediarsonic acid	—	120
	(3-Amino-4-hydroxyphenylarsonic acid)		

C_7

Formula	Compound	Yield	Reference
$C_7H_5AsClNO_5$	7-Chlorobenzoxazolone-5-arsonic acid	—	121
$C_7H_6AsNO_3S$	p-Thiocyanophenylarsonic acid	50% *	122 *
$C_7H_6AsNO_6$	Nitro-p-aldehydophenylarsonic acid	—	123
$C_7H_5AsN_2O_7$	6-Nitrobenzoxazolone-5-arsonic acid	—	15
$C_7H_6AsNO_5$	6-Arsonobenzoxazolone	42%	37
$C_7H_6AsNO_5$	Benzoxazolone-5-arsonic acid	—	121
$C_7H_6AsNO_6$	3-Nitro-4-arsonobenzaldehyde	47%	46
$C_7H_6AsNO_7$	2-Carboxy-4-nitrophenylarsonic acid	76%	44
$C_7H_6AsO_7$	6-Nitro-3,4-methylenedioxyphenylarsonic acid	37% or 74%	124
$C_7H_7AsN_2O_3S$	6-Arsono-2-mercaptobenzimidazole	—	114
$C_7H_7AsO_3$	o-Hydroxymethylphenylarsonic acid anhydride	14%	23
$C_7H_7AsO_4$	p-Arsonobenzaldehyde	22%	45
		— *	102 *
		—	125
		—	123
$C_7H_7AsO_4$	m-Arsonobenzaldehyde	4%	46
		0%	45
$C_7H_7AsO_5$	p-Carboxyphenylarsonic acid	50–60%	42
		37, 40%	14
		67%	22

COMPOUNDS PREPARED BY THE BART REACTION—*Continued*

Formula	Compound	Yield	Reference
$C_7H_7AsO_5$	o-Carboxyphenylarsonic acid	50–60%	43
		44, 56%	14
		56%	126
		65%	22
$C_7H_7AsO_5$	m-Carboxyphenylarsonic acid	76% *	18 *
		36%	14
$C_7H_7AsO_5$	3,4-Methylenedioxyphenylarsonic acid	42%	124
$C_7H_7AsO_6$	3-Carboxy-4-hydroxyphenylarsonic acid	40%	107
		37%	38
$C_7H_8AsClO_3$	2-Methyl-4-chlorophenylarsonic acid	9%	127
$C_7H_8AsNO_5$	2-Nitro-4-methylphenylarsonic acid	88%	128
		69%	129
		58%	52
$C_7H_8AsNO_5$	3-Nitro-4-methylphenylarsonic acid	40% *	18 *
		15%	52
$C_7H_8AsNO_5$	2-Nitro-6-methylphenylarsonic acid	50%	52
		—	100
$C_7H_8AsNO_5$	2-Methyl-4-nitrophenylarsonic acid	55%	52
		—	100
$C_7H_8AsNO_5$	2-Methyl-5-nitrophenylarsonic acid	35%	52
$C_7H_8AsNO_6$	2-Hydroxy-4-nitro-5-methylphenyl-arsonic acid	30%	24
$C_7H_8AsNO_6$	2-Hydroxymethyl-4-nitrophenylarsonic acid	78%	23
$C_7H_8AsNO_6$	3-Hydroxymethyl-4-nitrophenylarsonic acid	42%	23
		—	130
$C_7H_8AsNO_6$	2-Nitro-4-hydroxymethylphenylarsonic acid	75%	23
$C_7H_8AsNO_6$	2-Methoxy-4-nitrophenylarsonic acid	60%	100
$C_7H_8AsNO_6$	3-Nitro-4-methoxyphenylarsonic acid	—	10
$C_7H_8AsNO_6$	2-Nitro-4-β-hydroxyethylphenylarsonic acid	43%	23
$C_7H_8AsNO_6$	2-Methoxy-6-nitrophenylarsonic acid	—	100
$C_7H_9AsO_3$	o-Toluenearsonic acid	60–73%	131
		49%	14
		40%	7
		19%	127
		63%	22
$C_7H_9AsO_3$	m-Toluenearsonic acid	49%	131
		45%	14
		54%	22

References 88–231 appear on pp. 451–454.
* Scheller's modification was used (see p. 418).

COMPOUNDS PREPARED BY THE BART REACTION—*Continued*

Formula	Compound	Yield	Reference
$C_7H_9AsO_3$	*p*-Toluenearsonic acid	73%	22
		50–65%	7
		57%	131
		54%	14
		47%	132
		20%	21
		—	10
$C_7H_9AsO_3S$	*p*-Methylthiophenylarsonic acid	50% *	133 *
$C_7H_9AsO_4$	2-Hydroxy-3-methylphenylarsonic acid	—	134
$C_7H_9AsO_4$	2-Hydroxy-5-methylphenylarsonic acid	—	134
$C_7H_9AsO_4$	*p*-Hydroxymethylphenylarsonic acid	20%	23
		— *	135 *
$C_7H_9AsO_4$	*m*-Hydroxymethylphenylarsonic acid	12%	23
$C_7H_9AsO_4$	*o*-Methoxyphenylarsonic acid	58%	100
$C_7H_9AsO_4$	*p*-Methoxyphenylarsonic acid	—	100
		—	10
$C_7H_9AsO_5$	3-Hydroxy-4-methoxyphenylarsonic acid	26%	39
$C_7H_9AsO_5$	3-Methoxy-4-hydroxyphenylarsonic acid	34%	39
$C_7H_9AsO_5S$	4-Methylsulfonylphenylarsonic acid	36%	75
$C_7H_{10}AsNO_4$	3-Aminomethyl-4-hydroxyphenylarsonic acid	—	136
$C_7H_{10}As_2O_6$	Methyl-*p*-phenylenediarsonic acid (3-Methyl-4-aminophenylarsonic acid)	17%	48

C₈

Formula	Compound	Yield	Reference
$C_8H_7AsN_2O_7$	7-Nitro-3-hydroxy-1,4-benzisoxazine-6-arsonic acid	—	15
$C_8H_7AsO_6$	6-Arsonopiperonal	44%	137
$C_8H_7AsO_7$	2,3-Dicarboxyphenylarsonic acid	50–70%	138
		50–55%	139
$C_8H_8AsBrO_4$	2-Bromo-4-acetylphenylarsonic acid	18%	45
$C_8H_8AsBrO_4$	2-Bromo-5-acetylphenylarsonic acid	—	45
$C_8H_8AsBrO_4$	2-Acetyl-4-bromophenylarsonic acid	—	45
$C_8H_8AsNO_3$	*p*-Cyanomethylphenylarsonic acid	— *	135 *
$C_8H_8AsNO_5$	3-Hydroxy-1,4-benzisoxazine-6-arsonic acid	46%	107
$C_8H_8AsNO_5$	7-Methylbenzoxazolone-5-arsonic acid	—	121
$C_8H_8AsNO_6$	2-Nitro-4-acetylphenylarsonic acid	—	45
$C_8H_8AsN_3O_3$	1-(*p*-Arsonophenyl)-1,2,3-triazole	—	140

References 88–231 appear on pp. 451–454.
* Scheller's modification was used (see p. 418).

COMPOUNDS PREPARED BY THE BART REACTION—*Continued*

Formula	Compound	Yield	Reference
$C_8H_8AsN_3O_5$	2-Methyl-6-nitro-5-benzimidazolearsonic acid	60%	141
$C_8H_8AsNO_7$	Nitrohydroxyacetophenonearsonic acid	—	123
$C_8H_9AsClNO_5$	3-Acetylamino-4-hydroxy-5-chloro-phenylarsonic acid	—	142
$C_8H_9AsN_2O_3$	2-Methylbenziminazole-5-arsonic acid	30%	143
$C_8H_9AsN_2O_6$	2-Nitro-4-acetamidophenylarsonic acid	47%	144
$C_8H_9AsN_2O_6$	2-Nitro-5-acetamidophenylarsonic acid	67%	27
$C_8H_9AsO_4$	p-Acetylphenylarsonic acid	70%	22
$C_8H_9AsO_4$	o-Arsonoacetophenone	75%	45
		25%	145
$C_8H_9AsO_4$	m-Arsonoacetophenone	25–45%	45
$C_8H_9AsO_4$	p-Arsonoacetophenone	67% *	102 *
		66%	45
		65%	145
		35–40%	146
		— *	17 *
$C_8H_9AsO_5$	2-Hydroxy-5-acetylphenylarsonic acid	35%	147
$C_8H_9AsO_5$	3-Hydroxy-4-acetylphenylarsonic acid	—	45
$C_8H_9AsO_5$	3-Acetyl-4-hydroxyphenylarsonic acid	—	45
$C_8H_9AsO_5$	p-Arsonophenylacetic acid	20%	133
		35% *	133 *
$C_8H_9AsO_5$	Saligeninmethylenether-5-arsonic acid	31–44%	148
$C_8H_{10}AsNO_4$	p-Acetamidophenylarsonic acid	42%	14
		—	11
$C_8H_{10}AsNO_5$	2-Acetamido-3-hydroxyphenylarsonic acid	20–25%	149
$C_8H_{10}AsNO_5$	3-Acetamido-2-hydroxyphenylarsonic acid	20–25%	149
$C_8H_{10}AsNO_5$	3-Acetamido-4-hydroxyphenylarsonic acid	30%	149
		—	142
$C_8H_{10}AsNO_5$	3-Hydroxy-4-acetamidophenylarsonic acid	10%	104
	(5-Aminoethenyl-o-aminophenol)	30%	149
$C_8H_{10}AsNO_5$	2,5-Dimethyl-4-nitrophenylarsonic acid	35%	52
$C_8H_{10}AsNO_6$	2-Nitro-4-ethoxyphenylarsonic acid	—	15
$C_8H_{10}AsNO_6$	3-Nitro-4-ethoxyphenylarsonic acid	—	10
$C_8H_{10}AsNO_6$	2-Hydroxy-4-nitro-5-ethylphenylarsonic acid	42%	24

References 88–231 appear on pp. 451–454.
* Scheller's modification was used (see p. 418).

COMPOUNDS PREPARED BY THE BART REACTION—*Continued*

Formula	Compound	Yield	Reference
$C_8H_{11}AsO_3$	2,4-Dimethylphenylarsonic acid	55%	38
$C_8H_{11}AsO_3$	2,5-Dimethylphenylarsonic acid	40%	132
$C_8H_{11}AsO_3$	2,6-Dimethylphenylarsonic acid	30%	30
		0% *	18 *
$C_8H_{11}AsO_3S$	p-Ethylthiophenylarsonic acid	24% *	122 *
$C_8H_{11}AsO_4$	p-Ethoxyphenylarsonic acid	>90%	14
		—	10
		73%	22
$C_8H_{11}AsO_4$	o-β-Hydroxyethylphenylarsonic acid	—	23
$C_8H_{11}AsO_4$	p-β-Hydroxyethylphenylarsonic acid	—	23
$C_8H_{11}AsO_4S$	p-β-Hydroxyethylthiophenylarsonic acid	48%	150
$C_8H_{11}AsO_5$	o-β-Hydroxyethoxyphenylarsonic acid	10%	34
$C_8H_{11}AsO_5$	m-β-Hydroxyethoxyphenylarsonic acid	53%	40
$C_8H_{11}AsO_5$	p-β-Hydroxyethoxyphenylarsonic acid	—	151
$C_8H_{11}AsO_5$	3,4-Dimethoxyphenylarsonic acid	—	39
$C_8H_{12}AsNO_3$	p-Dimethylaminophenylarsonic acid	24%	152
$C_8H_{12}AsNO_4$	3-Methyl-4-hydroxy-5-aminomethyl-phenylarsonic acid	—	136

C_9

Formula	Compound	Yield	Reference
$C_9H_6AsClN_2O_5$	5-Chloro-6-nitroquinoline-8-arsonic acid	37%	153
$C_9H_7AsBrNO_3$	8-Bromoquinoline-5-arsonic acid	49%	153
$C_9H_7AsClNO_3$	2-Chloroquinoline-5-arsonic acid	24%	154
$C_9H_7AsClNO_3$	2-Chloroquinoline-6-arsonic acid	18%	154
$C_9H_7AsClNO_3$	2-Chloroquinoline-8-arsonic acid	11%	154
$C_9H_7AsClNO_3$	5-Chloroquinoline-8-arsonic acid	57%	153
$C_9H_7AsClNO_3$	8-Chloroquinoline-5-arsonic acid	57%	153
$C_9H_7AsN_2O_5$	8-Nitroquinoline-7-arsonic acid	—	155
$C_9H_7AsN_2O_6$	6-Nitro-5-hydroxyquinoline-8-arsonic acid	45%	153
$C_9H_8AsNO_3$	Quinoline-5-arsonic acid	15%	156
$C_9H_8AsNO_3$	Quinoline-6-arsonic acid	18%	156
$C_9H_8AsNO_3$	Quinoline-8-arsonic acid	33%	156
$C_9H_8AsNO_3$	Isoquinoline-?5-arsonic acid	—	156
$C_9H_8AsNO_3S$	p-(4-Thiazolyl-)phenylarsonic acid	40–60%	157
$C_9H_8AsNO_4$	2-Hydroxyquinoline-5-arsonic acid	23%	154
$C_9H_8AsNO_4$	2-Hydroxyquinoline-6-arsonic acid	55%	156
		—	158

References 88–231 appear on pp. 451–454.
* Scheller's modification was used (see p. 418).

COMPOUNDS PREPARED BY THE BART REACTION—*Continued*

Formula	Compound	Yield	Reference
$C_9H_8AsNO_4$	2-Hydroxyquinoline-7-arsonic acid	13%	154
$C_9H_9AsN_2O_3$	Glyoxaline-4-phenyl-*p*-arsonic acid	4%	159
$C_9H_9AsN_2O_5S_2$	*p*-(Benzenesulfonamido-2-thiazole)-arsonic acid	55% *	133 *
$C_9H_9AsO_5$	*p*-Arsonocinnamic acid	30% *	133 *
$C_9H_{10}AsNO_6$	2-Acetamido-3-carboxyphenylarsonic acid	—	132
$C_9H_{10}AsNO_6$	3-Carboxy-4-acetamidophenylarsonic acid	57%	132
$C_9H_{10}AsNO_6$	*p*-Arsonohippuric acid	—	132
$C_9H_{11}AsO_4$	Propiophenone-*o*-arsonic acid	75%	45
$C_9H_{11}AsO_4$	Propiophenone-*p*-arsonic acid	—	123
$C_9H_{11}AsO_4$	Propiophenone-*m*-arsonic acid	46%	45
$C_9H_{11}AsO_5$	β-*p*-Arsonophenylpropionic acid	23%	160
$C_9H_{11}AsO_5$	*m*-Arsonophenoxyacetone	2%	161
$C_9H_{11}AsO_5$	*p*-Carbethoxyphenylarsonic acid	60%	22
$C_9H_{11}AsO_5$	2-Methoxy-5-acetylphenylarsonic acid	60%	147
$C_9H_{11}AsO_6$	6-Arsono-3,4-dimethoxybenzaldehyde	46%	162
$C_9H_{11}AsO_6$	2-Methoxy-4-hydroxy-5-acetylphenyl-arsonic acid	58%	163
$C_9H_{12}AsNO_4$	*p*-Arsonobenzylacetamide	62%	152
$C_9H_{12}AsNO_5$	3-Methoxy-4-acetamidophenylarsonic acid	—	164
$C_9H_{12}AsNO_5$	3-Acetamido-4-hydroxy-5-methylphenyl-arsonic acid	—	142
$C_9H_{12}AsNO_6$	3-Hydroxy-4-carbethoxyaminophenyl-arsonic acid	20%	149
$C_9H_{12}AsNO_6$	3-Carbethoxyamino-4-hydroxyphenyl-arsonic acid	—	14
		—	10
$C_9H_{13}AsO_5$	α-Methyl-β-2-arsonophenoxyethanol	15%	99

C_{10}

Formula	Compound	Yield	Reference
$C_{10}H_8AsClO_3$	2-Chloro-1-naphthalenearsonic acid	56%	165
$C_{10}H_8AsNO_5$	2-Nitro-1-naphthalenearsonic acid	63%	166
$C_{10}H_8AsNO_5$	4-Nitro-1-naphthalenearsonic acid	80%	167
		40%	166
$C_{10}H_8AsNO_5$	1-Nitro-2-naphthalenearsonic acid	68%	167
		67%	166

References 88–231 appear on pp. 451–454.
* Scheller's modification was used (see p. 418).

COMPOUNDS PREPARED BY THE BART REACTION—*Continued*

Formula	Compound	Yield	Reference
$C_{10}H_8AsNO_5$	6-Nitro-2-naphthalenearsonic acid	47%	168
$C_{10}H_8AsNO_5$	8-Nitro-2-naphthalenearsonic acid	40%	167
$C_{10}H_8AsN_3O_7$	1-(*p*-Arsonophenyl)-4,5-dicarboxy-1,2,3-triazole	—	140
$C_{10}H_9AsClNO_3$	2-Chloro-4-methylquinoline-7-arsonic acid	7%	154
$C_{10}H_9AsO_3$	Naphthalene-1-arsonic acid	20%	53
$C_{10}H_9AsO_3$	Naphthalene-2-arsonic acid	26%	169
$C_{10}H_9AsO_4$	4-Hydroxynaphthalene-1-arsonic acid	3% *	170 *
$C_{10}H_9AsO_5$	7-Methylcoumarin-6-arsonic acid	—	171
$C_{10}H_9AsO_6S$	4-Sulfonaphthalene-1-arsonic acid	0%	51
$C_{10}H_{10}AsClN_2O_3$	1-(4'-Arsonophenyl)-3-methyl-5-chloro-pyrazole	—	172
$C_{10}H_{10}AsNO_3$	2-Methylquinoline-3-arsonic acid	—	156
$C_{10}H_{10}AsNO_4$	2-Hydroxy-4-methylquinoline-6-arsonic acid	18%	173
$C_{10}H_{10}AsNO_4$	2-Hydroxy-4-methylquinoline-7-arsonic acid	31%	154
$C_{10}H_{10}AsNO_4$	6-Methoxyquinoline-8-arsonic acid	—	155
$C_{10}H_{10}AsNO_4$	8-Methoxyquinoline-6-arsonic acid	—	155
$C_{10}H_{10}AsNO_4S$	6-Arsonobenzene-3-ketodihydro-1,4-thiazine	—	114
$C_{10}H_{10}AsN_3O_4$	Glyoxaline-4'-carboxy-*p*-aminophenyl-arsonic acid	36%	159
$C_{10}H_{11}AsO_7$	Dimethyl 4-arsonophthalate	80%	174
		77–80%	175
		41%	132
$C_{10}H_{12}AsNO_7$	2-Acetamido-4-arsonophenoxyacetic acid	—	164
$C_{10}H_{12}AsN_3O_3$	1-(*p*-Arsonophenyl)-3,4-dimethyl-1,2,5-triazole	47%	177
$C_{10}H_{13}AsN_2O_5$	3,4-Diacetamidophenylarsonic acid	50%	178
		—	179
$C_{10}H_{13}AsO_5$	γ-*p*-Arsonophenylbutyric acid	75%	133
$C_{10}H_{13}AsO_6$	2,4-Dimethoxy-5-acetylphenylarsonic acid	56%	72
$C_{10}H_{14}AsNO_5S_2$	N-(*p*-Arsonophenylsulfonyl)-(1,4)thiazan	59%	98
$C_{10}H_{14}AsNO_6$	3-Acetamido-4-β-hydroxyethoxyphenyl-arsonic acid	—	164
$C_{10}H_{15}AsN_2O_4$	2-Hydroxy-1,2,3-trimethyl-2,3-dihydro-benzimidazole-5-arsonic acid	30%	180

References 88–231 appear on pp. 451–454.
* Scheller's modification was used (see p. 418).

COMPOUNDS PREPARED BY THE BART REACTION—*Continued*

Formula	Compound	Yield	Reference
$C_{10}H_{15}AsN_2O_5$	2-Diethylamino-5-nitrophenylarsonic acid	17%	181
$C_{10}H_{15}AsO_3$	*o*-Butylphenylarsonic acid	12%	25
$C_{10}H_{15}AsO_4$	2-Hydroxy-3-arsono-*p*-cymene	—	182

C_{11}

$C_{11}H_{10}AsN_3O_5$	3-Nitro-4-(*p*-arsonophenylamino)-pyridine	25%	183
$C_{11}H_{10}AsN_3O_5$	2-(*m*-Arsonophenylamino)-5-nitropyridine	12%	183
$C_{11}H_{10}AsN_3O_5$	2-(*p*-Arsonophenylamino)-5-nitropyridine	28%	183
$C_{11}H_{11}AsN_2O_5S$	*p*-Arsono-N-2-pyridylbenzenesulfonamide	25% *	133 *
$C_{11}H_{11}AsO_5$	4,7-Dimethylcoumarin-6-arsonic acid	—	171
$C_{11}H_{12}AsNO_4$	2-Hydroxy-4,7-dimethylquinoline-6-arsonic acid	4%	173
$C_{11}H_{12}AsNO_4$	6-Ethoxyquinoline-8-arsonic acid	—	155
$C_{11}H_{12}AsNO_4$	2-Hydroxy-4,8-dimethylquinoline-6-arsonic acid	10%	173
$C_{11}H_{13}AsO_5$	Ethyl *o*-arsonocinnamate	—	184
$C_{11}H_{15}AsO_6$	2,4-Dimethoxy-5-propionylphenylarsonic acid	61%	72
$C_{11}H_{16}AsNO_6$	3,4-Dihydroxyphenylarsonic acid diethylcarbamate	—	117

C_{12}

$C_{12}H_8AsNO_5$	3-Keto-3-pyrano(3,2-*f*)quinoline-2-arsonic acid	—	185
$C_{12}H_8AsNO_6$	8-Nitro-3-dibenzofurylarsonic acid	35%	60
$C_{12}H_9AsBrNO_4$	2-Bromo-2′-nitrodiphenylarsinic acid (*o*-Nitroaniline)	51%	186
$C_{12}H_9AsN_2O_6$	4,4′-Dinitrodiphenylarsinic acid (*p*-Nitroaniline)	—	14
$C_{12}H_9AsO_4$	3-Dibenzofurylarsonic acid	12% 70%	187 188
$C_{12}H_9AsO_4$	2-Dibenzofurylarsonic acid	6%	187

References 88–231 appear on pp. 451–454.
* Scheller's modification was used (see p. 418).

COMPOUNDS PREPARED BY THE BART REACTION—*Continued*

Formula	Compound	Yield	Reference
$C_{12}H_{10}AsBrO_2$	p-Br-diphenylarsinic acid (p-Bromoaniline)	40%	96
$C_{12}H_{10}AsBrO_4$	2-Arsono-4'-bromodiphenyl ether	20%	189
$C_{12}H_{10}AsBrO_4$	4-Arsono-4'-bromodiphenyl ether	—	187
$C_{12}H_{10}AsClO_4$	2-Arsono-4-chlorodiphenyl ether	25%	190
$C_{12}H_{10}AsClO_4$	2-Arsono-2'-chlorodiphenyl ether	18%	190
$C_{12}H_{10}AsClO_4$	2-Arsono-3'-chlorodiphenyl ether	18%	190
$C_{12}H_{10}AsClO_4$	2-Arsono-4'-chlorodiphenyl ether	24%	190
$C_{12}H_{10}AsClO_4$	4-Arsono-4'-chlorodiphenyl ether	—	187
$C_{12}H_{10}AsFO_4S$	m-Sulfonylfluoridediphenylarsinic acid (m-Aminobenzenesulfonylfluoride)	35% *	97 *
$C_{12}H_{10}AsNO_3$	Carbazole-2-arsonic acid	27%	191
$C_{12}H_{10}AsNO_4$	o-Nitrodiphenylarsinic acid (o-Nitroaniline)	87% / 54%	12 / 13
$C_{12}H_{10}AsNO_4$	m-Nitrodiphenylarsinic acid (m-Nitroaniline)	51%	96
$C_{12}H_{10}AsNO_4$	p-Nitrodiphenylarsinic acid (p-Nitroaniline)	—	192
$C_{12}H_{10}AsNO_5$	4-Nitrobiphenyl-4'-arsonic acid	34% *	170 *
$C_{12}H_{10}AsNO_{12}S_3$	3,6,8-Trisulfocarbazole-1-arsonic acid	—	193
$C_{12}H_{10}As_2N_2O_{10}$	3,5'-Dinitro-4,4'-biphenyldiarsonic acid	65%	194
$C_{12}H_{11}AsN_2O_4$	2-Hydroxy-5-arsonoazobenzene	50%	14
$C_{12}H_{11}AsN_2O_5$	3-Nitro-4-aminophenyl-4'-arsonic acid (3-Nitrobenzidine)	15%	170
$C_{12}H_{11}AsO_2$	Diphenylarsinic acid	—	14
$C_{12}H_{11}AsO_3$	Biphenyl-4-arsonic acid	40% *	20 *
$C_{12}H_{11}AsO_3$	2-Biphenylarsonic acid	60%	195
$C_{12}H_{11}AsO_3S$	o-Arsonodiphenyl sulfide	12%	196
$C_{12}H_{11}AsO_4$	p-Arsonodiphenyl ether	26%	187
$C_{12}H_{11}AsO_4$	o-Arsonodiphenyl ether	32% / —	190 / 197
$C_{12}H_{11}AsO_5S$	p-Sulfodiphenylarsinic acid (p-Sulfanilic acid)	17%	19
$C_{12}H_{11}As_2NO_8$	3-Nitro-4,4'-biphenyldiarsonic acid (3-Nitrobenzidine)	19%	170
$C_{12}H_{12}AsClO_4$	2-Arsono-4-chloro-4'-methyldiphenyl ether	12%	198
$C_{12}H_{12}AsNO_3$	4'-Aminobiphenyl-4-arsonic acid	19%	194
$C_{12}H_{12}AsNO_3$	4'-Aminobiphenyl-2-arsonic acid	—	199
$C_{12}H_{12}AsNO_4S$	p-Sulfonamidodiphenylarsinic acid (p-Sulfanilamide)	29–32% * / 11, 23%	19 * / 19

References 88–231 appear on pp. 451–454.
* Scheller's modification was used (see p. 418).

COMPOUNDS PREPARED BY THE BART REACTION—*Continued*

Formula	Compound	Yield	Reference
$C_{12}H_{12}AsNO_5S$	N-*p*-Arsonophenylbenzenesulfonamide	—	10
$C_{12}H_{12}As_2O_5$	*o*-Arsonodiphenylarsinic acid (*o*-Arsanilic acid)	47%	13
$C_{12}H_{12}As_2O_5$	*o*-Arsonodiphenylarsinic acid (*o*-Aminodiphenylarsinic acid)	26%	13
$C_{12}H_{12}As_2O_6$	2,4'-Biphenyldiarsonic acid	—	199
$C_{12}H_{12}As_2O_6$	Biphenyl-4,4'-diarsonic acid (Benzidine)	55%	194
		—	201
		3%	170
$C_{12}H_{16}AsNO_6$	3,4-Dihydroxyphenylcarboxylic acid piperidide-1-arsonic acid	—	117
$C_{12}H_{20}AsNO_4$	*p*-β-Diethylaminoethoxyphenylarsonic acid	2%	41

C_{13}

Formula	Compound	Yield	Reference
$C_{13}H_7AsBrNO_7$	9-Keto-nitrobromoxanthenearsonic acid	—	185
$C_{13}H_8AsNO_7$	9-Keto-8-nitro-1-xanthenearsonic acid	—	185
$C_{13}H_8AsNO_7$	9-Keto-7-nitro-2-xanthenearsonic acid	—	185
$C_{13}H_9AsO_3$	*o*-Carboxydiphenylarsinic acid anhydride (Anthranilic acid)	40%	202
$C_{13}H_9AsO_3$	*o*-Carboxydiphenylarsinic acid anhydride (Aniline)	—	126
$C_{13}H_9AsO_4$	2-Fluorenonearsonic acid	55%	203
		22%	55
		—	204
$C_{13}H_9AsO_5$	9-Keto-3-xanthenearsonic acid	—	185
$C_{13}H_9AsO_5$	1,2-α-Naphthopyrone-6-arsonic acid	—	171
$C_{13}H_{10}AsNO_2S$	*p*-Thiocyanodiphenylarsinic acid (*p*-Thiocyanoaniline)	16% *	122 *
$C_{13}H_{10}AsNO_3$	Acridine-1-arsonic acid	30% *	205 *
$C_{13}H_{10}AsNO_3$	Acridine-2-arsonic acid	38% *	205 *
$C_{13}H_{10}AsNO_3$	Acridine-3-arsonic acid	18% *	205 *
$C_{13}H_{10}AsNO_3S$	2-(4-Arsonophenyl)-benzothiazole	26%	206
$C_{13}H_{10}AsNO_3S$	2-Phenyl-6-arsonobenzothiazole	5%	206
$C_{13}H_{10}AsNO_4$	Acridone-2-arsonic acid	38%	158
$C_{13}H_{10}AsNO_4S$	2-(2-Hydroxy-5-arsonophenyl)-benzothiazole	7%	207

References 88–231 appear on pp. 451–454.
* Scheller's modification was used (see p. 418).

COMPOUNDS PREPARED BY THE BART REACTION—*Continued*

Formula	Compound	Yield	Reference
$C_{13}H_{11}AsBrNO_4$	2'-Bromo-2-nitro-4-methyldiphenyl-arsinic acid (3-Nitro-*p*-toluidine)	22%	208
$C_{13}H_{11}AsBrNO_4$	2'-Bromo-2-nitro-6-methyldiphenyl-arsinic acid (3-Nitro-*o*-toluidine)	29%	208
$C_{13}H_{11}AsN_2O_3$	2-Aminoacridine-8-arsonic acid	8% *	205 *
$C_{13}H_{11}AsO_3$	2-Fluorenearsonic acid	19%	55
		—	204
$C_{13}H_{11}AsO_4$	*o*-Carboxydiphenylarsinic acid	50%	202
$C_{13}H_{11}AsO_4$	Benzophenone-*p*-arsonic acid	—	123
		—	125
$C_{13}H_{11}AsO_5$	3-Hydroxybenzophenone-4'-arsonic acid	—	123
$C_{13}H_{12}AsNO_3$	9-Methylcarbazole-3-arsonic acid	35%	181
$C_{13}H_{12}As_2O_7$	Benzophenone-4,4'-diarsonic acid	—	123
		—	125
$C_{13}H_{13}AsO_2$	*p*-Methyldiphenylarsinic acid (*p*-Toluidine)	42%	192
$C_{13}H_{13}AsO_2$	*p*-Methyldiphenylarsinic acid (Aniline)	35%	192
$C_{13}H_{13}AsO_3$	*o*-Arsonodiphenylmethane	27%	210
$C_{13}H_{13}AsO_3S$	*p*-Benzylthiophenylarsonic acid	—	211
$C_{13}H_{13}AsO_4$	2-Arsono-4'-methyldiphenyl ether	20–40%	188
$C_{13}H_{13}AsO_4$	2-Arsono-2'-methyldiphenyl ether	20–35%	189
$C_{13}H_{13}AsO_4$	2-Arsono-3'-methyldiphenyl ether	30–40%	189
$C_{13}H_{13}AsO_4$	2-Arsono-5-methyldiphenyl ether	0%	189
$C_{13}H_{13}AsO_4$	4-Arsono-4'-methyldiphenyl ether	47%	95
$C_{13}H_{13}AsO_5$	2-Arsono-4'-methoxydiphenyl ether	11%	189
$C_{13}H_{14}As_2O_6$	Diphenylmethane-4,4'-diarsonic acid (4,4'-Diaminodiphenylmethane)	36%	212
		—	213

C_{14}

Formula	Compound	Yield	Reference
$C_{14}H_9AsO_5$	Anthraquinone-1-arsonic acid	46%	54
		53%	214
$C_{14}H_9AsO_5$	Anthraquinone-2-arsonic acid	23%	54
$C_{14}H_9AsO_6$	4-Hydroxyanthraquinone-1-arsonic acid	70%	54
$C_{14}H_{10}AsNO_5$	4-Aminoanthraquinone-1-arsonic acid (1,4-Diaminoanthraquinone)	31%	54
$C_{14}H_{10}As_2O_{10}$	Anthrarufin-4,8-diarsonic acid	64%	32

References 88–231 appear on pp. 451–454.   * Scheller's modification was used (see p. 418).

COMPOUNDS PREPARED BY THE BART REACTION—*Continued*

Formula	Compound	Yield	Reference
$C_{14}H_{11}AsO_5$	4-Methyl-1,2-α-naphthopyrone-6-arsonic acid	—	171
$C_{14}H_{13}AsO_4$	p-Arsonophenylbenzylketone	—	123
$C_{14}H_{14}AsNO_4$	N-Acetyldiphenylamine-4-arsonic acid	47%	186
$C_{14}H_{14}AsNO_5$	3-Arsono-6-hydroxy-N-benzoylbenzylamine	—	215
$C_{14}H_{15}AsO_4$	2-Arsono-2',5'-dimethyldiphenyl ether	13%	189
$C_{14}H_{15}AsO_4$	2-Arsono-2',4'-dimethyldiphenyl ether	12–16%	189
$C_{14}H_{15}AsO_4$	2-Arsono-3',5'-dimethyldiphenyl ether	12%	189
$C_{14}H_{16}AsN_3O_5$	6-Nitro-5-piperidinoquinoline-8-arsonic acid	57%	153
$C_{14}H_{16}As_2O_6$	3,5'-Dimethylbiphenyl-4,4'-diarsonic acid (o-Tolidine)	44%	194
$C_{14}H_{17}AsN_2O_3$	8-Piperidinoquinoline-5-arsonic acid	0%	153

C_{15}

Formula	Compound	Yield	Reference
$C_{15}H_{12}AsNO_3S$	2-p-Arsonophenyl-4-phenylthiazole	—	216
$C_{15}H_{12}AsNO_6$	N-Phthalimido-2-hydroxy-5-arsono-benzylamine	—	136
$C_{15}H_{14}AsNO_4$	2-Acetamidofluorene-7-arsonic acid	2%	55
$C_{15}H_{14}AsNO_5$	4-Acetamidobenzophenone-3'-arsonic acid	—	123
$C_{15}H_{14}AsNO_7$	2-Benzamido-4-arsonophenoxyacetic acid	—	164
$C_{15}H_{15}AsN_2O_3S$	2-(2-Arsonophenyl)-6-dimethylamino-benzothiazole	0%	217
$C_{15}H_{15}AsN_2O_3S$	2-(3-Arsonophenyl)-6-dimethylamino-benzothiazole	18%	217
$C_{15}H_{15}AsN_2O_3S$	2-(4-Arsonophenyl)-6-dimethylamino-benzothiazole	18%	217

C_{16}

Formula	Compound	Yield	Reference
$C_{16}H_{10}AsNO_5$	12-Keto-12-xantheno(2,1-b)pyridine-10-arsonic acid	—	185
$C_{16}H_{12}AsNO_5$	2-Phenyl-4-carboxyquinoline-6-arsonic acid	24%	218

References 88–231 appear on pp. 451–454.

COMPOUNDS PREPARED BY THE BART REACTION—*Continued*

Formula	Compound	Yield	Reference
$C_{16}H_{12}AsNO_6$	ω-Phthalimidoacetophenone-*p*-arsonic acid	—	123
$C_{16}H_{14}AsNO_6$	3-Arsono-5-methyl-6-hydroxybenzyl-phthalimide	—	215
$C_{16}H_{15}AsO_4$	4,4′-Diacetyldiphenylarsinic acid	—	219
	(*p*-Aminoacetophenone)	—	220

C_{17}–C_{25}

Formula	Compound	Yield	Reference
$C_{17}H_{17}AsN_2O_4$	*m*-6′-Methoxy-2′-methyl-4′-quinolyl-aminophenylarsonic acid	19%	221
$C_{17}H_{17}AsN_2O_4$	*p*-6′-Methoxy-2′-methyl-4′-quinolyl-aminophenylarsonic acid	6–41%	221
$C_{18}H_{14}AsN_3O_8$	Tri-*p*-nitrophenylarsine oxide hydrate	—	4
$C_{18}H_{15}AsO$	Triphenylarsine oxide	—	4
$C_{18}H_{16}As_2O_4$	Phenylene-1,2-diphenylarsinic acid (*o*-Aminodiphenylarsinic acid)	28%	222
$C_{23}H_{21}AsN_2O_4$	4′-(6″-Methoxy-2″-methyl-4″-quinolyl-amino)biphenyl-4-arsonic acid	48%	221
$C_{24}H_{23}AsN_2O_4$	*p*-6-Methoxy-2-methyl-4-quinolylamino-diphenylmethane-*p*′-arsonic acid	—	223
$C_{25}H_{25}AsN_2O_4$	4′,6″-Methoxy-2″-methyl-4″-quinolyl-amino-3,3′-dimethylbiphenylarsonic acid	45%	223
$C_{25}H_{25}AsN_2O_6$	4′,6″-Methoxy-2″-methyl-4″-quinolyl-amino-3,3′-dimethoxybiphenylarsonic acid	74%	223

COMPOUNDS PREPARED BY THE BECHAMP REACTION

C_6

Formula	Compound	Yield	Reference
$C_6H_6AsNO_6$	3-Nitro-4-hydroxyphenylarsonic acid	0%	68
$C_6H_7AsClNO_3$	2-Amino-5-chlorophenylarsonic acid	—	67
$C_6H_7AsClNO_3$	3-Chloro-4-aminophenylarsonic acid	—	59
$C_6H_7AsN_2O_5$	2-Amino-5-nitrophenylarsonic acid	—	65, 66, 37
$C_6H_7AsN_2O_5$	3-Nitro-4-aminophenylarsonic acid	—	64, 63
$C_6H_7AsO_4$	*o*-Hydroxyphenylarsonic acid (Phenol)	3%	224

References 88–231 appear on pp. 451–454.

COMPOUNDS PREPARED BY THE BECHAMP REACTION—*Continued*

Formula	Compound	Yield	Reference
$C_6H_7AsO_4$	p-Hydroxyphenylarsonic acid	33%	78
		33%	225
		22%	226
		23%	224
		33%	80
		33%	227
$C_6H_7AsO_5$	2,4-Dihydroxyphenylarsonic acid	62%	71
$C_6H_8AsNO_3$	p-Arsanilic acid	26%	77, 111
		11–14%	79
		18–19%	209
		30%	228
		—	110
		—	76

C_7

Formula	Compound	Yield	Reference
$C_7H_9AsO_4$	2-Hydroxy-3-methylphenylarsonic acid	1%	62
$C_7H_9AsO_4$	2-Hydroxy-6 (or 4)-methylphenylarsonic acid	—	62
$C_7H_9AsO_4$	2-Methyl-4-hydroxyphenylarsonic acid	20%	62
$C_7H_9AsO_4$	3-Methyl-4-hydroxyphenylarsonic acid	8%	62
$C_7H_9AsO_5$	2-Methoxy-4-hydroxyphenylarsonic acid	31%	71
$C_7H_{10}AsNO_3$	2-Amino-5-methylphenylarsonic acid	—	67
$C_7H_{10}AsNO_3$	3-Methyl-4-aminophenylarsonic acid	14%	61
		—	229
		—	59
		—	230
$C_7H_{10}AsNO_3$	2-Methyl-4-aminophenylarsonic acid	—	59
$C_7H_{10}AsNO_4$	3-Methoxy-4-aminophenylarsonic acid	—	73

C_8–C_{24}

Formula	Compound	Yield	Reference
$C_8H_{11}AsO_5$	2,4-Dimethoxyphenylarsonic acid	44%	71
$C_8H_{12}AsNO_3$	2-Amino-3,5-dimethylphenylarsonic acid	—	67
$C_8H_{12}AsNO_3$	2,5-Dimethyl-4-aminophenylarsonic acid	—	59
$C_9H_{12}AsNO_6$	2-Hydroxy-4-carbethoxyaminophenylarsonic acid	—	70
		—	35
$C_{10}H_{10}AsNO_3$	1-Aminonaphthalene-2-arsonic acid	20–30%	58
		—	229
		—	231

References 88–231 appear on pp. 451–454.

COMPOUNDS PREPARED BY THE BECHAMP REACTION—*Continued*

Formula	Compound	Yield	Reference
$C_{10}H_{13}AsO_6$	2,4-Dimethoxy-5-acetylphenylarsonic acid (2,4-Dihydroxyacetophenone)	7%	72
$C_{11}H_{15}AsO_6$	2,4-Dimethoxy-5-propionylphenylarsonic acid	11%	72
$C_{12}H_9AsO_4$	2-Dibenzofurylarsonic acid	11%	60
$C_{12}H_{11}AsN_2O_5$	2'-Nitrodiphenylamine-4-arsonic acid	8%	200
$C_{12}H_{11}AsN_2O_5$	3'-Nitrodiphenylamine-4-arsonic acid	6–8%	200
$C_{12}H_{11}AsN_2O_5$	4'-Nitrodiphenylamine-4-arsonic acid	8%	200
$C_{12}H_{11}AsO_4$	2,4'-Dihydroxydiphenylarsinic acid (Phenol)	—	224
$C_{12}H_{11}AsO_4$	4,4'-Dihydroxydiphenylarsinic acid (Phenol)	3%	224
$C_{12}H_{12}AsNO_3$	Diphenylamine-*p*-arsonic acid (Diphenylamine)	18%	74
$C_{12}H_{13}AsN_2O_2$	4,4'-Diaminodiphenylarsinic acid (Aniline)	20–30% — 3%	76 176 230
$C_{12}H_{13}As_2NO_6$	Diphenylamine-4,4'-diarsonic acid (Diphenylamine)	—	74
$C_{13}H_{10}AsNO_4S$	2-(2-Hydroxy-5-arsonophenyl)-benzothiazole	19%	207
$C_{13}H_{10}AsNO_5S$	2-(5-Arsono-2,4-dihydroxyphenyl)-benzothiazole	20%	207
$C_{14}H_{15}AsO_4$	2,4'-Dihydroxy-3,3'-dimethyldiphenylarsinic acid (*o*-Cresol)	—	62
$C_{14}H_{15}AsO_4$	3,3'-Dimethyl-4,4'-dihydroxydiphenylarsinic acid (*o*-Cresol)	—	62
$C_{14}H_{17}AsN_2O_2$	3,3'-Dimethyl-4,4'-diaminodiphenylarsinic acid (*o*-Toluidine)	— —	230 176
$C_{24}H_{21}AsN_2O_2$	Bisdiphenylaminearsinic acid (Diphenylamine)	—	74

[88] Freres and Fourneau, Brit. pat., 279,379 (1926) [*Chem. Zentr.*, I, 807 (1929)].
[89] Hac, M. S. Thesis, University of Nebraska, 1931.
[90] Balaban, *J. Chem. Soc.*, **1930**, 183.
[91] Balaban, *J. Chem. Soc.*, **1928**, 809.
[92] King, *J. Chem. Soc.*, **1927**, 1049.
[93] Keimatsu and Yokota, *J. Pharm. Soc. Japan*, **510**, 629 (1924) [*C.A.*, **19**, 2481 (1925)].
[94] Schmidt and Hoffmann, *Ber.*, **59**, 560 (1926).
[95] Maclay and Hamilton, *J. Am. Chem. Soc.*, **54**, 3310 (1932).

[96] Blicke and Webster, *J. Am. Chem. Soc.*, **59**, 534 (1937).

[97] Steinkopf and Jaeger, *J. prakt. Chem.*, **128**, 63 (1930).

[98] Cragoe, University of Nebraska, private communication.

[99] Binkley and Hamilton, *J. Am. Chem. Soc.*, **60**, 134 (1938).

[100] Johnson and Adams, *J. Am. Chem. Soc.*, **45**, 1307 (1923).

[101] Parker, M. S. Thesis, University of Nebraska, 1938.

[102] Scheller, Ger. pat., 522,892 (1926) [*Chem. Zentr.*, II, 313 (1931)].

[103] Kirkhgof and Terent'eva, Russ. pat., 51, 422 [*C.A.*, **33**, 6882 (1939)].

[104] Newbery and Phillips, *J. Chem. Soc.*, **1928**, 116.

[105] Mueller, M. S. Thesis, University of Nebraska, 1941.

[106] Bart, U. S. pat., 1,061,587 (1913) [*C.A.*, **7**, 2286 (1913)].

[107] Newbery, Phillips, and Stickings, *J. Chem. Soc.*, **1928**, 3051.

[108] Lucius and Bruning, Ger. pat., 267,307 (1911) [*Chem. Zentr.*, II, 2067 (1913)]; Brit. pat., 24,668 (1912) [*C.A.*, **8**, 402 (1914)].

[109] Adams and Palmer, *J. Am. Chem. Soc.*, **42**, 235 (1920).

[110] Hamilton and Simpson, *J. Am. Chem. Soc.*, **51**, 3158 (1929).

[111] Hamilton and Sly, *J. Am. Chem. Soc.*, **47**, 435 (1925).

[112] Bullard and Dickey, *Org. Syntheses*, **15**, 59 (1935).

[113] Norris, *J. Ind. Eng. Chem.*, **11**, 825 (1919).

[114] Streitwolfe, Fehrle, Herrmann, and Hilmer, Ger. pat., 536,996 (1930) [*Chem. Zentr.*, I, 254 (1932)].

[115] Gilta, *Bull. soc. chim. Belg.*, **42**, 119 (1933) [*C.A.*, **27**, 4784 (1933)].

[116] Blas, *Anales soc. españ. fís. quím.*, **37**, 116 (1941) [*C.A.*, **36**, 3160 (1942)].

[117] Streitwolfe, Herrmann, and Hilmer, Brit. pat., 359,610 (1931) [*Chem. Zentr.*, I, 583 (1932)]; Ger. pat., 559,733 (1931) [*Chem. Zentr.*, II, 3273 (1932)].

[118] Lieb and Wintersteiner, *Ber.*, **56**, 1283 (1923).

[119] Berlin, *J. Gen. Chem. U.S.S.R.*, **9**, 1856 (1939) [*C.A.*, **34**, 4061 (1940)].

[120] Keimatsu and Kakinuma, *J. Pharm. Soc. Japan*, **520**, 520 (1925) [*C.A.*, **20**, 392 (1925)].

[121] Benda and Sievers, Brit. pat., 261,133 (1925) [*Chem. Zentr.*, I, 2014 (1927)].

[122] Cherline and Iacoubovitch, *Bull. soc. chim.*, [5] **1**, 1367 (1934).

[123] Margulies, Brit. pat., 220,668 (1923); Fr. pat.. 562,460 (1923) [*Chem. Zentr.*, II, 616 (1925)].

[124] Balabin, *J. Chem. Soc.*, **1929**, 1088.

[125] Albert, U. S. pat., 1,472,778 (1924) [*C.A.*, **18**, 400 (1924)].

[126] Aeschlimann and McCleland, *J. Chem. Soc.*, **125**, 2025 (1924).

[127] Karrer, *Ber.*, **48**, 305 (1915).

[128] Maschmann, *Ber.*, **57**, 1764 (1924).

[129] McCluskey, *J. Am. Chem. Soc.*, **51**, 1462 (1929).

[130] Ellis, Brit. pat., 366,183 (1930) [*Brit. Chem. Abs.*, B, 528 (1932)].

[131] Parmelee and Hamilton, *J. Am. Chem. Soc.*, **55**, 1463 (1933).

[132] Cohen, King, and Strangeways, *J. Chem. Soc.*, **1931**, 3236.

[133] Doak, Steinman, and Eagle, *J. Am. Chem. Soc.*, **62**, 3012 (1940).

[134] Finzi, *Atti II congr. naz. chim. pura applicata*, **1926**, 1302 [*Chem. Zentr.*, I, 2173 (1928)].

[135] Sherlin, Braz, Yakubovich, and Konovalchik, *J. Gen. Chem. U.S.S.R.*, **9**, 985 (1939) [*C.A.*, **33** 8584 (1939)].

[136] Schmidt, U. S. pat., 1,835,433 (1932) [*C.A.*, **26**, 1067 (1932)].

[137] Balaban, *J. Chem. Soc.*, **1931**, 885.

[138] Bogle, M. S. Thesis, University of Nebraska, 1927.

[139] Hamilton and Frazier, *J. Am. Chem. Soc.*, **48**, 2414 (1926).

[140] Sommer, M. S. Thesis, University of Nebraska, 1942.

[141] Phillips, *J. Chem. Soc.*, **1930**, 1409.

[142] Benda and Sievers, U. S. pat., 1,739,820 (1930) [*C.A.*, **24**, 864 (1930)]; Ger. pat., 487,420 (1925) [*Chem. Zentr.*, II, 467 (1930)].

[143] Phillips, *J. Chem. Soc.*, **1928**, 3134.

[144] Haythornthwaite, *J. Chem. Soc.*, **1929**, 1011.

[145] Ogden and Adams, *J. Am. Chem. Soc.*, **47**, 826 (1925).

[146] Clark, Ph. D. Thesis, University of Nebraska, 1942.

[147] Banks and Hamilton, *J. Am. Chem. Soc.*, **61**, 357 (1939).

[148] Beers, M. S. Thesis, University of Nebraska, 1935.

[149] Phillips, *J. Chem. Soc.*, **1930**, 2685.

[150] Morgan, Ph. D. Thesis, University of Nebraska, 1943.

[151] Herrmann, Hampe, and Sievers, Ger. pat., 675,959 (1939) [*C.A.*, **33**, 7048 (1939)]

[152] Doak, Eagle, and Steinman, *J. Am. Chem. Soc.*, **62**, 3010 (1940).

[153] Slater, *J. Chem. Soc.*, **1932**, 2104.

[154] Capps and Hamilton, *J. Am. Chem. Soc.*, **60**, 2104 (1938).

[155] Fourneau, Trefouel, and Benoit, *Ann. inst. Pasteur*, **44**, 719 (1930) [*C.A.*, **26**, 1592 (1932)].

[156] Binz and Rath, *Ann.*, **453**, 238–248 (1927).

[157] Ochiai and Suzuki, *J. Pharm. Soc. Japan*, **60**, 353 (1940) [*C.A.*, **34**, 7289 (1940)].

[158] Barnett, Gillieson, and Kermack, *J. Chem. Soc.*, **1934**, 433.

[159] Balaban and King, *J. Chem. Soc.*, **1925**, 2701.

[160] Walton, *J. Chem. Soc.*, **1939**, 156.

[161] Joyce, M. S. Thesis, University of Nebraska, 1936.

[162] Shamshurin, *J. Gen. Chem. U.S.S.R.*, **11**, 647 (1941) [*C.A.*, **35** 6937 (1941)].

[163] Banks and Hamilton, *J. Am. Chem. Soc.*, **60**, 1370 (1938).

[164] Benda and Sievers, Ger. pat., 552,267 (1930) [*Chem. Zentr.*, II, 2109 (1932)]

[165] Bowers and Hamilton, *J. Am. Chem. Soc.*, **58**, 1573 (1936).

[166] Lawrence, Ph. D. Thesis, University of Nebraska, 1932.

[167] Saunders and Hamilton, *J. Am. Chem. Soc.*, **54**, 636 (1932).

[168] Sweet and Hamilton, *J. Am. Chem. Soc.*, **56**, 2408 (1934).

[169] Brown, *Trans. Kansas Acad. Sci.*, **42**, 209 (1939).

[170] Doak, Eagle, and Steinman, *J. Am. Chem. Soc.*, **64**, 1064 (1942).

[171] Gaswami and Das Gupta, *J. Indian Chem. Soc.*, **9**, 91 (1932).

[172] Lucius and Bruning, Ger. pat., 313,320 (1917) [*Chem. Zentr.*, IV, 262 (1921)].

[173] Balaban, *J. Chem. Soc.*, **1930**, 2346.

[174] Jenkins, M. S. Thesis, University of Nebraska, 1931.

[175] Hamilton and Jelinek, *J. Am. Chem. Soc.*, **49**, 3165 (1927).

[176] Benda, *Ber.*, **41**, 2367 (1908).

[177] Coles, M. S. Thesis, University of Nebraska, 1942.

[178] Phillips, *J. Chem. Soc.*, **1928**, 3134.

[179] Phillips, *J. Chem. Soc.*, **1928**, 172.

[180] Phillips, *J. Chem. Soc.*, **1931**, 1143.

[181] Burton and Gibson, *J. Chem. Soc.*, **1927**, 2386.

[182] Bellavita and Battistelli, *Ann. chim. applicata*, **25**, 631 (1935) [*C.A.*, **30**, 5952 (1936)].

[183] Hatlelid, Ph. D. Thesis, University of Nebraska, 1942.

[184] Das Gupta, *J. Indian Chem. Soc.*, **14**, 397 (1937).

[185] Das Gupta, *J. Indian Chem. Soc.*, **9**, 393 (1932).

[186] Burton and Gibson, *J. Chem. Soc.*, **1926**, 450.

[187] Davies and Othen, *J. Chem. Soc.*, **1936**, 1236.

[188] Lesslie and Turner, *J. Chem. Soc.*, **1934**, 1170.

[189] Mole and Turner, *J. Chem. Soc.*, **1939**, 1720.

[190] Roberts and Turner, *J. Chem. Soc.*, **127**, 2004 (1925).

[191] Sherlin and Berlin, *J. Gen. Chem. U.S.S.R.*, **5**, 938 (1935) [*C.A.*, **30**, 1055 (1936)].

[192] Kamai, *Trans. Kirov. Inst. Chem. Tech. Kazan*, **3**, 49 (1935) [*C.A.*, **29**, 3319 (1935)]

[193] Muth and Schmelzer, U. S. pat., 1,973,012 (1934) [*C.A.*, **28**, 7035 (1934)].

[194] Bauer and Adams, *J. Am. Chem. Soc.*, **46**, 1925 (1924).

[195] Aeschlimann, Lees, McCleland, and Nicklin, *J. Chem. Soc.*, **1925**, 66.

[196] Roberts and Turner, *J. Chem. Soc.*, **1926**, 1207.

[197] Turner and Sheppard, *J. Chem. Soc.*, **127**, 544 (1925).

[198] Lesslie, *J. Chem. Soc.*, **1938**, 1001.

[199] Finzi and Bartelli, *Gazz. chim. ital.*, **62**, 545 (1932).

[200] Wintersteiner and Lieb, *Ber.*, **61**, 1126 (1928).

[201] Hill, *J. Am. Chem. Soc.*, **46**, 1855 (1924).

[202] Sakellarios, *Ber.*, **59**, 2552 (1926).

[203] Golden, M. S. Thesis, University of Nebraska, 1930.

[204] Morgan and Stewart, *J. Chem. Soc.*, **1931**, 620.

[205] Sherlin et al., *Ann.*, **516**, 218 (1935).

[206] Bogert and Corbitt, *Proc. Natl. Acad. Sci. U. S.*, **11**, 768 (1923).

[207] Bogert and Hess, *Rec. trav. chim.*, **48**, 904 (1929).

[208] Gibson and Johnson, *J. Chem. Soc.*, **1930**, 1124.

[209] Yang and Lo, *J. Chin. Chem. Soc.*, **4**, 477 (1936) [*C.A.*, **31**, 3892 (1937)]

[210] Gump and Stoltzenberg, *J. Am. Chem. Soc.*, **53**, 1428 (1931).

[211] Takahashi, *J. Pharm. Soc. Japan*, **55**, 875 (in German, 164–165) (1935) [*C.A.*, **30**, 721 (1936)].

[212] Zappi and Salellas, *Bull. soc. chim.*, [5] **4**, 400 (1937).

[213] Salellas, *Rev. facultad cienc. quím.*, **11**, 59 (1936) [*C.A.*, **33**, 556 (1939)].

[214] Steinkopf and Schmidt, *Ber.*, **61**, 675 (1928).

[215] Schmidt, Ger. pat., 507,638 (1927) [*Chem. Zentr.*, I, 360 (1931)].

[216] MacCorquodale and Johnson, *Rec. trav. chim.*, **51**, 483 (1932).

[217] Bogert and Updike, *J. Am. Chem. Soc.*, **49**, 1373 (1927).

[218] Calvery, Noller, and Adams, *J. Am. Chem. Soc.*, **47**, 3058 (1925).

[219] Elson and Gibson, *J. Chem. Soc.*, **1931**, 2381.

[220] Sergeev and Kudryashev, *J. Gen. Chem. U.S.S.R.*, **7**, 1488 (1937) [*C.A.*, **31**, 8517 (1937)].

[221] Slater, *J. Chem. Soc.*, **1930**, 1209.

[222] McCleland and Whitworth, *J. Chem. Soc.*, **1927**, 2753.

[223] Slater, *J. Chem. Soc.*, **1931**, 107.

[224] Jacobs and Heidelberger, *J. Am. Chem. Soc.*, **41**, 1440 (1919).

[225] Lawrence, M. S. Thesis, University of Nebraska, 1930.

[226] Conant, *J. Am. Chem. Soc.*, **41**, 431 (1919).

[227] Hamilton and Johnson, *J. Am. Chem. Soc.*, **48**, 1405 (1926).

[228] Fichter and Elkind, *Ber.*, **49**, 239 (1916).

[229] Adler and Adler, *Ber.*, **41**, 931 (1908).

[230] Pyman and Reynolds, *J. Chem. Soc.*, **93**, 1180 (1908).

[231] Andreev, *J. Russ. Phys. Chem. Soc.*, **45**, 1980 (1913) [*C.A.* **8** 1422 (1914)].

INDEX

Numbers in bold-face type refer to experimental procedures